Engineering GNVQ: Advanced

Engineering GNVQ: Advanced

Editor:

Mike Tooley
Dean of Faculty, Brooklands College of Further and Higher Education

Authors:

John Bird
Senior Lecturer, Highbury College of Technology

Lloyd Dingle
Associate Head of Faculty, Brooklands College of Further and Higher Education

John Green
Visiting Lecturer, Brooklands College of Further and Higher Education

Bruce Newby
Head of School of Electrical and Electronic Engineering, Brooklands College of Further and Higher Education

Roger Timings
Head of Department of Engineering (retired), Henley College, Coventry

Gerry Wood
Head of Faculty of Technology, Brooklands College of Further and Higher Education

BUTTERWORTH
HEINEMANN

Butterworth-Heinemann
Linacre House, Jordan Hill, Oxford, OX2 8DP
A division of Reed Educational and Professional Publishing Ltd

$\mathcal{R}$ A member of the Reed Elsevier plc group

OXFORD BOSTON JOHANNESBURG
MELBOURNE NEW DELHI SINGAPORE

First published 1996

British Library Cataloguing in Publication Data
Engineering GNVQ: advanced
    1 Engineering   2 Engineering – Problems, exercises, etc.
    I Tooley, Michael H. (Michael Howard), 1946–
    620'.0071141

ISBN 0 7506 2595 3

Printed and bound in Great Britain
Composition by Genesis Typesetting, Rochester, Kent

Contents

Preface

Welcome to the challenging and exciting world of engineering! This book is designed to help get you through the core units of the Advanced General National Vocational Qualification (GNVQ) in Engineering. It contains all of the material that makes the essential underpinning knowledge required of a student who wishes to pursue a career in any branch of engineering.

The book has been written by a team of Further and Higher Education Lecturers. They each bring their own specialist knowledge coupled with a wealth of practical teaching experience. The team worked closely during the production of the book and this has helped to ensure that the book uses a common format and approach.

About GNVQ

General National Vocational Qualifications (GNVQ) are available in schools and colleges throughout England, Wales and Northern Ireland. Their main aim is to raise the status of vocational education in the UK within a new system of high quality vocational qualifications which can be taken as an alternative to the well-established General Certificate of Secondary Education (GCSE) and General Certificate of Educational Advanced Level (GCE A level) qualifications. The Government intends that GNVQs, together with National Vocational Qualifications (NVQs), will replace other vocational qualifications and become the main national provision for vocational education and training.

Although GNVQs are primarily aimed at 16- to 19-year-olds, they are also available to adults. Furthermore, credit towards GNVQs is being gained by 14- to 16-year-olds in secondary education. One of the main objectives of GNVQs is to provide a valued alternative to A level qualifications for the increasing number of students staying on in full-time education beyond 16. In particular, the Advanced GNVQ is designed to be of comparable standard to that set by A levels.

GNVQs provide a broad-based vocational education that continues many aspects of general secondary education. As well as acquiring the basic skills and body of knowledge that underpin a vocational area, all students have to achieve *core skills*. The attainment of both vocational *and* core skills provides a foundation from which students can progress either to further and higher education, or into employment with further training appropriate to the job concerned.

GNVQs, like NVQs, are unit-based qualifications. Each is made up of a number of units which can be assessed separately, and this allows credit accumulation throughout a course. A certificate can be obtained for each unit when necessary and credit transfer on some units can be made between qualifications. To maintain this fundamental characteristic of GNVQs, assessment is based on the unit rather than the qualification.

The mandatory units for each GNVQ have been developed jointly by the National Council for Vocational Qualifications (NCVQ) and the GNVQ Awarding Bodies – BTEC, City and Guilds and RSA Examinations Board. NCVQ has taken a lead role in the evaluation and revision of the mandatory units. Each awarding body develops its own optional and additional units, and takes responsibility for their evaluation and revision. NCVQ has developed, evaluated and revised the core skills units.

Core skills

Core skills are a vital part of any GNVQ programme. Three core skills units, Communication, Application of Number, and Information Technology are mandatory requirements for all students. Indeed, the same core skills units are taken by all students taking GNVQs at the same level (e.g., level 3 core skills units are taken by all students following any Advanced GNVQ programme irrespective of the vocational area or the awarding body). Other core skills may be taken as 'additional units'.

How to use this book

This book covers the eight mandatory units that make up the GNVQ Advanced Engineering programme. One chapter is devoted to each unit. Each chapter contains text, worked examples, 'test your knowledge' questions, activities, and multi-choice practice questions.

The worked examples will not only show you how to solve simple problems but they will also help put the subject matter into context with typical illustrative examples.

The 'test your knowledge' questions are interspersed with the text throughout the book. These questions allow you to check your understanding of the preceding text. They also provide you with an opportunity to reflect on what you have learned and consolidate this in manageable chunks.

Most 'test your knowledge' questions can be answered in only a few minutes and the necessary information, formulae, etc., can be gleaned from the surrounding text. Activities, on the other hand, require a significantly greater amount of time to complete. Furthermore, they often require additional library or resource area research coupled with access to computing and other information technology resources.

Activities make excellent vehicles for gathering the necessary evidence to demonstrate that you are competent in core skills. To help you identify the opportunities for developing core skills and acquiring evidence, we have included core skills icons in the text, as shown below:

Communication

Application
of number

Information
technology

Look out for these icons as they will provide you with some clues as to how to go about developing and enhancing your own core skills!

Finally, here are a few general points worth noting:

- Allow regular time for reading – get into the habit of setting aside an hour, or two, at the weekend to take a second look at the topics that you have covered during the week.

- Make notes and file these away neatly for future reference – lists of facts, definitions and formulae are particularly useful for revision!

- Look out for the inter-relationship between subjects and units – you will find many ideas and a number of themes that crop up in different places and in different units. These can often help to reinforce your understanding.

- Don't expect to find all subjects and topics within the course equally interesting. There may be parts that, for a whole variety of reasons, don't immediately fire your enthusiasm. There is nothing unusual in this, however, do remember that something that may not appear particularly useful now may become crucial at some point in the future!

- However difficult things seem to get – don't give up! Engineering is not, in itself, a difficult subject, rather it is a subject that *demands* logical thinking and an approach in which each new concept builds upon those that have gone before.

- Finally, don't be afraid to put new ideas into practice – get out there and do it!

Good luck with your GNVQ Engineering studies!

Mike Tooley

Unit 1 Engineering and commercial functions in business

Summary

This unit begins by exploring the business context in which the engineer works. It is clear that engineers cannot ignore the commercial framework and must remain aware of the commercial impact of their work and in particular how activities such as design, development and manufacture are linked to satisfying the needs of customers. Getting a product to market is seen as a co-operative venture between all of the business functions. This co-operation is achieved by creating a suitable organization so that specialists can interface their activities effectively.

The unit examines the basic structure of businesses in our society from primary industries to secondary industries through to tertiary activities. It then focuses on the way a business can organize itself in the business environment and then internally; thus hierarchical, matrix and other structures are considered and compared. The main functions of business are studied and the interface between each and the engineering function is analysed. Financial techniques for managerial and cost control are explained and you should be able to understand the use of these techniques in the quest for commercially viable products and well run businesses

Structure of business in a complex society

This section examines the structure of business in relation to its place in the economy, whether primary, secondary or tertiary. It then explains some of the complexities of business organizations and the way they grow and develop, including the legal framework for businesses of different size such as sole traders, partnerships and limited companies.

Industry classification

The usual classification for industries which produce goods and services is based on a natural sequence, starting from the most basic to the most complex as outlined below.

Primary sector

Primary industries produce goods directly from natural resources and include:

- agriculture, forestry and fishing
- mining, oil extraction, quarrying.

Many of the goods grown or extracted become the raw materials for use in the secondary sector described below. A good example is quarrying which extracts broken stones from the ground and sorts them into sizes suitable for roads or other construction projects. In agriculture the production of sugar beet provides raw material for food manufacture, including refined sugar used in our homes. Oil is a valuable raw material used to produce petrol and diesel fuels, chemicals, pharmaceuticals and lubricants.

Secondary sector

The secondary sector includes manufacturing and construction which make use of the raw materials produced by primary industries. Manufacturing industries include:

- chemicals, pharmaceuticals and artificial fibres
- metals and mineral products
- engineering and allied industries
- food, drink and tobacco
- textiles, footware, clothing and leather.

Construction industries are:

- building, e.g. housing, factories and offices
- civil engineering, e.g. roads, bridges and dams.

The term *production industries* is used to describe businesses that operate in both primary and secondary sectors. A good example is the oil industry which is involved in prospecting for, extracting and processing of oil and oil products.

Tertiary sector

Tertiary sector industries provide services, and examples are:

- transport
- wholesale and retail distribution
- banking, finance and insurance
- hotels and catering
- education
- post and telecommunication
- Government (local and national)
- medical and health services
- any other services.

More complex structures

The analysis above suggests a fairly simple division between sectors and appears very straightforward. However, you should note that many real business organizations are not as simple.

Some businesses operate according to the concept of *vertical integration*. This means they may be involved in primary and secondary forms of production. A company in the food industry could grow cane sugar, transport it to its own factories for refining and produce food products which include sugar as a raw material. If it owns its own fleet of vehicles or even ships then its business spans all three sectors of industry. A company might operate this way because it can increase its control over the market or because it can operate more efficiently. The starting point for this process could be that a primary industry wants to protect its market so it buys the company that processes its raw material. This is called *forward integration*. Or a manufacturer might want to secure its supply of raw materials so it buys the company that extracts it. This is called *backward integration*.

Horizontal integration is where a business expands to take over similar industries in its sector. For example a retail newsagent could expand by taking over other retail newsagents in other towns and cities to build a chain of similar outlets. This can produce what are called economies of scale, perhaps in the control and management of the business or in the purchasing power it brings over its own suppliers.

Similar things have happened in the engineering industry where a manufacturer takes over small factories and integrates them into one large business. This can make production cheaper by enabling large volume production, with each factory specializing in fewer products.

Lateral integration is where a company diversifies into different businesses thereby spreading its business risk, because it is no longer reliant on a single product or on a narrow range of products for its survival. That is why a motor manufacturer might make cars, trucks and tractors. Each serve different markets which may grow or shrink at different rates and times and spread the risk.

However, when a business grows too large there comes a point when the economies of scale disappear and the dis-economies of scale appear. A very large company has many more management problems and often cannot respond to change as quickly as smaller companies can. This is analogous to an oil tanker, which cannot manoeuvre as quickly as a cross-channel ferry. To avoid disaster the big organization has to be able to forecast and plan for change if it is to match the performance of more nimble and flexible smaller companies.

Types of business organization

Sole traders

The smallest business structure is that of sole trader. Many very large businesses may have started as sole traders. A sole trader owns and controls all the business. He has the benefit of all the profits and has to stand all the losses. Sole traders may employ many people but these people will always work under the direction of the owner as his employees.

The advantages of operating as a sole trader are:

- personal contact with customers and employees
- rewards are direct, the owner benefits from his efforts
- quick personal decisions and actions
- minimum legal and accounting requirements
- business remains private, accounts not published
- such a business can be set up virtually overnight.

There are disadvantages and these are:

- long hours, onerous responsibility
- full personal liability for business debts
- lack of capital for growth
- the owner has to do everything but cannot be good at everything.

Partnerships

Many sole traders convert into partnerships as they grow in size. A legal framework exists in the form of the Partnerships Act 1890. A partnership is defined as an association of 2 to 20 partners (except that firms of accountants, solicitors and members of the stock exchange are not so limited). Thus normally, if more than 20 people wish to run a business, a limited company would be formed. Excepting a special case of a 'limited partner' all partners are liable to the full extent of their personal wealth for the whole of the liabilities of the firm. Usually each partner would have to pay his share of any deficiency. A limited partner has to be registered under the Limited Partnership Act of 1907, and such a partner is liable only for the amount of his investment in the business.

A partnership can exist without any formal written agreement, however, it is usually prudent to have a partnership deed drawn up by a solicitor which will prevent many of the possible misunderstandings and disagreements that could arise between partners. An example of the things that might be covered in a partnership deed are:

- the capital to be contributed by each partner
- the ratio for sharing profits/losses
- the rate of interest on capital before profits shared
- partners salaries if any.

Among the advantages of partnerships are:

- more capital can be contributed
- partners can specialize according to skills
- shared responsibility, provides backup.

However the disadvantages are:

- the partners have to consult on decisions
- a partner who leaves may cause financial problems
- each partner can make contracts – risk of bad decisions of one partner being suffered by the others.

Limited companies

Limited companies are more complicated than partnerships and are governed by a more detailed legal framework. A company is a form of corporation and is therefore a legal person or entity. Being a legal entity, it can sue or be sued, shareholders have limited liability and it is potentially immortal, since shares can be sold or passed on indefinitely. A private company cannot advertise its shares for sale to the public, but a public limited company (plc) can. This legal status requires the completion of prescribed forms which have to be submitted to the Registrar of Companies. He issues a Certificate of Incorporation which is the proof that all legal requirements have been met. It states the date of incorporation and cannot be withdrawn once it is issued. The documents required are *The Memorandum of Association*, *The Articles of Association* and *The Prospectus*. The Memorandum of Association contains six clauses:

- name of company
- the address of the registered office
- the objects/powers of the company
- the limitation of liability of members
- the amount of the nominal share capital and its division into shares and their denominations
- association of the persons named and their addresses who agree to take up the shares listed against their names. Their signatures are made and witnessed (minimum two persons).

The Articles of Association is a document that lays down the rules for internal governance and how the business will be conducted. It must be laid out into numbered paragraphs, signed by the subscribers of the Memorandum and witnessed. Main matters dealt with are:

- application of specified tables from the Companies Acts (these tables give model articles for various forms of company)
- preliminary contracts (made on behalf of the new company)
- allotment/transfer/transmission of shares
- borrowing powers
- changes to capital invested
- meetings, directors, dividends, reserve funds, accounts and audit matters
- notices and winding-up procedures.

The Prospectus is issued when a company 'goes public'. A limited company may be private or public. A public company (plc) offers its shares for public subscription. Usually a private limited company converts to plc when it needs more capital to fund growth. This is when The Prospectus is issued. This is defined as 'a notice, circular, advertisement or other invitation offering to the public for subscription or purchase any shares or debentures of a company'.

The prospectus must be registered with the registrar and it must comply with the rules of the stock exchange. It must contain or have attached the following information:

- written consent of any expert to statements made by him
- copy of every material contract mentioned
- statement of any adjustments to financial reports.

Other matters about companies

A company which enters into a contract which it has no power to do so is said to be *'ultra vires'*. Directors can be sued for allowing this.

If a prospectus contains untrue statements and the directors knew that to be the case, they could be fined or imprisoned.

Companies are usually managed by a board of directors and they are governed by detailed rules contained in the Companies Acts which relate to duties and responsibilities.

The disadvantage of limited company status is that the original owners will have to share decision-making with the other new shareholders and also its accounts are in the public domain and can be examined by any member of the public by application to the registrar. Public companies have all the advantages and disadvantages of private companies, except that they have better opportunities of raising capital for expansion via the stock market. They may also be prey to hostile takeover bids, thus the original owners may risk losing altogether the company they created.

Franchises

This is a relatively new approach to business ownership. It normally involves a well-known, well-established company permitting a franchisee to make or sell its products within a defined area. Some well-known names in this type of business are McDonalds Restaurants, Wimpey Restaurants, Spud U Like and Prontaprint.

The franchisor helps the franchisee to set up in business and gives advice about marketing and selling and location of premises and may supply equipment and materials. The franchisor will usually charge a royalty fee for services rendered which may be in the form of a lump sum and a percentage share of the profits.

Co-operatives

These types of business have been around for much longer than franchises. They usually involve a number of small units who band together for mutual protection and can make savings from bulk buying and joint advertising. The two main forms are retail societies and producer co-operatives. The Co-operative Movement began in 1844 as the Rochdale Equitable Pioneers Society. It was started by a group of workers who were fed up with the deal they were getting from others. They aimed to supply their members with good quality mechandise at fair prices, with profits being returned to them as dividend. It was very successful and grew rapidly in Britain.

The main characteristics of co-operatives are:

● owned by members
● one member one vote, regardless of shares
● each regional society was independent
● run via an elected board of directors.

The dividend is shared by the owners in proportion to their purchases. Alternatively some societies give discounts or dividend stamps.

The Co-operative Wholesale Society (CWS) was formed in 1863 and supplies up to 60% of goods sold by the retail societies. There is even a Co-operative Bank. Another organization called the Co-operative Union is an association to which the CWS and the retail societies belong. It provides advice on a range of matters and acts as a co-ordinating body for the Co-operative Movement as whole.

Producer co-operatives are common in agriculture and have been very successful in New Zealand, Denmark and Spain. In the UK up until the 1970s only farming co-operatives existed. This changed when some firms had financial problems and they were bought out by their employees in order to save the business. By means of Co-operative Development Agencies there are now about 1500 producer co-operatives in the UK.

Public corporations

As a result of privatization, many former nationalized industries are now in the private sector as Public Limited Companies. These include British Telecom, the water companies, the electricity industry and others.

However, there are still some significant organizations run as public enterprises and these include the Post Office and the British Broadcasting Corporation.

Public corporations are controlled by parliament through a government minister down to a chairman and board of directors. The minister determines general policy and the chairman and the board handle day-to-day matters. Such industries attempt to provide a good public service at a reasonable cost. However, these industries are still expected to meet a 'required rate of return' on the assets employed, as laid down by government.

Government departments and Local Authorities

Some central government departments operate businesses. These include the Royal Mint, Her Majesty's Stationery Office (HMSO), the Forestry Commission and the Central Office of Information.

Apart from providing local services like refuse collection and education some Local Authorities operate tourism and leisure businesses.

The reasons for having businesses run by local and central government are various and include the need to centrally plan some services or the need to run relatively unprofitable businesses which are in the public interest and may not survive if placed in the private sector.

Test your knowledge 1.1

1 Distinguish between primary, secondary and tertiary industries, and give an example of each.
2 State what is (a) vertical integration and (b) horizontal integration.
3 Distinguish between a sole trader, a partnership, a private limited company and a public limited company. Give a good reason why 'limited' companies came into being as a type of business structure.
4 Describe the main documents required to set up a limited company.
5 Distinguish between the Co-operative Movement and Producer Co-operatives and say why they came into being.
6 What are the advantages of operating a franchised business?
7 What two reasons can you give for central or local government departments to run businesses?

Activity 1.1

Contact your Local Authority and find out:

(a) What main services they offer.
(b) What *trading activities* they are engaged in.
(c) Discuss whether or not some of these services could be provided by a private company and say why you think so.

How businesses are organized

This section discusses the internal organization of business. It outlines basic theories of organization and explains how organizations can be designed using hierarchical and matrix structures. It looks at the essential management activities that are carried out within the framework of the organization.

Theories of organization

We are all affected by the activities of organizations. A school or a college is an organization. Most of us will have attended one and been influenced by one or both, whether we like it or not. Other parts of our lives are affected by business, government, charitable organizations and organizations that provide entertainment. Organizations are all-pervasive in our modern society.

Reasons for creating organizations

Why do organizations exist? Because they are the most rational and efficient forms of social groupings that we have been able to devise. Since an organization co-ordinates large numbers of human actions they can be powerful social tools.

Organizations bring together people skills, machines and raw materials to create products and services to meet the goals of our modern society. Much of what we take for granted in our world, such as our material prosperity, would not be possible without the co-operative nature of organizations.

Organizations are not modern inventions. The Pharaohs used them to build the pyramids and the Chinese used them to build the Great Wall of China. However, modern organizations are more effective and efficient than ancient ones because we have been able to develop them in ways that take account of human needs and happiness. That does not mean that *all* modern organizations do this, but we do have the knowledge to make such a result possible.

Thus the objective should be to construct an organization that is both rational and effective and produces the maximum human satisfaction. Given that we defined organizations as social structures the two aspects should go hand-in-hand. It is also true that many of the most successful business organizations are also places in which the employees can achieve job satisfaction and happiness.

Organizational effectiveness and efficiency

Organizational *effectiveness* can be defined in terms of how well it achieves its goals. It also involves doing the right things. *Efficiency* of an organization is a measure of the amount of resources needed or consumed to produce a unit of output. If the organization is effective then it is doing the right things. Efficiency in doing the right things is essential, since it is quite futile to be efficient at doing the wrong things. The unit of output is a measure of whatever an organization manufactures. However the *goals* of the organization are likely to be profit, output simply being a means to that end.

Generally effectiveness and efficiency go together, but in reality this does not always happen. A company might make excellent products in demand by the market, but fails to produce them at a cost that generates good profit. Such a company is effective but not very efficient. Alternatively a company might be very good at producing goods cheaply and quickly, but the market does not want all of those goods. Such a company is efficient but not very effective.

The search for organizations which are both effective and efficient led to the development of a number of theories of organization. We will examine some of the most important ones below.

Scientific management (1880–1930)

The most famous proponent of this school of thought was F.W.Taylor. He was a distinguished American engineer who lived from 1856 to 1917. He gave up studying law at Harvard to become an apprentice machinist and rose to become chief engineer of the Midvale Steel Company. At the age of 43 he organized his own company and introduced scientific management practices.

In essence this approach combined time and motion study with an economic approach which exploited the fear of hunger and motive for profit. Out of this arose piecework systems, bonus schemes, job analysis and work measurement. According to Taylor motivation to work was based on being able to earn high wages, with little or no emphasis on other factors.

Anyone who has ever worked in the engineering industry will recognize the influence of scientific management. The use of bonus schemes, piecework and work study are commonplace. There can be no doubt that Taylor's systematic and rational approach to the organization of work have contributed enormously to industrial efficiency.

The human relations school (1930–1950)

The scientific management theory had many critics because it took a very narrow view of human behaviour in industrial organizations. The assumption that high wages was the only or main motivation to work was challenged. The human relations school arose out of this and started to place emphasis on things like communication, participation and leadership.

This led to the idea that workers were also motivated by non-economic rewards. The theories were based on numerous experiments and field studies, the most famous of which were the Hawthorne Studies. These studies showed that social rules set by the workers themselves, non-pay rewards and sanctions all had a powerful effect on worker productivity. They also established that workers functioned as part of groups which had significant influences on individual worker behaviour. The study showed that high productivity could be achieved irrespective of pay levels and even if conditions were poor.

Current ideas on organization (1950 – present)

In many ways scientific management and human relations approaches to organization were diametrically opposed, but they both provided partial understanding about how organizations function.

Test your knowledge 1.2

1 What is scientific management?
2 What is the 'human relations' view of management?
3 Why should an organization be both effective and efficient?

Between them they gave insights into both *formal* and *informal* organizations. Scientific Management was concerned with formal structured methods while the human relations school was concerned with informal human interactions which had a major impact on how organizations worked.

Scientific management has led to such things as refinements in industrial engineering, and the development of operations research (the use of mathematical methods to understand business operating systems).

Human relations approaches have led to improved personnel management practices, better industrial relations and to a new understanding of motivation at work and the effect of different leadership styles.

Activity 1.2

A company called in consultants to carry out a full work study exercise on the work of production operatives. The purpose was to improve the accuracy of the costing system for products and to be able to make better estimates of plant capacity. Eventually it was intended to institute a full standard costing system throughout the manufacturing activity. When the consultants started work the shop stewards immediately called a general meeting of their members and it was agreed by a large majority to strike immediately unless the study was discontinued. The stewards said that their members were not prepared to work in a 'sweat shop'. They alleged that the study was intended to extract more work out of operatives with a view to reducing the size of the workforce. They also objected to the fact that the Union was not consulted before the study was undertaken.

With your tutor's help divide into groups of 5 or 6 and try to explain the reasons for the workers' behaviour. Be prepared to discuss your ideas with the whole group by appointing one of your members as spokesperson.

Organization design

Purpose

Organizations are not always designed in any rational sense. They grow from small beginnings and evolve to meet the perceived needs of the business. However, most large organizations do design and redesign their organization structure according to rational principles. This process includes:

● determining activities required to meet goals
● grouping activities into a logical pattern
● assigning activities to positions and people

- setting up co-ordinating systems
- defining authority and power
- describing responsibilities and accountabilities.

Authority, power, responsibility and accountability are such important aspects of organizational design they are further discussed below.

Authority and power

Authority is defined as the *right to do something*. A manager can require a subordinate to carry out a legitimate instruction. Authority arises out of rank and position in the organization, and can be *delegated* to subordinates so that required actions can be carried out. Authority can also arise out of the personal qualities of the manager concerned.

Power

Authority is the *right to do something* but power is the *ability to do something*. The two are often confused. Power means that a manager can compel a subordinate to do something by using sanctions such as withdrawing rewards, threatening and/or carrying out punishment. In a more positive way a manager can exercise power by giving or promising rewards.

If a manager has authority but no power or alternatively has power but no authority there is an imbalance. The proper situation is where power and authority are equal. In such a case power is legitimate and authority is workable. This means that there are rational limits to the exercise of power, preventing its abuse. It also means that authority rights can be enforced when it is necessary.

Consider the analogy of a police force. It has authority from the state to ensure that the law is kept. It also needs the powers to enforce the law so that it can deal with violent criminals and armed gangs. If it does not have power, the ability to enforce, it cannot exercise its authority.

Responsibility and accountability

Responsibility is the *obligation to do something*. This is the duty placed upon managers and employees to perform organizational tasks. They would normally be specified in some form of itemized job description. Whereas authority and power can be delegated, ultimate responsibility cannot. Thus if a manager delegates a task to be done he cannot escape final responsibility for accomplishing the task.

Managers get their job done through others, but remain in charge, and will have to accept responsibility for the subordinate's failure. Is this fair? Yes, because if the subordinate fails the manager has to accept some blame at least because he made an error of judgement in assigning a job to a subordinate who failed to do the job properly. While he can hold a subordinate personally accountable to him for the action, the manager has to take responsibility for the action when accounting to his own superiors.

Accountability

An organization member is accountable for his action to a higher authority. Each person given authority in an organization has to account to his superior for his performance. Each member of an organization has to report to his superior on the way he has exercised his individual responsibility. The refusal of organizational members to accept responsibility and accountability will cause the organization to malfunction, since it creates friction, lack of decisive action, and wasted energy. Hence the organization has to document the jobs of all post-holders so that authority, power, responsibility and accountability is clearly stated and communicated to all.

Line and staff

This expression is often misunderstood and has led to confusion and friction. This is because 'line' managers see themselves as directly in control of the important activities of the business, while 'staff' managers are functional or advisory and theoretically could be dispensed with first in the event of the contraction of the business. Despite the practical problems the concept is a useful way of understanding how different parts of the organization function. There are basically two definitions:

Line and staff as functions

This definition assumes that 'line and staff' are different functions of the business. Line managers are those who have direct responsibility for operations which accomplish the objectives of the business. An example is a Works Manager who directs the work of manufacturing workers. Any manager that is part of this direct chain of command, from director to workshop foreman is 'line'. All other functions are 'staff'. Examples of the latter are the Research and Development Manager, Financial Controller and Company Secretary.

In this definition we see that two aspects of the organization are distinguished, those that supervise the operations and those that provide backup service activities.

Line and staff as authority relationships

This definition views 'line' as referring to the relationship a manager has with subordinates, regardless of who the manager is. This then applies to a Financial Controller and to a Works Manager, since they both directly supervise their own staff, and are thus in a direct line relationship. However, when the Financial Controller is giving instructions or advice to the Works Manager he is operating in a 'staff' role. The Controller is exercising a functional role and is not the direct line manager to the Works Manager.

Centralization and decentralization

The concept of centralization is related to the level of decision-making in the organization. If decision-making is at the top level in the organization then it is said to be highly centralized. Also some business units are considered as of such importance that they are located centrally or at Head Office and are the source of decision-making for that function. Example functions are Accounting and Finance and Information Systems Management.

Usually highly centralized organizations inhibit lower level flexibility and initiative. This works well in very stable environments and where employees at the operating level are less well educated or are engaged in routine or low-skilled work. This could include workers such as production line operatives, stores personnel or sales assistants.

Decentralization is when the organization permits decisions to be made at lower levels in the organization, usually as close to the associated activity as possible. This allows the organization to be more adaptable and flexible and enables local autonomy for managers. This kind of structure works well in fast-changing and unpredictable environments or where the employees at the operating level are well educated or professionally qualified, and who are engaged in tasks of a complex or unstructured nature. Such people would include accountants, engineers or teachers.

Bureaucratic structure

The German sociologist, Max Weber described a structure which is called bureaucratic. This word tends to have negative connotations when used in the popular sense, and is often used as a way of denigrating the activities of civil servants or other public officials. The view of bureaucracy as discussed by Weber is somewhat different, and we shall see how Weber helps us to understand what it is.

Weber distinguishes three types of authority in organizations:

- traditional authority
- charismatic authority
- legal authority.

Traditional authority is rooted in historical structures in society, such as the authority of kings and emperors, Lords and Patriarchs. In such systems authority was often hereditary or based on military power.

Charismatic authority rests on the personality, abilities and values of an individual leader, and in ancient times such a leader would be a 'sage' or wise man, a prophet or warrior hero. Charisma is that certain something that inspires followers to devotion and enthusiasm. By its nature it is fickle, since a leader's mistakes can result in a fall from grace and the desertion of his or her followers. Sometimes charismatic authority develops into traditional authority as the power is transferred to successors, often these were the children of the charismatic leader.

Legal authority rests on the enactment of laws. The governing body is either appointed or elected, and authority stems from the application of rules, regulations and procedures. The authority of the 'ruler' is legitimized by the legal foundation and by the practice of professional skills and specialized knowledge. This kind of organization is rational, somewhat impersonal, and hierarchical in structure (see below for a discussion on such forms of organization). This form of authority is described as bureaucratic and is common in modern business and government.

Thus in the sense that Weber described it, many large business organizations are bureaucracies and are governed by the concepts of rules, specialization and hierarchy. Modern Companies operate within a framework of business law and are governed by their own internal procedures and regulations. This kind of structure is a pre-requisite to being able to direct and control an organization which may employ many thousands of people, sometimes on a global scale. However, there is still room for charismatic leadership in modern business. Many successful entrepreneurs and business leaders have this quality, which has often been crucial to the development and growth of particular businesses.

Organic structure

As observed above, bureaucracies work well in stable environments. When the reverse is true they function less well. In unstable or fast-changing conditions an organization needs to be adaptable and flexible. There is no time to create policies and procedures which can be used and referred to frequently, as by the time the policies are in place they may be irrelevant or out-of-date. Bureaucracies are by their nature *mechanistic* and unable to adapt quickly. However, *organic* structures are adaptable and flexible and have the following characteristics:

Communication
Organic organizations place emphasis on lateral or horizontal flows of information, not just those which flow up and down a hierarchy.

Authority of knowledge
The individual's formal position in the organization is less important than his knowledge and expertise. Those with these essential skills can solve problems better than their superior managers can.

Wide perspective
Organization members can take a wider view and are not bound by narrow departmental loyalties, instead they work for the benefit of the whole business.

Imprecise job definitions
Because the environment is changing rapidly job descriptions become out-of-date. Thus members are more concerned about their overall role within which tasks would change frequently.

Professionalism
Many members have as great a commitment to their profession as to their company. For example a Chartered Engineer will identify strongly with the values and ethics of his professional association.

The definitions of mechanistic and organic organizations are really at two ends of a continuum, and in reality most businesses will be somewhere in between. Some will tend to be organic while others will tend to be bureaucratic. Most organizations are mixtures of these two extremes.

Test your knowledge 1.3

1 Why must power and authority go together?
2 Can a manager escape responsibility for the failures of his subordinate?
3 What is meant by the word bureaucracy?
4 State two characteristics of an organic organization.
5 State the characteristics of (a) a de-centralized organization and (b) a centralized organization.

Types of structures

The design principles outlined above apply to all types of organizational structures. Job descriptions and organization charts are commonly used to define authority, power, responsibility and accountability. In addition there will be standing orders, procedures and legal obligations which particular managers will be charged with fulfilling. Understanding how a particular organization operates may be possible only by studying these documents alongside the organization charts.

There are various ways of describing organizational structures and we will consider these one at a time. Note that the descriptions are not necessarily mutually exclusive, thus one description may also overlap with other descriptions.

Flat structures

Flat structures have few levels from top to the bottom. Figure 1.1 shows a flat organization where five managers report directly to a Board of Directors. The five managers are described as 'first line managers' because they directly supervise the activities of people who do the actual job. The latter are often described as 'operatives'.

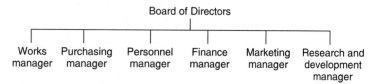

Figure 1.1 *Flat heirarchical structure*

The 1990s in Great Britain has seen a significant move towards having flat organizations. The process has been described as 'de-layering' and is regarded as an organization structure which has better communications up and down organizational levels. It is also seen as more cost-effective and responsive in dealing with demands placed on modern businesses.

Note that flat organizations are also hierarchical. A hierarchy is an organization with grades or classes ranked one above another. A flat organization meets that criterion also.

Tall structures

These are opposite to flat structures and contain many layers. Figure 1.2 shows an example. Tall structures usually exist only in large organizations because of the necessity of dividing the tasks into chunks of work that can be handled by individual managers, departments and sections.

Tall structures are also hierarchies, only they contain many more levels than flat structures.

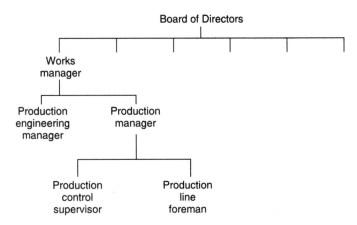

Figure 1.2 *Tall heirarchical structure*

Hierarchical structures

These are structures which have many or few layers showing rank order from top to bottom. They show a chain of command, with the most senior posts at the top and the most junior posts at the bottom. Plain hierarchies are the most common representations of organizations, as some aspect of hierarchy exists in all organizations.

The organization chart is a useful way of representing the overall structure, but it tells only part of the story. You should be aware that other documents are needed to fully understand how the organization works, as we observed earlier.

Hierarchical organizations can take many forms. We have already examined flat and tall structures. There are several other forms with which you should be familiar. One of the most common is the *functional* design. Figure 1.3 shows a functional organization. The main functions of a commercial business are marketing, finance, purchasing and supply, manufacturing, research and development and personnel. Notice how each functional manager reports to the managing director who co-ordinates their activities. There are a number of advantages in functional designs:

- specialists can be grouped together
- it appears logical and easy to understand
- co-ordination is achieved via operating procedures
- suits stable environments and few product lines
- works well in small to medium size businesses.

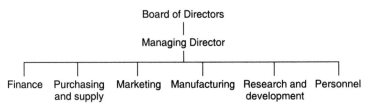

Figure 1.3 *Functional design*

As a business grows the functional design becomes less and less useful. This is because there are many more products and these may be manufactured in separate divisions of a company, especially if economies of scale are introduced into the manufacturing process.

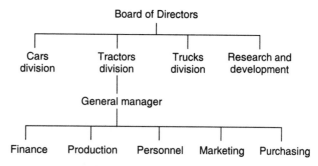

Figure 1.4 *Federal or divisional design*

Figure 1.4 shows a design based on major product lines and is really a federal structure which still has functional activities, but at a lower level in the organization, except for the research and development (R&D) function which is centralized. The managers of these operating divisions will control most of the functions required to run the business. In many conglomerate businesses this federal arrangement is achieved by having a holding company, which may be a public limited company (plc), which wholly owns a number of subsidiary companies, which are in effect divisions of the main business. Figure 1.5 shows an example.

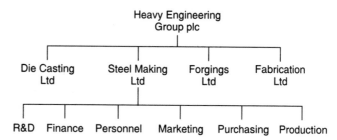

Figure 1.5 *A conglomerate organization*

An alternative to the product-based divisional design is one based on geographical divisions. Figure 1.6 shows a geographical design which still has many of the functions located at a head office, but which has branches dispersed around the country. These branches or divisions handle sales and manufacture, but are supported by head office for the other functions.

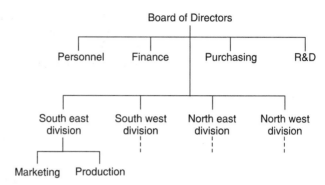

Figure 1.6   *Geographical divisions*

Matrix structures

A matrix structure as its name implies has a two-way flow of authority. Departmental or functional authority flows vertically and project management authority flows horizontally. Such a structure is shown in Figure 1.7. This depicts a company that designs and makes machines and tools to customer specifications.

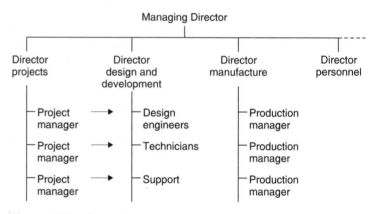

Figure 1.7   *A matrix structure*

Some businesses operate as a series of projects. This is common, for example, in construction and in some types of engineering company, especially those that design one-off products or who design manufacturing equipment used by other manufacturers. As the chart shows, there are the familiar functional divisions, and members of functional departments still report to their functional line manager. However, the project manager has the job of co-ordinating the work of functional specialists to ensure that the project is completed on time, to specification and within cost limits.

In the main, project managers do not have direct line authority, but have to influence and persuade others to achieve targets. They may have formal authority over project budgets and can set time schedules and decide what work is to be done, but little else. They also work as an interface with clients and subcontractors and their influence is often critical to the success of the project. Although they do not have formal authority over individual staff or their line managers, they never-the-less operate with the full support of senior managers. This means that functional specialists are obliged to provide the fullest co-operation and help, otherwise they become answerable for failure to their own senior line managers.

The matrix system works very well in project-based industries, and that is why the design is used. It still retains many of the ingredients of other structures, and still has substantial hierarchical elements.

Hybrids

The structures discussed above are just examples of the main design principles for organizations. There are numerous variations and rarely do we find 'pure' forms of organization structure. We need to remember that organizations are created to serve the goals of their owners and that the precise structure will be designed to meet the needs of the business.

Management activities

Planning

Planning is absolutely fundamental to the correct functioning of organizations. If no planning is done then activities are almost certainly going to be very ineffective. What is planning? It is the sum of the following activities:

- setting organization goals
- forecasting the environment
- determining the means to achieve goals.

Setting goals or objectives must be the first step. It determines the direction an organization is going. It encourages all organization members to work towards the same ends, otherwise members are likely to set their own objectives which will conflict with each other. Good objectives make for rational organizations that are more co-ordinated and effective. The objectives must therefore be set by the top management group in an organization so that its members can be given clear direction. If the goals are clearly stated, logical and appropriate for the business then they act both as motivators and yardsticks for measuring success. They also help to achieve consensus among organization members because they can be generally accepted by all.

Once the organization has clear direction the next step is to analyse the environment and forecast its effect on the business. For example an engineering company that makes lawn mowers may set objectives such as:

- achieve 30% share of the market
- be the technological leader
- be highly competitive on price
- operate internationally

When it forecasts its environment it discovers that:

- new designs are being marketed by competitors
- manual lawn mowers are in sharp decline.

Its designs are technically very sound but are being threatened by new rotary designs which are proving attractive to customers. It has to decide how to deal with the threat, either to improve its existing design concept so that customers continue to find them attractive or to follow the new trend and produce products based on new design concepts.

Forecasting the environment allows the company to set new objectives and to prepare plans to meet its revised goals. Companies that fail to go through this process will go into decline in the long run because they are ignoring the changing world around them.

Once the goals have been refined and changed in the light of environmental forecasting then plans can be made to achieve the goals. Some plans will not change that much others will be dramatically affected by the changing environment. For this reason plans can be classified as follows:

- standing plans
- single-use plans
- strategic plans
- tactical plans.

Standing plans are those that are used many times, and remain relatively unaffected by environmental change. Examples are employment, financial, operating and marketing policies and procedures. For example hiring new employees involve standard procedures for recruitment and selection. Another example would be the annual routines for establishing budgets.

Single-use plans are those that are used once only, such as those for the control of a unique project or specific budgets within an annual budget. (Budgets themselves are single-use plans, even though the procedures used for producing them are standing plans.)

Strategic plans are the broad plans related to the whole organization and include forecasting future trends and overall plans for the development of the organization. They are often in outline only and very often highly subjective, involving judgements made by top managers. For example a plan may be made to build an entirely new factory based on forecasts of demand. This plan is strategic, and if it is wrong and the sales forecasts on which it is based do not materialize, the results for a company could be devastating.

Tactical plans operate within the strategic plan. The new factory has to be brought into commission and production has to be scheduled and controlled. Plans for the latter are tactical, since they focus on how to implement the strategic plan.

Control

The pre-requisite of control is planning. Controlling involves comparing events with plans, correcting deviations and ensuring that the planned events happen. Sometimes deviations are so fundamental that they require a revision to the plan so that later events are controlled against a new plan. For example the original sales forecast may turn out to be too optimistic, and production plans may have to be reduced to bring output into line with what sales are possible.

There are various ways in which control can be exercised. It can be predictive as in the case of a cash-flow forecast. This forecast may indicate a shortfall of cash in August but a surplus in September. The finance manager may need to arrange additional finance with the bank in August and then in September he might deposit surplus funds onto the money market. The point here is that variances are predicted in advance, thereby promoting cash control.

In the case of monthly comparisons between budgeted expenditures and actual expenditures an overspend might be revealed. This triggers action which holds back expenditure until spending comes back into line with budget. This is historical control since action is based on a report of events in the recent past.

Concurrent control is 'real time' such as that which might occur in controlling a continuous process or a production line. In this case the system has built in 'feedback' which enables it to remain in balance by regulating inputs and outputs. An example of concurrent control would be where a production process requires temperature regulation. The control system is designed to switch off heating when temperature reaches a threshold or switch on heating when it drops to a minimum level. The 'feedback' is information on temperature. The same principle applies in some stock control systems, where stocks are maintained at pre-determined minimum and maximum levels, with supplies being switched on and off to maintain equilibrium.

Leadership and direction

Planning and control activities are the tasks of management: however, they are only achieved through people. People will work effectively if they are led and directed properly. This implies that top managers must be in touch with the business and be visible. They must have a clear vision for the future, reinforced by specific objectives which are communicated to their employees.

This approach to leadership is apparent in some of our best companies as exemplified by Marks & Spencer. Such companies have a clear mission and objectives, and have a visible committed top management. This philosophy permeates the whole organization stimulating better performance from all employees.

Motivating good performance from all employees is the responsibility of all managers. What motivates individuals and groups within commercial organizations is a complex and important subject, the detail of which is well beyond the scope of this book. However, it is still worth saying that managers must discover what it is that will stimulate employees to work productively.

In general people respond best to 'considerate' styles of management, whereby their personal contributions are fully recognized. It is also true that there has to be an atmosphere of discipline coupled with a work-oriented culture. The task has to be accomplished, and being considerate does not extend to the toleration of slack or sloppy practices and behaviour.

Clear direction, sound and explicit guidelines, well worked out procedures all of which are well communicated, ensure that the organization works smoothly.

Allocation and supervision of work

This is the practical implementation of all that we have discussed in this section. An organization exists to fulfil the goals of its owners. It has to function in a co-ordinated and rational way. The people who are its members have to work together and understand their specific roles and functions. They need to receive directions and work has to be allocated. There has to be supervision of these activities. An organization is analogous to a machine or a living organism. In order to function properly everything has to work together smoothly. The managers have the task of ensuring that this work takes place according to plan and within the organization's stated objectives.

Test your knowledge 1.5

1 Can effective control be exercised without planning? If not, why not?
2 Why is it important to have good leadership and direction in an organization?

Activity 1.3

A case study on organization

A company makes diesel engines for use in a variety of products and environments. It had one division which shipped 'knocked down' kits (KD) to overseas assemblers (these assemblers were foreign subsidiaries of the company). These firms assembled the kits into working engines and sold them on to other manufacturers for incorporation into their products. The kits were put together based on engineering specifications for each type of engine. A pre-production control department was responsible for translating the engineering specifications into packing lists used to prepare and pack the kits for export. Engineering specifications were constantly being updated to improve designs and to correct faults which came to light during service. Changes often had to be carefully planned so that the KD parts shipped were compatible and of the same engineering level.

The KD operation received many complaints about the kits. Some assemblers said they could not assemble the engines because of specification errors or because the wrong parts were shipped. The pre-production control department was very sceptical about these complaints and was slow to respond. A proportion of the complaints were ill-founded so requests for urgent replacements were given a low priority and normal packing operations deadlines were considered more important than sending out urgent miscellaneous orders to enable the overseas assembly locations to complete their work.

The management were under heavy pressure to meet their own packing deadlines which were constantly threatened by supply problems of all kinds and by frequent changes to orders from overseas assemblers. The kits normally took between six weeks and three months to reach their destination by sea-freight, while miscellaneous orders had to be air-freighted at high cost.

The problems continued to worsen as complaints from overseas companies grew. These companies tried to anticipate problems by comparing the packing documentation with the manufacturing engineering process sheets and faxing in queries on all discrepancies. This generated so many queries that it was impossible to respond quickly even if pre-production activities wished to. This actually generated even more inertia on their part. In the end Head Office appointed a senior manager as troubleshooter and sent him in to solve the problems.

What is wrong with this organization?
What role should the manufacturing engineering activity play here?
What should be the troubleshooter's first priority?
What do you think his actions should be for a longer-term solution?

Discuss this in small groups and prepare a brief presentation on your proposed solution.

Commercial functions and engineering

This section examines some of the main functional areas of businesses and shows the interface between them. It discusses the variety of jobs done by engineers in business, and how engineering techniques are used with other techniques in fulfilling the needs of the business.

Finance and accounting

The Director of Finance will manage the company's cash flow, short-term and long-term investments and supervise the company's accounting and budgetary system. His job is to ensure that the company has sufficient cash to support day-to-day operations. He should also ensure that cash that is not immediately required is made to work for the company. This is done by arranging short-term investments on the money markets or by switching funds into building society or bank deposit accounts. He may also be involved with international money flows and the 'hedging' of risk against exchange rate losses.

The financial accountant will be in charge of all recording in the financial accounting system. All business transactions are recorded in a system called double entry accounts. These records are called this because every business transaction has a two-fold effect, and to make a complete record this two-fold aspect has to be recorded. For example if £100 was spent to buy raw materials, there has to be a record in the bank account of the money spent and then the existence of materials bought must be recorded in a purchases account. This method of recording enables the business to produce a profit and loss account and a balance sheet, which summarize all the transactions so that financial performance can be tracked and reported to shareholders and other interested parties, including the tax authorities.

The management accountant will administer the budgetary control and costing system. This system enables the business to forward plan its profit and loss and its overall financial position, as well as being able to control and report on costs of operation. Thus a budgeted profit and loss account and balance sheet is produced, called a Master Budget. This Master Budget summarizes the budgets for all cost centres or operating divisions. The management accountant monitors actual results against the budget and will use data from the double entry accounts system referred to above. This monitoring enables departmental managers to correct deviations to budget, control and manage the cost of running their departments.

Part of management accounting is the process of investment appraisal to plan the purchase of fixed assets and to ensure the best choices are made for new and replacement equipment. The management accountant will also prepare reports and analyses of various kinds for management.

The cashier, who is likely to report to the financial accountant, will deal with all bank and cash transactions. In a large company the number of transactions is considerable, especially those that deal with receipts from customers and payments to suppliers. The work of this section is important because forecasting and monitoring cash flow is vital to the financial well-being of the business.

The credit controller will be concerned with authorizing new credit customers and controlling the amount of credit granted and reducing or preventing bad debts. A budget will be prepared giving planned levels for outstanding debtors. This figure really represents a short-term investment of capital in customers. This investment has to be managed within budgeted limits otherwise the company's finance costs would increase and there would be further risks of non-payment. The credit controller would monitor the financial stability of existing customers or vet the standing of new customers. He might do this through a combination of bank references, credit agencies and studying the customers' own published accounts.

Other activities carried out in accounting include payment of wages and salaries, depreciation of fixed assets, maintaining shareholder records and paying shareholder dividends.

A typical organization structure for the accounting and finance function is given in Figure 1.8 which shows the departmental divisions indicated above.

Figure 1.8 *The finance organization*

Finance functions which involve engineers

In some businesses, especially manufacturing, engineers will be involved with costing of complex products. This costing activity may require cost accounting expertise coupled with engineering skills and knowledge, so that a new product's costs can be determined. This may also involve value engineering and value analysis in a team that includes accountants. This is a product improvement approach which simplifies the product or substitutes cheaper materials. The product's functionality is maintained, but is achieved more cheaply. For example a metal component might be replaced by a cheaper plastic alternative.

The costing of manufacturing processes and the determination of methods for charging overhead costs to products may be subject to advice from manufacturing or production engineers.

Interfaces with other functions

The finance and accounting function interfaces with all other functions within the business. Its recording and monitoring activities are central to, and have a major impact on, the whole business. Some of the details of these interfaces are given below as we discuss the work of other important functions.

Test your knowledge 1.6

1 Briefly outline the jobs of:
   Financial accountant
   Management accountant
   Cashier
   Credit controller.

Marketing, sales and distribution

Marketing

Marketing is said to be the most important function in the business, since if customers cannot be found for the company's products the company will go out of business, regardless of how financially well run or efficient it is.

Although sales is considered separately later, it is really part of the marketing function. Marketing is all about matching company products with customer *needs*. If customer needs are correctly identified and understood, then products can be made which will give the customer as much as possible of what he wants. Companies which view the customer as 'sovereign' are those companies that stay in business, because customers will continue to buy products that meet their requirements.

Hence marketing activities are centred around the process of filling customers' known needs, discovering needs the customer does not yet know he has and exploiting this by finding out how to improve products so that customers will buy this company's products in preference to other goods. Some of the most important activities are:

● market research
● monitoring trends in technology and customer tastes
● tracking competitor's activities
● promotion activities
● preparing sales forecasts.

Remember that in some businesses the marketing activity is directed at end-consumers, members of the public. This has to be done by national forms of advertising, such as TV commercials, direct mail, newspapers or through major retailers selling to the consumer. The methods used may be somewhat different if the customers are other companies. Although the principle of meeting customer needs is the same, the approach taken may be much more technical and may include the services of sales engineers to provide technical backup and advice. The publicity methods are more likely to be centred around trade fairs, exhibitions, advertisements in the trade press or technical journals for example. You should note these two distinct marketing approaches are called, respectively, consumer marketing and industrial marketing.

Sales

The sales department is concerned with advertising and selling goods. It will have procedures for controlling sales and the documentation required. The documents used are the same as for purchasing, described below, except from the supplier's viewpoint rather than from the customer's. It may employ commercial travellers or have a resident sales force. It is involved with many possible ways of publicizing the company's products such as trade fairs, wholesalers' displays, press and TV advertising, special campaigns, promotional videos, etc. It will also be concerned about the quality of goods and services as well as administering warranty and guarantee services, returns and repairs, etc.

Sales will maintain contacts with customers which will entail the following customer services:

● technical support
● after-sales service, service engineering
● product information, prices and delivery
● maintaining customer records.

A typical marketing and sales organization for a company engaged in industrial marketing is shown in Figure 1.9.

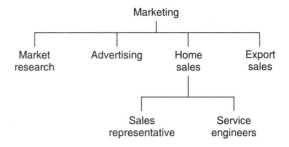

Figure 1.9 *Marketing and sales organization*

Distribution – consumer markets

For companies operating in the consumer marketing field distribution can be accomplished through a variety of ways. This can include wholesalers, retailers, mail order or direct selling through the company's own retail outlets. Some companies may use all of these methods. We will examine the wholesale and retail systems, as well as the pricing aspects.

Retail outlets

These outlets sell direct to the consumer. Most of these are shops or mail order businesses. Retailers fall into several types, hypermarkets, supermarkets, multiple shops, departmental stores, co-operative retail societies, independent retailers, voluntary retail chains, franchise outlets, discount stores.

The purpose of retailing is to provide for the availability of goods close to where consumers live. Retailers also study consumer preferences and stock goods accordingly. They also keep manufacturers informed of what it is that consumers want so that supply matches demand.

Wholesale outlets

If a retailer requires a large range of goods in relatively small quantities it is not very convenient to buy direct from manufacturers. Think of the number of different manufacturers that a small independent grocer would have to deal with if he did deal direct with each manufacturer. Hence the continuing need for wholesalers, who stock goods from many manufacturers and can supply smaller quantities to retailers.

The wholesaler is a middle man and it is said that his presence puts up prices. This is not necessarily the case, since manufacturers can sell to him in bulk quantities and save on transport and administration costs. In effect, wholesalers operate as intermediate storage depots for retailers and therefore provide a useful service. They can usually provide retailers with credit terms of trading, often enabling small businesses to sell before they have to pay for goods, or at least to reduce the impact of the cost of carrying a large range of stock items.

They can also act as a buffer to smooth out demand for manufacture. If demand is seasonal they can buy regularly through the year, thus making it easy for manufacturers to make goods in economic runs and then store stock to meet heavy demand, but which does not place excessive loads on the manufacturer's capacity.

Wholesalers as such have been in decline in recent times, thus many manufacturers have started to deal direct, especially with large retailers, such as the supermarkets. However, they have had to take over the functions of storage, transport and dealing directly with retailers.

Mail order

Companies may decide to deal directly with the public through mail order, thus bypassing the wholesaler and retailer. Mail order depends on a good postal service or the existence of transport operators who can provide a similar service. It has the advantage of being nationwide or even international, thus extending the potential market enormously.

In some cases there are very large mail order retailers who buy from manufacturers and sell on to consumers. These companies sometimes operate normal retail outlets as well.

Price structure

It is common for distributor prices to be expressed at a percentage discount from the price to be paid by the consumer. Thus manufacturers give discounts to wholesalers as an incentive to stock their goods and to provide a profit margin for him. A similar system will be used by the wholesaler when dealing with the retailer. However, if a price to the final consumer is not envisaged or fixed, then the situation is less clear and each party must charge a price which his particular market will stand and depending on what quantities he needs to sell and what his actual costs are going to be.

In addition to wholesale and trade discounts, quantity discounts may be offered to encourage distributors to buy in large quantities which may be more economical to supply and deliver, since there are economies of scale to be had, such as lower manufacturing, administrative and transport costs.

Further incentives may be offered in giving cash discounts. Cash discounts reward immediate or early payment. This may enable the manufacturer or wholesaler to reduce his need for working capital and reduce credit collection and control costs.

Discount structures are therefore used for many purposes. First to increase sales, secondly to influence the pattern of sales and thirdly to reduce the costs of production and distribution. Sometimes discounts can produce more sales but have very little effect on profits since higher volumes and lower costs may not compensate for lower margins.

You should be aware that price is influenced by many factors:

(a) actual cost of manufacture
(b) what the market will stand
(c) what others are charging for similar products
(d) consumers' perceptions of quality and value.

The interaction of supply and demand is complex and outside the scope of this course. However, if supply exceeds demand, in general this exerts a downward pressure on prices, as manufacturers and distributors seek to sell goods they have made or bought. The costs of storage and distribution may so high as to force sale at prices which might be below average cost. This is especially true of perishable goods and foodstuffs.

Alternatively, if demand exceeds supply that tends to bid up the price as consumers search for supplies. In some cases the increase in price then serves to limit demand since some potential buyers drop out when the price goes too high, this then acts to dampen demand again and tends to bring equilibrium between supply and demand.

As you can appreciate this can get very complicated when manufacturers, wholesalers and retailers start to offer the different discounts to try to influence events in their favour. Sometimes the competition is so cutthroat that the only winner is the consumer. In some cases the weaker players go under, leaving the more efficient firms to operate in a less hostile environment. Sometimes the bigger, stronger firms deliberately cut prices so low as to force others out of business and then exploit the consumer when they can dominate the market. However, this can go in reverse again if then prices go too high and this attracts new players into the market who will then increase supply which will then produce a downward pressure again on prices, and so it goes on.

Distribution – industrial markets

For industrial market distribution the situation is more variable. Frequently the seller will have his own fleet of vehicles and may have warehousing facilities or geographically dispersed depots. An example might be a company which manufactures components for the motor industry. It may manufacture in one or more locations and have storage depots located near its customers. It may also deliver products direct to the motor manufacturer's plant either using its own transport or by using an independent haulier.

If the company makes products for international markets it may have to prepare and package products for sea- or air-freight. This could include using haulage contractors who will deliver direct into Europe using roll-on roll-off ferries.

Price structure

This is also very variable, but is usually based on negotiation between the seller and buyer. It may be done through a process of enquiry and quotation or may simply be based on price lists and discounts separately negotiated.

Marketing functions that involve engineers

Where technical support is required the marketing function may employ sales engineers who can advise the customer on aspects of product design, product functionality and the technical characteristics of given products. They will be able to advise on the most suitable engineering solutions to meet customer requirements. In some environments companies will employ service engineers who carry out servicing and repairs, often on customers premises.

Below in the discussions on the interface of marketing with other functions there are frequent contacts with engineers operating within these functions.

Interfaces with other functions

Interface with manufacturing

Sales forecasts will be used to prepare factory schedules. Production may be sent to a warehouse and then put into the delivery and distribution system. From there the sales force will ensure that customers receive their orders when required. Alternatively delivery of specific customer orders may be made directly to customers.

Interface with research and development

Marketing will identify customer needs and will liaise with product development activities on possible new products or modifications to existing products. R&D will initiate design studies and prototypes for new products and may supply some items for market testing. Engineers involved with design and development will be given information on customer needs and preferences and will be expected to produce designs which meet those requirements.

Test your knowledge 1.7

1 What is the most important function of marketing?
2 What is the purpose of market research?
3 Why do some companies use wholesalers rather than sell direct?
4 Name two ways of determining the price of a product.
5 What does a sales engineer do?

Interface with finance and accounting

Marketing will supply information on prices. Prices may be determined primarily by the market rather than the cost of manufacture. Finance may provide cost information, but marketing may make the final pricing decisions.

Research and development (R&D)

New product design and development is often a crucial factor in the survival of a company. In an industry which is fast changing firms must continually revise their design and range of products. This is necessary because of the relentless progress of technology as well as the actions of competitors and the changing preferences of customers.

A good example of this situation is the motor industry. The British motor industry has gone through turbulent times, caused by its relative inefficiency compared with Japan and Germany and also because the quality of its products was below that of its competitors. This difficult position was then made worse by having products which lacked some of the innovative features of the competition.

Strategies for product development

There are three basic ways of approaching design and development:

● driven by marketing
● driven by technology
● co-ordinated approach.

A system driven by marketing is one that puts the customer needs first, and only produces goods which are known to sell. Market research is carried out which establishes what is needed. If the development is technology driven then it is a matter of selling what it is possible to make. The product range is developed so that production processes are as efficient as possible and the products are technically superior, hence possessing a natural advantage in the marketplace. Marketing's job is therefore to create the market and sell the product.

Both approaches have their merits, but each of them omit important aspects, hence the idea that a co-ordinated approach would be better. With this approach the needs of the market are considered at the same time as the needs of the production operation and of design and development. In many businesses this interfunctional system works best, since the functions of R&D, production, marketing, purchasing, quality control and material control are all taken into account.

However, its success depends on how well the interface between these functions is managed and integrated. Sometimes committees are used, as are matrix structures or task forces (the latter being set up especially to see-in new product developments). In some parts of the motor industry a function called 'programme timing' co-ordinates the activities of the major functions by agreeing and setting target dates and events using network planning techniques.

The development process

The basic process is outlined as follows:

- idea generation
- selection of suitable products
- preliminary design
- prototype construction
- testing
- final design.

This is a complex process and involves co-operative work between the design and development engineers, marketing specialists, production engineers and skilled craft engineers to name some of the major players.

Ideas can come from the identification of new customer needs, the invention of new materials or the successful modification of existing products. Selection from new ideas will be based on factors like:

- market potential
- financial feasibility
- operations compatibility.

This means screening out ideas which have little marketability, are too expensive to make at a profit and which do not fit easily alongside current production processes.

After this, preliminary designs will be made within which trade-offs between cost, quality and functionality will be made. This can involve the processes of value analysis and value engineering. These processes look at both the product and the methods of production with a view to maintaining good product performance and durability while achieving low cost.

Prototypes are then produced, possibly by hand and certainly by not by using mass production methods. This is followed by rigorous testing to verify the marketing and technical performance characteristics required. Sometimes this process will involve test marketing to check customer acceptance of the new product.

Final design will include the modifications made to the design as a result of prototype testing. The full specification and drawings will be prepared so that production can be planned and started.

R&D functions that involve engineers

It goes without saying that R&D of manufactured products is going to centre around the employment of professional engineers of various levels, all the way down to various grades of craftsmen and machine operators. The Professional Engineers (in the UK these will be Chartered or Incorporated) will lead and supervise the design of new products and will be involved with the testing of prototypes. Various grades of technicians will be involved with the production of drawings and a range of support functions including diagnosis, fault-finding, testing and data gathering. Craftsmen will make prototypes and will also make the modifications for further testing.

Interfaces with other functions

The interface with marketing, manufacturing and purchasing is covered the sections devoted to those functions.

Interface with finance

There will be a need to communicate details of the costs of new products or redesigned products. The processes required to produce new components or whole new products will also require costing. R&D may specify the manufacturing process, but manufacturing engineering departments located at the production facility will implement them, and may also share in the costing process.

Manufacturing operations

The production or manufacturing operation is at the heart of the business. It translates the designs for products, which are based on market analysis, into the goods wanted by customers.

The production process can be seen within a framework of five main areas which we will now discuss.

Process and facilities management

Decisions have to be made in relation to location of the factory and the design and layout of production facilities. The design of production processes is interactive with product design, requiring close co-operation with research and development and marketing functions.

Selecting the process of production is important and is strategic in nature. This means that it has a wide impact on the operation of the entire business. Decisions in this area bind the company to particular kinds of equipment and labour force because the large capital investments that have to be made limit future options. For example a motor manufacturer has to commit very large expenditures to lay down plant for production lines to mass produce cars. Once in production the company is committed to the technology and the capacity created for a long time into the future.

There are three basic methods for process design:

- line flow
- intermittent flow
- project.

Line flow is the type of system used in the motor industry for assembly lines for cars. It also includes continuous-type production of the kind that exists in the chemicals and food industries. Both kinds of line flow are characterized by linear sequences of operations and continuous flows and tend to be highly automated and highly standardized.

Intermittent flow is the typical batch production or job shop, which uses general-purpose equipment and highly skilled labour. This system is more flexible than line flow, but is much less efficient than line flow. It is most appropriate when a company is producing small numbers of non-standard products, perhaps to a customer's specification.

Finally, project-based production is used for unique products which may be produced one at a time. Strictly speaking there is not a flow of products, but instead there is sequence of operations on the product which have to be planned and controlled. This system of production is used for prototype production in R&D and is used in some engineering companies who produce major machine tool equipment for other companies to use in their factories.

Capacity planning

Once facilities for production have been put in place the next step is to decide how to flex the capacity to meet predicted demand. Production managers will use a variety of ways to achieve this from maintaining excess capacity to making customers queue or wait for goods, to having stocks to deal with excess demand. The process is complex and may require the use of forecasting techniques, together with careful planning.

Scheduling activities are different for each process method and require the use of a variety of techniques. The objectives of good scheduling are:

- meeting customer delivery dates
- correct loading of facilities
- planning starting times
- ensuring jobs are completed on time.

Inventory control

With any manufacturing facility good inventory control is an absolute essential. It is estimated that it costs up to 25% of the cost value of stock items per year to maintain an item in stock. Proper control systems have to be used to ensure that there is sufficient stock for production while at the same time ensuring that too much stock is not held. If stock levels are high there are costs associated with damage, breakage, pilferage and storage which can be avoided.

Workforce management

This is related to the need to have a labour force trained to use the facilities installed. The important aspects here are:

- work and method study
- work measurement
- job design
- health and safety.

The production manager has to establish standards of performance for work so that the capacity of the factory can be determined and so that the labour costs of products can be calculated. Work study, method study and work measurement activities enable this to be done, as well as helping to promote efficient and safe methods of working. The design of jobs is important in respect of worker health as well as effective work. Good job design can also make the work more interesting and improves employee job satisfaction, which in turn can improve productivity.

Quality control

Quality is a key objective for most business organizations. It is especially important to the production function which is making the product for the customer.

What is meant by the word quality? It is generally defined as 'fitness for purpose'. In effect this means meeting the identified needs of customers. Thus it is really the customer that determines whether or not a company has produced a quality product, since it is the customer who judges value received and registers satisfaction or dissatisfaction.

This does bring problems for manufacturers since customer perceptions of quality vary, some customers will like a product more than other customers will. Hence a manufacturer has to use some more objective criteria for assessing fitness for purpose. It has been suggested that this must include:

● design quality
● conformance quality
● reliability
● service.

Design quality is the primary responsibility of R&D and Marketing. It relates to the development of a specification for the product that meets identified needs. Conformance quality means producing a product that conforms to the design specification. A product that conforms is a quality product, even if the design itself is for a cheap product. That seems contradictory, but consider the following example. A design is drawn up for a 'budget' camera, which is made from inexpensive materials and has limited capability. This camera serves a particular market. If the manufacture conforms to the specification then the product is of high quality, even though the design is of 'low' quality compared with other more up-market cameras.

Reliability includes things like continuity of use measured by things like 'mean time between failure' (MTBF). Thus a product will operate for a specified time, on average, before it fails. It should also be maintainable when it does fail, either because it can easily and cheaply be replaced or because repair is fast and easy. Service relates to after sales service, guarantees and warranties.

Quality control is therefore concerned with administering all of these aspects. In the UK there are general standards for quality systems, the most relevant one here is BS 5750 and the international counterpart, ISO 9000. The activities of quality control include the following:

● Inspection, testing and checking of incoming materials and components.
● Inspection, testing and checking of the company's own products.
● Administering any supplier quality assurance systems.
● Dealing with complaints and warranty failures.
● Building quality into the manufacturing process.

Some of these activities are done after the event to monitor quality, other activities may be carried out to prevent problems before they occur. Some activities may be carried out to determine causes of failure that relate to design rather than manufacturing faults.

Production functions that involve engineers

As in research and development, engineers are a vital part of the production function. Manufacturing and production engineers are concerned with the setup and maintenance of machines and equipment for production. They will have a crucial role to play in conformance to design specifications and in ensuring manufacturing quality. They will ensure that there is sufficient capacity to meet demand and they will be responsible for the design of jobs and processes.

Interfaces of production with other functions

The interface with marketing and purchasing is discussed in the sections dealing with these functions.

Interface with research and development

New products will have different characteristics, and perhaps be made from different materials from previous products with similar functionality. This will require liaison between design engineers and manufacturing engineering on methods for production and in deciding what manufacturing equipment and machine tools are required. Detailed process sheets may be required which show how products are to be assembled or made.

While the particular methods of production are the province of production management, the designer has to be aware of the implications for his design of different methods of manufacture, whether this be batch production, assembly lines or one-off projects. Detailed specifications of the new and changed product will be communicated and there may liaison on temporary and permanent deviations to original specifications in order to facilitate production.

When quality problems appear and are related to faulty design there will be liaison on ways in which design modifications can be phased into production as soon as possible.

Interface with finance

There will be proposals for the replacement of machines and equipment. This function may require quite sophisticated techniques for what is called 'investment appraisal' so that the company can choose the best methods of manufacture from several alternatives.

Also important is the control of raw materials and component stocks, especially the levels of 'work-in-process'. Finance will want to restrict stock levels to reduce the amount of capital tied up in stocks, while the production manager will be concerned with having sufficient stock to maintain production, but avoiding congestion of factory floor space.

Budgetary control of production cost centres will involve regular contact and advice from the finance function. Matters of interest will be costs of production, wastage rates, labour costs, obsolescent stock, pilferage, etc.

Test your knowledge 1.9

1 Explain the purpose of the following production functions:
   manufacturing/production engineering
   capacity planning
   inventory control
   quality control.
2 State and briefly describe the three methods of process design.
3 Name three techniques used in workforce management.

Purchasing and supply

Main functions

In large businesses purchasing is done by professional buyers, and is therefore a centralized activity. When a company has a large purchasing budget this makes economic sense, since the large purchasing power gives advantages in negotiating for keen prices, better delivery times or increased quality. In small businesses the purchasing function is not centralized, usually because the operation is not large enough to support the employment of specialists. However, the basic principles of purchasing are the same, whatever the organizational structure. The main functions are:

- researching sources of supply
- making enquiries and receiving quotations
- negotiating terms and delivery times
- placing contracts and orders
- expediting delivery
- monitoring quality and delivery performance.

The basic documents used are as follows:

- requisitions from departments to buyer
- enquiry forms or letters to suppliers
- quotation document in reply to enquiry
- order or contract to buy
- advice note – sent in advance of goods.
- invoice – bill for goods sent to the buyer
- debit note – additional/further charge to invoice
- credit note – reduction in charge to invoice
- consignment note – accompanies goods for international haulage, containing full details of goods, consignee, consignor, carrier and other details
- delivery note – to accompany goods.

Purchasing procedures involve raising a requisition to buy. This may then require obtaining quotations or estimates in order to choose the best supplier. Orders are sent to the chosen supplier. Goods are despatched by the supplier, together with a delivery or advice note. When goods are received they are checked to see that the details on the delivery note agree with the actual goods received and that the goods have in fact been ordered. Goods not ordered may be refused. Accepted deliveries are signed for on the supplier's copy and given back to the driver. A goods received note is raised and sent to the purchasing department, so that the accounting function can be given confirmation of delivery before making payment against receipt of invoice.

These procedures are for the purpose of making sure that the goods are delivered on time, in the correct quantities, of the correct specifications and of the desired quality. Only if all is well is payment authorized.

A typical large, centralized purchasing organization would be as shown in the organization chart in Figure 1.10. It is common for there

Figure 1.10 *A centralized purchasing function*

to be a purchasing manager and buyers who will specialize in particular types of commodity. Sometimes the products being purchased require that the buyer is technically qualified.

Purchasing functions that involve engineers

When the products being purchased are technically complex and the decisions being made require the buyer to be able to interpret engineering drawings and specifications and to make judgements on the technical merits of a given supplier's products then an engineer may be employed as a buyer.

In such cases he will liaise with the company's own engineers and with the supplier's R&D engineers or sales engineers. An example could be where a manufacturer requires new machine tools to produce a new range of products in his factory. The manufacturing engineer will specify the type of machine required and provide a technical specification and perhaps a list of preferred suppliers. The engineer/buyer would then proceed to obtain quotations and technical details from potential buyers and will act as the link between manufacturing engineering and the supplier.

Interfaces between purchasing and other functions

These will depend on the kind of business but will include some or all of the following:

Interface with research and development
Specifications and drawings will be sent to the buyer for new products or machines for purchase. Problems of design and delivery will be discussed, modifications to designs will be sent to suppliers through the buying department. New product launches will be co-ordinated with R&D, the supplier, and of course, the factory. The buyer would be involved with supplies of new raw materials, new designs for components and will negotiate costs of tooling and long-term contracts.

Interface with manufacturing
Liaison with factory management on initial supplies for new materials or components. Assistance may given by the buyer to deal with quality and inspection problems and in dealing with return and replacement of defective materials. Sometimes buyers may be an interface with production and research and development in dealing with temporary or permanent deviations from the original engineering specifications. Chasing deliveries and ensuring supplies for factory use may be a major daily routine for some buying departments.

Systems for quality control may include some form of supplier quality assurance. The buying department will represent company interests to suppliers and may only use suppliers who have passed the company's quality assurance standards. The buyer will be involved with searches for new suppliers who can meet existing and new quality requirements.

Stock control systems used within the factory will affect the way purchasing is done. Economic order quantities may be established which the buyer has to take into account when arranging supplies. Deliveries may have to be phased according to minimum and maximum and re-order stock levels. The buyer will need a clear understanding of the importance of deliveries which enable the company to control its inventory costs, while at the same time ensuring a reliable supply of materials and components for production. The company may operate a 'just-in-time' system (JIT). JIT originated in Japan and is a way of delivering supplies at the point in time they are required by production, and avoids the costs of holding buffer stocks of raw materials and components. It works well when suppliers are dependable and when transport systems are good. The buyer will liaise with the factory on the establishment of JIT for given products.

Interface with accounting and finance

There will be the routine matters of passing invoices for payment of goods or dealing with returns for credit so that accounts department can pay for goods received. Materials purchasing will be subject to budgetary constraints like most other company activities. The purchasing department will be involved, either directly or indirectly in budgets for inventory levels, and in setting up minimum, maximum and re-order levels for stocks. Monthly monitoring of inventory levels will be done by the accounting function and purchasing activities may be responsible for ensuring that stocks of components and raw materials stay within agreed levels.

> **Test your knowledge 1.10**
>
> 1 Outline the basic documents for purchasing goods and the sequence in which they are used.
> 2 List the main functions of a purchasing department.

Financial and operational factors

The usual techniques for costing, budgeting, inventory control, investment appraisal, make or buy decisions and forecasting are examined and compared using examples drawn from a variety of situations. Cost control is concerned with collecting operating cost data and then monitoring and controlling these costs. Budgeting is the process of forecasting the financial position and providing a plan against which to monitor profitability. Inventory control is the establishment of economic levels of stock while maintaining production. Investment appraisal enables managers to choose the best projects for investment using discounted cash-flow techniques. Other techniques are examined that enable choices to be made to make or buy and to forecast sales and production.

Cost control

Cost accounting is part of the management accounting function, indeed, without a system for cost accounting effective management accounting could not exist. Management accounting exists to provide information for the internal control and management of a business. Thus cost accounting is necessary for a company to be able to identify responsibility for costs and to exercise control over actual costs compared with planned expenditure.

This is a very important function in respect of research and development as well as manufacturing activities. Engineers are subject to the discipline of budgetary control as are other specialists and it is essential that costs can be monitored and controlled so that engineering projects, for example, meet target costs and profits.

The elements of cost

A manufacturing example

The elements of cost in a typical manufacturing company can be analysed as follows:

Example 1.1 Cost analysis

Cost analysis	£
Direct materials	1200
Direct labour	800
Direct expenses	200
Prime cost	2200
Factory indirect expenses	1100
Production cost	3300
Administration expenses	1300
Selling and distribution expenses	2100
Finance expenses	900
Total cost	7600

Direct costs (for materials, labour and expenses) are costs which can be identified with a particular product or cost unit, and as such would not have been incurred had that product or cost unit not existed. These costs are quite easy to identify. For example, a car headlamp assembly will be based on an engineering bill-of-materials, specifying components and quantities required. Similarly the standard times for assembly will be known, either by work measurement or from actual data, so the direct labour cost can be calculated. If the assembly has to be delivered to the customer then the direct expense of the specific delivery can easily be obtained.

However, separately identified direct expenses are relatively rare. This is because costs for deliveries, for example, are often included in the buying price for materials or the selling price of finished goods. But something like royalties payable to a patent or copyright owner are common in some industries, such as in publishing. *Prime cost* is therefore the total of these three elements.

Factory indirect expenses (another term used is manufacturing overhead) are all the other expenses concerned with the manufacturing process which cannot be traced, or it is not worth tracing, to the product or cost unit. These costs may include power usage, supervision, plant maintenance, non-production consumable materials, etc. Together with prime cost these make up the total *works* or *production cost* of manufacture.

The remaining overheads are for the administration, selling and distribution and finance costs. When added to production cost the whole or *total cost* of operations is obtained.

Although the example is that of manufacture, these elements of cost are universally applicable to all industries and commercial operations.

How cost information is collected

Materials

It may seem that materials costs can be accounted for easily, and that is true in terms of the identification of direct materials that are part of the physical product. However, pricing of materials may be quite tricky, since prices for some items will vary up or down over time and it may not be clear which price should be used. This is not a problem where a company makes products for specific orders and therefore only buys in materials to fulfil such orders. In such cases the specific price paid is explicitly known and identified. However, when a business keeps stocks of raw materials which are purchased periodically to maintain such stocks it is a different matter, since purchase prices will vary over time and a decision has to be made at the point in time materials issues are made to production departments. This is not the simple decision that it first appears to be for a number of reasons, not least of which is the matter of being able to compare product costs over time and being able to value inventories for accounting purposes.

Methods for pricing stores issues
There are numerous methods of doing this and we shall look at several in common use.

First in – first out (FIFO)
This method assumes that stock delivered first is used first. This assumption may actually be a fiction, although it could reflect what really happens, for instance perishable goods will almost certainly be used in rotation. However, what actually happens is irrelevant, since we are only concerned with *pricing* stock issues according to a logical pattern, in this case according to earliest prices first. Example 1.2 shows how the stock account would look under FIFO when there are price differences.

Apart from the obvious assumption of issuing stock in rotation FIFO has the following characteristics:

● based on actual costs
● product costs lag behind price rises/falls
● can be time consuming if many entries made.

The lag effect identified above is important. In a period of inflation it leads to undercosting of products compared with current

Example 1.2   Stock ledger for FIFO

Mild steel strips

Date	Receipts Qty	Receipts Price	Issues Qty	Issues Price	Balance Qty	Balance Price
Feb. 1	20	£1			20	£1
Mar. 1	20	£1.10	15	£1	5	£1
					20	£1.10
Apr. 1			5	£1		
			10	£1.10	10	£1.10
May 1	20	£1.15			10	£1.10
					20	£1.15

conditions. Logically it can also lead to overstatement of profit because current prices are not reflected in costs. If many products are affected this can be very significant, leading to other undesirable situations like paying too much tax because profit is overstated. Of course this is reversed when prices are falling, and may therefore be beneficial. However, it is probably just as bad to understate profits as to overstate them. The ideal situation would be, of course, to state profit accurately.

Last in – first out (LIFO)
Unlike FIFO, LIFO is used to reflect current prices in product costs. That is because the latest price of goods in stock is used to price stores issues as shown in Example 1.3.

Example 1.3   Stock ledger for LIFO

Mild steel strips

Date	Receipts Qty	Receipts Price	Issues Qty	Issues Price	Balance Qty	Balance Price
Feb. 1	20	£1			20	£1
Mar. 1	20	£1.10	15	£1.10	20	£1
					5	£1.10
Apr. 1			5	£1.10		
			10	£1	10	£1
May 1	20	£1.15			10	£1
					20	£1.15

Although the pricing assumes issue in reverse rotation, that is not the case physically, and would be quite foolish for perishable goods. The characteristics of LIFO are as follows:

● based on actual costs
● latest prices are used giving current costs
● can be time consuming if many entries needed.

In a period of inflation LIFO enables current costs to be used and prevents profit from being overstated. The reverse would be true if prices were falling. However, if issues outstrip receipts, pricing will be based on earlier deliveries, which does introduce further distortions in product costs.

It is also true that LIFO tends to be less acceptable to the tax and regulatory authorities in the UK, since it can been used to massage accounts and avoid taxation. Certainly, swapping to LIFO when there is rapid inflation would be seen as manipulative by the authorities and would be contrary to the accounting principle of consistency in reporting business results.

Average Cost (AVCO)

This method of pricing is somewhere in between FIFO and LIFO in its effects and may be the preferred option because it reduces the effect of distortion caused by price changes. Example 1.4 shows how the stock ledger would appear.

Example 1.4   Stock ledger for AVCO

Mild steel strips

Date	Receipts Qty	Receipts Price	Issues Qty	Issues Price	Balance Qty	Balance Price
Feb. 1	20	£1			20	£1
Mar. 1	20	£1.10	15	£1.05	25	£1.05
Apr. 1			15	£1.05	10	£1.05
May 1	20	£1.15			30	£1.12

It should be noted that this is a weighted average, since it is calculated using the quantities at each purchase price to arrive at the average. Obviously the average has to be re-calculated after each new receipt of materials. For simplicity in our example only two decimal places are used to calculate averages, in practice greater accuracy would be required if significant rounding errors were to be avoided. The characteristics of AVCO are as follows:

● it evens out price fluctuations
● stock balances are valued at one price
● the lag effect of FIFO is reduced
● the calculations bring the risk of error.

How profit calculations are affected by pricing methods

We can see now that while the cost of materials appeared easy to get, especially for direct materials, the reality is very different. The various effects of the methods used, together with price changes, do distort costings to such a degree that it is probably impossible, in some circumstances, to arrive at a cost for products with absolute accuracy. Something we have to bear in mind when we study costing methods later.

To emphasize the effect of using different methods, Example 1.5 shows the standard way profit is calculated in company accounts and uses the data from the three examples of pricing given above. We can see that our caution is justified, as each method gives a different profit figure.

Example 1.5   The effect of pricing methods on profit calculation

	FIFO		LIFO		AVCO	
Sales		100		100		100
LESS cost of sales:						
Purchases	65		65		65	
Closing stock	(34)		(33)		(33.60)	
		31		32		31.40
Profit		69		68		68.60

The situation here is one of price inflation. We can see that FIFO gives the highest profit, LIFO the lowest and AVCO something in between.

These actual figures are, of course, trivial. But if we imagine that this effect is multiplied several thousand times to include all products manufactured, it will be seen that profit calculations can vary substantially. It is also clear that the valuation of closing stock (or ending stock) is different and is the cause of the different profits calculated above. Since this method of profit calculation is used in company accounting reports the effect of stock values and product cost values is of central importance.

Activity 1.4

Determine, from the information below, the value of the remaining stock after April 1 using in turn FIFO, LIFO, and AVCO.

Receipts:
  Jan. 1 50 @ £5
  Feb. 1 30 @ £5.20

Issues:
  Mar. 1 20
  Apr. 1 35

Labour costs

Labour costs are collected in two basic ways:

- time-based systems
- activity-based systems.

In time-based systems time sheets or mechanical time clocks will be used to record hours worked. Time clocks are generally used to record attendance time not activity time. If activity time must be recorded then some form of time sheet is likely to be used. Weekly time sheets are suitable for indirect workers, such as maintenance mechanics and daily sheets can be more useful for direct workers who may operate machines for making products.

If a job costing system is used then job sheets may have to be completed so that times can be recorded for each job worked on. In any case where activity or job time is different from attendance time some form of lost time analysis is needed so that causes of such wastage can be determined.

We can see that these processes are prone to errors and are no more precise than accounting for materials. However, even if errors are probable it is still possible to produce credible cost data from which to construct product costings.

The introduction of standard costs

The problems of collecting actual direct costs and then charging them to products have been clearly shown above. To overcome this it is possible to establish standard costs. These costs are pre-determined as opposed to collecting actual costs (or historical costs as they are called) and charging these to products. For labour costs this involves specifying each production process or operation and estimating the time required for each. From this a standard time for each product can be determined. A similar view is taken of wage rates, so that a standard rate can be used for given products. This allows the labour cost to be pre-determined for known products or processes.

Physical standards for direct materials can be determined from engineering standards and specifications from which a bill-of-materials is produced. The price for these materials can be pre-determined by estimating for possible price increases/decreases, wastage rates, scrap or spoilage.

The standard costing approach means that product costs can be determined before actual costs are collected. It facilitates managerial control because actual costs can be monitored against standard and variances calculated. It means that products can be costed, when needed, to a high degree of accuracy. Standard costs can be applied for each of the costing methods described below.

Costing methods

Absorption costing

The direct costs of products are easy to obtain and identify with a given product. The overheads or indirect costs are more difficult, since they may be totally unrelated to a given product, but are still part of the total cost of running the enterprise. Absorption costing is sometimes called total costing or full costing. It is called this because it adds overheads to direct costs, to obtain the total cost of a given product, by a process of *allocation*, *apportionment* and *absorption*.

Allocation

Indirect costs or overheads can be allocated as whole items to cost centres, such as production or service departments. Such costs are easily identified to these centres, but still cannot be specifically identified to products. (In cost accounting terminology cost centres are responsibility centres and are usually departmental units that are the domain of a given manager.)

Apportionment

Indirect costs which cannot be allocated as whole items have to be divided up or apportioned on some equitable basis. The basis of apportionment should be related to the incidence of cost. For example a machine maintenance department's costs could be divided between production departments on the basis of the number or perhaps more appropriately the value of machines in each case. Other costs such as business rates might be allocated on area used. Thus the apportioning method should correlate with the incidence of cost in some way. Generally costs which happen as a result of activity (termed variable costs) should be apportioned on an activity related basis, whereas costs which would be incurred even if no activity occurred (termed fixed costs), should be related to capacity provision. The two examples following are in accord with this principle.

Example 1.6 shows how indirect costs have been allocated and then apportioned from service departments to the production departments. The basis for apportioning the cost of service departments is machine value in each production department. Note that the direct costs of products would have already been identified with those products – what we are concerned with here are the indirect costs which have been charged to the various cost centres.

Example 1.6   Allocation and apportionment

	Production cost centres			Service cost centres	
	1	2	3	A	B
Indirect labour	1000	2000	1500	1800	1400
Other costs	3000	2500	1900	2700	2200
	4000	4500	3400	4500	3600
Apportion A	1500	1800	1200	(4500)	
Apportion B	1200	1440	960		(3600)
	6700	7740	5560	–	–

In example 1.6 the value of machines in each department is; Dept. 1 £5000, Dept. 2 £6000, Dept. 3 £4000, and this is used as the basis for apportionment of service costs. Therefore sharing service department A between these production departments has been done as follows:

Dept. 1   £4500 × £5000/15 000 = 1500
Dept. 2   £4500 × £6000/15 000 = 1800
Dept. 3   £4500 × £4000/15 000 = 1200

A similar process has been followed for service department B.

This method of allocation and apportionment between cost centres is commonly called the *elimination method*. There are more complex approaches, using the *algebraic method* or the *continuation method*. The former uses simultaneous equations and the latter involves continual reciprocal apportionments until all values have been transferred. These methods are more accurate and may be preferred, but are beyond the scope of this course. However, whether it is worth using more complex methods depends on how important it is to get extra accuracy. Our interest here is to understand the basic process of overhead allocation and apportionment, and the elimination method illustrated above serves our purpose well.

Our example is also a simple one so that the underlying principle can be clearly seen. In the real world of manufacture the number of production and service departments may be much greater and some service departments may serve other service departments, creating a much more complicated set of calculations.

Absorption
The final stage is to absorb the indirect costs into the product itself. This requires the development of an overhead recovery rate or overhead absorption rate that enables the cost to be shared according to the benefit received by the cost unit, product, job or project. There are numerous approaches to this and the following list is typical:

● direct wage percentage rate
● direct labour hour rate (£x per hour)
● machine hour rate (£x per hour)

- cost unit rate (£x per cost unit)
- standard cost rate (£x per pre-defined rate).

Which method is chosen depends on the kind of business and the way in which overhead costs are incurred. For example, if the occurrence of overhead cost is directly linked to machine usage, a machine hour rate might be appropriate. In a department where the work is labour intensive and most overheads are related to this, a labour hour rate or wage percentage rate might be the best.

If we return to Example 1.6 we can use the calculations to arrive at product costs. For this we will choose Department 1 costs as shown in Example 1.7.

Example 1.7   Department 1 product direct costs and time data

	Job 1	Job 2
Direct Costs	£300	£500
Machine hours	30	45
Labour hours	40	50

It has been ascertained that most of the indirect costs are related to machine usage rather than labour hours, i.e. for this cost centre a machine hour rate is used. It is known that the total machine hours produced are 2000, covering the same period as for the overhead costs. Therefore the machine hour recovery rate is £6700/2000 = £3.35. Thus, the total cost of each product can be shown as in Example 1.8.

Example 1.8   Department 1 total product costs

	Job 1	Job 2
Direct costs	£300	£500
Overheads	£100.50	£150.75
Total cost	£400.50	£650.75

This kind of calculation will be made for each cost centre so the basis might be different in other cost centres. From Example 1.6 it is known that department 3 is more labour intensive and that most costs are related to labour used rather than machines. In this case a labour rate is more appropriate. If the total labour hours worked in a given period comparable with the incidence of overhead is £5000 then a suitable recovery rate would be £5560/,000 = £1.11 per labour hour.

Usually such recovery rates are pre-determined based on past data so that product costs can be calculated quickly. This does introduce some error, but the ability to arrive at acceptably accurate costs quickly will often outweigh this.

It is therefore true that the actual costs of production cost centres may differ from the amounts that are absorbed by products using an overhead recovery rate and this has to be accounted for in some way. The cost book-keeping records will in fact show if the overheads have been over-recovered (too much has been charged to products) or under-recovered (too little has been charged to products). These differences will inevitably arise out the fact that no absorption costing system can be totally accurate, since it is usual for pre-determined overhead recovery rates to be used. If, for example, such recovery rates were only calculated after all costs had been collected then the costs charged to products would be more accurate, but the information would be totally historical and very little use in controlling and managing cost within cost centres.

Overhead recovery is an area where the cost accountant will decide a rate which is both convenient and practical, even if this means that costs are not quite as accurate as they could otherwise be. There is of course the question of cost–benefit to consider here and whether or not it is worth the effort of attempting to get very precise costings, when close approximations are more than adequate.

It should now be clear that cost information is used not only for getting at the cost for a job or a product but also for controlling costs at departments (termed cost centres). This enables responsibility to be established for particular costs such as labour and materials usage and prices.

Pre-determined recovery rates are calculated so that these costs are known quickly, giving managers information in time to take corrective action if things are going wrong. Frequently this means that speed is more important than precision.

All this can be used as part of a budgetary control system that enables corrective action to take place when costs vary from budgeted levels.

Activity 1.6

There are three types of product made in each of three separate production departments: 1, 2 and 3. There are two service departments, A – plant maintenance and B – works canteen. The maintenance department serves only the production departments, whereas the works canteen serves all departments. Overhead costs have been allocated to these departments and shown below, together with other relevant data:

	Production			Service	
	1	2	3	A	B
Costs	3000	5000	2500	1500	2500
Employees	20	10	25	10	N/A
Machine hours	2000	1000	500	N/A	N/A
Labour hours	1000	2000	1500	N/A	N/A

The incidence of cost in production department 1 is related to machine usage, for the other production departments it is labour based. The canteen costs are to be distributed to all other departments based on number of employees. The plant maintenance department's costs are to be distributed to the production departments in proportion to machine usage.

In production department 2 the following products and their direct costs are given:

	Job 1	Job 2
Direct materials	£350	£550
Direct labour	£250	£450
Labour hours	50	90

Using the information provided, you are required to produce:

1 A table showing the distribution of overhead costs to the production departments. (Hint: examine the distribution of the canteen costs before you look at the plant maintenance and remember that this alters the overhead costs of plant maintenance.)
2 Overhead recovery rates for each production department.
3 Absorption costs for jobs 1 and 2.

Marginal costing

The concept of marginal cost is an important one for engineers and managers. It is an alternative way of looking at costs and provides insights into the way costs behave. In particular it enables the engineer or manager to observe the interaction between costs, volumes and profit. Some costs vary with the level of activity (volume) others do not, thus total costs of products will vary depending on the volume produced. This effect is significant and has an important bearing on decisions such as make or buy or whether or not to accept lower prices for part of a factory's output.

Accountants define marginal cost as:

The amount by which aggregate costs change if the volume of output is increased or decreased by one unit.

Figure 1.11 shows the behaviour of costs based on the marginal cost concept. The vertical axis of Figure 1.11 shows aggregate costs and revenues in £ (pounds). The horizontal axis shows the units of output. The fixed costs are shown as a straight line across all levels of output. Fixed costs are costs which are unaffected by activity, at least in the short term. Figure 1.11 assumes that such costs do not vary for the whole range of output possible. Fixed costs include things like:

- insurance premiums
- business rates
- subscriptions
- audit fees
- rental charges
- fixed elements of power and telephone charges.

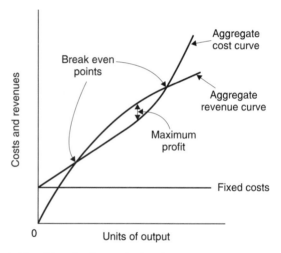

Figure 1.11   *Marginal cost behaviour*

The aggregate cost curve starts from the fixed cost line. This curve increases steadily with increases in output and for a time can be virtually a straight line. Its slope represents the incremental increase in variable costs as output increases. Variable cost is defined as cost which is incurred to actually make the product, such as direct materials and direct labour. It therefore *varies* with the level of activity, more product, more materials, etc. However, as volume increases beyond a certain point variable costs increase more steeply, since an extension in capacity is likely to cost more (an example is overtime premiums paid to operatives). Thus the aggregate cost curve becomes steeper. The aggregate revenue curve, which starts from the origin, also increases as output is sold to customers. At a certain point it crosses the aggregate cost line. Here the total cost is equal to total revenue, thus enough units have been produced to recover all fixed and variable costs. Beyond this point revenue is greater than cost so that a profit is earned. However, at a certain point sales become more difficult to achieve as the market becomes saturated so that revenue per unit declines. One reason for this would be price discounts to encourage customers to buy more. Economics teaches us that if supply outstrips demand prices will decline and that is what could be happening here.

The slope of the revenue line becomes less steep and eventually crosses the aggregate cost line for a second time. At that point a new breakeven point is reached where revenues and costs are again equal. The point of maximum profit is the point at which the revenue line is above and farthest away from the aggregate cost line. Attempting to push activity beyond this point is self-defeating, since total profit is lower – the business is working harder for fewer gains.

This concept of marginal costs forms the basis of an alternative to absorption costing discussed earlier. This new philosophy of costing provides a model of costing which is extremely useful for management purposes. It is also related to other new concepts which help us to more fully understand product costs, and these are discussed immediately below.

Fixed costs are costs which arise out of management decisions and are really the costs of providing productive capacity for a period of time. They are defined as period costs. They have to be charged in the period in which they are incurred, because by definition they cannot be related to any past or future period. Absorption costing breaks this principle since products are deemed to absorb period costs and such finished goods are valued at this total cost. Hence these absorbed costs are, in effect, carried forward to succeeding periods. When using marginal costs this does not happen, because finished goods and work-in-progress are valued at marginal cost (or variable cost).

This leads to another important concept. If period costs have to be met, whether or not production takes place, then revenues must cover these costs as well as the marginal (or variable) costs before a profit can be declared. Similarly when sales revenue occurs the income from each unit sold is reduced by its marginal cost. The difference between the revenue and marginal cost is called contribution. This contribution initially pays the fixed costs and what is left over is profit.

Marginal costing takes a different view of the world and is also much more sensitive to changes in stock levels and profitability.

Example 1.9 shows two profit and loss statements, one based on absorption costing and the other based on marginal costing.

Example 1.9   Profit and loss statements

Absorption cost basis	£k	Marginal cost basis	£k
Sales	100	Sales	100
Factory costs	(70)	Marginal cost	(40)
Gross profit	30	Contribution	60
Admin, etc.	(10)	Period costs	(50)
Profit	20		10

In this case output exceeds sales by 500 units. Each unit in the absorption costing statement was charged £20 fixed costs. As 500 units were unsold then 500 × £20 = £10 000 was carried over into the next period. This explains why the profit in the absorption costing example is greater by this amount. The marginal costing profit statement does not include fixed costs in the value of finished goods, so it does not carry over these costs into the next period, which means that it shows a lower profit.

From a management point of view the marginal costing approach is superior since it gives advance warning of the effect of declining revenues and output is unchanged.

You should note that the marginal costing approach is only acceptable for management accounts. For published accounts the absorption cost approach is mandatory, being required by the authorities because valuation of finished stock must include production overheads.

Another use of marginal costing is in short-term decision-making when there is an opportunity to sell extra products, but at lower prices. Example 1.10 shows cost data for this product.

Example 1.10 Product costs for job xl

	£	
Direct labour	10	
Direct materials	10	
Production overhead	20	(£17 fixed £3 variable)
Total Cost	40	
Normal Selling price	50	

There is an opportunity to sell 1000 more units at £27 per unit. In this case the current production is sufficient to pay for all variable and fixed costs and provide a profit. Example 1.11 shows a summary Profit and Loss Account based on present output which is 5000 units.

Example 1.11   Profit and loss

	£000s
Sales	250
Direct Labour	(50)
Direct Materials	(50)
Overheads	(100)
Profit	50

If an absorption cost approach was used then the new offer price would be seen as inadequate, since the total cost (absorption cost) of £40 is greater than the new offer price of £27. The order would not be accepted. However, that would be the wrong decision because acceptance of the order would in fact increase profit, but this situation is only revealed by the marginal costing approach. The marginal cost of the extra production is shown in Example 1.12.

Example 1.12   Marginal cost of extra 1000 units

	£000s	
Direct labour	10	
Direct materials	10	
Variable overheads	3	(this is a non-period cost)
Marginal cost	23	

The new offer price is £27. Thus profit will increase by £4 × 1000 = £4000. Assuming that the fixed overhead does not increase then the additional production is well worth doing.

This approach to costing of products is used frequently by businesses which can segment their markets enabling them to charge different prices in different segments. British Rail is a prime example. It charges full cost fares to commuters who have to travel at rush hours to get to and from work. This is their core business and enables them to recover the fixed overheads. Lower prices charged off-peak are based on marginal costs, and enable the rail company to increase its overall profit. This technique works fine unless the market suffering the higher price can switch into the market paying the lower price.

This kind of thinking can extend to costing for a range of products. Sometimes absorption costing reveals that some products make losses if full overheads (fixed and variable) are charged. An alternative marginal costing approach can show that such products can make a contribution which increases profit in exactly the same way as shown in Example 1.12. Thus to discontinue such 'unprofitable products' would cause a decline in overall profitability. Hence marginal costing enables an accurate view to be taken for a range of products and their costs, and identifies the most profitable range to offer. Of course the total contribution from all products must be sufficient to cover all period costs and all direct costs and still leave sufficient funds to provide a profit.

Breakeven analysis

Breakeven analysis is an application of the ideas behind marginal costing. The technique is limited but helpful in getting an understanding of cost behaviour and perceiving the interaction between profit, volumes and costs. Because it is frequently presented in graphical form it is used to communicate such information to managers and engineers.

All costs must be covered before a business makes a profit. When contributions from products equal the total costs then it is said that the 'breakeven point' has been achieved. This breakeven point can be obtained from a formula as follows:

$$BE \; point \; (\text{units}) = \frac{FC}{SP - VC}$$

where FC is the total fixed cost, SP is the selling price per unit and VC is the variable cost per unit. Using the selling price the breakeven point in units can be converted into sales value or turnover. Example 1.13 shows how this works.

Example 1.13   Breakeven point

	£
Fixed cost	6000
Selling price per unit	20
Variable cost per unit	10

$$BE = \frac{6000}{20 - 10} = 600 \text{ units or } £12\,000$$

This can be represented in a breakeven chart as shown in Figure 1.12.

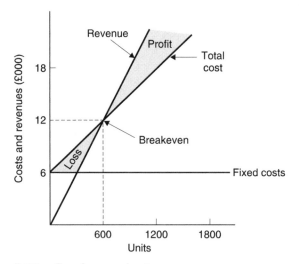

Figure 1.12   *Breakeven chart*

The chart in Figure 1.12 is not unlike Figure 1.11 except that it represents the data using straight lines. The assumption made is that in the period represented in the graph the prices and costs remain the same. Note the shaded areas for profit and loss. It is possible to see the degree of profit and loss at different levels of output. You can see also how the composition of cost changes with different levels of output. At low levels fixed costs are a greater proportion and at high levels they are a smaller proportion. Thus the *total cost* per unit decreases as production increases. It is not a static value, thus you can only define total cost for products at given levels of output. This, of course, explains why absorption costing can be so misleading.

However, you should note that breakeven analysis has limitations since it makes the assumption that costs and prices remain unchanged. In reality this is not the case. Also if the chart has been drawn based on a portfolio of products then any change in their mix will alter the relationships shown. It also assumes that everything that is made is also sold, a very big assumption. But in spite of its limitations breakeven analysis does provide some useful insights into how costs behave and does help to make cost information meaningful.

Activity 1.7

Use the following cost data and construct a breakeven chart using suitable graph paper. Identify the breakeven point in units and sales turnover. Verify the result of your chart by using the breakeven formula.

Fixed costs: £10 000
Variable cost per unit: £5
Sales price per unit: £10
Total sales (maximum capacity) is 5000 units

Budgetary planning and control

General principles

Budgets are used as a means of achieving planning and control objectives in most businesses and non-commercial organizations. A budget has been defined as:

A financial or quantitative statement prepared and approved, prior to a defined period of time, of the policy to be pursued during that period for the purpose of attaining given objectives.

The benefits that derive from budgetary control arise from the ability to co-ordinate policy, plans and action and to be able to monitor the financial consequences of carrying out the plans.

The basic procedure is as follows:

(a) Formulate policy and long term plans.
(b) Prepare forecasts for sales, production, stocks, costs, capital expenditure and cash.
(c) Compile these separate forecasts into a master forecast.
(d) Consider all the alternatives available and select the plan which gives the best results, for example, in terms of profit and long-term financial stability.
(e) Review limiting factors and *the principal budget factor*. This process takes place concurrently with item (d) and enables work to begin on the framing of the budgets mentioned below in item (f).
(f) Prepare individual budgets and finally the *master budget* which includes a forecasted profit and loss account and balance sheet.

This process is shown in Figure 1.13 and indicates the sequence of events starting from the top of the chart to the bottom. These aspects will be explained further in the following section.

Corporate planning

The starting point of budgetary control is with the Board of Directors who will determine the scale and nature of the activities of the company. This policy and objective setting is done within the

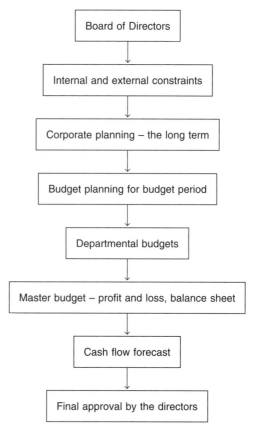

```
┌─────────────────────┐
│  Board of Directors │
└─────────────────────┘
           │
           ▼
┌───────────────────────────────┐
│ Internal and external constraints │
└───────────────────────────────┘
           │
           ▼
┌───────────────────────────────┐
│ Corporate planning – the long term │
└───────────────────────────────┘
           │
           ▼
┌─────────────────────────────────┐
│ Budget planning for budget period │
└─────────────────────────────────┘
           │
           ▼
┌─────────────────────┐
│ Departmental budgets │
└─────────────────────┘
           │
           ▼
┌──────────────────────────────────────────┐
│ Master budget – profit and loss, balance sheet │
└──────────────────────────────────────────┘
           │
           ▼
┌─────────────────────┐
│  Cash flow forecast │
└─────────────────────┘
           │
           ▼
┌──────────────────────────────┐
│ Final approval by the directors │
└──────────────────────────────┘
```

Figure 1.13 *The budget planning process*

constraints which exist at the time. For example plans may have to be made within the current capacities and capabilities of the company, since making changes to the location of operations, the size and composition of the work force and the product range are usually long-term matters. The budget is essentially for the short term, usually for one year, and created within the framework of long-term corporate planning. Successive budgets will be influenced by the preparation of long-term plans, but will always relate to the current period.

Some organizations prepare outline budgets over much longer periods perhaps for a 5 to 10 year time horizon, but such budgets are really part of the long-term corporate planning activity and subject to major revision before being used as a basis for current period budgetary planning. We are only concerned with the annual budget planning process and the monitoring and control functions used to track actual results against the plan.

External factors will exercise considerable effects on the company in preparing its forecasts and budgets. Government policy, the proximity of a general election, taxation, inflation, world economic conditions and technological development will all combine to constrain or influence the budget planning process. Once the Board has settled on a policy within the prevailing situation, then the process of turning the policy into detailed quantitative statements can begin.

We assume a budget period of one year, which is usual for most industries. It is therefore recognized that the budget period is fixed in relation to the needs of the organization concerned and could be any period ranging from 3 months to 5 years. The shorter the period the more accurate the forecasts will be and that is why most companies find that an annual budgeting procedure is a satisfactory compromise.

Behavioural aspects

Budgetary planning and control requires that departments and individuals work together and co-ordinate their activities. It can therefore be used to create a unified and co-operative approach to the business of managing the enterprise. Because all managers with significant responsibility will have a share in the framing of the budgets they will also have commitment to achieving the proposed results. This provides a powerful motivator to good performance because realistic objectives are set and performance can be monitored against those objectives.

Budget centres

The concept of a budget centre (synonymous with cost centre or profit centre) is central to the budgetary control process because it is then possible to control costs at the point where they are incurred. What is a budget centre will vary according to the needs of each business, but it is common in manufacturing industry for these to be similar to the following functional areas:

- sales and marketing
- production
- personnel
- research and development
- purchasing
- material control
- finance and accounting
- administration.

Principal budget factor

There is always some limitation on the budgeting process which constrains what can be done in a given period. For example, it might be possible to sell 10 000 widgets but it is only possible to make 7000. In this case there is no point in framing a budget which is based on selling 10 000 widgets, unless something can be done during the budget period to remove the capacity constraint.

Other limiting factors could include the availability of skilled labour or the ability to obtain a given piece of machinery. Sometimes the supply of raw materials will be a limiting factor or delivery lead times for certain components may cause delays.

What the company has to do is to identify the principal limiting factor which restricts all the other activities. For many businesses this is likely to be sales. In this case the current budget will start from the sales forecast and build all the other budgets around this. The assumption is made that capacity exists to meet all forecasted sales levels.

Preparation of forecasts

Each manager will forecast his own budget, based on his understanding the situation. If sales are the starting point then forecasts for labour, materials, expenses, etc., naturally follow. Forecasting techniques will discussed later.

Functional budgets

The principal functional budgets are:

- marketing budget
- manufacturing budget
- administration budget
- research and development budget
- capital expenditure budget
- cash budget.

We will discuss each in turn.

The marketing budget

Depending on the business this is probably the most important budget. No profit can be made unless sales take place. In effect everything follows from this budget. There are rare businesses that can sell all they can produce, in which case the manufacturing budget becomes the key, since sales are dependent on how much can be produced. This situation is of course related to the principal budget factor identified earlier.

The marketing budget may be sub-divided into:

(a) sales
(b) selling
(c) distribution.

It is also common in bigger businesses for further divisions to be made into geographical areas. Each of these areas may produce the three budgets listed in (a) to (c) above, which would then be aggregated into the whole company equivalents.

A sales budget would look like Example 1.14, which shows products, volumes, selling prices and revenue.

The methods for arriving at this estimate vary from mathematical methods such as exponential smoothing, moving averages to just plain guesswork based on an intimate knowledge of the marketplace. It is often necessary to break down this budget into monthly intervals to deal with seasonal fluctuations in demand.

Both the selling budget and the distribution budget would be based on the sales budget. The former would include costs relating to sales

Example 1.14 Sales budget

Product	Units	£ Selling price	£s Revenue
1	3500	3.40	11 900
2	2700	4.50	12 150
3	1400	9.00	12 600
			36,650

activities, sales staff salaries, commissions, travelling costs, sales office costs, advertising and publicity, while the latter would include the costs of packaging, warehousing and transport. Thus all three (sales, selling and distribution) would comprise the complete marketing budget.

Activity 1.8

With reference to the sales budget in example 1.14 the marketing manager has done some research which indicates that a 10% reduction in price affects sales as follows:

Product	Revised sales
1	4000
2	2900
3	2400

Recast the sales budget based on these changes. What does this do to revenues? Is this the best situation, and if not, what further changes would you suggest that will maximize revenues?

Manufacturing budget

As with marketing this major functional budget can also be sub-divided into other more detailed budgets. Examples of such sub-divisions are:

(a) production budget
(b) direct materials budget
(c) direct labour budget
(d) factory overhead budget.

Example 1.15 shows a production budget.

Example 1.15 Production budget

	Item 1	Item 2	Item 3
Forecast Sales	3500	2700	1400
Opening stock	1000	500	400
Production	3000	3300	1200
	4000	3800	1600
Planned closing stock	500	900	200

Notice the crucial importance of stock levels, both at the beginning of the period and at the end. Note that this shows the stock of finished goods, later we will discuss raw materials and components. Levels of stock have to be planned for several reasons. There are storage costs and warehouse capacities to consider as well as the risk of pilferage, damage and deterioration.

Also matters related to seasonal fluctuations need to be planned for. There are two possible scenarios here:

(a) Use stock levels to smooth production output. Stockpile when demand is low, then run down stocks at peak demand. This way production can be held steady, avoiding overtime and less economic working.
(b) Maintain static stock levels and flex production around seasonal changes in demand by working overtime or temporarily decreasing capacity by short-time working.

These possibilities may mean that the production budget would have to be prepared for monthly intervals with opening and closing stocks being planned for each month.

Activity 1.9

Recast the production budget with the revised sales based on the 10% price reduction given in the previous test your knowledge. Assume that planned closing stock is the same. The factory manager says that product C maximum capacity is 1800 units. What actions could be taken to meet the extra demand?

The direct materials budget is shown in Example 1.16. It shows a simplified bill of materials for each item in the production budget multiplied by the planned production volumes.

Example 1.16   Direct materials budget

Product	Qty	Part No	Units	£ Price	£ Value	£ Totals
A	3000	x1	6000	0.50	3000	
		x2	3000	0.75	2250	
						5250
B	330	y1	9900	0.25	2475	
		y2	3300	1.00	3300	
						5775
Grand total						11025

Example 1.16 illustrates the basic principles which are simple enough. In a business of any size the amount of work could be quite daunting, and it is likely that computer assistance would be used to produce the data.

The direct materials budget would be used to derive the direct materials purchase budget. This will be different from the direct materials budget itself because opening stocks and closing stocks of raw materials would have to be taken into account so that the actual purchases would be known. The calculation to arrive at the required purchases is as shown in Example 1.17.

Example 1.17   How purchase quantities are determined

	Item x1 Units	Item x2 Units
Opening stock	400	250
Production (see Example 4.13)	6000	3000
Total stock	6400	3250
Planned closing stock	450	300
Purchases	5950	2950

The direct labour budget is shown in Example 1.18.

Example 1.18   Direct labour budget

	Product A	Product B
Quantity produced	3000	3300
Standard hours per item	0.5	0.25
Total hours	1500	825
Wage rate	£4	£3.50
Total labour cost	£6000.00	£2887.50

Direct labour budgets are derived from estimates or standards for production. Whatever the type of business there will be methods for determining direct labour hours so that a budget can be produced.

In a service industry such as a college the unit of output could be a course such as a GNVQ in Engineering. In this case a college could determine standard hours for each course and cost each course on the basis of an hourly rate derived from salaries data. A college may not relate budgets to individual courses in this way, but will calculate aggregate teacher salaries in departments or faculties. Each department or faculty will deliver a range of courses (or products), so that the salaries of the teachers would be the direct labour cost of delivery. Because the standard working hours of staff are known and the standard hours of courses are known the college can determine a faculty budget for a planned range of courses. This is the college equivalent of preparing a manufacturing budget for a production department based on sales budget data.

You can see that although the details are different to that of a manufacturing company the underlying principles are the same, namely to quantify the labour cost of making the product, whether this product is manufactured or is a service of some kind. It is important to note, that although we are discussing budgets in a manufacturing context, the broad principles are applicable to all types of organizations and businesses.

Activity 1.10

Refer to Example 1.18. The factory manager has reviewed the methods of manufacture and by using more highly skilled labour he can reduce the standard hours per product by 20%. However, the wage rates will increase by 10%. Prepare a new direct labour budget.

Finally there is the budget is for manufacturing overheads. It can be quite complicated because these costs may occur in three different ways:

- variable (related to output or volume)
- semi-variable (partially related to output or volume)
- fixed (not related to output or volume).

In the earlier discussion of absorption costing you may remember that such costs were charged to products by the process of allocation, apportionment and absorption. Clearly, the budget planning process has to be in harmony with the system for cost ascertainment, otherwise the cost information collected will not be directly comparable with the budget.

Example 1.19 shows a flexible overhead budget which uses standard labour hours for calculating the variable content of the overheads costs. Remember that the basis for calculation has to relate to the incidence of cost, in other words, there must be some correlation between the occurrence of the cost and its calculation.

Example 1.19   A flexible manufacturing overhead budget

Overhead (Item)	Fixed	Variable (per Std Hr)	Output 1 (Units)	Output 2 (Units)
			100 000	120 000
Variable costs:				
Wastage		0.02	2 000	2 400
Coolant		0.01	1 000	1 200
Semi-variable costs:				
Electricity	500	0.03	3 000	3 600
Water	400	0.015	1 500	1 800
Fixed costs:				
Bus. Rates	5 000			
Rent	7 000			
Salaries	80 000			
Total fixed costs			92 000	92 000
Total Overheads			99 500	101 000

In Example 1.17 we said that the costs being calculated are incurred in proportion to standard labour hours worked. This enables us to flex the budget according to different levels of activity. This is superior to just preparing a fixed budget which assumes that output or volume does not vary.

A flexible budget improves the process of control when actual results are compared with the budget. This is because the comparison removes the distorting effect of changes in volume and enables the manager to concentrate on variances in cost levels for a given output, rather than variances that occur with changes in volume, which may be outside his/her control.

Other overhead budgets

Budgets for administration, research and development also have to be prepared. The level of these budgets will relate to the size of the business, but may not vary according to sales volumes as shown for marketing and manufacturing. The budgets will be framed within policy decisions made by management on the level of service needed to support business operations. Methods for deciding this are many and varied and may not be very scientific. However, expenditure budgets are required both to control the costs of these activities and to calculate an overall or master budget.

Cash budgets

These budgets are crucially important to all businesses. This is because a shortage of actual cash can destroy a business, even if it is very profitable. This may seem contradictory, but is true because cash flow occurs at different time intervals to profit. If a company cannot pay employees and creditors when payment falls due it is in real trouble, even if profits are excellent and will generate cash later on.

Cash budgets will almost invariably start from the opening cash balance and the flow of expected revenues from sales. However, as cash flows occur later than the sales which generate them, the budget has to account this time phasing.

Example 1.20 shows how this can be done.

Example 1.20 Cash flow budget 6 month period Jan.–June

	Dec	Jan	Feb	Mar	Apr	May	Jun
Sales	200	400	600	800	500	400	400
Balance B/F		100	(100)	(200)	(300)	0	100
Receipts		200	400	600	800	500	400
		300	300	400	500	500	500
Payments		400	500	700	500	400	300
Balance C/F		(100)	(200)	(300)	0	100	200

Notice the timing differences for cash flow from sales. It is normal for businesses to give customers trade credit. This is typically 30 days or one month. Our example assumes this and time phases receipts from sales a month later. Even this assumption is somewhat optimistic, since most well-run British companies are likely to experience a lag in cash flow equivalent to an average of 60 days. When this budget is set the accountant must make realistic assumptions about the actual arrival of cash.

Notice that negative figures are identified by brackets, which is a convention in common use. You will also note that there are several months when the business has a shortfall in cash. In itself this is not bad, because the money arrives eventually. However, the company has to bridge this gap somehow if it is to pay wages and creditors.

Temporary shortfalls of cash can be met in several ways. The company might liquidate some investments such as bank deposits, stocks and shares or it might arrange a bank overdraft. The production of a cash flow forecast enables the company to do proper financial planning. Banks are happy to provide short-term overdrafts if they are planned, but are much less happy with businesses who fail to plan for these eventualities, for obvious reasons.

The cash budget illustrated is a summary and some simplifying assumptions have been made. Receipts have been assumed to be for sales only. However, receipts may include interest on investments, disposals of fixed assets, etc. Payments will represent purchase of supplies, wages, purchase of equipment, overdraft interest, auditors fees, payment of loan interest or dividend paid to shareholders. Much of the information will come from the functional budgets which give details on various expenditures.

The master budget

Figure 1.13 showed the overall budget planning process and indicated the production of a master budget. The master budget is in effect a forecasted profit and loss statement and balance sheet.

Budgets may be redrafted if the initial master budget is unsatisfactory. It may not contain sufficient profit or some expenses may be too high. This is an iterative process, whereby the information is refined and operating problems solved.

Example 1.21 shows a typical master budget drawn up for one year.

The master budget shows the complete financial position of the company for the year in question. The profit and loss account shows the results of operations based on the budgets which have been planned for all the functional areas. It shows that the company plans to make a profit of £6500 during this year after all costs have been met.

The balance sheet summarizes the financial position as at the end of the budget year. The balance sheet is a snapshot of the position at 31 December, after the events of the year have taken place, whereas the profit and loss account is a period statement which gives a summary of the year's activities.

The balance sheet shows two vital facts:

● where the money came from to run the business
● what was done with the money obtained.

If you look at Example 1.21 you can see that the sources of funds are share capital and the accumulated profit and loss position. Sometimes firms make losses and that is also shown here. However, this year's operations show a profit which adds to the funds available. The funds from shareholders and profits are the sole source of long-term funding for this business.

The use of funds (or capital employed) is shown in the fixed assets and current assets totals. Fixed assets are the long-term property of the business and current assets are the circulating assets of the business. The latter are called this because they constantly change through time, reflecting day-to-day business operations. The net current asset figure is an important figure because it shows what is left of current assets after current liabilities are met. Since current liabilities are sums of money owed to creditors (usually the

Example 1.21   Master budget

Profit and loss account for 1 January to 31 December

	£	£
Sales		20 000
Less cost of goods sold:		
Opening stock of finished goods	2 500	
Cost of completed goods	8 000	
	10 500	
Less closing stock of finished goods	3 500	
		7 000
Gross profit		13 000
Selling and distribution costs	3 000	
Administration and finance costs	1 500	
Research and development costs	2 500	
		6 500
Net profit		6 500

Balance sheet as at 31 December	£	£
Assets employed:		
Net fixed assets		
Premises	21 000	
Equipment	6 000	
	27 000	
Current assets		
Stock	1 900	
Debtors	2 300	
Cash	2 100	
	6 300	
Less current liabilities		
Creditors	(1 400)	
Overdraft	(1 000)	
Net current assets		3 900
		30 300
Financed by		
Share capital		28 000
Profit and loss account		
Brought forward		(4 200)
This year		6 500
		30 300

company's suppliers) or to employees for wages, they have to be met out of current assets. Current assets are usually stock, debtors and cash. Stock turns into debtors when it is sold to customers on credit, debtors being customers who buy goods on credit, debtors turn into cash when they pay for goods. The flow of cash from these operations enables liabilities to be settled. If a company cannot meet its obligations in this way it is said to be insolvent.

The net current assets figure is also called working capital. It must be sufficient to support day-to-day business operations. If it is too small the business has difficulty in meeting its commitments. Thus you can see the importance of producing this budget. If the budget shows that working capital is too small the company can make plans to obtain more capital to support the business. The working capital position is closely linked to the cash flow forecast we discussed earlier. The cash flow statement will show in detail where there is a shortfall in cash, and will help the company decide whether it needs more long-term investment in the business or whether a temporary overdraft is more suitable.

Activity 1.11

Refer to Example 1.20 and redraft the cash flow statement on the assumption that cash from sales comes in 40% in the month following sales and 60% in the month after that.

Depreciation of fixed assets

Depreciation is the estimate of the cost of a fixed asset consumed during its useful life. If a company buys a car, to be used by a sales representative, for £15000 it has to charge the cost in some reasonable way to the profit being earned. This process is essential, otherwise the whole cost of running the business cannot be obtained, and profit figures would be overstated. If it is estimated that the car will be worth £6000 in three years time when it is to be sold, then it could be charged to profit at (15 000–6000)/3 = £3000 for each year of use.

Depreciation is discussed here as a prelude to our discussion about investment appraisal. The way companies accumulate funds with which to replace fixed assets is to charge depreciation as an overhead cost. In the case of our car this recovers £9000 which together with the sale price of the used car generates a fund of £14 000 towards the purchase of a replacement. It is also possible that the sums so deducted from profit can be invested to offset inflation until the time comes to replace the asset.

Because depreciation is an estimate and is deducted from profit it has the effect of keeping the money available in the business. Many companies use the aggregate depreciation charged as the basis for the fund against which investment appraisal is done. (See the following section for a detailed discussion of investment appraisal.)

There are two main methods used by accountants to calculate depreciation. We will outline each in turn.

Straight line method

This charges an equal amount as depreciation for each year of the asset's expected life. It is called straight line method because if the annual amounts were plotted on a graph they would form a straight line. The formula is:

$$d = (p - v)/n$$

where d = annual depreciation, p = purchase price, v = residual value and n = years of asset life.

The method used for the car in the above example is straight line. It is a very popular and easy to use method.

Reducing balance method

In this method a fixed percentage is applied to the written down balance of the fixed asset. The formula for establishing this fixed percentage is:

$$r = 1 - \sqrt[n]{\frac{v}{p}}$$

where r = the percentage rate, n = number of years, v = residual value and p = asset purchase price.

v must be a significant amount, otherwise the rate will be very large and somewhat meaningless.

Using our car example above the reducing balance rate is:

$$1 - \sqrt[3]{\frac{6000}{15\,000}} = 1 - 0.7368 \quad = 26.31\%$$

Applying this, the depreciation pattern is as follows:

Purchase price		£15 000
1st year	26.31%	3 946
Reduced balance		11 054
2nd year	26.31%	2 908
Reduced balance		8 116
3rd year	26.31%	2 135
Residual value (approx)		5 981

The reducing balance system means that a greater sum is taken in earlier years, but reduces year on year since the percentage rate is applied to the reduced balance. This method is more complex but it is more logical because a new asset gives better service than an old asset and should suffer more depreciation in earlier years. Certainly, with regard to motor cars the early years depreciation is very heavy in relation to resale prices.

Investment appraisal

Introductory ideas

The process of investment appraisal is necessary in order to select the best projects for investment, whether they be replacement machines for the factory, office equipment or new cars for managers and sales representatives.

Major factors to consider are:

- risk and return
- time scale
- time value of money
- evaluating alternative choices.

The first one, that of risk and return is important. A good general rule is to expect a high return if the investment is risky. That is why interest rates on mortgages are less than interest rates on loans for consumer durables. A bank will regard loans against property as low risk because a house is a better security than a refrigerator if something goes wrong.

For commercial businesses some capital investment projects carry low risk, such as those which merely involve a replacement of a machine which is being used to make a product for which there is a regular demand. However, the risk is much greater for investment in a new factory for a range of new products. These different risk profiles have to be taken into account when comparing different projects for investment.

Time scale is important too. If the project is going to take five years to be completed, then many things could change before completion. Inflation, government action, market conditions, competitive pressures, etc. The investment decision must take account of all these risk factors as well and this is not an easy process, because of the need to forecast up to five years into the future.

Money has time value. This fact lies at the heart of the investment appraisal process. If you could choose to have £5 today or £5 in a year's time which would you prefer and why?

Hopefully you would take account of the risk of not getting your £5 in a year's time and would prefer to avoid risk and get it now. Also you should have thought about the fact that if you had the £5 now you could invest it for a year, so that it would be worth more than £5 in a year's time.

The time value of money exists because of these two aspects, risk and return. Most people who decide to save money instead of spending it look for a secure and lucrative place to keep it until they wish to spend it. If your risk preference is low you would probably put your money into a building society account. If you were more adventurous you might buy shares. The risks attached to buying shares are greater than a building society account, but the return may be greater.

The essence of the capital investment decision is no different to this. A company must decide whether or not to keep its money in the bank or invest in the business. If it chooses to invest in the business it must expect a better return than merely leaving it in the bank. It is for this reason that certain techniques for evaluating projects have arisen. There are numerous approaches, which we will describe briefly below, but we shall confine our detailed discussion to the mainstream technique which is the most theoretically sound method, and is called net present value (NPV) technique.

Traditional methods for investment appraisal

Accounting rate of return (ARR)

This is the sort of profit figure that would be reported on the profit and loss account which was discussed in an earlier section. It is sometimes called Annual Rate of Return. For example if £10 000 was invested for 5 years and the average annual returns after depreciation were £1000, then the ARR is:

$$\frac{1000}{5000} = 20\% \text{ per annum}$$

Notice that the average capital is used, and this is because the depreciation implies a repayment of capital throughout the life of the project. (You should note that depreciation is an accounting device to recover capital costs from annual profits.) The assumption is that capital invested is £10 000 at the start and zero at the end, the average being, in this case: £10 000/2 = £5 000.

The problems with this method are various, especially that ARR has no universally accepted method for calculation, which makes comparisons difficult. Furthermore it takes no account of the actual flows of cash, it just uses an average. Timing of cash flows has a very significant effect on both risk and return as we shall see more clearly when we discuss net present value techniques.

Payback

This is a simple method and in essence calculates the period of time it takes to recoup the initial investment from the cash flows arising. For example if £10 000 was invested and the positive cash flows were £5000 per year, then the payback is 2 years. It also has problems. While it does take limited account of timing and just uses cash flows arising from the project, it does not actually provide a true overall profit, and is therefore very limited.

Net present value method (NPV)

Net present value is the most theoretically sound technique since it takes account of all of the important factors:

- it uses actual cash flows
- the time value of money is evaluated
- it measures the increase in wealth.

The use of cash flow rather than the use of accounting profit removes several distorting influences. Accounting profits are calculated using accounting rules which are related to periods of time, and furthermore will use non-cash flow adjustments which are not relevant. What matters for a specific project are the sums of money which arise only from that project, and the only way to get at these figures directly is to use incremental cash flows. Incremental cash flows are flows (in and out) which can only arise from that project and in no other way.

The time value of money is accounted for by using what is called a discount rate. This is the rate of return expected from the project, taking account of the company's cost of raising capital and any additional risk factors it estimates. Why is this rate called a discount rate? It is called this because the cash flows are discounted back to present day values using a discount factor. An example will make this clear.

Example 1.22   Discounted cash flows

Discount rate is 20%.
The factor is based on the formula $1/(1 + r)^n$ when r = discount rate and n = number of years.

End of year	Investment	Return	Factor	Net CF
0	(10 000)		1.0000	(10 000)
1		3 000	0.8333	2 500
2		3 000	0.6944	2 083
3		4 000	0.5787	2 315
4		5 000	0.4822	2 411
NPV (Net Present Value)				(691)

The table shows that £10 000 was invested at the end of year zero. This cash flow is as at now, therefore its discount factor is one. It is invested at present day value.

However, the income or return at end of year 1 is discounted by 20% and is only worth £2500 in present value. The calculation is made by multiplying the factor by the gross cash flow as follows:

$$0.8333 \times £3000 = £2500$$

This is because if it was received today the assumption is made that it could have been invested at 20% so that it would grow to £3000 by end of year 1.

Similarly the later cash flows are discounted back to present day values. The return of £5000 at the end of year 4 is only worth £2411 in today's money since £2411 invested at 20% yields £5000 in four years' time.

You can check all these numbers using the formula with a scientific calculator, if you wish. In the past the factors would be calculated from a table for various rates of discount. These days such calculations would be done using a spreadsheet, which has built-in functions for NPV.

Now that we have taken account of the time value of money we need to discover whether or not we have increased our wealth. In the case of Example 1.22 we have in fact suffered a loss of wealth to the sum of £691, not a very satisfactory position! If we had borrowed the money at 20% our position would have been as shown in Example 1.23.

Example 1.23   Loan repayment

(End of)	Loan	Interest	CF	Bal C/F
1	(10 000)	(2000)	3000	(9000)
2	(9 000)	(1800)	3000	(7800)
3	(7 800)	(1560)	4000	(5360)
4	(5 360)	(1072)	5000	(1432)

The table reveals what is called a net terminal value of minus £1432 which is worth minus £690 in present value terms, which is the NPV loss shown above, and proves the accuracy of the technique.

NPV technique gives a clear signal, do not invest unless the NPV is positive, otherwise you suffer loss. Given that your forecasts for income are correct this is the only method which gives a satisfactory way of determining whether or not a project is worth doing.

However, you might want to compare the actual rate of return of the above project with the cost of raising the money. This would require the calculation of the internal rate of return (IRR). This still based on the concept of discounted cash flow, but provides a measure of the actual percentage return a given project achieves. Today is very easy to calculate the IRR using a spreadsheet function, but you should also be familiar with a manual method which will give a reasonable approximation. We will continue to use the data from the example above to show how it can be done.

IRR is defined as the discount rate that gives a zero NPV. This then represents the return for that project regardless of the hurdle rate (the required rate of return, which in the above example is 20%). However, as we saw the actual rate of return must have been less than the hurdle rate since the NPV was negative at £691. We want to discover what the actual IRR is.

To do this we need to recalculate the NPV at a discount rate that will give a positive rate of return. We have done this in Example 1.24.

Example 1.24   Revised NPV calculation

Discount rate use is 15%

End of Year	Investment	Return	Factor	Net CF
0	(10 000)		1.0000	(10 000)
1		3000	0.8695	2 609
2		3000	0.7561	2 268
3		4000	0.6575	2 630
4		5000	0.5717	2 859
NPV (Net Present Value)				366

You can see that if finance could be obtained for 15% this project would become viable. However, we still do not know the IRR. To obtain this we will have to use interpolation to give an approximation. This is done as follows:

$$\text{IRR} = 15\% + (5\% \times 366/1057) = 16.73\%$$

This formula starts with the discount rate that produces a positive NPV (15% in this case) plus the difference between that and the rate that produces a negative NPV (in this case 20% − 15% = 5%). Then it multiplies the 5% by the positive NPV of £366 divided by the difference between the positive NPV and the negative NPV (in this case $366-(-691) = 1057$). This gives 16.73% IRR. The process appears very complicated but you can prove it is approximately right by using 16.73% as the discount rate as shown in Example 1.25.

Example 1.25   NPV equal to IRR

Discount rate use is 16.73%

End of Year	Investment	Return	Factor	Net CF
0	(10 000)		1.0000	(10 000)
1		3000	0.8567	2570
2		3000	0.7339	2202
3		4000	0.6287	2515
4		5000	0.5386	2693
NPV (Net Present Value)				(20)

You can see our approximation is close enough, and we can see that our project falls short of the required return by about 3.27%. IRR is theoretically very close to NPV in giving a correct answer to our problem, but as you can see, without a spreadsheet it is rather tedious to calculate. It may not always give the right signal however, since it gives a rate of return not a total increase or decrease in wealth. It is sometimes true that a project with a lower IRR will generate a larger NPV amount as shown in Example 1.26.

Example 1.26   IRR and NPV compared

	Year 0	Year 1	Year 2	Year 3
Project 1	(13 000)	4000	6100	8000
Project 2	(13 000)	8500	5400	3000

	NPV at 10%	IRR
Project 1	1688	16.4%
Project 2	1444	17.4%

Note that NPV would rank project 1 as best whereas IRR ranks project 2 as best. Which technique is giving the right signal? The answer is NPV, since it will always give the correct signal, regardless of the situation. This is because NPV is a measure of wealth creation, which is what we are looking for. IRR is merely a rate of return and will give misleading results in some cases, depending on the shape of the numbers.

Test your knowledge 1.14

1 What is the relationship between risk and return?
2 What is meant by 'the time value of money'?
3 Explain why ARR and payback techniques are not as useful as NPV.

However, even with NPV technique you should be aware of the fact that as always, when trying to forecast the future, the cash flows and other projections are liable to error and will not necessarily occur as planned. But given these obvious problems NPV is the best tool we have for investment appraisal.

Activity 1.12   + ÷ ×

Calculate the NPV and IRR for the following two projects and choose which of the two you will invest in.

	Investment	Positive cash flows		
	Year 0	Year 1	Year 2	Year 3
Project 1	(25 000)	10 000	13 000	13 000
Project 2	(25 000)	10 000	17 000	9 000

Make or buy decisions

These decisions require the involvement of more than one functional area. They almost certainly require the involvement of the production function, production control and engineers from design and manufacturing. Before an actual decision is made certain questions must be addressed:

(a) Could the item be made with existing facilities?
(b) If the answer to (a) is yes, is capacity adequate?

If the answer to (a) is no, then it indicates that new plant and equipment may be needed, or indeed that the company has no experience in this area of manufacture, which might therefore mean a move toward vertical integration, which involves a change to its basic business. The latter involves top level policy decisions and will not yet even be considered at the functional level at all. Theoretically any item, whether already manufactured or purchased outside can be reviewed for alternative sourcing, but in practice only those items will be considered for change that do not involve major changes to the business. Therefore, we will confine our analysis to decisions that can be made within the functional areas we described earlier.

Thus if a purchased item is being considered for manufacture then there must be suitable facilities available and sufficient capacity. If a manufactured item is being considered for purchase there must be alternative uses for the capacity or there should be an intention to reduce that capacity rather than leave it unused.

The other major factors to account for are:

● incremental costs of alternatives
● quality control problems
● multi-sourcing
● costs of tooling
● strategic importance.

What is incremental cost? This is the additional or unavoidable cost incurred for an item purchased outside or being manufactured inside. The point to note is that many overhead costs will be unaffected by the make or buy decision. Thus overhead or indirect costs are almost certainly irrelevant to the decision and only the direct or marginal costs are important. Thus comparison between the outside purchase price and the marginal or incremental manufactured price must be made to give a true picture.

If an item is being outsourced then quality control will need to be considered. Potential suppliers may not have in place suitable quality procedures or may not be part of any supplier quality assurance scheme. If multi-sourcing is necessary then this problem is even greater.

If an item for outside purchase is a special design to the company's own specification then capital investment costs will have to be accounted for. It is common in these circumstances for the customer and supplier to share the investment in tooling and this could be quite significant.

An item or component which is of strategic importance in the company's own manufacturing process presents risks if it is manufactured outside. This may be true if it is a crucial safety item or is something upon which other production processes depend. Thus a cessation of supply or quality problems could have serious consequences. Before arranging outside purchase these risks have to be evaluated and some form of risk reduction undertaken before committing to outside sourcing.

1 Why are incremental costs the only relevant costs when considering make or buy decisions?
2 What other major factors affect the make or buy decision?
3 What major business functions are likely to be involved with make or buy decisions?

Inventory control

To avoid confusion we will use the term inventory control rather than stock control. In essence these terms are interchangeable.

Inventory control is of major importance in a manufacturing company. It has an impact upon production operations, marketing and finance. In many respects there are conflicting objectives between production, finance and marketing, thus a good inventory control system should achieve a satisfactory trade-off between these disparate needs. For example finance would seek to keep inventory levels as low as possible so that capital costs are reduced. Production might prefer large stocks of raw materials to ensure security of supply and to enable long production runs and smooth production. Marketing would like high stocks of finished goods in order to provide a high level of customer service, whereas finance would like to reduce the costs of warehousing, risk of pilferage and damage.

From this you can see that 'inventory' can be a stock of raw materials, components, work-in-process (semi-finished goods) or finished goods. You can also see that these different inventories represent the materials flow process as raw materials become components, which are put into assemblies and finally transformed into finished goods.

Pareto analysis or the '80/20' rule

Often a first step in achieving the control of inventory is to classify stock according to usage and value. There is little point in establishing expensive and sophisticated control techniques for items which are very inexpensive and/or are infrequently used. The technique used is called Pareto analysis or the 80/20 rule or simply ABC analysis.

Studies have shown that for most inventory systems 80% of the use by value is accounted for by only 20% of the items in the inventory. Therefore parts are classified into A, B and C with possible percentages as follows:

A class   10% of items, 70% of value
B class   20% of items, 20% of value
C class   70% of items, 10% of value

The value is not simply the piece price of the item, it is the 'use by value' cost. For example a part may cost £0.20 each but is used at a rate of 2000 per day. Its use by value is £400. Whereas another item costing £2 is only used at a rate of 10 per day, thus its use by value is only £20. The latter item will be in a lower category than the first item, even though it is individually more expensive.

Figure 1.14 shows the Pareto curve for a particular inventory. It is based on the following analysis:

● annual use by value is calculated for each item
● the items are sorted in descending order of use by value
● compute the percentage use by value of each item
● show cumulative use by value percentage and cumulative percentage of items.

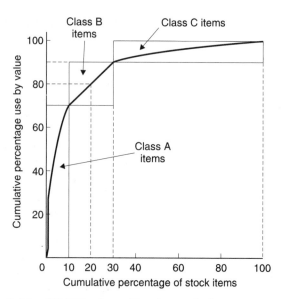

Figure 1.14   *'80/20' rule or Pareto analysis*

Our figure shows an exact correspondence with the 80/20 rule, but in reality this is rarely the case. However, it is likely to conform to the general idea behind the 80/20 rule, namely that most of the use by value is caused by a minority of items. The percentages for A, B and C items may also vary in practice, depending the company's own objectives.

The analysis is used to decide the degree of control required for items in each class. A typical approach might be:

- A class items will be physically counted frequently (say monthly) and reconciled with book records.
- B class items will be physically counted less frequently (say 3 monthly) and reconciled with book records.
- C class items will be physically counted every 6 months and reconciled with book records.

Sometimes no book record or 'perpetual inventory' is kept for C class items. Control may simply be exercised by using a bin system, which is replenished when a certain level of stock is reached as marked on the bin.

The basic principles of inventory systems

A neat way of looking at inventory is to use the analogy of a water tank as shown in Figure 1.15.

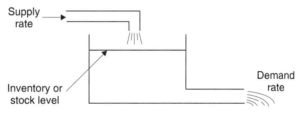

Figure 1.15 *Water tank analogy*

This shows a flow into the tank which represents the rate of supply of raw materials and components. The water level represents the stock of materials. The flow out of the tank represents the demand for inventory by the production facility. If demand exceeds supply the inventory level drops, if supply exceeds demand the level of inventory rises. The actual level of inventory then provides a buffer against changes and interruptions in supply and demand. This analogy helps us to understand more fully what are the primary functions of carrying inventories:

- ensure against uncertainties
- permit economic production and supply
- contingency against changes in supply/demand
- allow for transit time.

The uncertainties are related to things like day-to-day supply delays and interruptions and in predicting customer demands. Adequate stock allows the production function to make in economic batch sizes, thus reducing the costs of machine setup times. It also enables purchasing to buy in bulk if necessary to keep prices and transport costs down. There are also the unexpected changes that can be caused by strikes or wars, or the creation of additional demands brought about by special promotions of products. Finally there is the matter of transit time, both in relation to initial supply and between production facilities in the factory, and into the finished goods warehouse.

Multiple choice questions

1 An organization which allows decision-making at the lowest possible levels is described as

A a matrix organization
B a decentralized organization
C a hierarchical organization
D a tall organization.

2 A sheep farm business is classified as a

A primary business
B tertiary business
C secondary business
D service business.

3 Which one of the following departments would be responsible for employee welfare?

A Finance
B Production
C Purchasing
D Personnel.

4 Which of the following activities would require an engineer?

A Cost accounting
B Stock control
C Demand forecasting
E Process specification.

5 Company activities have an interface between

A Marketing and Product Development
B Finance and Manufacture
C Quality Control and Purchasing
D Sales and Production Planning.

6 Which is the company interface that will operate where a supplier delivers faulty goods to the factory?

A Marketing with Product Development
B Finance with Manufacture
C Quality Control with Purchasing
D Sales with Production Planning.

7 Which one of the following costs cannot be identified directly with the product?

A Prime cost
B Material cost
C Overhead cost
D Variable cost.

8 A fixed cost is

A one that does not vary at all
B one that does not vary when volume of production varies
C one that does not vary when volume of production varies, but may do so in later periods
D one that is decided by the accountant.

9 The following figures relate to the production of a small component:

Fixed costs:	£20 000
Variable cost per unit:	£4
Selling price:	£6

Which one of the following gives the breakeven point in sales turnover?

A £20 000
B £30 000
C £40 000
D £60 000.

10 The Production Manager's salary is:

A a direct cost
B a prime cost
C an overhead cost
D a direct labour cost.

Unit 2 Engineering systems

Summary

This unit provides an introduction to systems and their relevance to engineering. The unit is divided into two elements:

- describing engineering systems
- investigating engineering systems.

The first element introduces the basic concepts of systems while the second element delves deeper into the operation of some typical engineering systems.

Describing engineering systems

This element introduces some of the basic ideas behind the systems found in engineering. In particular, we shall focus our attention on:

- identifying the key features of a variety of engineering systems
- describing the purpose of a number of engineering systems
- identifying the inputs to, and outputs from, a variety of engineering systems using simple block diagrams.

We begin by explaining what a system is and why it is important in engineering.

What is a system?

Systems are all around us. Indeed, we ourselves are examples of a complex system that in turn contains its own nervous, respiratory, and muscular sub-systems.

We use the word system so liberally and in such a wide range of contexts that it is difficult to explain what the term means in just a few words. However, at the risk of over-simplification, we can say that every system conforms to the following main points:

(a) it has a function or purpose
(b) it has inputs and outputs

(c) it has a boundary

(d) it comprises a number of smaller components or elements linked together in a particular way.

These fundamental concepts of systems are so important that it is worth expanding on each of them in turn.

Systems have a function or purpose

Actually, some people may argue with the assumption that *every* system must have a function or purpose. They may, for example, ask what is the purpose of the solar system other than, perhaps, providing us with a home! When considering engineering systems, however, we are on pretty safe ground since, by definition, an engineered system *must* have a defined function or purpose.

Systems have a number of inputs and outputs

A system without inputs and outputs cannot interact with its environment and is thus useless! It's worth noting, however, that not all inputs and outputs may be desirable. An example of an undesirable input to a telecommunication system would be noise picked up by the cables and wires along which the signals travel. In effect, this noise presents itself as an unwanted signal superimposed on top of the wanted signal. An example of an undesirable output from a system would be the exhaust gases produced by an internal combustion engine.

Systems have a boundary

Because all systems have a boundary, it is possible to say what is inside the system and what is outside it. This sometimes becomes important when there are a number of systems (and/or subsystems) and they interact with one another.

Sometimes the boundary of a system is not very clearly defined. That said, it is usually possible to construct a diagram for a system showing all of the components and elements within the system and then place this inside a box that contains the system as a whole. We sometimes refer to this as a 'black box', see Figure 2.1.

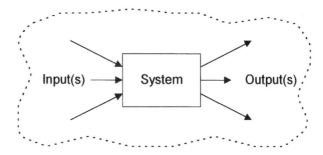

Figure 2.1 *A 'black box' system*

System components are linked in a particular way

The elements, parts, components or sub-systems that make up a system are connected together (i.e. linked) in a particular way. This may sound obvious but it is quite an important point. Consider a box of bicycle parts that can be assembled to produce a fully working bicycle. The box of bicycle parts *does not* constitute a system whereas the fully assembled bicycle *does* constitute a system. Exactly the same physical parts are present in both cases – what *is* important is the way in which the parts are connected together so that they can interact with one another. Figure 2.2 illustrates this point.

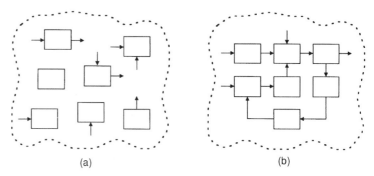

Figure 2.2 *(a) not a system; (b) a system*

Definition of a system

Systems comprise a number of elements, components or sub-systems that are connected together in a particular way. The individual elements of an engineering system interact together to satisfy a particular functional requirement.

Types of system

Various types of system are used in engineering. Listed below are some of the most common types of system. You will already be familiar with some of them but others may be completely new to you.

Electromechanical systems	e.g. a vehicle electrical system comprising battery, starter motor, ignition coil, contact breaker, distributor, etc.
Fluidic systems	e.g., a vehicle braking system comprising foot-operated lever, master cylinder, slave cylinder, piping, fluid reservoir, etc.
Electrochemical systems	e.g. a cell that uses gas as a fuel to produce electricity, pure water and heat.
Information systems	e.g. a computerized airport flight arrival system.

Communiction systems	e.g. a local area network comprising file server, coaxial cable, network adapters, several computers and a laser printer.
Control systems	e.g. a microcomputer-based controller that regulates the flow and temperature of material used in a diecasting process.
Transport systems	e.g. an overhead conveyor for transporting gravel from a quarry to a nearby processing site.

Activity 2.1

A 'heat engine' is an example of a thermodynamic system. Use your library to investigate the operation of ONE type of heat engine. Write a brief report explaining how the system operates and include relevant diagrams.

Test your knowledge 2.1

State THREE different energy sources that can be used as the primary energy source in an electrical generating station.

Test your knowledge 2.2

List the raw materials and energy sources used in each of the following systems:

(a) a foundry that produces motor vehicle engine housings
(b) a paper making plant
(c) a steel rolling mill.

Test your knowledge 2.3

Identify the inputs to, and outputs from, each of the following systems:

a traffic lights system
a domestic central heating system
a coal-fired power station
a nuclear power station

(Hint: Remember that there can be unwanted outputs from a system as well as wanted outputs!)

Function and purpose

By definition, an engineering system must have a defined purpose. This purpose is normally associated with the principal function of the system (e.g. the purpose of a manufacturing system is to produce a manufactured product).

Inputs

Inputs to a system may comprise raw materials, energy, and control values set by the operator or manufacturer. In practical, real-world systems we must also take into account disturbances (such as changes in ambient temperature) that may affect the performance of the system.

Outputs

Outputs from a system can comprise finished products, processed materials, converted energy, etc. We also need to give some consideration to the by-products produced by the system, such as waste heat, toxic materials, inert materials, chemically active materials, radiation, etc.

System components

Most systems comprise several different types of component. Some components provide the main function of a system (e.g. a boiler in a central heating system) while others monitor the output of the system (e.g. a room thermostat in a central heating system). Other components are used to set or determine the required output of the system (e.g. the human operator who interacts with the system through a programmable controller).

Test your knowledge 2.4

Complete the table shown below:

System	Main functional components (the 'doer')	Performance-checking component (the 'monitor')	Controlling component (the 'decision maker')
Central heating	Boiler and radiators	Thermostat	Gas valve
Car	Engine and transmission	Driver's eyes and ears	_____
Computer	Microprocessor and memory	_____	Application program
Railway	_____	Inspectors	Manager

The following categories can be applied to system components:

Functional components — Essentially, these are the components that do the work of the system.

Performance-checking components — These components ascertain the level of performance of the system. As such, they measure or in some way respond to the output produced by the system

Controlling components — These components are responsible for determining the level of performance of the system. They establish the desired output from the system and, in complex systems, manage the overall operation of the system.

As an example, a satellite positioning system might comprise the following:

Directional thrusters (functional components)
Fuel tank (functional component)
Control valve (functional component)
Earth-link antenna (functional component)
Command receiver/decoder (functional component)
Position computer (performance checking component)
Ground command station (the controlling component).

Activity 2.2

A domestic central heating system has the following components, inputs and outputs:

Inputs
Cold water supply (via expansion tank in loft)
Thermostat setting (set point)

Energy sources
Domestic gas supply
240 V a.c. mains electricity to operate the gas ignition system and water pump

Outputs
Heat from radiators
Waste heat and combustion products

Functional components
Gas-fired boiler
Gas ignition system
Room thermostat (adjustable)
Water pump
Water tank
Radiators
Gas valve (on/off)
Water valve (on/off)
Control panel

Sketch a diagram showing how the system components are connected together. Label your diagram clearly. (Hint: Take a look at your central heating system at home if you are not sure about how the system components are linked together).

Investigating the operation of engineering systems

This element introduces the techniques used for:

● describing systems using appropriate diagrams
● describing sub-system and component functions
● identifying the relationships between sub-systems and components
● identifying system control strategies
● investigating and modelling system performance

Systems diagrams

A simple processing system is shown in Figure 2.3. This system has a single input and a single output separated by a box marked 'process'. Practical engineering systems also require some form of energy source in order to operate and, to make the diagram complete, we also need to show this on our systems diagram together with unwanted inputs and outputs that may, or may not, be present (see Figure 2.4).

Figure 2.3 *A simple processing system*

Test your knowledge 2.5

In relation to the public address system in Figure 2.5:

(a) state TWO forms of noise that may be present
(b) identify the energy source for the system
(c) state ONE unwanted output produced by the system.

Energy supply

Unwanted input(s)

Unwanted output(s)

Input   Process   Output

Figure 2.4 *A more accurate representation of a processing system showing unwanted inputs (disturbances) and outputs*

A practical example of a simple system is illustrated in Figure 2.5. In this public address system, a microphone is used as an 'input transducer' to collect acoustic energy in the form of sound pressure waves and convert this to electrical energy in the form of small voltages and currents. The signal from the microphone is then amplified by means of an electronic circuit containing transistors and/or integrated circuits before it is applied to a loudspeaker. This 'output transducer' converts the electrical energy supplied to it back into acoustic energy.

Test your knowledge 2.6

Sketch block diagrams of each of the following systems, Clearly identify the system's inputs and outputs and the links between its various components:

a petrol engine ignition system
a hi-fi system
a computerized airport flight arrival system.

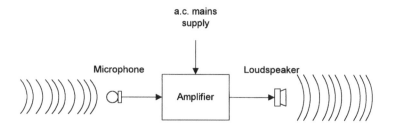

a.c. mains supply

Microphone   Amplifier   Loudspeaker

Positive feedback

Figure 2.5 *A public address system*

Test your knowledge 2.7

Classify the following list of system components under the headings: 'Input device', 'Processing device', 'Output device':

a rotary switch
a variable resistor
an actuator
a position sensor
a transformer
a signal lamp
a keyboard
an amplifier
a comparator
a visual display unit (VDU)

Activity 2.3

Read the following description of a nuclear power station based on a pressurized water cooled reactor (PWR). Draw a complete system diagram for the nuclear power station. Clearly label all of the inputs and outputs from the system and each of the elements within the system. Hint: If you need further information, refer to your library.

Within the nuclear reactor, uranium fuel undergoes fission – the splitting of atoms – which, in turn, produces heat. This heat is removed by water which is pressurized to prevent it from boiling. The water circulates through the reactor and heat exchangers (known as steam generators) in which the heat is given up to a separate secondary water circuit which operates at a lower pressure and therefore is able to boil.

Steam produced in the secondary circuit is used to drive a turbine generator, the power from which is transmitted via a transformer and switchgear to overhead high-voltage power lines. Exhausted steam from the turbines, its useful energy now expended, is condensed back to water via a seawater-cooled condenser before it is returned by pump to the steam generators where it is once again converted to steam.

Activity 2.4

Investigate ONE engineering system selected from EACH of the FOUR categories listed below:

Category A (Electromechanical systems)
    a portable electric drill
    a washing machine
    a robot arm.

Category B (Fluidic systems)
    a hydraulic ram
    a compressor
    a water pump.

Category C (Chemical systems)
    a PCB production plant
    an electroplating plant
    an oil refinery.

Category D (Information and data communication systems)
    a personal laptop computer
    a portable cellular telephone
    a PLC-based process controller.

Category E (Thermodynamic systems)
    an internal combustion engine
    a refrigerator
    a domestic central heating system.

Present your findings in the form of an illustrated report and include the following:

(a) a description of the purpose of the system
(b) a fully labelled block diagram of the system
(b) a list identifying and describing the inputs to the system
(c) a list identifying and describing the outputs from the system
(d) an explanation of the implications of the inputs to the system.

System control

The behaviour of most systems is subject to variations in input (supply) and in output (demand). The behaviour of a system may also change in response to variations in the characteristics of the components that make up the system. In practice it is desirable to include some means of regulating the output of a system so that it remains relatively immune to these three forms of variation.

System control involves maintaining the system output at the desired level regardless of any disturbances that may affect:

(a) the input quantitites
(b) any unwanted variations in systems components
(c) the level of demand (or 'loading') on the output.

Different control methods are appropriate to different types of system. The overall control strategy can be based on analogue or digital techniques and may also be classed as either sequential or combinational. We shall briefly consider each of these methods.

Analogue control

Analogue control involves the use of signals and quantities that are continuously variable. Within analogue control systems, signals are represented by voltage and currents that can take any value between two set limits. Figure 2.6 shows how the output of a typical analogue system varies with time.

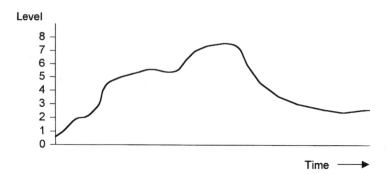

Figure 2.6 *Output of an analogue system shown against time*

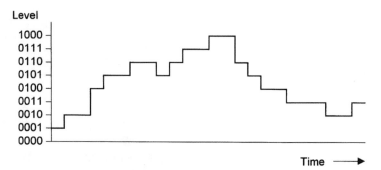

Figure 2.7 *Output of a digital system shown against time*

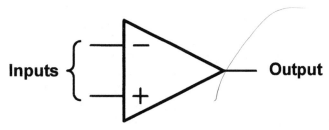

Figure 2.8 *An operational amplifier*

Analogue control systems are invariably based on the use of operational amplifiers (see Figure 2.8). These devices are capable of performing mathematical operations such as addition, subtraction, multiplication, division, integration and differentiation.

Digital control

Digital control involves the use of signals and quantities that vary in discrete steps. Values that fall between two adjacent steps must take one or other value as intermediate values are disallowed! Figure 2.7 shows how the output of a typical digital system varies with time.

Digital control systems are usually based on digital logic devices (see Figure 2.9) or microprocessor-based computer systems.

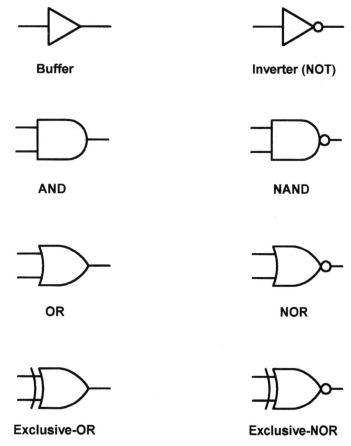

Buffer **Inverter (NOT)**

AND **NAND**

OR **NOR**

Exclusive-OR **Exclusive-NOR**

Figure 2.9 *A selection of digital logic gates*

Test your knowledge 2.9

How many different states can be represented by:

(a) a 4-bit binary code
(b) a 12-bit binary code?

Test your knowledge 2.10

A digital control system is required to represent values to a resolution of at least 1%. With how many bits should it operate?

Test your knowledge 2.11

Write down the sequence of operations required to start a conventional car engine.

(Hint: you might like to consider the operation of each of the following components: choke, petrol pump, ignition switch, battery, starter motor, etc.)

Values represented within a digital system are expressed in binary coded form using a number of signal lines. The voltage on each line can be either 'high' (representing logic 1) or 'low' (representing logic 0). The more signal lines the greater the resolution of the system. For example, with just two signal lines it is only possible to represent a number using two binary digits (or 'bits'). Since each bit can be either 0 or 1 it is only possible to represent four different values (00, 01, 10 and 11) using this system. With three signal lines we can represent numbers using three bits and eight different values are possible (000, 001, 010, 011, 100, 101, 110 and 111).

The relationship between the number of bits, n, and the number of different values possible, m, is given by, $m = 2^n$. So, in an 8-bit system the number of different discrete states is given by, $m = 2^8 = 256$

Sequential control systems

Many systems are required to perform a series of operations in a set order. For example, the ignition system of a gas boiler may require the following sequence of operations:

1 Operator's start button pressed
2 Fan motor operates
3 Delay 60 seconds
4 Open gas supply valve
5 Igniter operates for 2 seconds
6 If ignition fails, close gas supply valve, delay 60 seconds, then stop fan motor
7 If ignition succeeds, boiler will continue to operate until either stop switch operates or flame fails.

The components of simple sequential systems often include timers, relays, counters, etc., however digital logic and microprocessor-based controllers are used on more complex systems.

Combinational control systems

Combinational control systems take several inputs and perform comparisons on a continuous basis. In effect, everything happens at the same time – there are no delays or predetermined sequences that

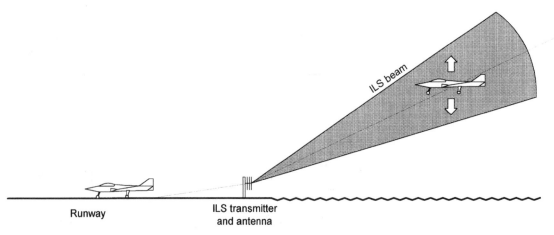

Figure 2.10 *An aircraft instrument landing system (ILS)*

would be associated with sequential controllers. An aircraft instrument landing system (ILS) for example, makes continuous comparisons of an aircraft's position relative to the ILS radio beam. Where any deviation is detected, appropriate correction is applied to the aircraft's flight controls (Figure 2.10).

Control methods

Open-loop control

In a system that employs open loop-control, the value of the input variable is set to a given value in the expectation that the output will reach the desired value. In such a system there is no automatic comparison of the actual output value with the desired output value in order to compensate for any differences.

A simple example of an open-loop control method is the manual adjustment of the regulator that controls the flow of gas to a burner on the hob of a gas cooker. This adjustment is carried out in the expectation that food will be raised to the correct temperature in a given time and without burning. Other than the occasional watchful eye of the chef, there is no means of automatically regulating the gas flow in response to the actual temperature of the food.

Closed-loop control

Clearly, open-loop control has some significant disadvantages. What is required is some means of closing the loop in order to make a continuous automatic comparison of the actual value of the output compared with the setting of the input control variable.

In the previous example, the chef actually closes the loop on an intermittent basis. In effect, the gas cooker relies on human intervention in order to ensure consistency of the food produced. If our cooking only requires boiling water, this intervention can be kept to a minimum, however, for 'haute cuisine' we require the constant supervision of a skilled human operator!

All practical engineering systems make use of closed-loop control. In some cases, the loop might be closed by a human operator who determines the deviation between the desired and actual output. In most cases, however, the action of the system is made fully automatic and no human intervention is necessary other than initially setting the desired value of the output. The principle of a closed-loop control system is illustrated in Figure 2.11.

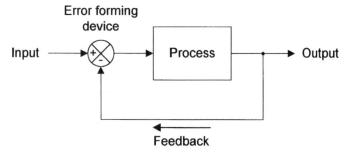

Figure 2.11   *A closed-loop system*

Consider each of the following systems and classify them in terms of the previous statements, 1 to 5 (Hint: more than one may apply!):

(a) Control of the fuel rods in a nuclear reactor
(b) An infra-red missile guidance system
(c) A computerized space shuttle landing system
(d) Control of solder temperature in a flow-soldering plant
(e) Controlling the frequency of a reference clock oscillator.

Reasons for making a system fully automatic include the following:

1 Some systems use a very large number of input variables and it may be difficult or impossible for a human operator to keep track of them.

2 Some processes are extremely complex and there may be significant interaction between the input variables.

3 Some systems may have to respond very quickly to changes in variables (human reaction times may just not be fast enough).

4 Some systems require a very high degree of precision (human operators may be unable to work to a sufficiently high degree of accuracy).

Example 2.1 An analogue closed-loop control system

The analogue closed-loop control system shown in Figure 2.12 provides speed control for the d.c. motor, M. The actual motor speed is sensed by means of a small d.c. tachogenerator, G, coupled to the output shaft. The voltage produced by the tachogenerator is compared with that produced at the slider of a potentiometer, R, which is used to set the desired speed. The comparison of the two voltages (i.e. that of the tachogenerator with that corresponding to the set point) is performed by an operational amplifier connected as a comparator. The output of the comparator stage is applied to a power amplifier that supplies current to the d.c. motor. Energy is derived from a mains-powered d.c. power supply comprising transformer, rectifier and smoothing circuits.

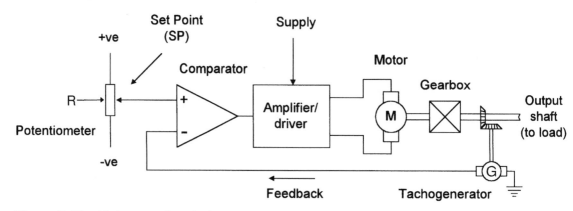

Figure 2.12 *Motor speed control system*

> ### Example 2.2 A digital closed-loop control system
>
> Figure 2.13 shows a microprocessor-based digital closed-loop control system developed by Lotus. This system provides active ride suspension control for a high performance road vehicle and it avoids the need for the road springs, dampers and anti-roll bars that are found in a conventional vehicle. The system allows the car to be 'self-levelling' and it can eliminate roll when the vehicle corners at both low and high speed. The overall ride can be set to 'hard' or 'soft' to suit the driver and also to cater for a variety of load conditions.
>
> The three principal input signals (all in analogue form) are derived from a load cell (which forms part of the suspension unit), an accelerometer, and a linear displacement (position) transducer attached to each wheel. These analogue signals are converted to digital signals that can be processed by the microprocessor by means of analogue to digital converters (ADC). The 8-bit digital signals produced by thee ADC are connected directly to the microprocessor's 8-bit data bus.
>
> The two main output signals are used to drive two servo control valves that regulate the supply of hydraulic fluid to the hydraulic ram arrangement. The supply of hydraulic fluid is powered by a small engine-driven pump.

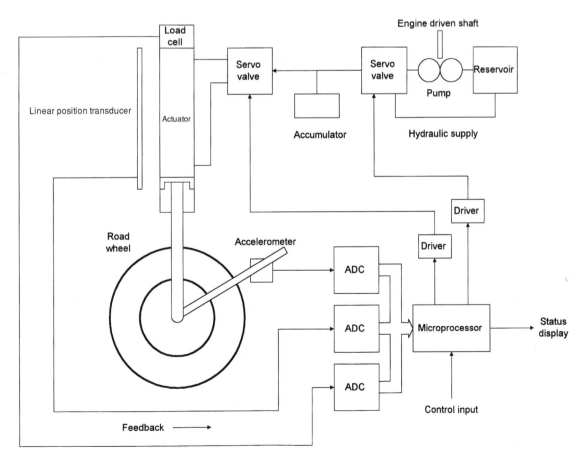

Figure 2.13 *Vehicle ride control system*

On/off control

On/off control is the simplest form of control and it merely involves turning the output on and off repeatedly in order to achieve the required level of output variable. Since the output of the system is either fully on or fully off *at any particular instant of time* (i.e., there is no half-way state), this type of control is sometimes referred to as 'discontinuous'.

Example 2.3   On/off control

The most common example of an on/off control system is that of a simple domestic room heater. A variable thermostat is used to determine the set point (SP) temperature value. When the actual temperature is below the SP value, the heater is switched on (i.e., electrical energy is applied to the heating element). Eventually, the room temperature will exceed the SP value and, at this point, the heater is switched off. Later, the temperature falls due to heat loss, the room temperature will once again fall below the SP value and the heater will once again be switched on (Figure 2.14). In normal operation, the process of switching on and off will continue indefinitely.

Hysteresis

In practice, a small amount of hysteresis is built into most on/off control systems. In the previous example, this hysteresis is designed to prevent the heater switching on and off too rapidly which, in turn, would result in early failure of the switch contacts fitted to the thermostat. Note, however, that the presence of hysteresis means that, at any instant of time, the actual temperature will always be somewhere between the upper and lower threshold values.

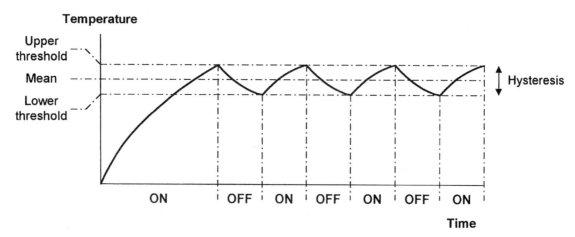

Figure 2.14   *Variation of output produced by a simple domestic heater using on/off control*

Activity 2.5

Locate a room heater (an electric fire, fan heater or a portable oil-filled radiator) fitted with a thermostatic control. Examine the thermostat carefully and see if you can determine the upper and lower thresholds as you rotate the control that determines the SP value (you should be able to detect a 'click' at these two points). If the control is calibrated, estimate the amount of hysteresis present.

Now set the heater up in its normal position and connected it to the mains supply. Obtain a reasonably sensitive thermometer and place this approximately half a metre away from the heater and 1 metre off the floor (do not place it directly above the heater). Set the thermostat to a temperature that is a few degrees (e.g. 5°C) above the current ambient temperature.

Note down the time that you first apply power to the heater and then and allow the room heater to bring the room temperature up to the point at which the thermostat first operates (removing power to the heater). Record the temperature at the measuring point regularly (say, every 2 minutes) and note down the time at which the thermostat first operates. Now wait for the temperature to fall back to the point at which power is re-applied to the heater, again recording time and temperature and noting the time at which the thermostat contacts next become closed. Continue to observe the operation of the thermostat for two or three further cycles then use the data that you have collected to construct a graph showing on and off times and recorded temperature starting at the point that you first applied power to the heater. Finally, if you are to obtain a satisfactory result for this activity you will need to take steps to avoid unwanted 'disturbances'. Can you give an example of an unwanted disturbance in the context of this investigation and say how you were able to minimize its effect on the performance of the system?

Proportional control

On/off control is crude but can be effective in many simple applications. A better method is to vary the amount of correction applied to the system according to the size of the deviation from the SP value. As the difference between the actual value and the desired output becomes less, the amount of correction becomes correspondingly smaller.

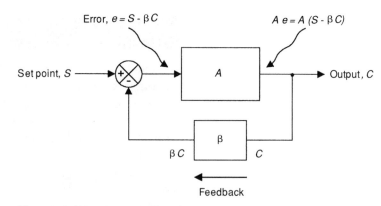

Figure 2.15 *A proportional controller*

Figure 2.15 shows the simplified block schematic of a proportional controller. The output of the controller, C, is proportional to the error signal, e. Now

$$C = Ae \text{ and } e = S - \beta Ae \text{ thus } e = S - \beta C \text{ or } \beta C = S - e$$

hence

$$C = \frac{S - e}{\beta} \tag{i}$$

but

$$C = A e \text{ thus } e = C/a \tag{ii}$$

Combining (i) and (ii) gives:

$$C = \frac{S - (C/A)}{\beta} = \frac{S}{\beta} - \frac{C}{\beta A}$$

thus

$$C + \frac{C}{\beta A} = \frac{S}{\beta}$$

or

$$C(1 + (1/\beta A) = S/\beta$$

or

$$C\left(1 + \frac{1}{\beta A}\right) = \frac{S}{\beta}$$

or

$$C = \frac{S}{(1 + (1/\beta A) \beta}$$

Hence

$$C = \frac{S}{(\beta + 1/A)}$$

or

$$C = k_p S$$

where

$$k_p = \frac{1}{(\beta + 1/A)}$$

Thus

$$k_p = \frac{A/\beta}{A/\beta(\beta + 1/A)} = \frac{A/\beta}{A + 1/\beta}$$

or

$$k_p = \frac{A}{1 + \beta A}$$

From the previous example you should note that k_p tends to $1/\beta$ as A becomes large. In a practical analogue control system, A can be made very large using an operational amplifier (such devices have typical open-loop voltage gains of more than 100 000).

Now consider what happens in Figure 2.15 when the output, C, exceeds the desired value, S (i.e., $C > S$). In this case, the error signal (e) becomes negative and, as a consequence, the output is reduced. Conversely, when the output, C, is less than the desired value, S (i.e. $C < S$), the error signal (e) becomes positive and, as a result, the output is increased. Finally, when the output, C, is equal to the desired value, S, the error signal (e) is zero and no further correction is applied.

Test your knowledge 2.13

Determine the constant, k_p, for each of the following conditions:

(a) $A = 10$, $\beta = 1/10$
(b) $A = 100$, $\beta = 1/10$
(c) $A = 1000$, $\beta = 1/10$
(d) $A = 10\,000$, $\beta = 1/10$

What can you say about k_p as A becomes large?

Test your knowledge 2.14

Determine the value of C and e in Figure 2.16.

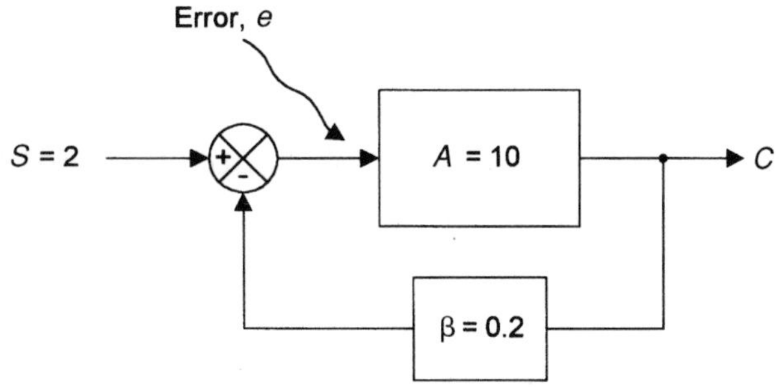

Figure 2.16   *See test your knowledge 2.14*

Choosing the right value for k_p

The overall (closed-loop) gain, k_p, of the proportional controller shown in Figure 2.15 is given by:

$$k_p = \frac{A}{1 + \beta A}$$

The value chosen for k_p determines the behaviour of the system as a whole. Small values of k_p result in relatively small correcting signals and poor response to large changes in output (e.g. as a result of increasing the demand or load imposed on the output). We can improve the response by increasing k_p (and correspondingly reducing S). If k_p is made too large, the system may become unstable. Hence the value chosen for k_p usually represents something of a compromise between responsiveness and freedom from instability.

Test your knowledge 2.15

Determine the closed loop gain, k_p, for all three cases shown in Figure 2.17. Also determine the input (S) required to produce an output (C) of 2 in each case.

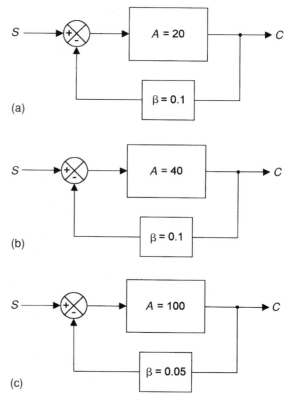

(a)

(b)

(c)

Figure 2.17   *See test your knowledge 2.15*

Adding an offset to the input

In many practical systems, a small constant input may be required before the output variable can reach its optimum value (see Figure 2.18). In such a system, the equation for the output, C, can be written:

$$C = A (e + k_i)$$

where k_i determines the control action when the error signal, e, is equal to zero. Proportional action takes place above and below this standing value.

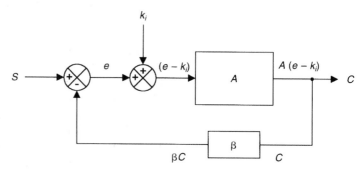

Figure 2.18   *Proportional controller with constant offset input*

Now

$$C = A (e + k_i) = A e + A k_i$$

Now

$$e = S - \beta C \text{ or } \beta C = S - e \text{ (as before)}$$

hence

$$C = \frac{S - e}{\beta} \tag{i}$$

but

$$C = A e + A k_i$$

thus

$$C - A k_i = A e$$

or

$$e = \frac{C - A k_i}{A} \tag{ii}$$

Combining (i) and (ii) gives:

$$C = \frac{S - ((C - A k_i)/A)}{\beta} = \frac{S}{\beta} - \frac{((C - A k_i)/A)}{\beta A}$$

$$C = \frac{S}{\beta} - \frac{C}{\beta A} + \frac{A k_i}{\beta A}$$

thus

$$C + \frac{C}{\beta A} = \frac{S}{\beta} + \frac{k_i}{\beta}$$

or

$$C \left(1 + \frac{1}{\beta A} \right) = \frac{S}{\beta} + \frac{k_i}{\beta}$$

or

$$C = \frac{S + k_i}{(1 + (1/\beta A) \beta}$$

Hence

$$C = \frac{S + k_i}{(\beta + 1/A)}$$

or

$$C = k_p (S + k_i) \text{ where } k_p = \frac{1}{(\beta + 1/A)}$$

As before,

$$k_p = \frac{A}{1 + \beta A}$$

Test your knowledge 2.16

For the system shown in Figure 2.19, find C when:

(a) $S = 0$
(b) $S = 0.5$

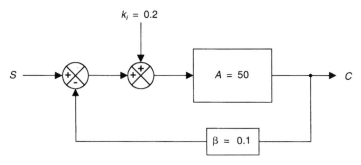

Figure 2.19 *See test your knowledge 2.16*

System response

In a perfect system, the output value, C, will respond instantaneously to a change in the input, S. There will be no delay when changing from one value to another and no time required for the output to 'settle' to its final value. This ideal state of affairs is illustrated in Figure 2.20(b). In practice, real-world systems take time to reach their final state. Indeed, a very sudden change in output may, in some cases, be undesirable. Furthermore, inertia is present in many

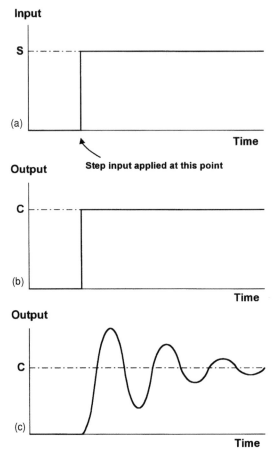

Figure 2.20 *(a) Step input. (b) Ideal response to a step input. (c) Response of a real system to a step input*

systems. Consider the case of the motor speed control system shown in Figure 2.21 where the output shaft is connected to a substantial flywheel. The flywheel effectively limits the acceleration of the motor speed when the set point (S) is increased. Furthermore, as the output speed reaches the desired value, the inertia present will keep the speed increasing despite the reduction in voltage (C) applied to the motor. Thus the output shaft speed overshoots the desired value before eventually falling back to the required value.

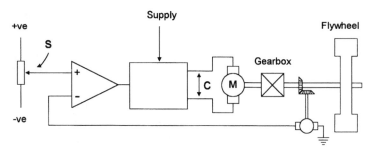

Figure 2.21 *Motor speed control system with inertia*

Increasing the gain present in the system will have the effect of increasing the acceleration but this, in turn, will also produce a correspondingly greater value of overshoot. Conversely, decreasing the gain will reduce the overshoot but at the expense of slowing down the response. The actual response of the system represents a compromise between speed and an acceptable value of overshoot. Figure 2.20(c) shows the typical response of a system to the step input shown in Figure 2.20(a).

Second-order response

The graph shown in Figure 2.20(c) is known as a 'second-order' response. This response has two basic components, an exponential growth curve and a damped oscillation (see Figure 2.22). The

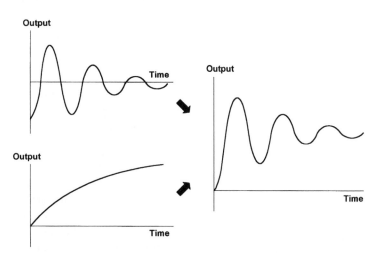

Figure 2.22 *System response resulting from adding damped oscillation to an exponential growth curve*

oscillatory component can be reduced (or eliminated) by artificially slowing down the response of the system. This is known as 'damping'. The optimum value of damping is that which *just* prevents overshoot. When a system is 'underdamped', some overshoot is still present. Converseley, an 'overdamped' system may take a significantly greater time to respond to a sudden change in input (see Figure 2.23 here).

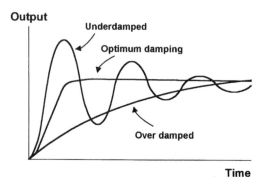

Figure 2.23 *System response with different amounts of damping*

Delay time, settling time and damping factor

The delay time for a system is the time taken for the output to reach 50% of its final (steady-state) value after the application of a step input (see Figure 2.24(a)). The settling time for a system is the time taken for the system to enter and remain within defined tolerance limits for its output. Typical values for tolerance limits are 5% or 10%. In relation to the steady-state step value, the size of the first overshoot is an indicator of the 'damping factor'. The smaller the damping factor, the larger the overshoot. Optimum damping is associated with a damping factor of unity.

Natural frequency

The natural frequency (f_n) of a system is the reciprocal of the time taken (t) for one cycle of the damped oscillation (see Figure 2.24(b)). Natural frequency is sometimes specified in hertz (Hz) or in terms of angular velocity, ω_n, where:

$$\omega_n = 2\,\pi\,f_n \text{ and } f_n = 1/t$$

Decrement

From Figure 2.24 you should note that each successive cycle of damped oscillation has a smaller amplitude than its predecessor. However, the amount of reduction in amplitude is constant from each peak to the next. This is known as the 'decrement' and it can be most easily measured from the ratio of the amplitude of the first undershoot to that of the first overshoot. In each case the amplitudes are measured either side of the steady-state value. If, for example, the amplitude of the first undershoot is 0.1 while that of the first overshoot is 0.2, the decrement is (0.1/0.2) or 0.5.

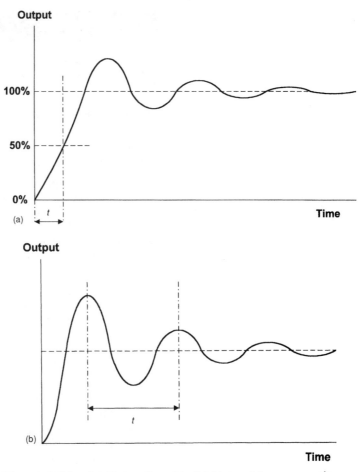

Figure 2.24 *(a) Delay time (t). (b) Natural frequency ($\frac{1}{t}$)*

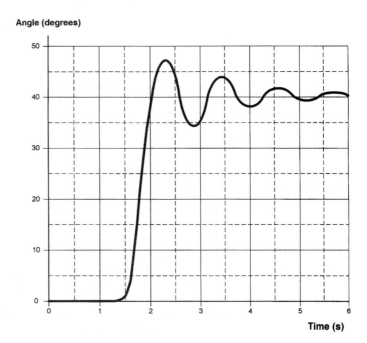

Figure 2.25 shows the response of a rotary position control system to a sudden change in input. Determine each of the following:

(a) the amplitude of the first overshoot
(b) the decrement
(c) the natural frequency
(d) the 10% settling time.

Figure 2.25 *See test your knowledge 2.17*

Activity 2.6

The following data refers to measurements made on a motor speed control system:

Time (s)	0	1	2	3	4	5	6	7	8	9	10
Output (rev/s)	0	2.1	11.0	19.5	25.0	28.6	29.8	28.8	24.5	20.5	17.0

Time (s)	11	12	13	14	15	16	17	18	19	20
Output (rev/s)	15.5	14.8	15.6	16.9	19.1	21.0	21.9	28.3	21.9	21.0

Plot the response of this system and use it to determine:

(a) the final (steady-state) value
(b) the delay time
(c) the 15% settling time
(d) the natural frequency.

Negative feedback

Most systems use negative feedback in order to precisely control the operational parameters of the system and to maintain the output over a wide variation of the internal parameters of the system. In the case of an amplifier, for example, negative feedback can be used not only to stabilize the gain but also to reduce distortion and improve bandwidth.

The amount of feedback determines the overall (or closed-loop) gain. Because this form of feedback has the effect of reducing the overall gain of the circuit, this form of feedback is known as 'negative feedback'. An alternative form of feedback, where the output is fed back in such a way as to reinforce the input (rather than to subtract from it) is known as 'positive feedback'.

We will put negative feedback into context by taking a look at an easily quantifiable example, that of a simple electronic amplifier. Figure 2.26 shows the block diagram of an amplifier stage with

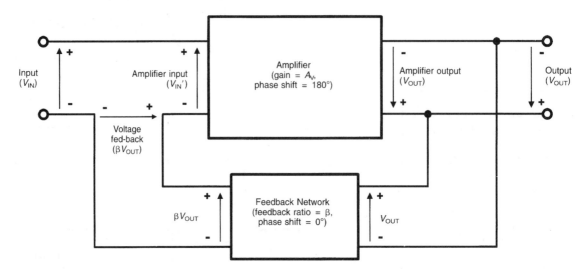

Figure 2.26   *An electronic amplifier with negative feedback applied*

negative feedback applied. In this circuit, the proportion of the output voltage fed back to the input is given by β and the overall voltage gain will be given by:

Overall gain $= V_{out}/V_{in}$

Now

$V_{in}' = V_{in} - \beta V_{out}$ (by applying Kirchhoff's Voltage Law)

(note that the amplifier's input voltage has effectively been reduced by applying negative feedback), thus

$V_{in} = V_{in}' + \beta V_{out}$

and

$V_{out} = A_v \times V_{in}'$ (A_v is the internal gain of the amplifier)

Hence,

$$\text{overall gain} = \frac{A_v \times V_{in}'}{V_{in}' + \beta V_{out}} = \frac{A_v \times V_{in}'}{V_{in}' + \beta (A_v \times V_{in}')}$$

Thus

$$\text{overall gain} = \frac{A_v}{1 + \beta A_v}$$

Hence, the overall gain with negative feedback applied, will be less than the gain without feedback. Furthermore, If A_v is very large (as is the case with modern integrated circuit operational amplifiers) the overall gain with negative feedback applied will be given by:

overall gain (when A_v is very large) $= 1/\beta$

Note, also, that the loop gain of a feedback amplifier is defined as the product of β and A_v.

Example 2.4   Gain with negative feedback applied

An amplifier with negative feedback applied has an open-loop voltage gain of 50 and one-tenth of its output is fed back to the input (i.e. β = 0.1). Determine the overall voltage gain with negative feeback applied.

With negative feedback applied the overall voltage gain will be given by:

$$\frac{A_v}{1 + \beta A_v} = \frac{50}{1 + (0.1 \times 50)} = \frac{50}{1 + 5} = \frac{50}{6} = 8.33$$

Example 2.5   Gain stabilization

If, in the previous example, the amplifier's open-loop voltage gain increases by 20%, determine the percentage increase in overall voltage gain.

The new value of open-loop gain will be given by:

$A_v' = A_v + 0.2 A_v = 1.2 \times 50 = 60$

The overall voltage gain with negative feedback will then be:

$$\frac{A_v}{1 + \beta A_v} = \frac{60}{1 + (0.1 \times 60)} = \frac{60}{1 + 6} = \frac{50}{6} = 8.57$$

Test your knowledge 2.18

An amplifier has an open-loop gain of 200 and is used in a circuit in which 5% of the output is fed back as negative feedback. Determine the overall voltage gain with negative feedback applied.

Test your knowledge 2.19

An amplifier is required to have a closed-loop voltage gain of 40. If the amplifier is to be based on an integrated circuit that exhibits an open-loop voltage gain of 800, determine the amount of negative feedback required.

The increase in overall voltage gain, expressed as a percentage will thus be:

$$\frac{8.57 - 8.33}{8.33} \times 100\% = 2.88\%$$

Note that this example illustrates one of the important benefits of negative feedback in stabilising the overall gain of an amplifier stage.

Example 2.6   Use of negative feedback to determine precise gain

An integrated circuit that produces an open-loop gain of 100 is to be used as the basis of an amplifier stage having a precise voltage gain of 20. Determine the amount of feedback required.

Rearranging the formula, $\dfrac{A_v}{1 + \beta A_v}$, to make β the subject gives:

$$\beta = \frac{1}{A_v'} - \frac{1}{A_v} = \frac{1}{20} - \frac{1}{100} = 0.05 - 0.01 = 0.04$$

where A_v' is the overall voltage gain with feedback applied, and A_v is the open-loop voltage gain.

Positive feedback

Positive feedback is an alternative form of feedback where the output is fed back in such a way as to reinforce the input (rather than to subtract from it). This form of feedback is associated with instability and oscillation rather than regulation and stabilization. Once again, we will attempt to put this into context by considering an example that is easily quantifiable.

Figure 2.27 shows the block diagram of an electronic amplifier stage with positive feedback applied. Note that the amplifier provides a phase shift of 180° and the feedback network provides a further 180°. Thus the overall phase shift is 0°. The overall voltage gain is given by:

$$\text{Overall gain} = \frac{V_{out}}{V_{in}}$$

Now $V_{in}' = V_{in} + \beta V_{out}$ (by applying Kirchhoff's Voltage Law)

thus $V_{in} = V_{in}' - \beta V_{out}$

and $V_{out} = A_v \times V_{in}'$ (A_v is the internal gain of the amplifier)

Hence, overall gain $= \dfrac{A_v \times V_{in}'}{V_{in}' - \beta V_{out}} = \dfrac{A_v \times V_{in}'}{V_{in}' - \beta(A_v \times V_{in}')}$

Thus overall gain $= \dfrac{A_v}{1 - \beta A_v}$

Now consider what will happen when the loop gain (βA_v) approaches unity. The denominator ($1 - \beta A_v$) will become close to

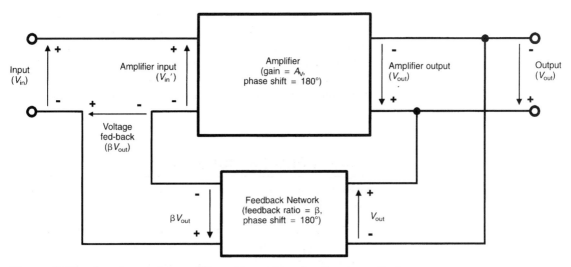

Figure 2.27 *An electronic amplifier with positive feedback applied*

zero. This will have the effect of increasing the overall gain, i.e., the overall gain with positive feedback applied will be greater than the gain without feedback.

It is worth illustrating this difficult concept using some practical Figures. Assume that you have an amplifier with a gain of 9 and one-tenth of the output is fed back to the input (i.e. $\beta = 0.1$). In this case the loop gain ($\beta \times A_v$) is 0.9.

With negative feedback applied (see page 104) the overall voltage gain will fall to:

$$\frac{A_v}{1 + \beta A_v} = \frac{9}{1 + (0.1 \times 9)} = \frac{9}{1 + 0.9} = \frac{9}{1.9} = 4.7$$

With positive feedback applied the overall voltage gain will be:

$$\frac{A_v}{1 - \beta A_v} = \frac{9}{1 - (0.1 \times 9)} = \frac{9}{1 - 0.9} = \frac{9}{0.1} = 90$$

Now assume that you have an amplifier with a gain of 10 and, once again, one-tenth of the output is fed back to the input (i.e. $\beta = 0.1$). In this example the loop gain ($\beta \times A_v$) is exactly 1.

With negative feedback applied the overall voltage gain will fall to:

$$\frac{A_v}{1 + \beta A_v} = \frac{10}{1 + (0.1 \times 10)} = \frac{10}{1 + 1} = \frac{10}{2} = 5$$

However, with positive feedback applied the overall voltage gain will be:

$$\frac{A_v}{1 - \beta A_v} = \frac{10}{1 - (0.1 \times 10)} = \frac{10}{1 - 1} = \frac{10}{0} = \text{infinity}$$

This simple example shows that a loop gain of unity (or larger) will result in infinite gain and, as a consequence, the amplifier will be unstable. In fact, the amplifier will oscillate since even the smallest disturbance will be amplified and will result in an output.

Clearly, as far as an amplifier is concerned, positive feedback may have an undesirable effect – instead of reducing the overall gain the effect is that of reinforcing any signal present and the output can build up into continuous oscillation if the loop gain is 1, or greater. To put this another way, oscillator circuits can simply be thought of as amplifiers that generate an output signal without the need for an input!

Conditions for oscillation

From the foregoing we can deduce that the conditions for oscillation are:

(a) the feedback must be positive (i.e. the signal fed back must arrive back in-phase with the signal at the input)
(b) the overall loop voltage gain must be greater than 1 (i.e. the amplifier's gain must be sufficient to overcome the losses associated with any frequency-selective feedback network).

Hence, to create an oscillator we simply need an amplifier with sufficient gain to overcome the losses of the network that provides positive feedback. Assuming that the amplifier provides 180° phase shift, the frequency of oscillation will be that at which there is 180° phase shift in the feedback network. A number of circuits can be used to provide 180° phase shift, however the essential point is that the feedback should be positive so that the output signal arrives back at the input in such a sense as to reinforce the original signal.

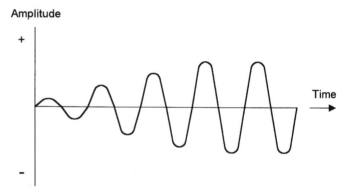

Figure 2.28 *See test your knowledge 2.20*

Test your knowledge 2.20

Figure 2.28 shows a system in which positive feedback is present. Explain the shape of the output signal. What factors determine the frequency of the signal produced?

Activity 2.27

Use your library to investigate one type of electronic oscillator circuit. Write a brief report explaining how the circuit works and illustrate your report with a labelled circuit diagram. Present your report in word processed form and use a drawing or CAD package to draw the circuit diagram.

Multiple choice questions

1 A computerized airport flight arrival system is an example of

  A an electromechanical system
  B a fluidic system
  C a chemical system
  D an information system.

2 An oil refinery is an example of

  A an electromechanical system
  B a fluidic system
  C a chemical system
  D an information system.

3 Which ONE of the following system components is a device used to store energy?

  A a flywheel
  B an actuator
  C a stepper motor
  D a battery charger.

4 Which ONE of the following is not a system control device?

  A a thyristor
  B a triac
  C a relay
  D an LED.

5 Which ONE of the following is not a system input device?

  A a microphone
  B a loudspeaker
  C a variable resistor
  D a rotary switch.

6 Which ONE of the following is likely to degrade the signal present in a communication system?

  A noise resulting from thermal agitation within components
  B long-term variations in component values
  C a significant increase in signal amplitude
  D use of negative feedback.

7 Which ONE of the following is a disadvantage of using negative feedback?

  A the stability of the system is increased
  B the system is more prone to variations in the characteristics of individual components
  C the performance of the system is less predictable
  D the overall gain produced by the system is reduced.

8 The system component shown in Figure 2.29 is

A a logic gate
B an operational amplifier
C a relay
D a flow control valve.

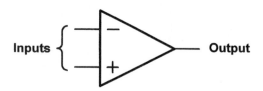

Figure 2.29 *See multiple choice question 8*

9 The block schematic of a motor speed controller is shown in Figure 2.30. The component marked X

A generates an error signal
B determines the set point
C compensates for speed fluctuations
D provides negative feedback.

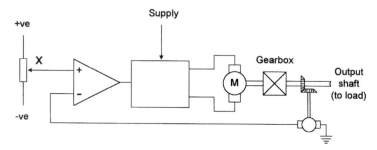

Figure 2.30 *See multiple choice question 9*

10 The block schematic of a proportional control system is shown in Figure 2.31. The signal at point X is

A the set point, *S*
B the output, *C*
C the feedback ratio, *B*
D the error, *e*.

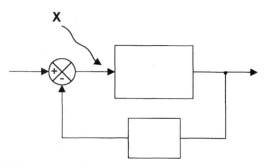

Figure 2.31 *See multiple choice question 10*

Unit 3 Engineering processes

Summary

This element introduces a range of workshop and manufacturing processes. Some of these processes you will eventually use in your project work. Others are more appropriate to the large-scale production of materials and components. This element starts by reviewing the selection of materials and processes used to make some common devices. It then looks at these processes, and others, in greater depth and breadth.

Products

Engineered products are usually assemblies of individual components. Such products can be divided into three main groups:

● Mechanical products such as gearboxes, pumps, engines and turbines.
● Electronic products such as the completed circuit boards used in computers, video recorders and television receivers.
● Electromechanical devices can range from washing machines to computer controlled machine tools. These are devices which combine electrical and mechanical components.

Electrician's screwdriver

Figure 3.1 shows an exploded view of a typical electrician's screwdriver. It has to combine the functions of a conventional screwdriver with the ability to indicate whether a mains circuit is live. It must be strong enough to tighten and undo the small brass screws found in the terminals of electrical accessories. It must be insulated to withstand the potentials (voltages) met in domestic, industrial and commercial installations. The current through the neon indicator lamp must be limited to a safe level under all conditions. It must be light in weight, compact and competitively priced.

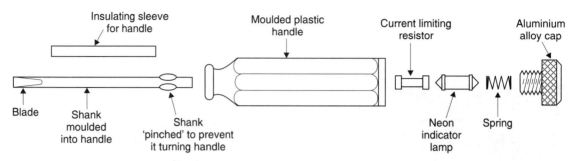

Figure 3.1 *A typical electrician's screwdriver*

These criteria can be met by careful selection of materials and manufacturing processes.

- The blade is made from a toughened medium carbon steel (0.8% carbon).
- The shank of the blade is insulated using a PVC sleeve.
- The handle is moulded from cellulose acetate. This is a tough, flame resistant plastic with good insulating properties. It is transparent so that the neon indicator lamp can be seen to light up. The blade would be moulded into the handle.
- The spring would be made from hard drawn phosphor bronze wire. This is a good conductor and corrosion resistant.
- The end cap would be made from an aluminium alloy on a computer numerically controlled (CNC) lathe. This material is light in weight, easily cut, a good conductor and corrosion resistant. The process of manufacture is suitable for large batch production.
- The neon indicator lamp and the current limiting resistor would be bought in as standard components.

All the materials chosen are readily available and relatively low in cost. They are selected for their fitness for purpose. Such screwdrivers are made and sold in large quantities and the manufacturing processes chosen lend themselves to large batch production.

Automatic opener for greenhouse ventilators

Figure 3.2 shows a schematic design and some details for a means of automatically opening and closing the ventilator lights of a large commercial greenhouse. This is a prototype and only one is to be made. Normal mechanical and electronic workshop equipment is available. Let's now look at some of the problems.

- Greenhouses are wet places so we should be looking for readily available, low cost, corrosion resistant materials that can be fabricated within the limitations of the equipment available.
- Greenhouses are wet places so we pay particular attention to the protection and insulation of all electrical equipment. We should be looking at the possibility of using low voltage equipment.

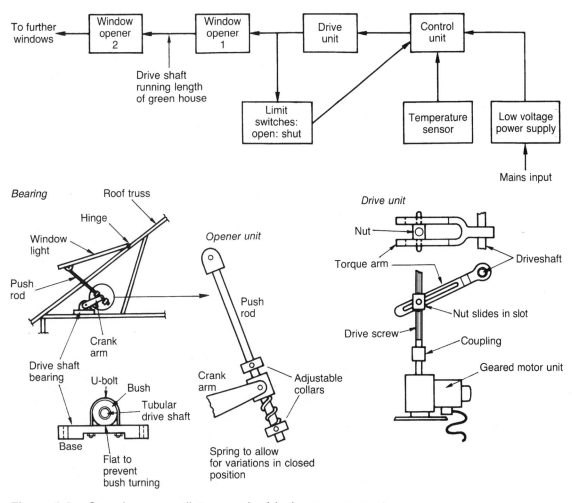

Figure 3.2 *Greenhouse ventilator opening/closing arrangement*

● Greenhouses are lightweight structures and tend to flex in high winds. Our design should also be strong but light. It should be able to 'give' with the structure.

● Greenhouse attendants are not engineering technicians. Our design must be capable of operating over long periods with minimal attention.

Let's now see how these objectives can be achieved:

● The main drive shaft needs to be light but strong, corrosion resistant and flexible. It must be cheap and readily available. We have an ideal solution in the stainless steel piping that is used as an alternative to copper for domestic plumbing. It is sold in long straight lengths. If we need to join several lengths together we can use standard plumbers' compression joint couplings.

● The bearing housings could be machined from aluminium alloy bar with nylon bearing bushes. Moisture is absorbed by nylon and acts as a lubricant. No oiling would be required. The U-bolts would be made from 18/8 stainless steel rod. This is readily available, easy to machine and relatively cheap in the smaller sizes.

- The arms and the push rods could be machined from aluminium, alloy such as 'duralumin', and 18/8 stainless steel rod. These are both corrosion resistant. The bearing bushes could be made from nylon rod and the pivot pins from 18/8 stainless steel rod. The pivot pins being cross-drilled and secured by stainless steel split pins.
- A drive motor would have to be 'bought-in'. This should be a geared unit with a very high ratio. Remember that the shaft running along the greenhouse will only need to make about a quarter of a turn. A low voltage motor should be chosen and its direction of rotation should be reversible.
- The output from the motor should be coupled to the master screw. The screw should have a coarse thread for strength. It could be turned from 18/8 stainless steel rod and the nut could be made from nylon rod or from 'tufnol'. The nut would need to be fairly long to withstand the wear. Again, I would remind you that neither nylon nor 'tufnol' would need lubrication and they are likely to last longer than a bronze nut, unless the bronze nut is regularly lubricated.
- All nuts and bolts and screws should be standard stainless steel items.
- Finally we come to the electronic control unit. This, and its associated power pack, could be developed using laminated plastic matrix boards with terminal pins. The circuit components would need to be bought in. If standard integrated circuits are to be used, then it will be easier to build up the circuit on perforated strip board. There would be little point in producing a printed circuit board (p.c.b.) for a 'one-off'.
- The control circuit, its power pack, the motor control relay and the low voltage transformer for the motor, all need to be housed in a moisture proof, corrosion resistant box. Plastic instrument cases are advertised in a number of catalogues. However these tend to retain heat. If any of the solid state devices require heat-sinks then an aluminium sheet-metal box would have to be fabricated with suitable ventilation louvres built in..

So you can see that, with a little ingenuity, what seemed a complex and expensive electromechanical device can be developed and produced quite cheaply using standard materials and components. Any machining can be carried out using normal workshop equipment including a lathe, a milling machine and a drilling machine. We will now look at the safe use of a range of workshop equipment and also at a range of larger-scale manufacturing processes.

> **Test your knowledge 3.1**
>
> List THREE main factors that must be considered when choosing a material for a given component.

Safety

Health and safety legislation

The Health and Safety at Work, etc., Act of 1974 makes both the employer and the employee (you) equally responsible for safety. Both are equally liable to be prosecuted for violations of safety regulations and procedures. It is your legal responsibility to take reasonable care for your own health and safety. The law expects you to act in a responsible manner so as not to endanger yourself or other workers or the general public. It is an offence under the act to misuse or or interfere with equipment provided for your health and safety or the health and safety of others.

Causes of accidents

Accidents result from a number of possible causes, including:

Human carelessness   Most accidents are caused by human carelessness. This can range from 'couldn't care less' and 'macho' attitudes, to the deliberate disregard of safety regulations and codes of practice. Carelessness can also result from fatigue and ill-health resulting from a poor working environment.

Personal habits   Personal habits such as alcohol and drug abuse can render workers a hazard not only to themselves but also to other workers. Fatigue due to a second job (moonlighting) can also be a considerable hazard, particularly when operating machines. Smoking in prohibited areas where flammable substances are used and stored can cuase fatal accidents involving explosions and fire.

Supervision and training   Another cause of accidents is lack of training or poor quality training. Lack of supervision can also lead to accidents if it leads to safety procedures being disregarded.

Environment   Unguarded and badly maintained plant and equipment are obvious causes of injury. However the most common causes of accidents are falls on slippery floors, poorly maintained stairways, scaffolding and obstructed passageways in overcrowded workplaces. Noise, bad lighting, and inadequate ventilation can lead to fatigue, ill-health and carelessness. Dirty surroundings and inadequate toilet and washing facilities can lead to a lowering of personal hygiene standards.

Accident prevention

Elimination of hazards   The work place should be tidy with clearly defined passageways. it should be well lit and ventilated. It should have well maintained non-slip flooring. Noise should be kept down to acceptable levels. Hazardous processes should be replaced with less dangerous and more environmentally acceptable alternatives. For example asbestos clutch and brake linings should be replaced with safer materials.

Guards   Rotating machinery, drive belts and rotating cutters must be securely fenced to prevent accidental contact. Some machines have interlocked guards. These are guards coupled to the machine drive in such a way that the machine cannot be operated when the guard is open for loading and unloading the work. All guards must be set, checked and maintained by qualified and certificated staff. They must not be removed or tampered with by operators. Some examples of guards are shown in Figure 3.3

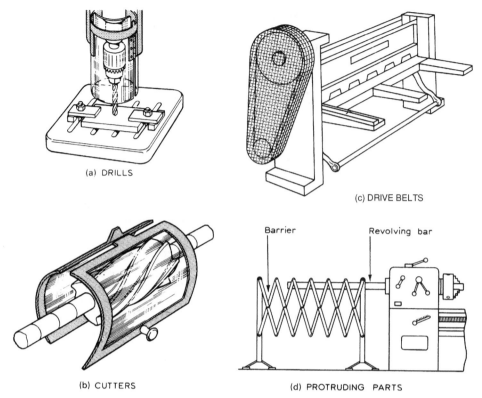

(a) DRILLS

(c) DRIVE BELTS

(b) CUTTERS

Barrier | Revolving bar

(d) PROTRUDING PARTS

Figure 3.3 *Examples of guards*

Maintenance Machines and equipment must be regularly serviced and maintained by trained fitters. This not only reduces the chance of a major breakdown leading to loss of production, it lessens the chance of a major accident caused by a plant failure. Equally important is attention to such details as regularly checking the stocking and siting of first-aid cabinets and regularly checking the condition and siting of fire extinguishers. All these checks must be logged.

Personal protection Suitable and unsuitable working clothing is shown in Figure 3.4.

Some processes and working conditions demand even greater protection, such as safety helmets, earmuffs, respirators and eye protection worn singly or in combination. Such protective clothing must be provided by the employer when a process demands its use. Employees must, by law, make use of such equipment. Some examples are shown in Figure 3.5.

Safety education This is important as it can help to produce positive attitudes towards safe working practices and habits. Warning notices and instructional posters should be displayed in prominent positions and in as many ethnic languages as necessary. Information, education and training should be provided in all aspects of health and safety. For example process training, personal hygiene, first-aid and fire procedures. Regular fire drills must be carried out to ensure that the premises can be evacuated quickly, safely and without panic.

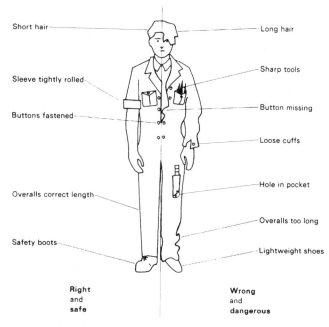

Figure 3.4 *Suitable and unsuitable work clothing*

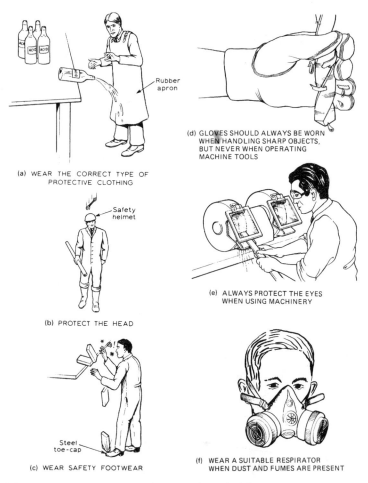

Figure 3.5 *Examples of protective clothing*

Test your knowledge 3.2

1 Who are equally responsible for Health and Safety in the workplace under the terms of the Act?
2 List SIX precautions you can take that will help to prevent an accident happening to you or other workers in your workplace.

Personal attitudes   It is important that everyone adopts a positive attitude towards safety. Not only your own safety but the safety of your workmates and the general public. Skylarking and throwing things about in the workplace or on site cannot be allowed. Any distraction that causes lack of concentration can lead to serious and even fatal accidents.

Housekeeping   A sign of a good worker is a clean and tidy working area. Only the minimum of tools for the job should be laid out at any one time. These tools should be laid out in a tidy and logical manner so that they immediately fall to hand. Tools not immediately required should be cleaned and properly stored away. All hand tools should be regularly checked and kept in good condition. Spillages, either on the workbench or on the floor should be cleaned up immediately.

Electrical hazards

Electrical equipment is potentially dangerous. The main hazards can be summarized as follows:

● electric shock
● fire due to the overheating of cables and equipment
● explosions set off by sparks when using unsuitable equipment when flammable vapours and gasses are present.

Personal safety

Before using any electrical equipment it is advisable to carry out a number of visual checks as shown in Figure 3.6(a).

● Check that the cable is not damaged or frayed.
● Check that both ends of the cable are secured in the cord grips of the plug or appliance and that none of the conductors is visible.
● Check that the plug is in good condition and not cracked.
● Check that the voltage and power rating of the equipment is suitable for the supply available.

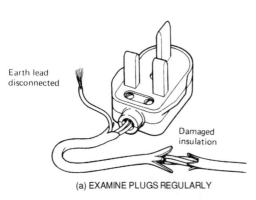

(a) EXAMINE PLUGS REGULARLY

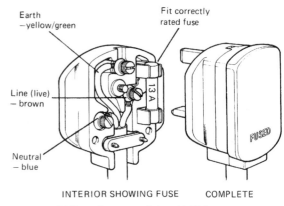

INTERIOR SHOWING FUSE   COMPLETE

(b) Correctly connected plug with 3A fuse

Figure 3.6   *Electric plug safety checks*

- If low voltage equipment is being used check that a suitable transformer is available.
- Check that whatever the voltage rating of the equipment, it is connected to the supply through a circuit breaker containing a residual current detector (RCD).
- Check that all metal clad electrical equipment has a properly connected earth lead and is fitted with a properly connected three-pin plug as shown in Figure 3.6(b).

Earthing

All exposed metalwork of electrically powered or operated equipment must be earthed to prevent electric shocks. Figure 3.7 shows the two ways in which a person may receive an electric shock. In Figure 3.7(a) the person is receiving a shock by holding both the live and neutral conductors so that the electric current can flow through his or her body. The neutral conductor is connected to earth, so it is equally possible to receive a shock via an earth path when holding a live conductor as shown in Figure 3.7(b). It is unlikely you would be so foolish as to deliberately touch a live conductor, but you might come into contact with one accidentally.

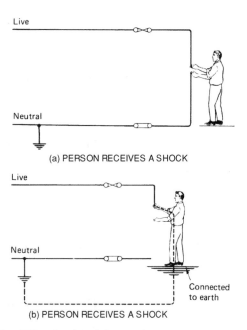

Figure 3.7 *Electric shock hazard*

For example, the portable electric drill shown in Figure 3.8(a) has a metal casing but no earth. The live conductor has fractured within the machine and is touching the metal casing. The operator cannot see this and would receive a serious or even fatal shock. The fault current would flow through the body of the user via the earth path to neutral.

Figure 3.8(b) shows the effect of the same fault in a properly earthed machine. The fault current would take the path of least

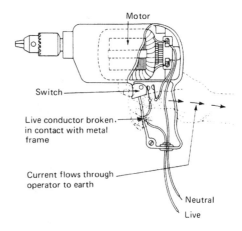

(a) ELECTRIC DRILL NOT EARTHED

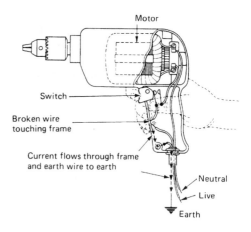

(b) ELECTRIL DRILL IS EARTHED

Figure 3.8   *Electric drill earthing*

resistance and would flow to earth via the earth wire. The operator would be unharmed. *Electrical equipment must be regularly inspected, tested, repaired and maintained by qualified electricians.* Note that 'double insulated' equipment does not need to be earthed.

Procedure in the event of electric shock

- Switch off the supply of current if this can be done quickly.
- If you cannot switch off the supply, do *not* touch the person's body with your bare hands. Human flesh is a conductor and you would also receive a severe shock. Drag the affected person clear using insulating material such as dry clothing, a dry sack, or any plastic material that may be handy.
- If the affected person has stopped breathing commence artifical respiration *immediately*. Don't wait for help to come or go to seek for help. If the affected person's pulse has stopped, heart massage will also be required. Use whatever method of resuscitation with which you are familiar.

Test your knowledge 3.3

1 State THREE causes of electrical accidents and suggest how they may be prevented.
2 List the checks you would make before using a portable electric power tool.

Fire

Fire is the rapid oxidation (burning) of flammable materials. For a fire to start, the following are required:

- A supply of flammable materials.
- A supply air (oxygen).
- A heat source.

Once the fire has started the removal of one or more of the above will result in the fire going out.

Fire prevention

Fire prevention is largely 'good housekeeping'. The workplace should be kept clean and tidy. Rubbish should not be allowed to accumulate in passages and disused storerooms. Oily rags and waste materials should be put in metal bins fitted with airtight lids. Plant, machinery and heating equipment should be regularly inspected, as should fire alarm and smoke detector systems. You should know how to give the alarm.

Electrical installations, alterations and repairs must only be carried out by qualified electricians and must comply with the current Institute of Electrical Engineers (IEE) Regulations. Smoking must be banned wherever flammable substances are used or stored. The advice of the fire prevention officer of the local brigade should be sought before flammable substances, bottled gases, cylinders of compressed gases, solvents and other flammable substances are brought on site.

Fire procedures

Regular fire drills must be held. Personnel must be familiar with normal and alternative escape routes. There must be assembly points and a roll call of personnel. A designated person must be allocated to each department or floor to ensure that evacuation is complete. There must be a central reporting point.

In the event of you discovering a fire, you should:

- Raise the alarm and call the fire service.
- Evacuate the premises.
- Keep fire doors closed to prevent the spread of smoke. Smoke is the biggest cause of panic and accidents, particularly on staircases. Emergency exits must be kept unlocked and free from obstruction whenever the premises are in use. Lifts must not be used in the event of fire.
- Only attempt to contain the fire until the professional brigade arrives if there is no danger to yourself or others. Always make sure you have an unrestricted means of escape. Saving lives is more important than saving property.

Extinguishers

Figure 3.9 shows a fire hose and a range of pressurized water extinguishers. These can be identified by their shape and colour which is RED. They are for use on burning solids such as wood, paper, cloth, etc. They are UNSAFE on electrical equipment at all voltages.

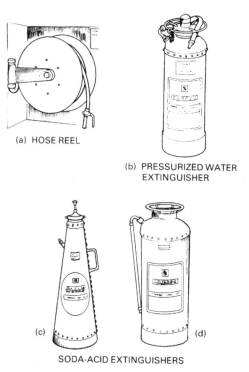

(a) HOSE REEL

(b) PRESSURIZED WATER
EXTINGUISHER

(c)   (d)

SODA-ACID EXTINGUISHERS

Figure 3.9   *Fire hose and pressurized extinguishers*

Figure 3.10 shows two types of foam extinguisher. These can be identified by their shape and colour which is CREAM. They are for use on burning flammable liquids. They are *UNSAFE* on electrical equipment at all voltages.

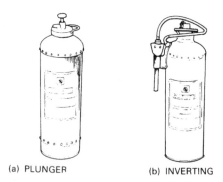

(a) PLUNGER   (b) INVERTING

Figure 3.10   *Foam extinguishers*

Figure 3.11 shows a variety of extinguishers that can be used on most fires and are safe for use on electrical equipment. Again, they can be identified by their shapes and colours.

- Dry powder extinguishers are coloured BLUE and are safe up to 1 000 volts (1 kV).
- Carbon dioxide (CO_2) extinguishers are coloured BLACK and are safe at high voltages.
- Vapourizing liquid extinguishers are coloured GREEN and are safe at high voltages.

(a) Dry powder extinguisher

(b) Carbon dioxide (CO₂) extinguisher

(c) Vaporizing liquid extinguisher

Figure 3.11 *Dry powder, CO₂ and vaporizing liquid extinguishers*

These latter two extinguishers act by replacing the air with an atmosphere free from oxygen. They are no good in draughts which would blow the vapour or gas away. Remember, if the fire can't breathe neither can any living creature. Evacuate all living creatures before using one of these types of extinguisher. When using this type of extinguisher, keep backing away from the gas towards fresh air, *otherwise it will put you out as well as the fire!*

Figure 3.12 shows a fire blanket. Fire blankets are woven from fire-resistant synthetic fibres and are used to smother fires. The old fashioned blankets made from asbestos must *NOT* be used. The blanket is pulled from its container and spread over the fire to exclude the air necessary to keep the fire burning. They are suitable for use in kitchens, in workshops, and in laboratories. They are also used where a person's clothing is on fire, by rolling the person and the burning clothing up in the blanket to smother the fire. Do not cover the person's face.

Figure 3.12 *A fire blanket*

Test your knowledge 3.4

1 State which sort of fire extinguisher you would use in each of the following instances:
    (a) Paper burning in an office waste bin.
    (b) A pan of fat burning in the kitchen of the work's canteen.
    (c) A fire in a mains voltage electrical machine.
2 A fire breaks out near to a store for paints, paint thinners and bottled gases. What action should be taken and in what order?
3 Consult the appropriate safety notices and describe how to carry out mouth to mouth resuscitation in the event of electric shock.
4 Describe how the guard over the end-train gears (change wheels) of a lathe can be interlocked so that the lathe cannot be operated with the guard open.
5 Explain why it is unsafe to use pressurized water and foam extinguishers on fires in mains voltage electrical equipment.

Activity 3.1

Consult the Health and Safety at Work Act and write a brief report explaining what is meant by each of the following:

(a) an 'improvement notice'
(b) a 'prohibition notice'

State who it is that issues these notices and identify those who can be prosecuted under the Act.

Inspection

Quality control is concerned with *fitness for purpose*. That is, will the component or assembly do the job for which it is designed. For this reason regular inspection is required. Bought-in materials and components should be inspected to ensure the supplier is maintaining the standards required by the purchaser. The components and assemblies made from such purchased materials must be inspected to see if they are up to specification.

Mechanical inspection

This is mostly concerned with the linear and angular measurement of size. Components may be measured or gauged. Measurement and gauging are comparator processes. The component is compared with a measuring instrument or a gauge.

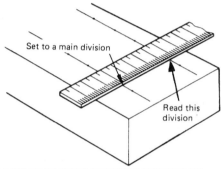

(a) MEASURING THE DISTANCE BETWEEN TWO
     SCRIBED LINES

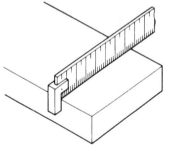

(b) MEASURING THE DISTANCE BETWEEN TWO
     FACES USING A HOOK RULE

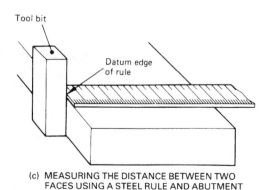

(c) MEASURING THE DISTANCE BETWEEN TWO
     FACES USING A STEEL RULE AND ABUTMENT

Figure 3.13 *Applications of a steel rule*

Direct measurement

Steel rule   These are made from spring temper stainless steel or matt chrome-plated carbon steel. They should be engine engraved for accuracy and clarity. The edges should be ground so that a rule can be used as a straight edge. The ground datum end of the rule must be carefully protected from wear and damage. Figure 3.13 shows some applications of a steel rule, and Figure 3.14 shows how a steel rule can be used in conjunction with internal and external calipers. These enable measurements to be made more accurately. A rule should not be used where an accuracy of better than ±0.5 mm is required.

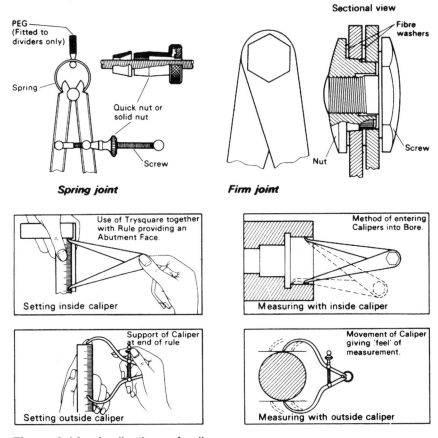

Figure 3.14   *Applications of calipers*

Vernier caliper   Figure 3.15 shows a typical vernier caliper and some of its applications. The scales vary with the make and the manufacturers instructions should always be read. Scales in 'inch' units may have a reading accuracy of either 0.001 or 0.002 inch. Scales in metric units may have a reading accuracy of either 0.01 mm or 0.02 mm. Figure 3.15(d) shows how to read a metric vernier scale.

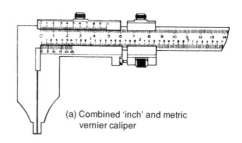

(a) Combined 'inch' and metric
vernier caliper

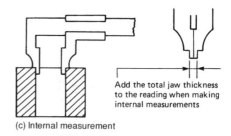

(b) External measurement

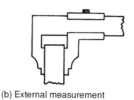

(c) Internal measurement

Add the total jaw thickness
to the reading when making
internal measurements

METRIC VERNIER

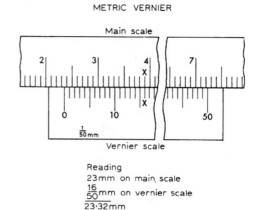

Main scale

Vernier scale

Reading
23mm on main scale
$\frac{16}{50}$mm on vernier scale
23·32mm

(d) Reading the metric vernier scale
23 mm on main scale plus 16 x 0.02 mm
on vernier scale gives total 23.32 mm

Figure 3.15 *A typical vernier caliper and applications*

Vernier calipers usually have scales in both 'inch' and metric units. They are made in a variety of sizes up to a scale length of 1,000 mm. They tend to be heavy to use and it is difficult to get an accurate 'feel' between the instrument and the workpiece. Also the scales can be difficult to read if you haven't got good eyesight. A magnifying glass is helpful.

Micrometer caliper Figure 3.16 shows a typical micrometer caliper and its scales in both 'inch' and metric units. It has a reading accuracy of 0.001 inch. or 0.01 mm. The micrometer caliper has a number of advantages compared with the vernier caliper:

● It is lighter and a more accurate 'feel' between it and the workpiece can be achieved.
● The scales are clearer to read.
● The ratchet enables a constant measuring pressure to be achieved.
● It is adjustable to compensate for wear.

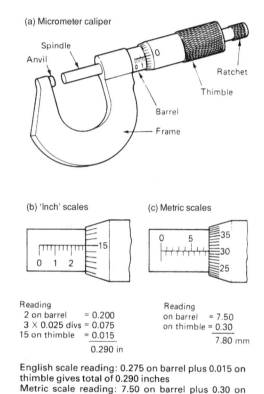

Figure 3.16 *Micrometer caliper*

Unfortunately the range of a micrometer scale is only 25 mm or 1 inch. Therefore a whole range of micrometers are required, increasing in size by 25 mm or 1 inch steps. Also different types of micrometer are required for internal measurements and depth measurements.

Angular measurement The accurate measurement of angles can involve the use of very sophisticated optical equipment. Here we are only concerned with protractors. Figure 3.17(a) shows a plain bevel protractor and its use. With care a plain bevel protractor can be read to 0.5 degrees (30 minutes) of arc. Figure 3.17(b) shows the scales of a vernier protractor. These can be read to 5 minutes of arc.

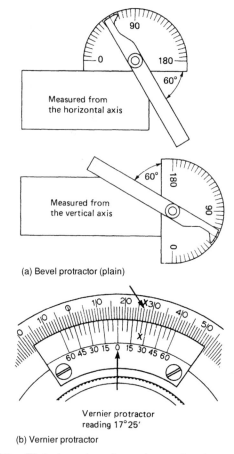

(a) Bevel protractor (plain)

Vernier protractor
reading 17°25′

(b) Vernier protractor

Figure 3.17 *Plain bevel and vernier protractors*

Main scale

0.02 mm

Vernier scale

(a)

(b)

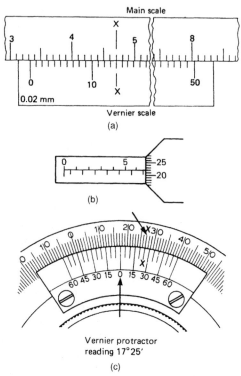

Vernier protractor
reading 17°25′

(c)

Figure 3.18 *See Test your knowledge 3.5*

Test your knowledge 3.5

1 Write down the reading of the vernier caliper scale shown in Figure 3.18(a).
2 Write down the reading of the micrometer scale shown in Figure 3.18(b).
3 Write down the reading of the vernier protractor scale shown in Figure 3.18(c).

Indirect measurement

Dial test indicator (plunger type) The dial test indicator (DTI), also known as a dial gauge or a 'clock', is used for making comparative measurements and for setting up machines. Figure 3.19 (a) shows a plunger type dial gauge. Movement of the plunger is magnified by a gear train and indicated by the movement of a pointer over a scale. The smaller pointer indicates the number of complete revolutions the main pointer has made. Various scales and magnifications are available. The plunger has a substantial range of movement.

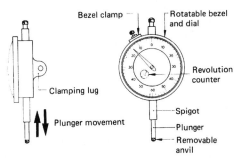

(a) PLUNGER-TYPE DIAL TEST INDICATOR

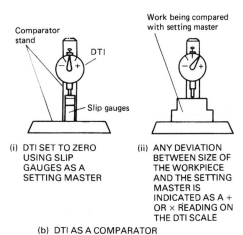

(b) DTI AS A COMPARATOR

Figure 3.19 *Dial test indicator*

Figure 3.19(b) shows a plunger type DTI set up on a stand for making comparative measurements. The DTI indicates the difference in size between the component being measured and a stack of master gauge blocks making up the correct size. Figure 3.20 shows a plunger type DTI being used for testing roundness and concentricity.

Dial test indicator (lever type) An example of a lever-type dial test indicator (DTI) is shown in figure 3.21(a). The magnification of the movement of the stylus is achieved using levers and a scroll. The stylus movement is very limited compared with the plunger

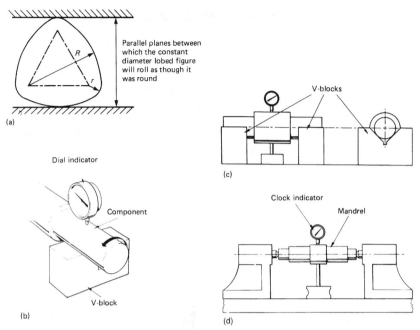

(a) Out-of-roundness which cannot be determined by micrometer or vernier calipers (b) use of V-block and DTI to determine out-of-roundness (c) and (d) testing for concentricity

Figure 3.20 *Plunger type dial test indicator*

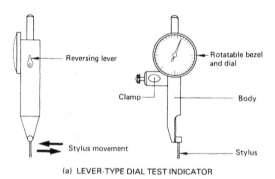

(a) LEVER-TYPE DIAL TEST INDICATOR

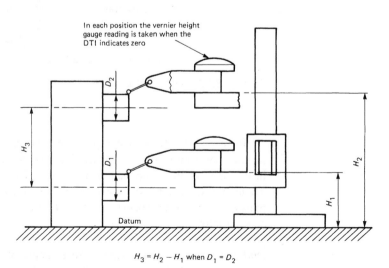

$$H_3 = H_2 - H_1 \text{ when } D_1 = D_2$$

(b) DTI AS A FIDUCIAL INDICATOR: $H_3 = H_2 - H_1$ WHEN $D_1 = D_2$: ZERO READINGS GUARANTEE CONSTANT MEASURING PRESSURE

Figure 3.21 *Lever type dial test indicator*

type. However it is very compact and this, coupled with the convenient position of its dial, makes it a very popular instrument for inspection and machine setting. An example of its use is shown in Figure 3.21(b).

Gauges

All the instruments and devices considered so far measure the actual size of a component feature. Gauges only check if the size of this feature is satisfactory. Gauges cannot measure size. Component features cannot be manufactured to an exact size, nor can measuring instruments measure to an exact size. Therefore we have to give components limits of size between which the component will work satisfactorily. The closer the limits, the more expensive manufacturing becomes.

The terminology associated with a toleranced dimension is explained in Figure 3.22. Let's consider Example 2. The component will be correct and it will function correctly, if its thickness lies anywhere between 20.2 mm and 20.8 mm.

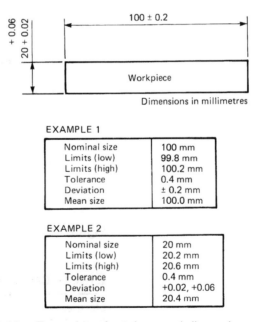

EXAMPLE 1

Nominal size	100 mm
Limits (low)	99.8 mm
Limits (high)	100.2 mm
Tolerance	0.4 mm
Deviation	± 0.2 mm
Mean size	100.0 mm

EXAMPLE 2

Nominal size	20 mm
Limits (low)	20.2 mm
Limits (high)	20.6 mm
Tolerance	0.4 mm
Deviation	+0.02, +0.06
Mean size	20.4 mm

Figure 3.22 *Examples of a toleranced dimension*

We don't need to know the actual thickness, only if it lies between these limits. We can check if this is so by use of a gap gauge as shown in Figure 3.23. The gauge shows whether the component thickness is within limits and acceptable, or whether it is too thick or too thin in which case it is rejected as scrap. Gauging is quicker and cheaper than measuring for batch and large volume production. However, for prototype production the cost of a special gauge is not warranted. Figure 3.23(d) shows a plug gauge for checking holes.

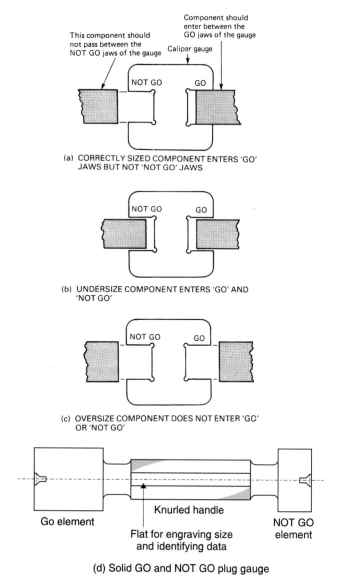

(a) CORRECTLY SIZED COMPONENT ENTERS 'GO'
JAWS BUT NOT 'NOT GO' JAWS

(b) UNDERSIZE COMPONENT ENTERS 'GO' AND
'NOT GO'

(c) OVERSIZE COMPONENT DOES NOT ENTER 'GO'
OR 'NOT GO'

(d) Solid GO and NOT GO plug gauge

Figure 3.23 *A gap gauge*

Electrical inspection

Electrical inspection requires the use of specialized instruments and 'meters'. The following instruments are commonly used:

Voltmeters   Voltmeters are used to measure the potential difference between two points in a circuit. Therefore voltmeters are always wired in *parallel* across these two points. You must always make sure that the voltmeter is able to withstand the potential applied across it.

Ammeters   Ammeters are used to measure the magnitude of the current flowing in a circuit. The current must flow through the ammeter. Therefore ammeters are always connected in *series* with a circuit. You must alway make sure that the ammeter can withstand the maximum current flowing in the circuit. Figure 3.24 shows a voltmeter and an ammeter wired into a circuit.

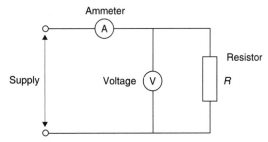

Figure 3.24 *Measurement of resistance by voltmeter/ammeter method*

Ohmmeters Resistance can be measured using an ohmmeter or by calculation using Ohm's Law. With reference to Figure 3.24:

$$R = V/I$$

where: R = resistance in ohms (Ω), V = potential in volts (V), I = current in amperes (A).

Multi-range meters These are widely used by service engineers. They can be switched to read potential (voltage), current, and resistance in ohms. For each of these modes they can be switched through various ranges. These meters are available with analogue (needle and scale) or digital readouts. Figure 3.25 shows simple examples of the use of a typical multi-range meter.

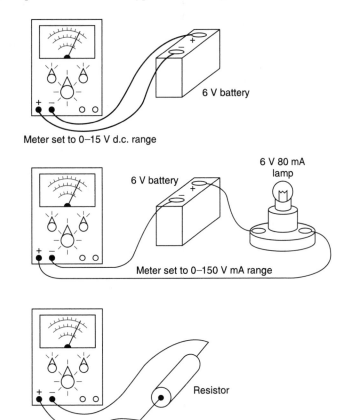

Meter set to 0–15 V d.c. range

Meter set to 0–150 V mA range

Meter switched to appropriate resistance range
Ohmic value is read directly off meter scale

Figure 3.25 *Examples of using a multi-range meter*

Meggers These can be battery powered or have a hand-cranked, internal generator. They produce a high voltage output for testing the insulation and continuity of wiring systems in domestic and industrial premises. They are used by installation electricians.

Oscilloscopes Oscilloscopes are used to display current form on the screen of a cathode-ray tube, rather like a small television set. The appearance of the front of an oscilloscope is shown in Figure 3.26(a). This shows the main controls. There is a transparent grid

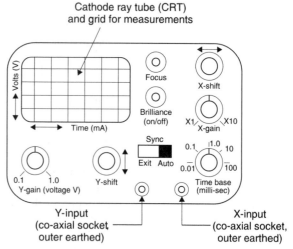

(a) Cathode ray oscilloscope (CRO) controls

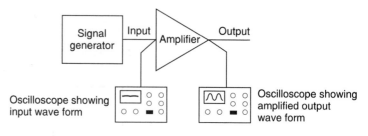

(b) Testing an amplifier

Figure 3.26 *The oscilloscope*

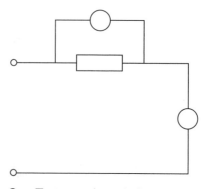

Figure 3.27 *See Test your knowledge 3.7*

over the screen so that measurements can be taken. Figure 3.26(b) shows how two oscilloscopes can be used to compare the input and output signals of an amplifier.

Activity 3.2

A small engineering company manufactures the component shown in Figure 3.28. Produce a set of illustrated instructions to give to a trainee production technician describing how he or she should go about measuring each of the the toleranced dimensions shown. State the instruments required for each measurement together with the reasons for your choice.

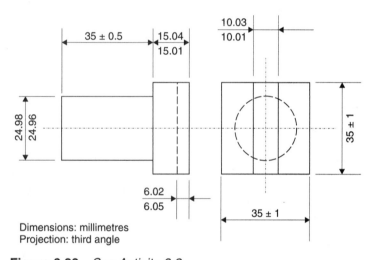

Dimensions: millimetres
Projection: third angle

Figure 3.28 *See Activity 3.2*

Activity 3.3

Investigate a manufacturer's or supplier's specifications for a basic multi-range meter. Produce a specification sheet for the instrument that you have chosen and explain why it is desirable for such an instrument to have a very high input resistance and a high sensitivity.

Material removal

Cutting tools

Basic hand and machine cutting tools were introduced at the intermediate level. It is now time to look at the cutting tools associated with drilling, turning and milling in greater detail. Figure 3.29 shows a single point cutting tool and the angles that are needed to make it cut.

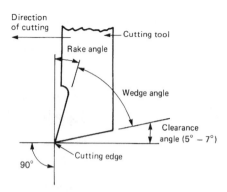

Figure 3.29 *Single point cutting tool*

Clearance angle This is required so that the tool can cut into the metal surface without rubbing. If the angle is too small the tool will rub and quickly wear out. It may also overheat and become soft and useless. If the angle is too large the tool will 'chatter' and produce a poor finish. In extreme cases the tool may 'grab' the component and throw it from the machine. This is very dangerous. Also the tool will usually be broken and the workpiece scrapped. The clearance angle should be kept to the minimum required for efficient cutting. Usually about 5°.

Wedge angle You can see from Figure 3.29, that this is the angle that remains when the sum of the clearance and rake angles is subtracted from 90°. The larger the wedge angle, the stronger will be the tool. Unfortunately a large wedge angle also results in a reduced rake angle. This reduces the cutting efficiency of the tool. Tool geometry is, therefore, a compromise between tool strength and cutting efficiency.

Rake angle This angle controls the cutting action of the tool. For ductile materials, the greater the rake angle, the more easily the tool cuts. Therefore, for such materials, the rake angle should be as large as possible without unduly weakening the tool (see wedge angle). Non-ductile (brittle) materials are usually cut with tools having a very small rake angle or a zero rake angle. High carbon steel and highspeed steel tools are usually given a positive rake angle, as shown in Figure 3.29.

Figure 3.30 compares positive, zero and negative rake angles. Tools with negative rake angles are usually tipped with carbide or ceramic inserts. These inserts are usually brazed or clamped to a

Key Facts 3.1

Material	Rake angle
Aluminium alloy	30°
Brass (ductile)	14°
Brass (free-cutting)	0°
Cast iron	0°
Copper	20°
Phosphor bronze	8°
Mild steel	25°
Medium carbon steel	15°

For high speed steel tools under normal workshop conditions

Test your knowledge 3.8

1 Calculate the size of the wedge angle of a cutting tool if the clearance angle is 5° and the rake angle is 15°C.
2 Explain why the rake angle is smaller when cutting high strength, tough materials such as alloy steels, than when cutting weaker materials such as low carbon steels.

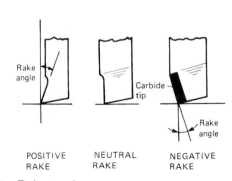

Figure 3.30 *Rake angle*

carbon steel shank. Negative rake tools are capable of high rates of metal removal but require very powerful and rigid machines to fully exploit their special properties. They can be used on both ductile and non-ductile materials.

Lathe tools

The application of the basic cutting angles to lathe (turning) tools is shown in Figure 3.31(a). They are the same as those shown in Figure 3.29 except that they have all been rotated through 90°. This time the cutting edge of the tool is in contact with a curved surface. Therefore we have to take the cutting angles from imaginary planes at the point of contact as shown. Because the curvature of the work is running away from the tool we can use a smaller clearance angle (3° to 5° is sufficient). The cutting angles vary if the tool point is moved above or below the centre height of the workpiece. This is shown in Figure 3.31(b).

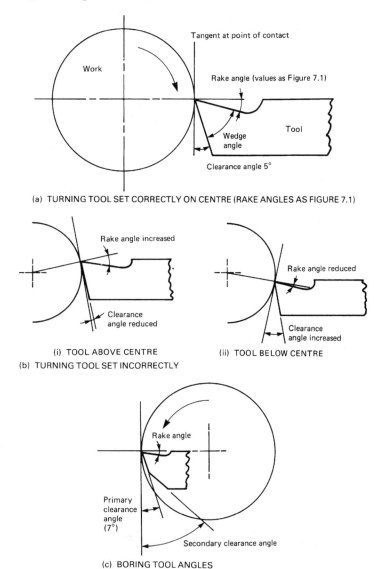

(a) TURNING TOOL SET CORRECTLY ON CENTRE (RAKE ANGLES AS FIGURE 7.1)

(i) TOOL ABOVE CENTRE (ii) TOOL BELOW CENTRE
(b) TURNING TOOL SET INCORRECTLY

(c) BORING TOOL ANGLES

Figure 3.31 *Lathe tools*

As well as external cutting tools used to turn the outside of the work piece we use boring tools for machining holes and recesses in a workpiece. An example is shown in Figure 3.31(c). You can see that a boring tool has an additional angle. This is called the *secondary clearance angle* and it prevents the 'heel' of the tool from fouling the surface of the bore.

When selecting a lathe tool for a particular turning operation we have to consider the *profile* of the tool as well as its cutting angles. Figure 3.32 shows some typical lathe tool profiles and their applications.

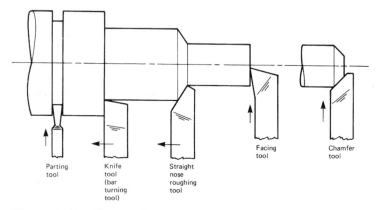

Figure 3.32 *Tool profiles*

Let's consider two of the tools shown in Figure 3.32:

● The cutting edge of the *knife* tool is at 90% to its direction of travel. Such a tool is said to be cutting *orthogonally* as shown in Figure 3.33(a).
● The cutting edge of the *roughing* tool is trailing at an angle to its direction of travel. Such a tool is said to be cutting *obliquely* as shown in Figure 3.33(b).

Where a square corner is not required it is better to use a tool that cuts obliquely. The oblique cutting action produces a radial component force as shown in Figure 3.33(b). This force takes up any wear and

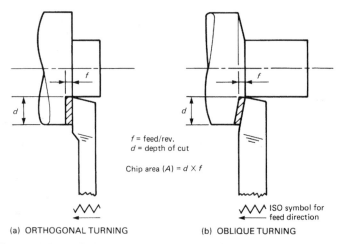

Figure 3.33 *Orthogonal and oblique turning*

backlash in the feed mechanism of the lathe and prevents the tool being drawn into the work by the action of the cut. This produces more stable cutting conditions, particularly when taking heavy cuts.

Twist drills

The application of the basic cutting angles to a twist drill is shown in Figure 3.34. Here the drill is compared with our original single-point cutting tool. You can see that the helix angle of the flutes represents the rake angle. This angle is not constant and becomes less towards the centre of the drill, with a corresponding reduction in cutting efficiency. The clearance angle is formed when grinding the point of the drill.

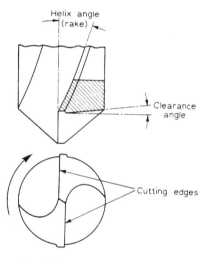

Figure 3.34 *Twist drill*

It is not possible to vary the rake angle of a drill to any great extent during regrinding. This is because the helix of the flutes is fixed at the time of manufacture. However, drills can be bought ready made with various combinations of point and helix angles for drilling different materials.

Key Facts 3.2				
Material to be drilled	Helix angle / HELIX ANGLE (RAKE)			Point angle / POINT ANGLE
Aluminium	40°	Quick spiral		90°
Brass	0–10°	Slow spiral		118°
Cast iron	0–10°	Slow spiral		118°
Copper	30°	Quick spiral		90°
Hard steel	5–10°	Slow spiral		130°
Mild steel	25°	Standard spiral		118°
Plastics	25°	Standard spiral		90°

Twist drill point and helix angles

Milling cutters

These are multi-tooth cutters and cut with a rotary action while the work is fed past the cutter as shown in Figure 3.35. You can see from the Figure that two different cutting actions can occur depending upon the direction in which the workpiece is fed into the cutter.

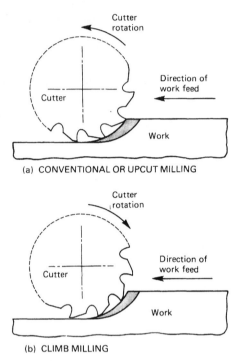

Figure 3.35 *Milling cutters*

Figure 3.35(a) shows *conventional* or *up-cut* milling. This is the most common method of milling. The work is fed against the direction of rotation of the cutter. This is the safest way of working since there is no tendency for the work to be drawn under the cutter. The feed force required to drive the work against the cutter takes up any wear and backlash in the feed mechanism and leads to safe and stable cutting conditions. However, this method of milling does have some disadvantages, particularly when taking heavy cuts.

- The feed force required heavily loads the feed mechanism of the milling machine.
- Figure 3.35(a) shows that there is a tendency for the teeth of the cutter to rub at the start of each cut. This tends to blunt the cutter.
- Figure 3.35(a) shows that the maximum chip thickness and, therefore, the maximum load on the cutter tooth occurs at the end of each cut. This sudden release of load on the cutter teeth can cause fatigue failure of the cutting edge. It also causes the transmission train in the machine to 'bounce' leading to premature wear.
- The cut tends to lift the work from the machine table. Always ensure that the work is secure.

Figure 3.35(b) shows *climb* or *downcut* milling. This should only be used by a skilled operator on a machine specially equipped for this technique and maintained in good condition. The disadvantage of this technique is that the work tends to be dragged under the cutter which, in turn, tries to climb over the work. This can be very dangerous. However, where this technique can be used it has a number of advantages.

● The feed force is reduced as the cutter tends to draw the work forward. In fact, the feed mechanism is acting as a brake to prevent the work being drawn into the cutter too quickly.
● Maximum chip thickness occurs at the start of the cut and there is no initial rubbing to blunt the cutter.
● The chip thickness and, therefore the load on the cutter tooth, is reduced progressively throughout the cut. There is no sudden release of the cutting load.
● The cutting action forces the work down onto the machine table.

Figure 3.36(a) shows how the basic cutting angles are applied to the teeth of milling cutters. In addition to the primary clearance angle, there is a secondary clearance angle to prevent the heel of the tooth from rubbing on the work surface. There is also a tertiary clearance angle which forms the 'gullet' between the teeth. This provides *chip clearance* to prevent the teeth becoming clogged up and breaking. Alternatively a parabolic tooth form may be used as shown in Figure 3.36(b).

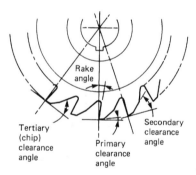

(a) BASIC TOOTH FORM

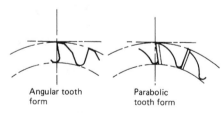

(b) ALTERNATIVE TOOTH FORMS

Figure 3.36 *Tooth forms of milling cutters*

Coolants and lubricants

Coolants and lubricants are used when cutting metals. Coolants are usually emulsions of water and a cutting oil plus an emulsifier. They keep the cutting tool and the work cool, improve the surface finish, flush away the chips (swarf) and lubricate the passage of the chips over the rake face of the tool. This greatly increases the cutting

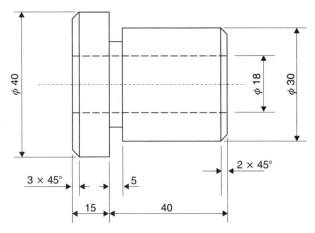

Material: free-cutting brass rod ϕ 50 m,
Dimensions: millimetres

Figure 3.37   *See Test your knowledge 3.9*

efficiency and reduces tool wear. Because the ratio of water to oil is high the cost is reduced. Great care must be taken in mixing and storing emulsified coolants if they are to act efficiently.

Lubricants are neat (undiluted) cutting oils with extreme pressure additives. They are only used for very severe machining operations such as thread cutting and gear cutting. The neat oil does not cool as well as an emulsion but its lubricating action prevents the early wear of very expensive form tools.

Coolants and lubricants should be flooded over the cutting zone in large volumes. This prevents the cutting fluid from overheating and degrading. An intermittent flow results in the tool continually heating up and cooling down. This results in thermal cracking of the tool. Ordinary lubricating oils should not be used. They give off noxious fumes when hot and are not effective under cutting conditions. Non-flammable synthetic coolants and lubricants are steadily taking over from traditional coolants based on mineral oils.

Drilling

This is a process for producing holes. The holes may be cut from the solid or existing holes may be enlarged. The purpose of the drilling machine is to:

● Rotate the drill at a suitable speed for the material being cut and the diameter of the drill.
● Feed the drill into the workpiece.
● Support the workpiece being drilled. Usually at right-angles to the axis of the drill. On some machines the table may be tilted to allow holes to be drilled at a pre-set angle.

Drilling machines

Drilling machines come in a variety of types and sizes. Figure 3.38 shows a hand held, electrically driven, power drill. This depends upon the skill of the operator to ensure that the drill cuts at

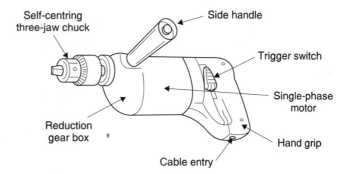

Figure 3.38 *A hand-held power drill*

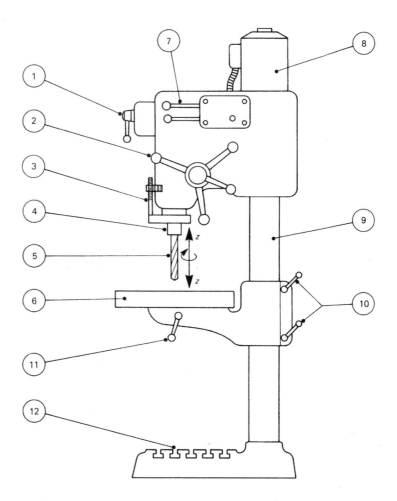

1	Stop/start switch (electrics).
2	Hand or automatic feed lever.
3	Drill depth stop.
4	Spindle.
5	Drill.
6	Table.
7	Speed change levers.
8	Motor.
9	Pillar.
10	Vertical table lock.
11	Table lock.
12	Base.

Figure 3.39 *A pillar drill*

right-angles to the workpiece. The feed force is also limited to the muscular strength of the user. Figure 3.39 shows a more powerful, floor-mounted machine.

The axis of the spindle of the milling machine shown in Figure 3.39 is perpendicular to the table of the machine. The spindle rotates the drill. It can also move up and down in order to feed the drill into the workpiece and withdraw the drill at the end of the cut. Large drills have taper shanks and are inserted directly into the spindle of the machine. They are located and driven by a taper as shown in Figure 3.40(a). The tang of the drill is for extraction purposes only. It does not drive the drill. The use of a drift to remove the drill is shown in Figure 3.40(b).

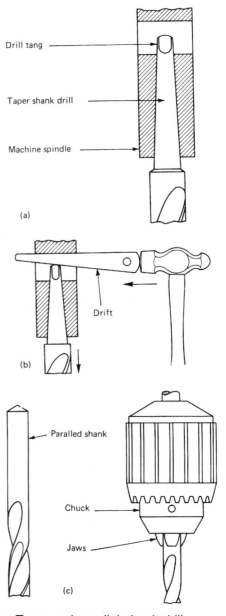

Figure 3.40 *Taper and parallel shank drills*

Small drills have parallel shanks and are usually held in a self-centering chuck as shown in Figure 3.40(c). The drill chuck has a taper shank which is located in, and driven by, the taper bore of the machine spindle.

Work-holding when drilling

It is dangerous to hold work being drilled by hand. There is always a tendency for the drill to grab the work and spin it round. Also the rapidly spinning swarf can produce some nasty cuts to the back of your hand. Therefore the work should always be securely fastened to the machine table.

Small work is usually held in a machine vice which, in turn, is securely bolted to the machine table. This is shown in Figure 3.41(a). Larger work can be clamped directly to the machine table as shown in Figure 3.41(b). In both these examples note how the work is supported on prallel blocks. You mount the work in this way so that when the drill 'breaks through' the workpiece it does not damage the

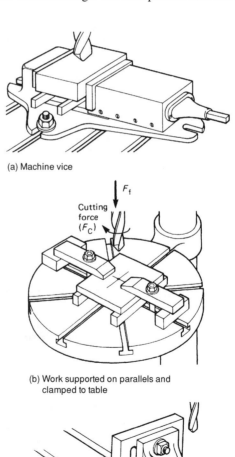

(a) Machine vice

(b) Work supported on parallels and clamped to table

(c) Use of angle plate

Figure 3.41 *Work-holders*

vice or the machine table. Figure 3.41(c) shows how an angle plate
can be used when the hole axis has to be parallel to the datum surface
of the work.

Round work is not easy to hold. You require three points of
support. Two examples are shown in Figure 3.42. Can you see how
the use of the vee-blocks and clamp provides three points of support
in Figure 3.42(a)? Can you see how the vee-block and the moving
jaw of the vice provides three points of support in Figure 3.42(b).
The first example shows the need for keeping vee-blocks in sets of
matched pairs if the work is to lie parallel to the machine table.

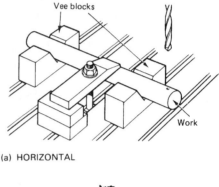

(a) HORIZONTAL

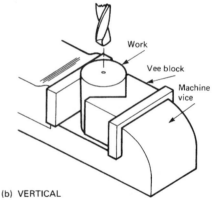

(b) VERTICAL

Figure 3.42 *Holding round work*

Miscellaneous drilling operations

Figure 3.43 shows some miscellaneous operations that are frequently
carried out on drilling machines.

Countersinking Figure 3.43(a) shows a countersink bit being used
to countersink a hole to receive the heads of rivets or screws. For this
reason the included angle is 90°. Lathe centre drills are unsuitable for
this operation as their angle is 60%.

Counterboring Figure 3.43(b) shows a piloted counterbore being
used to counterbore a hole so that the head of a capscrew or a cheese-
head screw can lie below the surface of the work. Unlike a
countersink cutter, a counterbore is not self centering. It has to have
a pilot which runs in the previously drilled bolt or screw hole. This
keeps the counterbore cutting concentrically with the original hole.

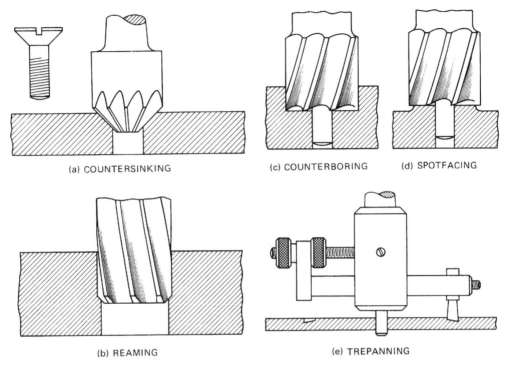

(a) COUNTERSINKING   (c) COUNTERBORING   (d) SPOTFACING

(b) REAMING   (e) TREPANNING

Figure 3.43 *Miscellaneous operations that can be carried out using drilling machines*

Spot-facing This is similar to counterboring but the cut is not as deep. It is used to provide a flat surface on a casting or a forging for a nut and washer to seat on. Sometimes, as shown in Figure 3.43(c), it is used to machine a boss (raised seating) to provide a flat surface for a nut and washer to seat on.

Reaming A reamer is used to produce a hole that is more accurate in size and of better surface finish than can be obtained with a twist drill. A reamer is only a finishing tool, removing a small amount of metal. The hole should first be drilled just below the required size and finished with a reamer as shown in Figure 3.43(d). A reamer always follows the existing hole. It cannot correct any positional error. Positional error can only be corrected by single-point boring. Boring is carried out after drilling and before reaming

Trepanning Trepanning cutters are used for cutting large-diameter holes in sheet metal and plate. This is shown in Figure 3.43(e). A narrow groove is cut through the plate at a preset distance from the axis of the required hole. The cutter is located by a pilot in a previously drilled hole of small diameter. The waste material is removed in the form of a disc.

Centre lathe turning

The main pupose of a centre lathe is to produce external and internal cylindrical and conical (tapered) surfaces. It can also produce plain surfaces and screw threads.

The centre lathe

Figure 3.44(a) shows a typical centre lathe and identifies its more important parts.

- The *bed* is the base of the machine to which all the other sub-assemblies are attached. Slideways accurately machined on its top surface provide guidance for the saddle and the tail stock. These slideways also locate the headstock so that the axis of the spindle is parallel with the the movement of the saddle and the tailstock. The saddle or carriage of the lathe moves parallel to the spindle axis as shown in Figure 3.44(b).
- The *cross-slide* is mounted on the saddle of the lathe. It moves at 90° to the axis of the spindle as shown in Figure 3.44(c). It provides in-feed for the cutting tool when cylindrically turning. It is also used to produce a plain surface when facing across the end of a bar or component.
- The *top-slide* (compound-slide) is used to provide in-feed for the tool when facing. It can also be set at an angle to the spindle axis for turning tapers as shown in Figure 3.44(d).

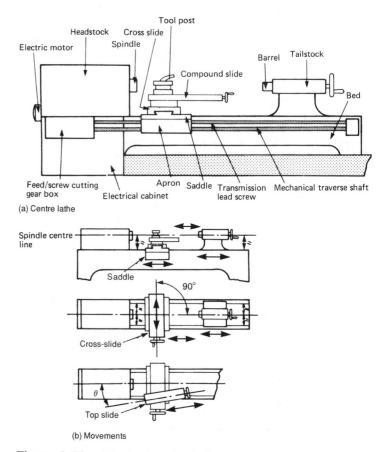

(a) Centre lathe

(b) Movements

Figure 3.44 *A typical centre lathe*

Workholding in the lathe

The work to be turned can be held in various ways. We will now consider the more important of these.

	Key Facts 3.3		
Cutting movement	*Hand or power traverse*	*Means by which movement is achieved*	*Turned feature*
Tool parallel to the spindle centre line	Both	The saddle moves along the bed slideways	A parallel cylinder
Tool at 90° to the spindle centre line	Both	The cross slide moves along a slideway machined on the top of the saddle	A flat face square to the spindle centre line
Tool at an angle relative to the spindle centre line	Hand	The compound slide is rotated and set at the desired angle relative the centre line	A tapered cone

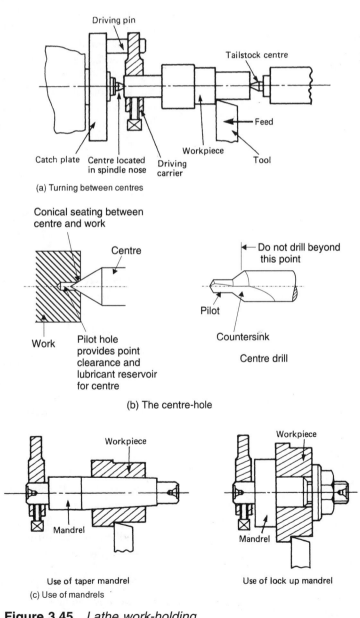

(a) Turning between centres

(b) The centre-hole

(c) Use of mandrels

Figure 3.45 *Lathe work-holding*

Between centres   The *centre-lathe* derives its name from this basic method of workholding. The general layout is shown in Figure 3.45(a). Centre holes are drilled in the ends of the bar and these locate on centres in the headstock spindle and the tailstock barrel. A section through a correctly centred component is shown in Figure 3.45(b). The centre hole is cut with a standard centre drill. The main disadvantage of this method of workholding is that no work can be performed on the end of the component. Work that has been previously bored can be finish turned between centres on a taper mandrel as shown in Figure 3.45(c).

Three-jaw chuck   The self-centring, three-jaw chuck is shown in Figure 3.46(a). The jaws are set at 120° and are moved in or out simultaneously (at the same time) by a scroll when the key is turned. This key must be removed before starting the lathe or a serious accident can occur. When new and in good condition this type of chuck can hold cylindrical and hexagonal work concentric with the spindle axis to a high degree of accuracy. It is provided with internal and external jaws for holding work as shown in Figure 3.46(b). Soft jaws are also available. These are bored out to suit the work immediately before use and ensure that the work runs concentrically with the spindle axis even when the chuck has become worn.

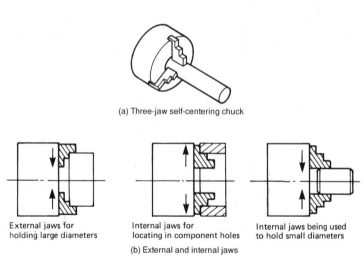

(a) Three-jaw self-centering chuck

External jaws for holding large diameters

Internal jaws for locating in component holes

Internal jaws being used to hold small diameters

(b) External and internal jaws

Figure 3.46   *Three-jaw chuck*

Four-jaw chuck   In this chuck the jaws can be moved independently by means of jack-screws. It clamps the work more tightly than the three-jaw chuck. Because the jaws can be moved independently, the work can be set to run concentrically to a high degree of accuracy with the aid of a dial test indicator DTI. Alternatively the work can be deliberately set off-centre to produce eccentric components as shown in Figure 3.47.

Face-plate   Figure 3.48 shows a component held on a face-plate so that the hole can be bored perpendicularly to the datum surface. This datum surface is in contact with the face-plate. Note that the face-

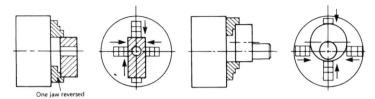

Figure 3.47 *Four-jaw chuck*

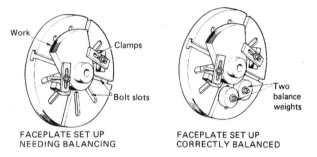

Figure 3.48 *Faceplate*

plate has to be balanced to ensure smooth running. Care must be taken to check that the clamps will hold the work securely and do not foul the machine. These must not only resist the cutting forces, but they must also prevent the rapidly rotating work from spinning out of the lathe.

Parallel Turning

Figure 3.49(a) shows a long bar held between centres. To ensure that the work is truly cylindrical with no taper, the axis of the tailstock centre must be in line with the axis of the headstock spindle. The saddle traverse provides movement of the tool parallel with the workpiece axis. You take a test cut and measure the diameter of the bar at both ends. If all is well, the diameter should be constant all along the bar. If not the lateral movement of the tailstock needs to be adjusted until a constant measurement is obtained. The depth of cut is controlled by micrometer adjustment of the cross-slide.

While facing and centre drilling the end of a long bar, a fixed steady is used. This supports the end of the bar remote from the chuck. A fixed steady is shown in Figure 3.49(b). If the work is long and slender it sometimes tries to kick away from the turning tool or even climb over the tool. To prevent this happening a travelling steady is used. This is bolted to the saddle opposite to the tool as shown in Figure 3.49(c).

Surfacing

A surfacing (facing or perpendicular-turning) operation on a workpiece held in a chuck is shown in Figure 3.50. The saddle is clamped to the bed of the lathe and the tool motion is controlled by

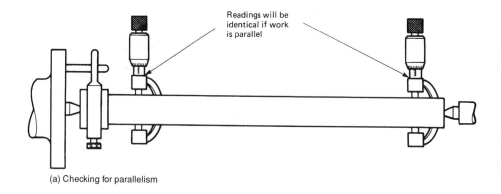

(a) Checking for parallelism

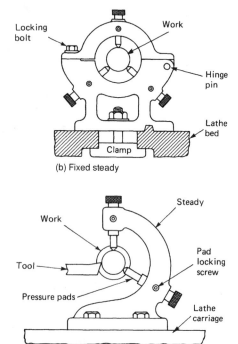

(b) Fixed steady

(c) Travelling steady

Figure 3.49 *Parallel turning*

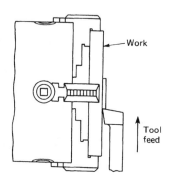

Figure 3.50 *Surfacing arrangement*

the cross-slide. This ensures that the tool moves in a path at right-angles to the workpiece axis and produces a plain surface. In-feed of the cutting tool is controlled by micrometer adjustment of the top-slide.

Boring

Figure 3.51 shows how a drilled hole can be opened up using a boring tool. The workpiece is held in a chuck and the tool movement is controlled by the saddle of the lathe. The in-feed of the tool is controlled by micrometer adjustment of the cross-slide. The pilot hole is produced either by a taper shank drill mounted directly into the tailstock barrel (poppet), or by a parallel shank drill held in a drill chuck. The taper mandrel of the drill chuck is inserted into the tailstock barrel.

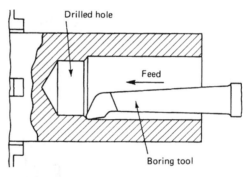

Figure 3.51   *Boring*

Figure 3.52 shows three ways of taper turning:

Compound slide   The top (compound) slide is being used in Figure 3.52(a). This is a useful method of producing short steep tapers and chamfers. No power feed is available.

Taper turning attachment   A taper turning attachment is being used in Figure. 3.52(b). The movement of the cross-slide is controlled by the guide-bar as the saddle is moved along the bed. The normal power traverse for the saddle can be used. This is a useful way of producing long tapered components. The range of angles available is limited.

Offset tailstock   A taper turning attachment is not a standard fitment on a centre lathe. An alternative method of producing long tapers is to offset the tailstock. Figure 3.52(c) shows how a tapered component can be produced by setting over the tailstock. Earlier we saw how lateral adjustment of the tailstock can be used to ensure parallel turning. This time the tailstock is being deliberately offset to produce a taper. The amount of taper is limited if damage to the centrehole and centre is to be avoided. However, the full length of the bed can be used and the power traverse for the saddle can also be used.

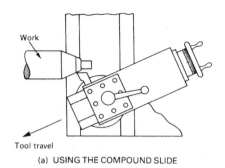

(a) USING THE COMPOUND SLIDE

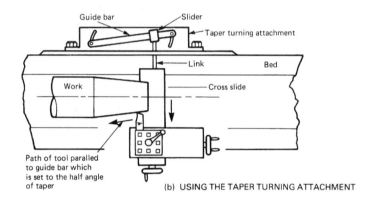

(b) USING THE TAPER TURNING ATTACHMENT

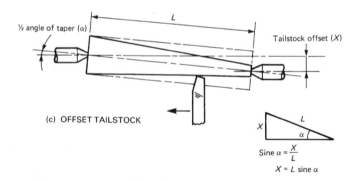

(c) OFFSET TAILSTOCK

$$\text{Sine } \alpha = \frac{X}{L}$$

$$X = L \text{ sine } \alpha$$

Figure 3.52   *Taper turning*

Screw threads

Standard, non-standard and large-diameter screw threads can be cut in a centre lathe by use of the lead-screw to control the saddle movement. This is a highly skilled operation. However, standard screw threads of limited diameter can be cut using a die-head mounted in the tailstock as shown in Figure 3.53(a).

The die adjusting screws (B) are slacked off and the adjusting screw (C) is tightened to spread the die open. A cut is taken along the previously turned diameter. A good cutting oil should be used. Once the die has started, it will feed itself along the component. The screw (C) is now slackened off slightly and the screws (B) are tightened to close the die slightly. The die will now take a light finishing cut and improve the finish of the thread. The thread should be checked with a nut or a screw thread gauge. If still tight, the die should be closed still further and another cut taken. This is repeated until the desired fit is obtained.

Internal screw threads can be cut with a screw thread tap as shown in Figure 3.53(b). Taps are very fragile and the workpiece should be rotated by hand with the lathe switched off and the gears disengaged.

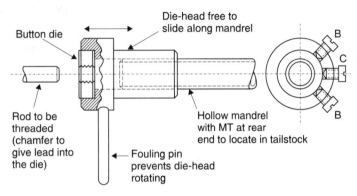

(a) Die-head for external threads

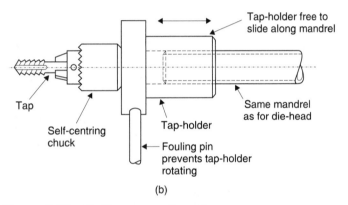

(b)

Figure 3.53   *Cutting screw threads*

Describe the operations, workholding devices, and tooling to produce the component shown in Figure 3.54. It is to be made from a free-cutting, low-carbon steel blank 75 mm diameter by 100 mm. long.

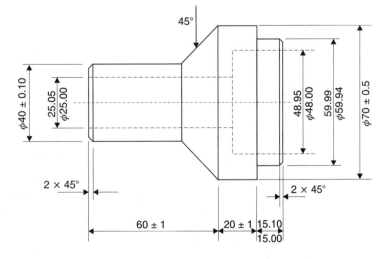

Dimensions: millimetres
All diametres to be concentric

Figure 3.54   *See Test your knowledge 3.11*

Milling

Milling machines are mainly used to produce plain surfaces parallel and perpendicular to the machine table using rotating multi-tooth cutters.

The horizontal milling machine

This machine gets its name from the fact that the axis of the spindle lies in the horizontal plane. An example of such a machine is shown in Figure. 3.55.

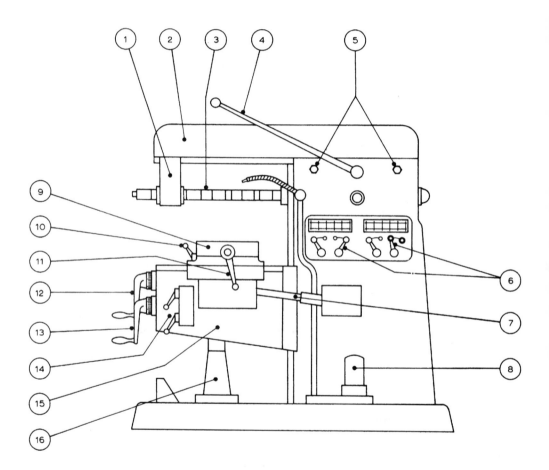

1   Arbor support or yoke (which slides on overarm).
2   Overarm.
3   Arbor (on which the cutter is mounted).
4   Clutch lever.
5   Overarm clamping screws.
6   Speed and feed selector levers.
7   Telescopic feedshaft.
8   Coolant pump.
9   Table which contains tee slots for clamping work or a vice.
10   Automatic table feed (longitudinal).
11   Longitudinal feed (hand).
12   Vertical feed (hand) which raises or lowers knee assembly.
13   Cross or transverse handle (hand).
14   Vertical and horizontal automatic-feed levers.
15   Knee which supports table and moves up and down on dovetail slides.
16   Knee elevating screw.

Figure 3.55   *Horizontal mill*

The cutter is mounted on an *arbor* as shown in Figure 3.56(a). One end of the arbor is located in a taper in the spindle nose of the machine and is retained by a draw-bolt passing through the spindle of the machine as shown in Figure 3.56(b). Drive to the arbor is positive. Blocks of metal called *dogs* fastened to the spindle nose engage in slots in the end of the arbor. The opposite end of the arbor is supported and located in an outrigger bearing supported by the overarm.

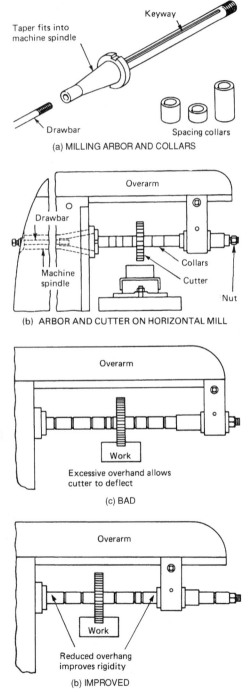

(a) MILLING ARBOR AND COLLARS

(b) ARBOR AND CUTTER ON HORIZONTAL MILL

(c) BAD

(b) IMPROVED

Figure 3.56 *Arbor and cutter positioning*

The cutter is positioned along the arbor by means of spacing collars. These should be arranged so that the overhang between the cutter and its nearest support bearing is as small as possible. Figure 3.56(c) shows the cutter badly positioned with excessive overhang. Figure 3.56(d) shows the cutter correctly positioned for improved rigidity.

For light cuts the cutter may be driven by friction alone. However, for heavy cuts the cutter should be keyed to the arbor to provide a positive drive. Cutters intended for use on horizontal milling machines have standard keyways in their bores. Arbors for horizontal milling machines have matching keyways. Some typical cutters for horizontal milling machines are shown in Figure 3.57.

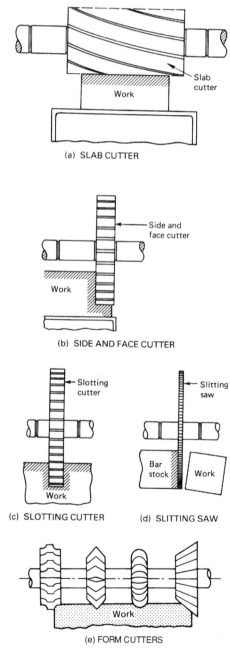

Figure 3.57 *Typical cutters for horizontal mills*

The vertical milling machine

This machine gets its name from the fact that the axis of its spindle lies in the vertical plane. An example of a vertical milling machine is shown in Figure 3.58.

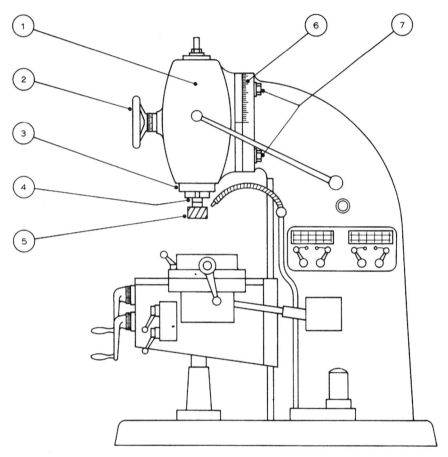

1	Vertical head which tilts.	5	Cutter.
2	Vertical feed handwheel.	6	Head tilts here.
3	Quill.	7	Head locking nuts.
4	Spindle.		

Note: Remaining parts are similar to the horizontal-type milling machine.

Figure 3.58 *Vertical mill*

The cutters for use with a vertical milling machine can be mounted in various ways. Large face mills are mounted directly on the spindle nose as shown in Figure 3.59(a). The body of a face mill is fitted with a stub-arbor that is located in the taper of the spindle nose. It is retained in position by a draw-bolt passing through the spindle. The face mill is driven positively by the spindle nose dogs engaging in slots in its shank. Figure 3.59(b) shows an end mill and its chuck. Slot drills can also be held in the same chuck. The chuck has a taper shank and is mounted in the spindle nose of the milling machine. It

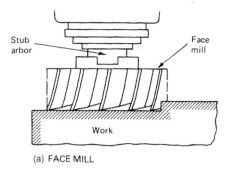

(a) FACE MILL

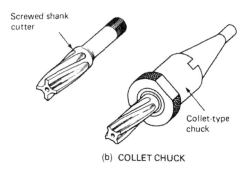

(b) COLLET CHUCK

Figure 3.59 *Face mill and end mill with chuck*

is retained by the draw bolt passing through the spindle and is driven positively by the dogs on the spindle nose. Most end mills and slot drills have parallel shanks with screwed ends so that they are positively secured in the chuck and can't be drawn out of the chuck by the cutting forces.

Figure 3.60 shows a typical end mill, a typical slot drill and the type of work such cutters are used for. End mills and shell end mills cannot be used for making pocket cuts from the solid. However, provided they can be fed into the work as shown in Figure 3.60(a). End mills can remove metal more quickly and with a better surface finish than slot drills because of their larger number of teeth. For making pocket cuts from the solid, a slot drill is used as shown in Figure 3.60(b).

Work may be held in a machine vice bolted to the machine table or it may be clamped directly to the machine table. The workholding techniques used are similar to those used for drilling but are rather more substantial to withstand the larger cutting forces. For batch and continuous production purposes a milling fixture is used. This is a custom-built workholding device which ensures that the components are located in the machine in the same place every time so that identical cuts are taken. It also ensures that all the components are correctly and securely clamped in the same manner.

Sometimes it is necessary to make a series of cuts around a circular component. Such an operation is called *indexing*. Figure 3.61 shows two methods of indexing. The dividing head can be used on both horizontal and vertical milling machines. The rotary table is normally used only on a vertical milling machine. The dividing head shown is called a 'simple' dividing head because the index plate locates the spindle directly. In the more sophisticated 'universal'

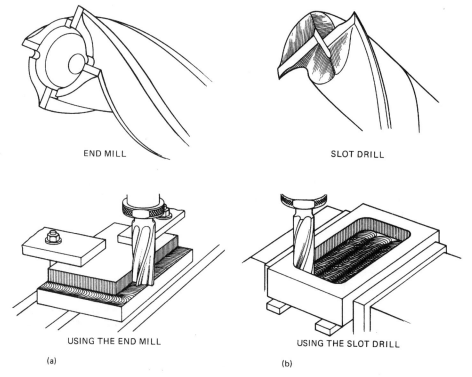

Figure 3.60 *End mill and slot drill*

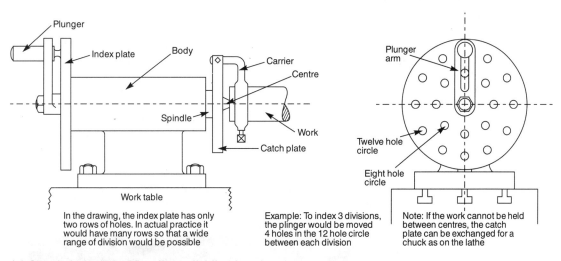

In the drawing, the index plate has only two rows of holes. In actual practice it would have many rows so that a wide range of division would be possible

Example: To index 3 divisions, the plinger would be moved 4 holes in the 12 hole circle between each division

Note: If the work cannot be held between centres, the catch plate can be exchanged for a chuck as on the lathe

(a) Simple indexing with a direct dividing head

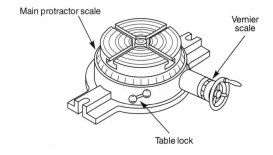

(b) Rotary table

Figure 3.61 *Indexing*

dividing head the index plate locates the spindle via a worm and worm wheel with a standard 40:1 ratio. This, together with a range of index plates, enables an almost unlimited number of divisions to be made.

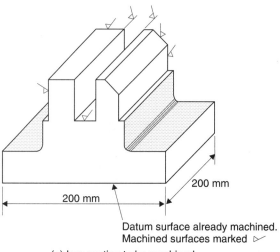

(a) Iron casting to be machined

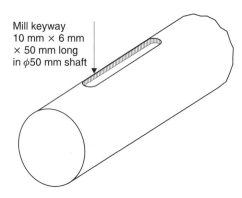

(b) Key-way to be milled in shaft

Figure 3.62   *See Test your knowledge 3.12*

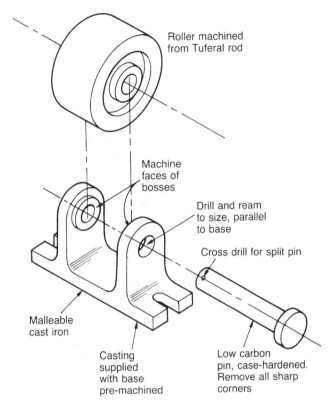

Roller machined
from Tuferal rod

Machine
faces of
bosses

Drill and ream
to size, parallel
to base

Cross drill for split pin

Malleable
cast iron

Casting
supplied
with base
pre-machined

Low carbon
pin, case-hardened.
Remove all sharp
corners

Figure 3.63 *See Activity 3.4*

Shaping materials (metals)

Sand casting

In this process molten metal is poured into a mould made from sand. The cavity in the sand is determined by a pattern the same shape as the required component. The pattern is made slightly larger than the required component to allow for shrinkage as the metal cools. Also additional metal may be required on certain surfaces to allow for machining. This is called a machining allowance. The pattern has a taper or draft on its vertical surfaces to allow it to be removed from the mould without disturbing the sand. Figure 3.64 shows a typical pattern made from wood. It is divided along its major axis to make moulding easier. The two halves of the pattern are aligned by dowels.

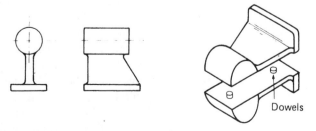

Dowels

Figure 3.64 *A typical wood pattern*

Making the mould

To make the mould, one half of the pattern is placed on the *turnover board*. The lower half of the moulding box or flask is placed round the half pattern as shown in Figure 3.65(a). The lower part of the mould is called the *drag*. The pattern and the turnover board are dusted with *parting powder* to prevent the sand from sticking to them. The moulding box or flask is then filled with *green sand* which is rammed into place to make it rigid. The term 'green sand' does not refer to the colour of the sand but to the fact that the sand is sufficiently moist to stick together. The sand used is specially blended for moulding purposes and must be chosen to suit the metal being cast.

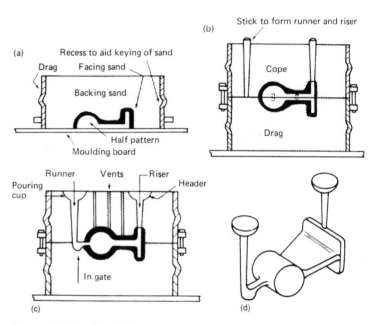

Figure 3.65   *Moulding*

The moulding flask and board are then turned over and the board is removed. The upper half of the pattern is placed in position over the lower half making sure that the location dowels are properly aligned. The upper moulding flask (called a *cope*) is placed round the pattern as before. The two halves of the moulding flasks are located by dowels which pass through lugs welded to the end of the flasks as shown in Figure 3.65(b). Parting powder is dusted over the parting surface of the sand and over the top half of the pattern. Tapered wooden dowels are placed in position to form the *runner* and the *riser* as shown in Figure 3.65(b). The cope is filled with moulding sand which is again rammed up as previously.

The mould is then opened up by removing the cope. The two halves of the pattern can now be withdrawn from the cope and the drag, respectively. To make this easier the pattern halves are lightly 'rapped' to loosen them in the sand. The tapered wooden dowels are also withdrawn. The *pouring cup* and the *in-gate* are carefully cut into the sand and the moulding flasks are re-assembled. A fine wire is used to make vent holes in the mould. This is necessary so that any steam generated when the hot metal comes into contact with the moist sand can escape. The mould is now ready for pouring as shown in Figure 3.65(c).

Pouring the metal

The molten metal is poured steadily into the mould via the pouring cup and runner. The air in the mould cavity escapes via the riser. Pouring continues until molten metal is visible at the top of the riser. As the metal cools and shrinks, additional metal can be drawn into the casting from the runner and riser which act as reservoirs. Pouring must not be too quick or the sand will be flushed from the walls of the mould to form unsightly *scabs*. Nor must pouring be too slow or the metal will solidify before the mould is full. That is, the metal will form a *cold shut* and the mould will not fill properly.

When the metal has solidified, the mould is broken open and the casting is removed. The casting will appear as shown in Figure 3.65(d). The casting now has to be *fettled*. That is, the casting has to be cleaned up ready to be sent to the machine shop. First the runner and riser are cut off. Then any surplus sand sticking to the casting is removed. Finally any *fins* are ground off. Fins are formed by metal leaking between the joint faces of the cope and the drag.

Test your knowledge 3.13

Figure 3.66 shows the pattern for an angle plate to be made from grey cast iron. Describe, with the aid of sketches, how a sand mould can be made for this angle plate.

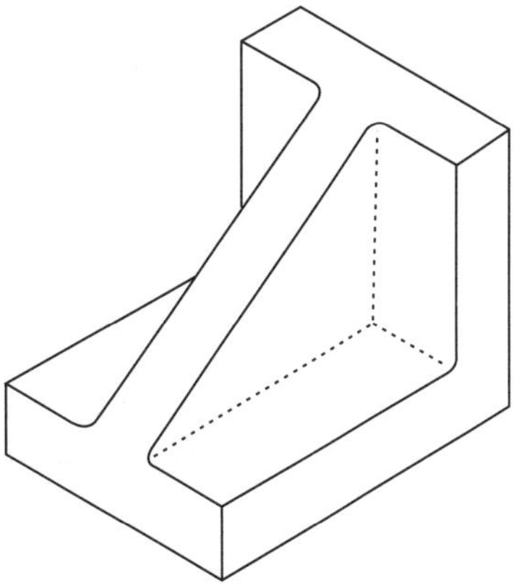

Figure 3.66 *See Test your knowledge 3.13*

Die-casting

In die-casting the metal is cast in heat resisting alloy steel dies. The metal to be cast must have a low melting temperature so as not to damage the dies. Neither must the hot metal being cast attack the dies chemically. Most die-castings are made from zinc-based alloys such as 'Mazak' or from suitable aluminium and magnesium alloys.

Gravity die-casting

This process gets its name from the fact that the molten metal is poured into the closed dies by gravity in the same way as pouring metal into a sand mould as previously described. Runners, risers and vents have to be machined into the dies at the time of their manufacture. Since the dies cannot be broken open they have to be designed so that they can be separated to release the casting. The dies are not porous like sand moulds so adequate venting is most important. The vents consist of grooves 0.5 mm deep milled into the joint faces of the dies.

The dies are very expensive to make and the process is only used where large quantities of identical castings are required. To protect the working surfaces of the die and to aid withdrawal of the casting, the die cavity is spray coated with a release agent immediately before closing the die and pouring the metal.

It is important to keep the dies at the correct casting temperature. Too cold and the molten metal will become chilled and cold shuts may occur (see sand moulding). Too hot and the metal dies may be damaged. Therefore small dies have to be preheated to about 200°C, while large dies may have to cooled after each pouring. Castings made in this manner have a better surface finish and accuracy than those produced by sand moulding.

Pressure die-casting

In this process the molten metal is injected into the closed dies under considerable pressure. Compared with gravity die casting, pressure die-casting has the following advantages:

- Thinner sections and finer detail can be reproduced.
- The surface finish and dimensional accuracy is better.
- The grain structure is compacted and this gives better mechanical properties to the casting .

Hot chamber pressure die casting   The principle of the hot chamber pressure die casting process is shown in Figure 3.67(a). The plunger forces the molten metal into the dies via the 'goose-neck' at a pressure between 2.5 MPa and 3.5 MPa. When the casting has solidified, the dies are opened automatically and the casting is

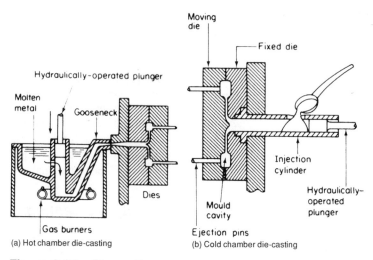

(a) Hot chamber die-casting
(b) Cold chamber die-casting

Figure 3.67   *Die-casting*

ejected automatically. With a fully automatic machine up to 2000 castings per hour can be produced using multiple impression dies. Aluminium alloys are rarely used with the hot chamber process since the molten metal reacts with the metal of the injection mechanism and the dies. Thus this process is mostly used with zinc and magnesium based alloys.

Cold chamber pressure die casting   The principle of cold chamber pressure die casting is shown in Figure 3.67(b). This process gets its name from the fact that the injection chamber is not immersed in the molted metal. The molten metal is only poured into the injection chamber immediately before injection takes place. Thus the injection chamber is able to cool down between each 'shot'. Also, the molten metal is in contact with the injection chamber for only a short period of time. This allows aluminium alloys to be die cast without damage to the equipment.

The injection pressure can be as high as 70 MPa although 14 MPa is a generally used pressure. The fact that the molten metal has to be ladled into the injection chamber by hand before each shot makes the process much slower than the hot chamber process. Also, the process cannot be automated to the same extent.

Forging

Forging is the the flow forming of metal to shape in the solid condition by squeezing it between a hammer and an anvil or between formed dies. Forging can be performed 'cold' (at room temperature) in the case of rivet heading. It can be performed 'warm' (just below red-heat), in the case of manufacturing constant velocity universal joint members from high-strength alloy steels for the automotive industry. Generally, however, forging is performed 'hot' at red-heat.

At the temperatures associated with red-heat, wrought iron and steels become malleable and plastic. They are more easily shaped and do not tend to work-harden and crack.

These temperatures are above the *temperature of recrystallization* for each metal. That is, above the temperature at which the metal crystals reform themselves after being distorted by the forging process. This is what prevents the metal from cracking.

The properties of most metals and alloys are improved by forging. This is due to the grain refinement and grain flow that takes place. Figure 3.68(a) compares the grain flow for a forged crankshaft with one machined from the solid. Figure 3.68(b) compares the grain flow of a forged spanner with one machined from the solid.

Test your knowledge 3.14

Draw up a table comparing the advantages and limitations of pressure die-casting and sand-mould casting.

Key Facts 3.4

Metal	Forging temperature (°C)	
	Min	Max
High speed steel	850	1100
High carbon steel	820	1100
Medium carbon steel	820	1200
Mild steel	840	1250
Wrought iron	850	1350

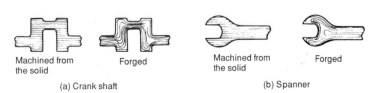

Machined from the solid   Forged   Machined from the solid   Forged

(a) Crank shaft   (b) Spanner

Figure 3.68   *Forging*

Open forging

This is done by squeezing the metal between a hammer and an anvil with or without the aid of standard forging tools. Small components in small quantities can be made by hand forging by a blacksmith. The metal is heated in a hearth (Figure 3.69(a)) and forged to shape by hammering it on an anvil (Figure 3.69(b)).

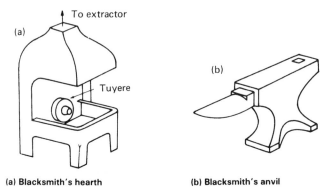

(a) Blacksmith's hearth   (b) Blacksmith's anvil

Figure 3.69   *Blacksmith's hearth and anvil*

Drawing down   This operation thins down and lengthens the bar being forged. The metal is forged between *fullers* as shown in Figure 3.70(a). The lower tool is held in the 'hardie hole' in the anvil. The handle of the top tool is held by the blacksmith. The blacksmith may strike the top fuller himself if only a light blow is required. A heavier blow may be given by the blacksmith's assistant or 'striker' wielding a sledge hammer. Alternatively the metal may be forged between a hammer and the 'beak' of the anvil as shown in Figure 3.70(b).

Setting down   This is similar to drawing down but the metal is spread in width as well as in length. This process can also be used for smoothing or 'flatting' metal that has previously been drawn down between fullers. The setting down process is shown in Figure 3.70(c).

Swaging   This process finishes work to a round section using the tools shown in Figure 3.70(d).

Upsetting   This process is used to shorten and thicken a component as shown in Figure 3.70(e). After heating the component in the hearth, it is cooled locally in water so that only the part to be thickened is left hot.

Cutting   This can be performed hot or cold. When cutting hot metal, a pair of chisels are used as shown in Figure 3.70(f). The bottom chisel is called a 'hardie' and is held in the 'hardie hole' in the anvil. When cutting cold, a single chisel is used and cutting takes place on the soft table where the beak joins the body of the anvil. This soft table avoids damage to the chisel as it breaks through the metal being cut.

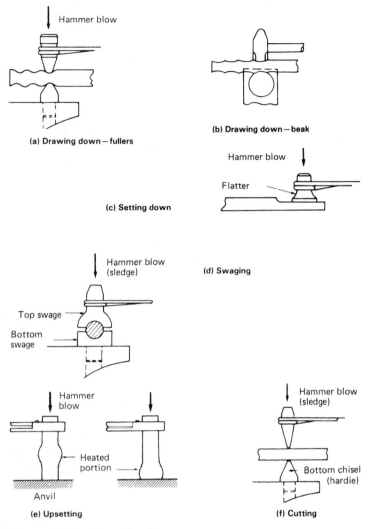

Figure 3.70   *Hand forging*

These basic processes are used irrespective of the size of the job. Moving up the scale, work that is too large to be hand forged can be forged under a self-contained pneumatic hammer. Medium sized work can be forged using a steam driven hammer. The largest work is forged under very powerful hydraulic presses.

Closed die forging

For repetition forging a *drop hammer* is used, as shown in Figure 3.71(a). Shaped dies are fitted to the tup and to the anvil. A section through such a die, when closed, is shown in Figure 3.71(b). The heated billet of metal is placed in the lower die and the dies are closed. More than one blow may be required to make the metal fill the impression in the dies. The finished forging is shown in Figure 3.71(c). Finally the forging is taken to a press to have the flash clipped off.

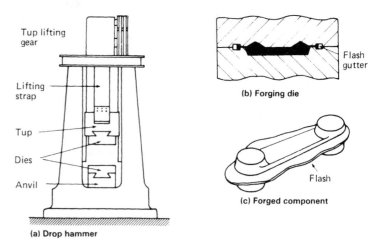

(a) Drop hammer

Figure 3.71 *Drop forging*

The principle of an upset forging machine is shown in Figure 3.72. The gripping dies open and the heated metal rod is fed into the machine. The dies then close and grip the metal as the heading die moves forward and forces the metal into the die cavity.

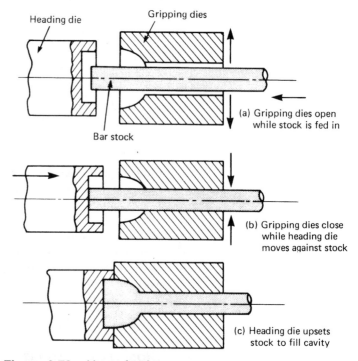

Figure 3.72 *Upset forging*

Rolling

This is a continuous forging process in which the metal is squeezed out longer and thinner between rollers instead of by hammering. Cast ingots are always hot rolled (above red-heat). This welds together any internal cavities in the metal and it also improves the grain structure. Hot rolling also speeds up the rate of size reduction. A *two-high* mill is used for this initial reduction as shown in Figure 3.73(a). This Figure shows a cast *ingot* being reduced to a rolled *bloom*.

The bloom is then reheated and rerolled into a *billet* for further reduction into bars and sections. Figure 3.73(b) shows how formed rolls are used to produce an 'I' section steel beam. The stages of production move progressively from left to right as the metal is passed backwards and forwards between the rollers. The rollers are reversed for each pass. Alternatively the bloom can be reheated and rerolled into a *slab* for further reduction into plate and sheet.

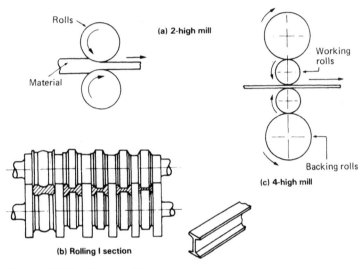

Figure 3.73 *Cold rolling*

Cold rolling is often carried out after hot rolling.

- Cold rolling improves the surface finish.
- Cold rolling improves the dimensional accuracy.
- Cold rolling improves the mechanical properties of the metal. This is particularly important for non-ferrous metals.

Because of the resistance of metals to cold rolling, this is only a finishing process. The metal is hot rolled to just over the finished size. It is then pickled in dilute acid to get rid of the scale (oxide film) from the surface of the metal and passed through a bath to neutralize the acid. It is oiled to prevent it becoming rusty. Finally, the hot rolled, pickled and oiled metal is cold rolled to the finished size. Because of the forces involved in cold rolling a *four-high* mill is used as shown in Figure 3.73(c). In this type of mill the working rollers are supported by massive backing rollers.

Cold drawing

The metal is first hot-rolled into long coils of rod using formed rollers. The coils of rod are pickled in dilute acid, as explained above, to remove the scale. The rod is then drawn (pulled) through a die to reduce its diameter and improve its finish and accuracy. The drawing process is carried out cold at room temperature. Figure 3.74(a) shows the principle of wire drawing.

There is a limit, depending upon the properties of the metal, to how much the diameter can be reduced in a single pass. Fine wire is produced on a multiple die drawing machine as shown in Figure 3.74(b).

Tube can also be cold drawn. Where precision tube is required with a closely controlled, uniform wall thickness, a fixed mandrel is used as shown in Figure 3.74(c). The length of the tube is limited by

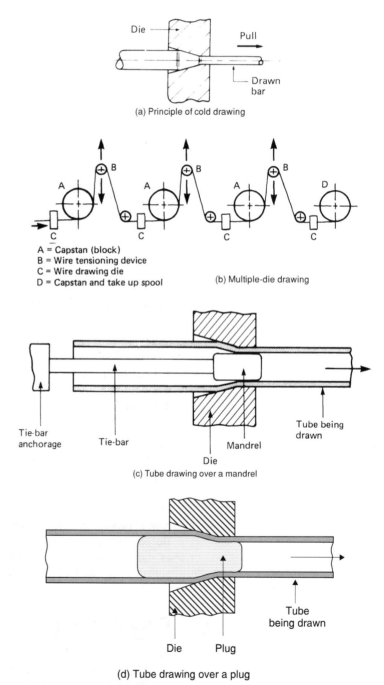

(a) Principle of cold drawing

A = Capstan (block)
B = Wire tensioning device
C = Wire drawing die
D = Capstan and take up spool

(b) Multiple-die drawing

(c) Tube drawing over a mandrel

(d) Tube drawing over a plug

Figure 3.74 *Cold drawing*

the length of the mandrel tie-bar. General purpose tubes, particularly in the smaller sizes, are drawn over a floating mandrel or 'plug'. This is shown in Figure 3.74(d).

Hot extrusion

This process is used to produce long lengths of continuous section, often of complex shape from non-ferrous metals such as brass, copper and aluminium and its alloys. A heated billet is forced through a die by a hydraulic ram as shown in Figure 3.75. It is a bit like squeezing toothpaste out of the nozzle of a toothpaste tube.

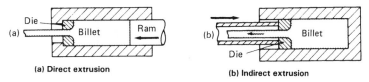

Figure 3.75 *Extrusion*

As with all hot working processes the accuracy and finish of extrusion leaves much to be desired. To improve the finish, accuracy and mechanical properties of the extruded section, it is often subjected to some cold-working after extrusion. This can range from simply applying a tensile load to slightly stretch the section, to drawing it through pre-formed dies. In the first case, stretching the metal straightens it and improves its strength and stiffness. In the second case, as well as improving its straightness, strength and stiffness, the surface finish and dimensional accuracy of the extrusion are also improved.

Cold impact extrusion

Unlike the process described above, this process is performed cold (at room temperature) on such metals as soft pure aluminium and lead. The principle is shown in Figure 3.76. A preformed *slug* of metal is struck by a rapidly moving punch (25 m/s), causing the metal to become plastic and flow through the gap between the punch and the die. Typical products produced by this process are toothpaste tubes and screen cans for electronic devices.

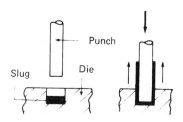

Figure 3.76 *Cold impact extrusion*

Presswork

Presswork processes range from simple bending operations to forming complex car body panels. These and other forming operations can be carried out in either a hand press as shown in Figure 3.77(a) or in a power press as shown in Figure 3.77(b) depending upon the force required. Note the extensive guarding associated with these potentially dangerous machines. Long, narrow components can be bent and folded using a manually-operated bending machine as shown in Figure 3.77(c) or in a power-operated brake press as shown in Figure 3.77(d). We are only concerned with simple bending operations at this stage.

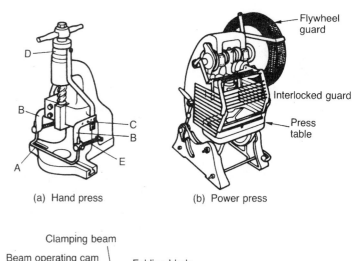

(a) Hand press (b) Power press

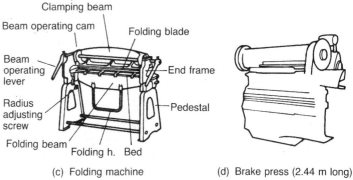

(c) Folding machine (d) Brake press (2.44 m long)

Figure 3.77 *Presswork machines*

Cutting operations

Before a component can be bent or drawn to shape, a metal *blank* of the appropriate shape has to be produced. The sequence of operations for making a box corner reinforcement is shown in Figure 3.78. You can see that the blank is the shape of the finished component when flattened out. This component is made in pairs, not only to increase the rate of production but also to balance the load on the bending tool and the blank. This prevents the blank from slipping while it is being bent in the tools.

Stamping out a blank is called a *blanking* operation. Punching a hole in a blank is called a *piercing* operation. For prototype work or

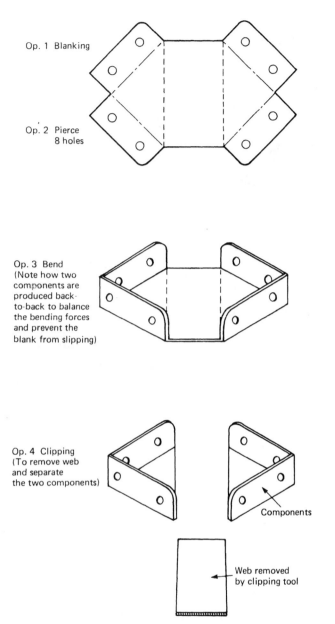

Op. 1 Blanking

Op. 2 Pierce
8 holes

Op. 3 Bend
(Note how two
components are
produced back-
to-back to balance
the bending forces
and prevent the
blank from slipping)

Op. 4 Clipping
(To remove web
and separate
the two components)

Components

Web removed
by clipping tool

Figure 3.78 *Operations required for making a box corner reinforcement*

when only a few simple blanks are required, the cost of an expensive blanking tool is not justified. Small blanks in thin metal can be cut with hand shears. Larger blanks in thicker metal can be cut using portable electric shears or a portable electric nibbling machine. Examples are shown in Figure 3.79.

V-bending

Figure 3.80(a) shows a simple V-bending tool. The metal blank is positioned in the location or 'nest' and the press closes the tool. This will form a strip of metal into a right-angled bracket. The tools themselves will have an angle that is slightly more acute than a right-angle to allow for *spring-back* of the metal when the tools open.

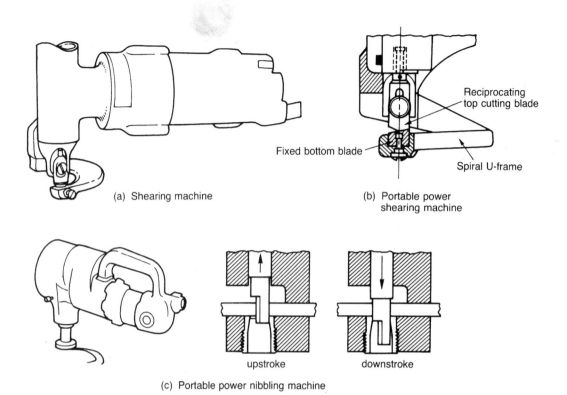

(a) Shearing machine

(b) Portable power shearing machine

Reciprocating top cutting blade

Fixed bottom blade

Spiral U-frame

upstroke

downstroke

(c) Portable power nibbling machine

Figure 3.79 *Shearing and nibbling machines*

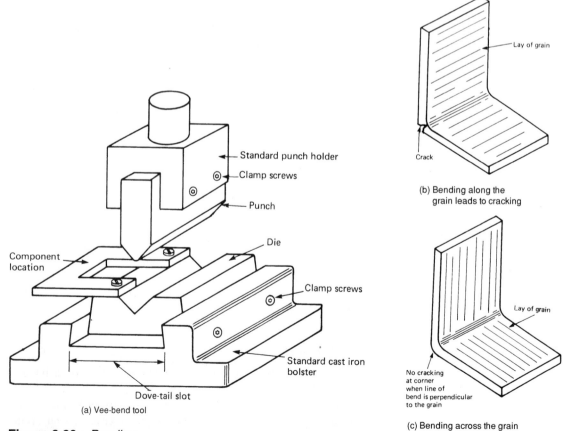

Standard punch holder

Clamp screws

Punch

Die

Component location

Clamp screws

Standard cast iron bolster

Dove-tail slot

(a) Vee-bend tool

Lay of grain

Crack

(b) Bending along the grain leads to cracking

Lay of grain

No cracking at corner when line of bend is perpendicular to the grain

(c) Bending across the grain reduces risk of cracking

Figure 3.80 *Bending*

Care must be taken when bending to prevent the metal from cracking. When metal is rolled out the grain is elongated in the direction of rolling. If you bend the metal along the grain it will crack as shown in Figure 3.80(b). If you bend the metal across the grain as shown in Figure 3.80(c) no cracking will occur. It's a bit like bending wood.

U-bending

Figure 3.81 shows a combination U-bending tool for making a clip. The blank is trapped between the left-hand punch and the corresponding pressure pad. The pressure pad stops the metal from slipping, keeps it flat, and ejects the bent component from the die. The partly formed component is transferred to the second die on the right-hand side of the tool and a new blank is placed over the left-hand die. The next stroke of the press finishes the first clip and part-forms the second clip.

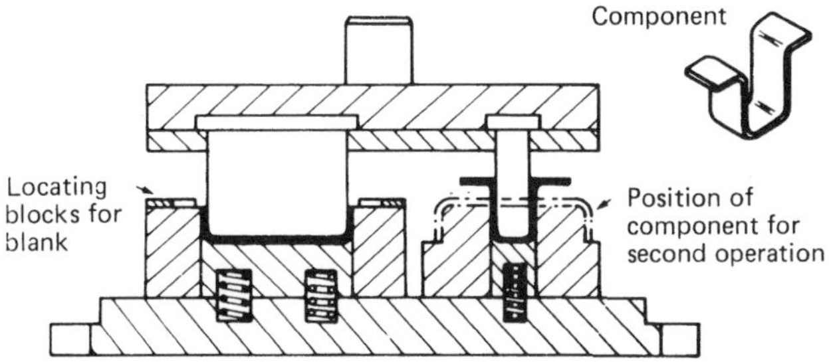

Figure 3.81 *U-bending*

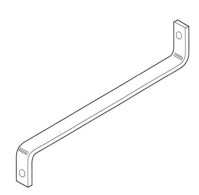

Figure 3.82 *See Test your knowledge 3.16*

Test your knowledge 3.16

1 Figure 3.77 shows a power press with a fixed transmission guard and an interlocked guard for the work zone.
  (a) Suggest why these types of guard have been chosen for their particular applications.
  (b) Find out how the interlocked guard works.
2 Figure 3.82 shows a simple bracket that is to be made in small batches. The strip metal blanks are supplied cut to length with the holes pierced in their ends.
  (a) State the most suitable type of bending tool that could be used.
  (b) Describe how the bracket is made from the blanks supplied.
3 With the aid of sketches explain how a CORE is used to make hollow castings.
4 A pressure die-casting machine can deliver 2 kg of metal per shot. With the aid of a sketch explain how the machine can economically produce components requiring only 250 g of metal each.
5 Choose suitable processes for making the following:
  (a) a rolled steel joist;
  (b) a small screening can for an electronic device from a soft aluminium 'slug';
  (c) a large diesel engine camshaft;
  (d) hexagon section free-cutting brass rod.

Activity 3.5

Compare the advantages and disadvantages of casting and forging as methods of manufacture. Present your findings in the form of a brief written report.

Activity 3.6

Figure 3.83 shows two pressed, aluminium alloy components that are fastened together with self-tapping screws to make an instrument case. Hint: think back to the greenhouse light project!

(a) Sketch the blank shapes for components.
(b) Sketch suitable bending tools for pressing the blanks to shape.

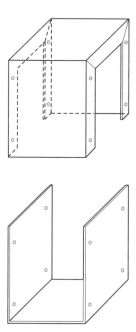

Figure 3.83   *See Activity 3.6*

Shaping materials (plastics)

Plastic materials are formed and moulded by a variety of operations. The choice of operation depends largely upon the type of plastic material being used as well as upon the shape of the component and the quantity required. You will learn about the composition and properties of materials elsewhere in this book. However, before considering the various forming processes, let's just revise some important points about plastics.

Thermoplastics   These soften every time they are heated. No chemical changes take place during the forming process so they can be ejected from the forming tools as soon as they are cool enough not to lose their shape. Such plastics can be injection-moulded, extruded and vacuum moulded.

Thermosets   Thermoset is a commonly used abbreviation for thermosetting plastic. These materials change chemically during the moulding process. The moulds have to be heated to the correct temperature for the change to take place. The moulds have to be kept closed long enough for the change to take place. The chemical change that takes place during moulding is called *curing*. Once cured, these plastics can never be softenend again by heating. Thermosets are generally more rigid than thermoplastics but tend to be more brittle.

Injection moulding

This is used mainly for moulding thermoplastics and is the most widely used moulding process. It is suitable for large volume production at low cost. Figure 3.84(a) shows a ram injection machine. Plastic granules from the hopper are fed by gravity into the injection chamber. They are then forced into the mould by a hydraulically operated ram. The *torpedo* spreads the granules so that they are heated uniformly. This heating is required to plasticize the granules before they enter the mould cavity. After injection, the moulds are opened automatically and the moulding is ejected.

Figure 3.84(b) shows a screw injection machine. A rotating screw is used to feed the granules into the mould. The action of the screw in feeding the granules past the heating elements ensures uniform heating without the need for a torpedo. This type of machine can handle larger volumes of granules per shot and is used for the largest mouldings. For example, car bumper mouldings made from high impact resistant plastics.

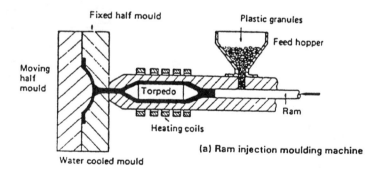

(a) Ram injection moulding machine

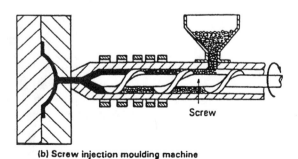

(b) Screw injection moulding machine

Figure 3.84 *Injection moulding*

When injection moulding the plasticizing temperatures can range between 150°C and 300°C depending upon the type of plastic material being moulded. The injection pressure can range between 100 MPa and 150 MPa. Injection moulding lends itself to total automation of the moulding cycle. This leads to high volumes of production and high levels of uniformity in product quality. Small components are produced in multiple impression moulds to ensure that the machine is fully loaded at every shot and running economically.

Extrusion

You can see from Figure 3.85(a) that the equipment for the extrusion of thermoplastic materials is very similar to the equipment for screw feed injection moulding. In extrusion moulding an open die is used instead of a closed die. As the moulded strip is extruded from the die it is sprayed with water to cool it and stop it losing its shape. It is supported on a roller-bed conveyor. In theory there is no limit to the

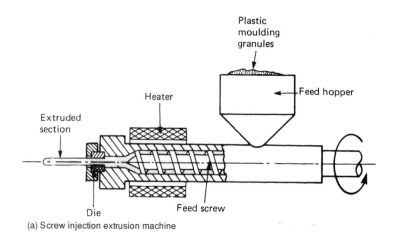

(a) Screw injection extrusion machine

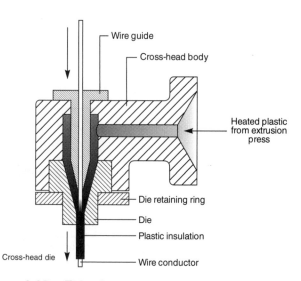

Figure 3.85 *Extrusion*

length of section that can be extruded provided the feed hopper is kept filled with plastic granules. In practice the extrusion is cut into convenient lengths for handling. Typical extrusions are the guttering that is fixed round the roofs of houses, curtain rails and plastic piping. Figure 3.85(b) shows a cross-head die used for insulating copper wire for electric cables.

Compression moulding

This is used when moulding thermosetting plastics. Moulding takes place in an upstroking hydraulic press as shown in Figure 3.86. Unlike injection moulding, where the moulds are cooled to ensure that the moulding can be ejected as quickly as possible, compression moulds are heated. This heating is needed to plasticize the granular material and to bring about its *curing* (polymerization). Also the mould is kept closed for a controlled period of time to ensure that the curing process is complete.

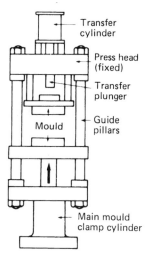

Transfer cylinder

Press head (fixed)

Transfer plunger

Guide pillars

Mould

Main mould clamp cylinder

Figure 3.86 *Upstroking hydraulic press*

Figure 3.87(a) shows a typical *flash mould*. To ensure that the mould is completely filled, excess moulding powder or granules are loaded into the die. The mould is then closed and any excess material is forced into the flash gutter. The flash land holds back the plasticized material to ensure the mould cavity is completely filled. After curing, the moulds are opened and the moulding is ejected. Although this method of moulding ensures uniform wall thickess and enables fine detail to be achieved, the material that spills over into the flash gutter is wasted. Also the flash has to be cut off and this is an extra operation.

Figure 3.87(b) shows a *positive mould*. This does not have a flash gutter and the exact amount of material has to be charged into the mould every time. Too much and the mould will not close properly leaving a flash. Too little and the moulding will not be complete. The main advantages of this technique are as follows:

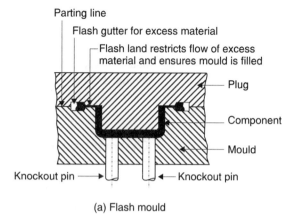

(a) Flash mould

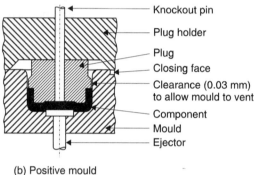

(b) Positive mould

Figure 3.87 *Flash and positive moulds*

- No flash has to be trimmed off.
- No flash material is wasted.
- The full force of the press is brought to bear on the moulding and none is wasted in producing the flash.

Note:

- When compression moulding thermosets, any flash or other waste material cannot be ground up and used again. Waste material from injection moulded thermoplastics can be reused.
- During curing, which is a chemical reaction, water vapour is produced in the form of steam. Vents have to be machined into the mould to release this steam.

Vacuum moulding and blow moulding

These two techniques produce similar products, for example bottles, buckets and washing-up bowls. Figure 3.88(a) shows the sequence of events for vacuum moulding. The heated sheet thermoplastic is stretched lightly across the mould. The air is exhausted from the mould by means of a vacuum pump. Atmospheric pressure then forms the sheet over the mould. Upon cooling the formed sheet retains its shape. No expensive press is required. The half mould can be made relatively cheaply. The gentle action of the air pressure allows thin sheet to be formed without tearing the sheet.

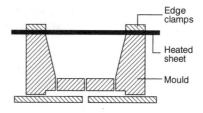

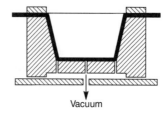

Vacuum

(a) Vacuum moulding

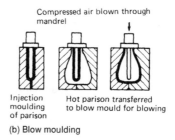

(b) Blow moulding

Figure 3.88 *Vacuum and blow moulding*

Figure 3.88(b) Shows the sequence of events for blow moulding. This process is used to make bottles and other hollow containers from thermoplastic materials. First of all a plastic blank called a *parison* is moulded onto a hollow mandrel. The mandrel and parison is transferred to a blow mould and heated. Air is blown down the hollow mandrel and inflates the parison, like a balloon, until it fills the mould. The moulding is then cooled and the mould – which is in two halves – is opened to remove the moulding. As can be seen from this example, re-entrant mouldings can be produced from which a shaped mandrel or plug could not be removed.

Sheet plastic fabrication

Rigid and semi-rigid plastic sheet can be fabricated like sheet metal. However, this material would break if bent cold. Therefore it has to be heated along the joint line so that it will bend through the required angle. A hot air gun can be used for short bends. For long bends electric strip heaters have to be used to ensure uniform heating. Care must be taken not to overheat and degrade the plastic. The bent shape is retained when the plastic cools.

Activity 3.7

1 List the factors that must be considered when choosing a suitable manufacturing process for a component made from a plastic material. Present the list in a logical sequence.
2 Sketch a section through a *transfer mould* and explain why it is superior to a simpler and cheaper positive mould.

Joining and assembly

The purpose of assembly is to put together a number of individual components to build up a whole device, structure or system. To achieve this aim attention must be paid to the following key factors:

Sequence of assembly   This must be planned so that as each component is added, its position in the assembly and the position of its fastenings are accessible. Also the sequence of assembly must be planned so that the installation of one component does not prevent access for fitting the next component or some later component.

Technique of joining   These must be selected to suit the components being joined, the materials from which they are made, and what they do in service. If the joining technique involves heating, then care must be taken that adjacent components are not heat sensitive or flammable.

Position of joints   Joints must not only be accessible for initial assembly, they must also be accessible for maintenance. You don't want to dismantle half a machine to make a small adjustment, or replace a part that wears out regularly.

Interrelationship and identification of parts   Identification of parts and their position in an assembly can usually be determined from assembly drawings or exploded view drawings. Interrelationship markings are often included on components. For example the various members and joints of structural steelwork are given number and letter codes to help identification on site. Printed circuit boards usually have the outline of the various components printed on them as well as the part number.

Tolerances   The assembly technique must take into account the accuracy and finish of the components being assembled. Much greater care has to be taken when assembling a precision machine tool or an artificial satellite, than when assembling structural steel work.

Protection of parts   Components awaiting assembly require protection against accidental damage and corrosion. In the case of structural steelwork this may merely consist of painting with red oxide primer and careful stacking. Precision components will require treating with an anti-corrosion lanolin-based compound that can be easily removed at the time of assembly. Bores must be sealed with plastic plugs and screw threads with plastic caps. Precision ground surfaces must also be protected from damage. Heavy components must be provided with eye-bolts for lifting. Vulnerable sub-assemblies such as aircraft engines must be supported in suitable cradles.

Joining (mechanical)

The joints used in engineering assemblies may be divided into the following categories:

Permanent joints These are joints in which one or more of the components and/or the joining medium has to be destroyed or damaged in order to dismantle the assembly. For example a riveted joint.

Temporary joints These are joints that can be dismantled without damage to the components. It should be possible to re-assemble the components using the original or new fastenings. For example a bolted joint.

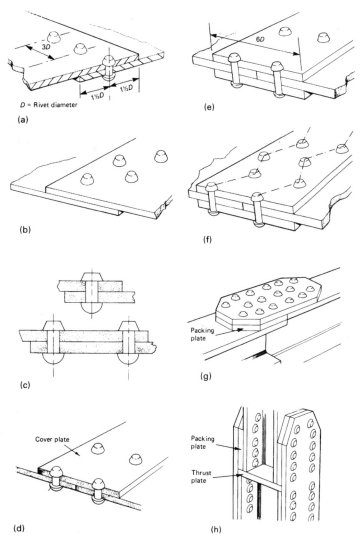

Figure 3.89 *Typical riveted joints*

Flexible joints   These are joints in which one component can be moved relative to another component in an assembly in a controlled manner. For example the use of a hinge.

Riveting

This is a long established method of making permanent joints. Some typical riveted joints are shown in Figure 3.89. Remember that the joint must be designed so that the shank of the rivet is in shear and carries most of the load. The head of the rivet is only intended to keep the rivet in place. It is not intended to carry major loads. Riveting may be carried out hot or cold. Small rivets may be closed in the cold condition but large rivets should be closed while they are red-hot. This not only makes the process easier, it prevents the rivet head from cracking. Also, as the rivet cools down, it shrinks and pulls the joint tightly together.

Figure 3.90(a) shows the stages in closing a solid rivet using simple workshop equipment. This technique is suitable providing

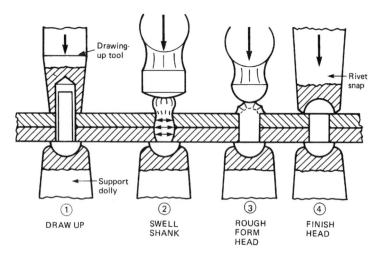

(a) Closing a rivet

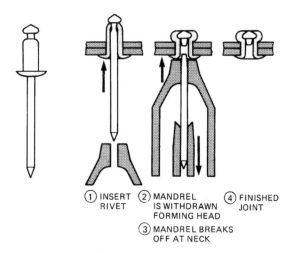

(b) Pop riveting

Figure 3.90   *Riveting*

you can get to both sides of a joint to support the rivet. For box sections in sheet metal, where this is not possible, 'pop' riveting is used. Figure 3.90(b) shows the stages in joining two pieces of sheet metal using a 'pop' rivet.

Fusion welding

Welding has largely taken over from riveting for many purposes such as ship and bridge building and for structural steelwork. Welded joints are continuous and, therefore, transmit the stresses across the joint uniformly. In riveted joints the stresses are concentrated at each rivet. Also the rivet holes reduce the cross-sectional areas of the members being joined and weaken them. However, welding is a more skilled assembly technique and the equipment required is more costly. The components being joined are melted at their edges and additional *filler metal* is melted into the joint. The filler metal is of similar composition to that of the components being joined. Figure 3.91(a) shows the principle of fusion welding.

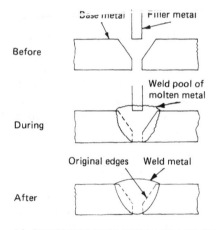

(a) FUSION WELDING WITH A FILLER ROD

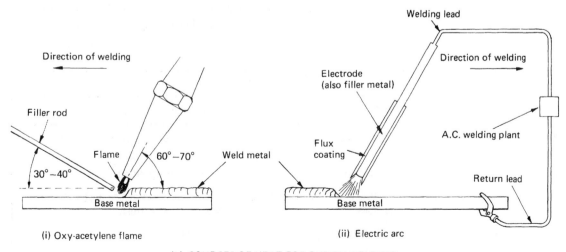

(i) Oxy-acetylene flame

(ii) Electric arc

(b) SOURCES OF HEAT FOR FUSION WELDING

Figure 3.91 *Welding*

High temperatures are involved to melt the metal of the components being joined. These can be achieved by using the flame of an oxy-acetylene blowpipe as shown in Figure 3.91(b) or an electric arc as shown in Figure 3.91(c). When oxy-acetylene welding (gas welding), a separate filler rod is used. When arc welding, the electrode is also the filler rod and is melted as welding proceeds.

No flux is required when oxy-acetylene welding as the molten metal is protected from atmospheric oxygen by the burnt gases (products of combustion). When arc welding, a flux is required. This is in the form of a coating surrounding the electrode. This flux coating is not only deposited on the weld to protect it, it also stabilizes the arc and makes the process easier. The hot flux gives off fumes and adequate ventilation is required.

Protective clothing must be worn when welding and goggles or a face mask appropriate for the process must be used. These have optical filters that protect the user's eyes from the harmful radiations produced during welding. The optical filters must match the process. The compressed gases used in welding are very dangerous and welding equipment must only be used by skilled persons or under close supervision. Gas bottles must only be stored and used in an upright position.

The heated area of the weld is called the *weld zone*. Because of the high temperatures involved, the heat affected area can spread back into the parent metal of the component for some distance from the actual weld zone. This can alter the structure and properties of the material so as to weaken it and make it more brittle. If the joint fails in service, failure usually occurs at the side of the weld in this heat affected zone. The joint itself rarely fails.

Soft soldering

Soft soldering is also a thermal jointing process. Unlike fusion welding, the parent metal is not melted and the filler metal is a low melting range alloy of tin and lead. Soft soldering is mainly used for making mechanical joints in copper and brass components (plumbing). It is also used to make permanent electrical connections. Low carbon steels can also be soldered providing the metal is first cleaned

---

Test your knowledge 3.17

State THREE advantages and THREE disadvantages of welding compared with riveting.

Key Facts 3.5

Flux	Metals	Characteristics
Killed spirits (acidulated zinc chloride solution)	Steel, tin plate, brass and copper	Powerful cleansing action but leaves corrosive residue
Dilute hydrochloric acid	Zinc and galvanized iron	As above, wash off after use
Resin paste or 'cored' solders	Electrical conductor and terminal materials	Only moderate cleansing action (passive flux), but non-corrosive
Tallow	Lead and pewter	As above
Olive oil	Tin plate	Non-toxic, passive flux for food containers, non-corrosive

and then 'tinned' using a suitable flux. The tin in the solder reacts chemically with the surface of component to form a bond. Figure 3.92 shows how to make a soft soldered joint.

- The surfaces to be joined are first degreased and physically cleaned to remove any dust and dirt. Fine abrasive cloth or steel wool can be used. A flux is used to render the joint surfaces chemically clean and to make the solder spread evenly through the joint.
- The copper 'bit' of the soldering iron is then heated. For small components and fine electrical work an electrically heated iron can be used. For joints requiring a soldering iron with a larger bit, a gas heated soldering stove can be used to heat the bit.
- The heated bit is then cleaned, fluxed and coated with solder. This is called 'tinning' the bit.
- The heated and tinned bit is drawn slowly along the fluxed surfaces of the components to be joined. This transfers solder to the surfaces of the components. Additional solder can be added if required. The work should be supported on wood to prevent heat loss. The solder does not just 'stick' to the surface of the metal being tinned. The solder reacts chemically with the surface to form an *amalgam* that pentrates into the surface of the metal. This forms a permanent bond.

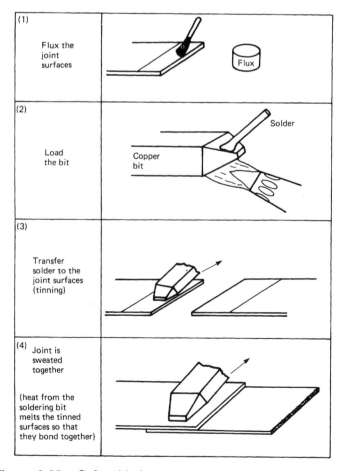

Figure 3.92   *Soft soldering*

● Finally the surfaces are overlapped and 'sweated' together. That is, the soldering iron is re-heated and drawn along the joint as shown. Downward pressure is applied at the same time. The solder in the joint melts. When it solidifies it forms a bond between the two components.

Figure 3.93 shows how a copper pipe is sweated to a fitting. The pipe and the fitting are cleaned, fluxed and assembled. The joint is heated with a propane gas torch and solder is added. This is usually a resin-flux cored solder. The solder is drawn into the close fitting joint by capillary attraction.

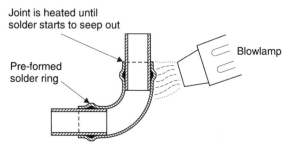

Figure 3.93 *A sweated joint*

Hard soldering

The melting range for a typical soft solder is 183°C to 212°C. The melting range for a typical hard solder is 650°C to 700°C. This is the difference between hard and soft soldering. Hard soldering uses a solder whose main alloying elements are copper and silver. This has a very much higher melting range but produces a very much stronger and more ductile joint.

The melting range is very much lower than the melting point of copper and steel but it is only just below the melting point of brass. Therefore great care is required when hard soldering brass to copper. Because the hard solder contains silver it is often referred to as 'silver solder'. A special flux is required based on borax.

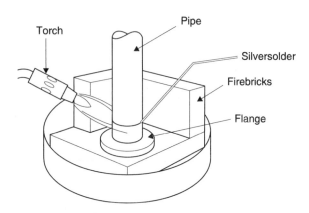

● The work is up to heat when the silversolder melts on contact with the work with the flame momentarily withdrawn.
● Add solder as required until joint is complete.

Figure 3.94 *Hard soldering*

1 Consult solder manufacturers' literature and draw up a table showing the composition of the standard soft solders and their typical applications.
2 List the advantages and limitations of silver soldering compared with soft soldering.

A soldering iron cannot be used because of the high temperatures involved. Heating is by a blow pipe. Figure 3.94 shows you how to make a typical hard soldered joint. Again cleanliness and careful surface preparation is essential for a successful joint. The joint must be close fitting and free from voids. The silver solder is drawn into the joint by capillary attraction.

Even stronger joints can be made using a brass alloy instead of a silver–copper alloy. This is called 'brazing'. The temperatures involved are higher than those for silver soldering. Therefore brass cannot be brazed. The process of brazing is widely used for joining the steel tubes and malleable cast iron fittings of bicycle frames.

Adhesive bonding

The advantages of adhesive bonding can be summarized as follows.

● The temperature rise from the curing of the adhesive is negligible compared with that of welding. Therefore the properties of the materials being joined are unaffected.
● Similar and dissimilar materials can be joined.
● Adhesives are electrical insulators. Therefore they reduce or prevent electrolytic corrosion when dissimilar metals are joined together.
● Joints are sealed and fluid tight.
● Stresses are transmitted across the joint uniformly.
● Depending upon the type of adhesive used, some bonded joints tend to damp out vibrations.

Bonded joints have to be specially designed to exploit the properties of the adhesive being used. You cannot just substitute an adhesive in a joint designed for welding, brazing or soldering. Figure 3.95(a) shows some typical bonded joint designs that provide a large contact area. A correctly designed bonded joint is very strong. Major structural members in modern high performance airliners and military aircraft are adhesive bonded. Figure 3.95(b) defines some of the jargon used when talking about bonded joints.

The strength of a bonded joint depends upon two factors:

Adhesion This is the ability of the adhesive to 'stick' to the materials being joined (the adherends). This can result from physical keying or interlocking, as shown in Figure 3.96(a). Alternatively specific bonding can take place. Here, the adhesive reacts chemically with the surface of the adherends, as shown in Figure 3.96(b). Bonding occurs through intermolecular attraction.

Cohesion This is the internal strength of the adhesive. It is the ability of the adhesive to withstand forces within itself.

As well as the design of the joint, the following factors affect the strength of a bonded joint:

● The joint must be physically clean and free from dust, dirt, moisture, oil and grease.

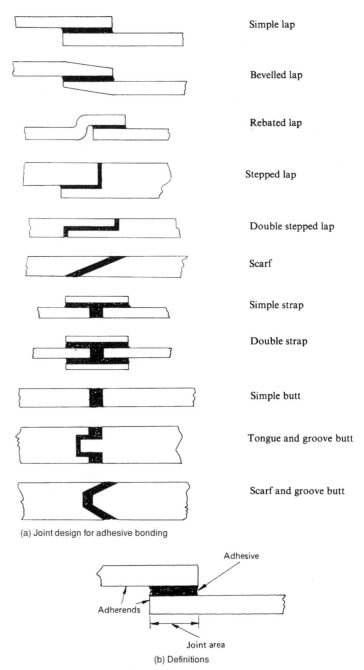

Simple lap

Bevelled lap

Rebated lap

Stepped lap

Double stepped lap

Scarf

Simple strap

Double strap

Simple butt

Tongue and groove butt

Scarf and groove butt

(a) Joint design for adhesive bonding

(b) Definitions

Figure 3.95   *Typical bonded joints*

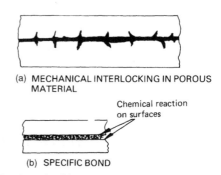

(a) MECHANICAL INTERLOCKING IN POROUS MATERIAL

(b) SPECIFIC BOND

Figure 3.96   *Interlocking*

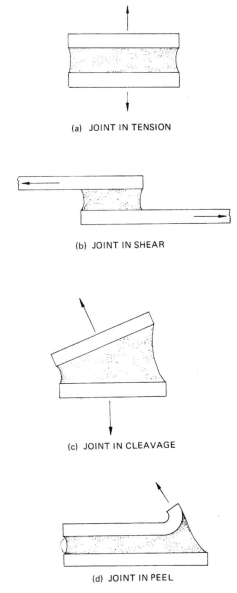

Figure 3.97   *Ways in which bonded joints can fail*

- The joint must be chemically clean. The materials being joined must be free from scale or oxide films.
- The environment in which bonding takes place must have the correct humidity and be at the correct temperature.

Bonded joints may fail in four ways. These are shown in Figure 3.97. Bonded joints are least likely to fail in tension and shear. They are most likely to fail in cleavage and peel.

Screwed fastenings

All the joints considered so far have been permanent joints. They have to be destroyed to separate the components. Screwed fastenings

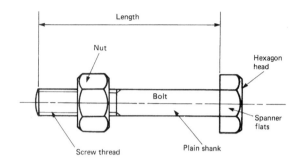

(a) HEXAGON HEAD BOLT AND NUT

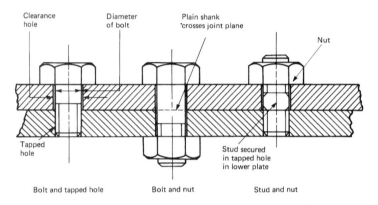

(b) TYPES OF SCREWED JOINT

Figure 3.98   *Typical screwed fastenings*

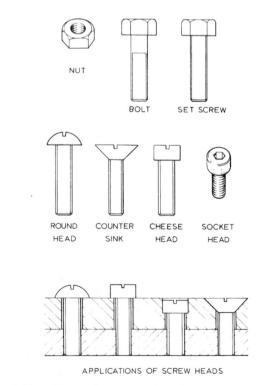

APPLICATIONS OF SCREW HEADS

Figure 3.99   *Alternative screw heads*

are temporary joints. Components secured by screwed fastenings can be assembled and separated without damage as often as is required. Figure 3.98 shows some typical screwed fastenings. Figure 3.99 shows some alternative screw heads.

Screwed fastenings must always pull down onto flat surfaces. Plain washers prevent the corners of the nut from damaging that surface. Taper washers are used when bolting up steel beams to prevent the bolt being bent. We don't want our screwed fastenings to work loose in service. This can be prevented by spring washers or self-locking nuts to increase the friction between the threads. Positive locking devices include tab washers and slotted (castle) nuts. Examples of these devices are shown in Figure 3.100.

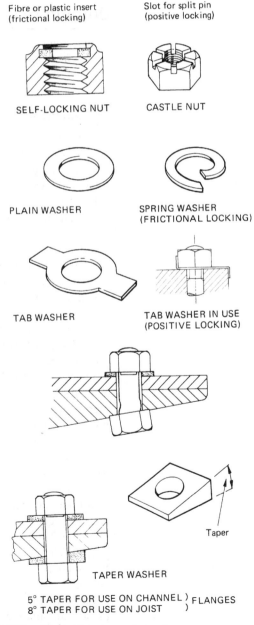

Figure 3.100 *Typical nuts and washers*

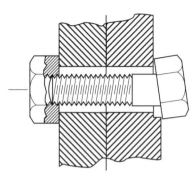

Figure 3.101 *See Test your knowledge 3.20*

Joining (electrical and electronic)

Again, joints may be permanent or temporary. Permanent joints are soldered or crimped. Temporary joints are bolted, clamped or plugged in.

Soldered joints

When soldering electrical and electronic components it's important not to overheat them. Overheating can soften thermoplastic insulation and completely destroy solid-state devices such as diodes and transistors. Very often some form of heat sink is required when soldering solid-state devices.

A high tin content low melting temperature solder with a resin flux core should be used. This is a *passive* flux. It only protects the joint. It contains no active, corrosive chemicals to clean the joint. Therefore the joint must be kept clean whilst soldering. Even the natural grease from your fingers is sufficient to cause a high resistance 'dry' joint.

Figure 3.102(a) shows how a soldered connection is made to a solder tag. Note how the lead from the resistor is folded around the tag. This gives mechanical strength to the connection. Soldering provides the electrical continuity.

Figure 3.102(b) shows a prototype electronic circuit assembled on a matrix board. The board is made from laminated plastic and is pierced with a matrix of equally spaced holes. Pin tags are fastened into these holes in convenient places and the components are soldered to these pin tags.

Figure 3.102(c) shows the same circuit built up on a strip board. This is a laminated plastic board with copper tracks on the underside. The wire tails from the components pass through the holes in the board and are soldered to the tracks on the underside. The copper tracks are cut wherever a break in the circuit is required.

Figure 3.102(d) shows the underside of a printed circuit board (p.c.b.). This is built up as shown in Figure 3.102(c), except that the tracks do not need to be cut since they are customized for the circuit.

Large volume assembly of printed circuit boards involves the use of pick and place robots to install the components. The assembled boards are the carried over a flow soldering tank on a conveyor. A

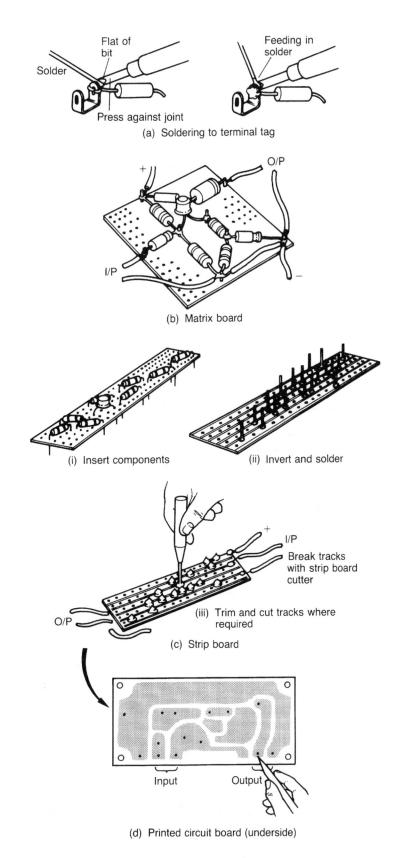

Flat of bit

Solder

Press against joint

(a) Soldering to terminal tag

Feeding in solder

+ O/P

I/P —

(b) Matrix board

(i) Insert components

(ii) Invert and solder

+ I/P

Break tracks with strip board cutter

O/P

(iii) Trim and cut tracks where required

(c) Strip board

Input Output

(d) Printed circuit board (underside)

Figure 3.102 *Typical soldered joints and electronic circuit boards*

roller rotates in the molten solder creating a 'hump' in the surface of the solder. As the assembled and fluxed board passes over this 'hump' of molten solder the components tags are soldered into place.

Wire wrapping is widely used in telecommunications where large numbers of fine conductors have to be terminated quickly and in close proximity to each other. Soldering would be inconvenient and the heat could damage the insulation adjoining conductors. Also, soldered joints are difficult to disconnect. A special wire wrapping tool is used that automatically strips the insulation from the wire and binds the wire tightly around the terminal pins. The terminal pins are square in section with sharp corners. The corners cut into the conductor and prevent it from unwinding. The number of turns round the terminal is specified by the supervising engineer.

Crimped joints

For power circuits, particularly in the automotive industry, cable lugs and plugs are crimped onto the cables. The sleeve of the lug or the plug is slipped over the cable and then indented by a small pneumatic or hydraulic press. This is quicker than soldering and, as no heat is involved, there is no danger of damaging the insulation. Portable equipment is also available for making crimped joints on site. Hand-operated equipment can be used to fasten lugs to small cables as shown in Figure 3.103.

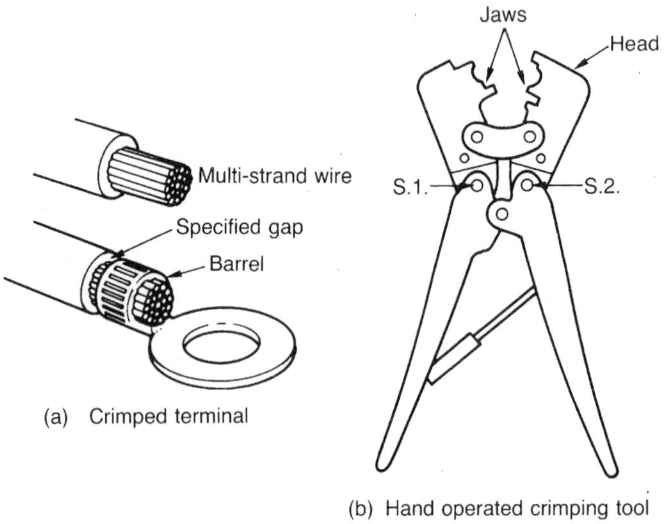

(a) Crimped terminal

(b) Hand operated crimping tool

Figure 3.103 *Crimping*

Clamped connections

Finally we come to clamped connections using screwed fastenings. You will have seen many of these in domestic plugs, switches and lamp-holders. For heavier power installations, cable lugs are bolted to solid copper bus-bars using brass or bronze bolts.

Activity 3.8

Write a brief report describing the advantages of an active soldering flux over a passive soldering flux and explain why an active flux is unsuitable for building electronic circuits. Also explain why silver soldering is unsuitable for securing components to a printed circuit board.

Activity 3.9

Consult manufacturers' literature and produce 'data sheets' describing the stages required to:

(a) make a wire wrapped joint;
(b) fit a multi-way ribbon cable to an insulation displacement connector (IDC) as used in data transmission circuits.

Illustrate your 'data sheets' with appropriate sketches and diagrams.

Heat treatment

The properties of many metals and alloys can be changed by heating them to specified temperatures and cooling them under controlled conditions at specified rates. These are called, respectively, critical temperatures and critical cooling rates. We are only going to consider the heat treatment of plain carbon steels.

Hardening

Figure 3.104 relates the critical temperatures for plain carbon steels to their various carbon contents. It also shows the corresponding hardening temperature ranges.

Key Facts 3.6		
(a) Effect of carbon content		
Type of steel	*Carbon content (%)*	*Effect of quench hardening*
Low Carbon	Below 0.3	Negligible
Medium Carbon	0.3–0.5	Becomes tougher
	0.5–0.9	Becomes hard
High Carbon	0.9–1.3	Becomes very hard
(b) Rate of cooling		
Carbon content (%)	*Quenching media*	*Required treatment*
0.3–0.5	Oil	Toughening
0.5–0.9	Oil	Toughening
0.5–0.9	Water	Hardening
0.9–1.3	Oil	Hardening

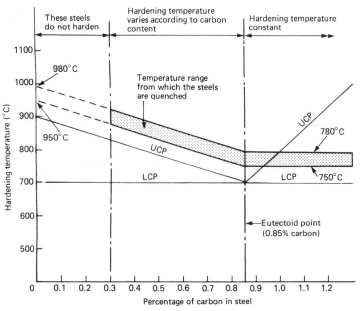

Figure 3.104 *Critical temperatures for carbon steel and hardening range*

The steel is heated to the temperature appropriate for its carbon content as shown in Figure 3.104. To harden the steel it is quenched (cooled rapidly) from this temperature by immersing it in a bath of cold water. The degree of hardness obtained depends upon two factors.

- The carbon content
- The rate of cooling

Hardening faults

Under heating If the temperature of a steel does not reach its temperature range as shown in Figure 3.104, the steel won't harden.

Overheating It is a common mistake to think that increasing the temperature from which the steel is quenched will increase its hardness. Once the correct temperature has been reached the hardess will depend only upon the carbon content of the steel and its rate of cooling. If the temperature of a steel exceeds its temperature range as shown in Figure 3.104, grain growth will occur and the steel will be weakened. Also overheating will slow the cooling rate and will actually reduce the hardness of the steel.

Cracking There are many causes of hardening cracks. Some of the more important are: sharp corners; sudden changes of section; screw threads; holes too near the edge of a component (these should all be avoided at the design stage); over-rapid cooling for the type of steel being used.

Distortion   There are many causes of distortion. Some of the more important are as follows:

● Lack of balance or symmetry in the shape of the component.
● Lack of uniform cooling. Long thin components should be dipped end-on into the quenching bath.
● Change in the grain structure of the steel causing shrinkage.

No matter how much care is taken when quench hardening, some distortion (movement) will occur. Also slight changes in the chemical composition may occur at the surface of the metal. Therefore precision components should be finish ground after hardening. The components must be left slightly oversize before grinding to allow for this. That is, a grinding allowance must be left on such components before hardening.

Tempering

Quench-hardened plain carbon steels are very brittle and unsuitable for immediate use. Therefore further heat treatment is required. This is called tempering. It greatly increase the toughness of the hardenend steel at the expense of some loss of hardness.

Tempering consists of re-heating the hardened steel and again quenching it in oil or water. Typical tempering temperatures for various applications are summaried in Key Facts 3.7. You can judge the tempering temperature by the colour of the oxide film. First, the component must be polished after hardening and before tempering. Then heat the component gently and watch for the colour of the metal surface to change. When you see the appropriate colour appear, the component must be quenched immediately.

Full annealing

This process is used to soften plain carbon steels that have been quench-hardened. It is also used to give the maximum ductility to materials that are to be severely cold worked.

Test your knowledge 3.22

Describe how you should harden and temper a cold chisel made from 0.8% carbon steel.

Key Facts 3.7		
Tempering temperatures		
Component	*Temper colour*	*Temperature (°C)*
Edge tools	Pale straw	220
Turning tools	Medium straw	230
Twist drills	Dark straw	240
Taps	Brown	250
Press tools	Brownish-purple	260
Cold chisels	Purple	280
Springs	Blue	300
Toughening (medium carbon steels)	–	450–600

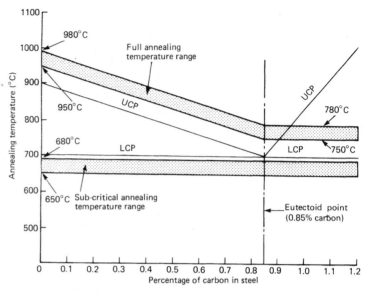

Figure 3.105 *Critical temperatures for carbon steel and annealing range*

Depending upon its carbon content, the metal is heated to the temperatures shown in Figure 3.105. Note that these are the same as for hardening. The metal is then allowed to cool down very slowly in the furnace with the energy supply turned off and the dampers closed. This will give maximum softness, ductility and grain growth.

Subcritical annealing

This is also known as process annealing and inter-stage annealing because it is used between the stages of cold-working processes and, if required, after cold working. As you can see from Figure 3.104, the temperature range for subcritical annealing is very much lower than that for full annealing.

The band of temperatures lies below the lower critial temperature line in the diagram. Hence the name subcritical annealing. This process will only work if the material has been hardened by cold working. It depends upon the stresses resulting from cold-working remaining locked up in the metal to trigger the annealing process.

When the metal is cold worked the metal crystals are deformed. This makes the metal hard and brittle. Process annealing causes new and undeformed crystals to grow from each stress point in the deformed crystals. Therefore, subcritical annealing is a recrystalization process. Cooling is again carried out very slowly as for full annealing.

Normalizing

After annealing the material is very soft and ductile, with an enlarged grain structure. This is ideal for cold manipulation but unsuitable for machining. Annealed steels tend to tear and leave a poor surface finish when machined. The turned components will also be weak

1 Describe the hardening and tempering of a carpenter's chisel made from a 1.2% carbon steel.

2 A large welded fabrication has to be finished by machining. How would you heat treat this fabrication so that it will machine to a good finish without distortion from the welding stresses?

3 Some components are to be made by bending them from cold rolled steel in a power press. How should the blanks be heat-treated to avoid cracking, using minimum energy.

because of the coarse grain structure. When the softened material is to be machined a normalizing process is used instead of annealing.

To normalize a steel it is heated, according to its carbon content, to the temperature range indicated in Figure 3.106. Although the temperature is higher for some of the steels, grain growth is less because the steel is cooled more quickly. Unlike annealing where the aim is to cool as slowly as possible, often over several days, normalized components are taken from the furnace and cooled more quickly in still air away from draughts. This results in a tougher structure, with a finer grain, that will machine to a good finish. Normalizing is used for the following purposes.

● Softening previously hardened steels that are to be machined.
● Stress relieving casting and forgings after rough machining so that they will not distort after finish machining.
● Stress relieving components before quench hardening to reduce the chance of cracking and distortion.

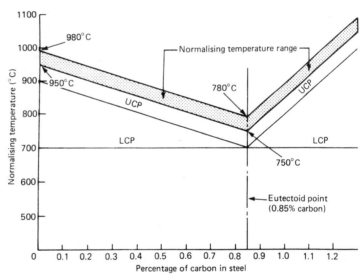

Figure 3.106 *Critical temperatures for carbon steel and normalizing range*

So far we have only considered plain carbon steels. Most non-ferrous metals cannot be quench hardened. They rely entirely on cold-working to increase their hardness and to increase their strength. Annealing such metals and alloys is entirely a recrystallization process. The temperature varies with the type of metal or alloy. Suitable temperatures are given in heat-treatment handbooks and metal manufacturers data sheets.

Chemical treatment

The chemical treatments that will be considered in this section are as follows.

● Chemical machining (etching) as used in the production of printed circuit boards.
● The coating of metal components with decorative and/or corrosion resistant finishes.

Etching

Printed circuit boards have already been introduced in the section on assembly. First the circuit is drawn out by hand or designed using a computer aided drawing (CAD) package. A typical circuit master drawing is shown in Figure 3.107. The master drawing of the circuit is then photographed to produce a transparent copy called a negative. In a negative copy the light and dark areas are reversed.

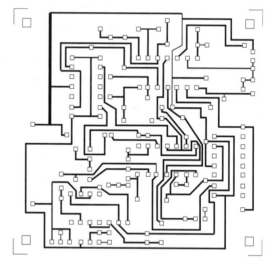

Figure 3.107   *A printed circuit layout*

The printed circuit board is made as follows:

- The copper-coated laminated plastic (tufnol) or fibre glass board is coated with a photoresist by dipping or spraying.
- The negative of the circuit is placed in contact with the prepared circuit board. They are then exposed to ultraviolet light. The light passes through the transparent parts of the negative. The areas of the board exposed to the ultraviolet light will eventually become the circuit.
- The exposed circuit board is then developed in a chemical solution that hardens the exposed areas.
- The photoresist is stripped away from the unexposed areas of the circuit board.
- The circuit board is then placed in a suitable etchant. Ferric chloride solution can be used as an etchant for copper. This eats away the copper where it is not protected by the hardened photo resist. The remaining copper is the required circuit.
- The circuit boards are washed to stop the reaction. The remaining photoresist is removed so as not to interfere with the tinning of the circuit with soft solder and the soldering of the components into position.

Note: This process is potentially dangerous. Ultraviolet light is very harmful to your skin and to your eyes. The ferric chloride solution is highly corrosive to your skin. The various processes also give off

harmful fumes. Therefore you should only carry out this process
under properly controlled and ventilated conditions. Appropriate
protective clothing should be worn.

A similar process can be used for the chemical engraving of
components with their identification numbers and other data.

Electroplating

The component to be plated is placed into a plating bath as shown in
Figure 3.108. The component is connected to the negative terminal of
a direct current supply. This operates at a low voltage but relatively
heavy current. The anode is connected to the positive terminal of the
supply. The anode is made from the same metal as that which is to
be plated onto the component. The electrolyte is a solution of
chemical salts. The composition depends upon the process being
carried out.

When the current passes through the bath the component is coated
with a thin layer of the protective and/or decorative metal. This metal
comes from the chemicals in the electrolyte. The process is self-
balancing. The anode dissolves into the electrolyte at the same rate as
the metal taken from the electrolyte is being deposited on the

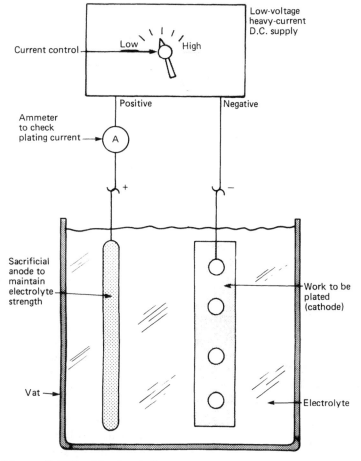

Figure 3.108 *Electroplating*

component. This applies to most plating processes such as zinc, copper, tin and nickel plating.

An exception is chromium plating. A neutral anode is used that does not dissolve into the electrolyte. Additional salts have to be added to the electrolyte from time to time to maintain the solution strength. Chromium is not usually deposited directly onto the component. It is usually nickel plated and polished and then a light film of chromium is plated over the nickel as a decorative and sealing coat.

The 'hard-chromium' plating used to build up worn gauges and tools is applied directly onto the steel. This is a specialized process outside the scope of this unit.

Galvanizing

This is the coating of low carbon steels with a layer of zinc.

Hot-dip galvanizing   This is the orignal process used for buckets, animal feeding troughs and other farming accessories. It is also used for galvanized sheeting. The work to be coated is chemically cleaned, fluxed and dipped into the molten zinc. This forms a coating on the work. A small percentage of aluminium is added to the zinc to give the traditional bright finish. The molten zinc also seals any cut edges and joints in the work and renders them fluid tight.

Electrolytic galvanizing   This is an electroplating process as described earlier. The metal deposited is zinc and the process is usually limited to flat and corrugated sheet. It is quicker and cheaper than hot-dip galvanizing but the coating is thinner.

Any corrosive attack on galvanized products eats away the zinc in preference to the iron. The zinc is said to be sacrificial. To prolong the life of galvanized sheeting it should be painted to protect the zinc itself from the atmosphere.

Anodizing

This is a protective process for aluminium and aluminium alloys. These metals resist corrosion by developing an oxide film on their surfaces which resists any further attack. This film is a drab grey colour that is unattractive.

Anodizing is a process for producing a thicker oxide film that can be coloured to make it more attractive. Unlike electroplating the work is made the anode of the bath. The electrolyte is usually a mixture of organic acids depending upon the finish required. The cathode is merely present to complete the circuit it is not involved in the reactions.

After the oxide film has been built up on the work, it can be coloured with dyes or left the natural colour produced by the process. Finally the work is steamed to seal the oxide film.

Test your knowledge 3.25

Give two examples of where each of the following processes would be appropriate:
(a) electroplating
(b) galvanizing
(c) anodizing
Do not repeat the examples in the text!

Finishing and Coating

Grinding

A grinding wheel consists of abrasive particles bonded together. It does not 'rub' the metal away, it cuts the metal like any other cutting tool. Each abrasive particle is a cutting tooth. Imagine an abrasive wheel to be a milling cutter with thousands of teeth. Wheels are made in a variety of shapes and sizes. They are also available with a variety of abrasive particle materials and a variety of bonds. It is essential to choose the correct wheel for any given job.

Precision surface grinding machines, precision cylindrical grinding machines and tool and cutter grinding machines are outside the scope of this book.

Polishing

Polishing produces an even better finish than grinding but only removes the minutest amounts of metal. It only produces a smooth and shiny surface finish, the geometry of the surface is uncontrolled. Polishing is used to produce decorative finishes, to improve fluid flow through the manifolds of racing engines, and to remove machining marks from surfaces that cannot be ground. This is done to reduce the risk of fatigue failure in highly stressed components.

Coating

Electroplating has already been discussed and is the coating of metal components with another metal that is more decorative and/or corrosion resistant. Metal components may also be coated with non-metallic surfaces.

Oxidizing

Oil blueing   Steel components have a natural oxide film due to their reaction with atmospheric oxygen. This film can be thickened and enhanced by heating the steel component until it takes on a dark blue colour. Then immediately dip the component into oil to seal the oxide film. This process does not work if there is any residual mill scale on the metal surfaces.

Chemical blacking   Alternatively, an even more corrosion resistant oxide film can be applied to steel components by chemical blacking. The components are cleaned and degreased. They are then immersed in the oxidizing chemical solution until the required film thickness has been achieved. Finally the treated components are rinsed, dewatered and oiled. Again, the process only works on bright surfaces.

Plastic coating

Plastic coatings can be both functional, corrosion resistant and decorative. The wide range of plastic materials available in a wide variety of colours and finishes provides a designer with the means of achieving one or more of the following.

- Abrasion resistance.
- Cushioning effects with coatings up to 6 mm thick.
- Electrical and thermal insulation.
- Flexibility over a wide range of temperatures.
- Non-stick properties (Teflon PTFE coatings).
- Permanent protection against weathering and atmospheric pollution, resulting in reduced maintenance costs.
- Resistance to corrosion by a wide range of chemicals.
- The covering of welds and the sealing of porous castings.

To ensure success, the surfaces of the work to be plasticized must be physically and chemically clean and free from oils and greases. The surfaces to be platicized must not have been plated, galvanized or oxide treated.

Fluidized bed dipping   Finely powdered plastic particles are suspended in a current of air in a fluidizing bath. The powder continually bubbles up and falls back and looks as though it is boiling. It offers no resistance to the work to be immersed in it. The work is preheated and immersed in the powder. A layer of powder melts onto the surface of the metal to form a homogenous layer.

Liquid plastisol dipping   This process is limited to PVC coating. A plastisol is a resin powder suspended in a liquid and no dangerous solvents are present. The preheated work is suspended in the PVC plastisol until the required thickness of coating has adhered to the metal surface.

Painting

Painting is used to provide a decorative and corrosion resistant coating for metal surfaces. It is the easiest and cheapest means of coating that can be applied with any degree of permanence. A paint consists of three components.

- *Pigment*   The finely powered pigment provides the paint with its opacity and colour.
- *Vehicle*   This is a film-forming liquid or binder in a volatile solvent. This binder is a natural or synthetic resinous material. When dry (set) it must be flexible, adhere strongly to the surface being painted, corrosion resistant and durable.
- *Solvent* (thinner). This controls the consistency of the paint and its application. It forms no part of the final paint film as it totally evaporates. As it evaporates it increases the concentration of catalyst in the 'vehicle' causing it to change chemically and set.

A paint system consists of the following components:

- *Primer*   This is designed to adhere strongly to the surface being painted and to provide a key for the subsequent coats. It also contains anti-corrosion compounds.

- *Putty* or *filler* This is used mainly on castings to fill up and repair blemishes. It provides a smooth surface for subsequent paint coats.
- *Undercoat* This builds up the thickness of the paint film. To produce a smooth finish, more than one under coat is used with careful rubbing down between each coat. It also gives richness and opacity to the colour.
- *Top coat* This coat is decorative and abrasion resistant. It also seals the paint film with a waterproof membrane. Modern top coats are usually based on acrylic resins or polyurethane rubbers.

There are four main groups of paint:

- *Group 1* The vehicle is polymerized (see thermosetting plastics) into a solid film by reaction with atmospheric oxygen. Paints that set naturally in this way include traditional linseed oil based paints, oleo-resinous paints, and modern general purpose air drying paints based on modified alkyd resins.
- *Group 2* Paints based on amino-alkyd resins that do not set at room temperatures but have to be stoved at 110°C to 150°C. When set these paints are much tougher than group 1 air-drying paints.
- *Group 3* These are the 'two-pack' paints. Polymerization starts to occur as soon as the catalyst is mixed with the paint immediately before use. Modern 'one-pack' versions of these paints have the catalyst diluted with a volatile solvent as mentioned earlier. The solvent evaporates after the paint has been spread and, when the concentration of the catalyst reaches a critical level, polymerization takes place and the paint sets.
- *Group 4* These paints dry by evaporation of the solvent and no polymerization occurs. An example is the cellulose paint used widely at one time for spray painting motor car body panels. Lacquers also belong to this group but differ from all other paints in that dyes are used as the colourant instead of pigments.

Paints may be applied by brushing, spraying or dipping. Whatever method is used great care must be taken to ensure adequate ventilation. Not only can the solvents produce narcotic effects, but inhaling dried particles and liquid droplets of paint can cause serious respiratory diseases. The appropriate protective clothing, goggles and face masks must be used.

Paints are also highly flammable and the local fire-prevention officer must be consulted over their storage and use. On no account can smoking be tolerated anywhere near the storage or use of paints.

Activity 3.10

A bumper for a small, home-made child's pedal car has been made from steel metal as a welded fabrication. List the operations required, in the correct order, from dressing the weld to the final polishing, including the plating processes. Consult a plating and finishing supplier's catalogue and data sheets for information on plating and polishing.

Activity 3.11

Identify a suitable application process and suitable coating medium for:

(a) painting washing machine body panels;
(b) painting pressed steel angle brackets;
(c) plastic cladding metal tubing for bathroom towel rails.

Multiple choice questions

1 An example of an electromechanical device is

A an electroplating bath
B a computer-controlled machine tool
C a digital voltmeter
D a car battery.

2 Inspection is an important manufacturing function, which

A ensures a product is pleasing to the eye
B selects the process by which a product is to be made
C reduces the cost of a product
D ensures a product satisfies its design specification.

3 The diameter of a precision turned component is best measured using

A a rule and calipers
B a GO and NOT GO gap (snap) gauge
C a micrometer caliper
D slip gauge blocks.

4 To reduce the cost of manufacture a designer would re-dimension a drawing to

A reduce the tolerances
B increase the tolerances
C leave the tolerances unchanged
D include close geometrical tolerances.

5 Metal cutting tools should have

A a rake angle alone
B a clearance angle alone
C both a rake and a clearance angle
D neither a rake nor a clearance angle.

6 The most economical method of producing a long, flat and accurate surface would be to use a

A hacksaw
B file
C milling machine
D lathe.

7 The cutting edge of a cold chisel should be heat treated by

A hardening and tempering
B normalizing and tempering

C hardening and normalizing

D tempering alone.

8 Small components are connected to printed circuit boards by

A soft soldering

B silver soldering

C spot welding

D adhesive bonding.

9 A portable fire extinguisher coloured black will contain

A foam

B water

C carbon dioxide

D CTC.

10 Planned maintenance reduces

A the chance of a major breakdown

B the cost of process planning

C the cost of process inspection

D the cost of routine maintenance.

Unit 4   Engineering materials

Summary

All branches of engineering are concerned with the behaviour of materials. Civil engineers need to ensure that the materials from which they build their roads, bridges and dams are suitable. Think about what might happen if they got their calculations wrong and selected the wrong type of material. For instance, if a bridge was built from the wrong material it might collapse under heavy loads. Even on a much smaller scale knowledge of materials is vitally important. An electrical engineer designing complex computer circuitry must ensure that the materials chosen do not prematurely deteriorate in service causing the computer to fail unexpectedly because, this too, could have catastrophic results. Imagine the consequences if the computer failed while controlling the automatic pilot of an aircraft just as the aircraft was landing!

A study of materials is, therefore, an essential part of every engineer's vocabulary and for this reason alone, is worthy of study. However, I also hope that the more you learn about materials, the more you will come to realize how fascinating and challenging a subject it is.

Materials and their properties

In the first element in this unit we are going to consider the important properties of the various types of materials used to make engineering products. Next we will look at typical measured values, for a variety of properties, for our chosen materials. Then, from appropriate literature and experimental tests, we will determine these data values and use them. Finally we will consider the way the chemical composition, types of bond, crystal and other structural features, affect the properties of the parent material.

Classes of Material

What do you already know?

For most engineering applications the most important criteria for the selection of the material to be used are that the material does its job properly as cheaply as possible. Whether a material does its job depends on its *properties*, which are a measure of how it reacts to the various influences to which it is exposed. For example, loads, atmospheric environment, electromotive forces, heat, light, chemicals and so on.

To aid our understanding of the different types of materials and their properties they are divided into four categories; metals, polymers, ceramics, and composites. Strictly speaking, composites are not really a separate group since they are made up from the other categories of material. However, because they display unique properties and are a very important engineering group, they are treated separately here.

Metals

You will be familiar with metals such as aluminium, iron, and copper, in the enormous variety of everyday applications: i.e. aluminium saucepans, copper water pipes and iron stoves. Metals can be mixed with other elements (often other metals) to form an *alloy*. Metal alloys are used to provide improved properties, i.e. alloys are often stronger or tougher than the parent pure metal. Other improvements can be made to metal alloys by *heat-treating* them as part of the manufacturing process. Thus steel is an alloy of iron and carbon and small quantities of other elements. If after alloying the steel is quickly cooled by quenching in oil or brine, a very hard steel can be produced. Much more will be said later about alloying and heat-treating metals.

Polymers

Polymers are characterized by their ability to be (initially at least) moulded into shape. They are chemical materials and often have long and unattractive chemical names. There is considerable incentive to seek more convenient names and abbreviations for everyday use. Thus you will be familiar with PVC polyvinyl chloride and PTFE polytetrafluoroethylene.

Polymers are made from molecules which join together to form long chains in a process known as *polymerization*. There are essentially three major types of polymer. *Thermoplastics*, which have the ability to be remoulded and reheated after manufacture. *Thermosetting plastics*, which once manufactured remain in their orginal moulded form and cannot be re-worked. *Elastomers* or *rubbers*, which often have very large elastic strains; elastic bands and car tyres are two familiar forms of rubber.

Ceramics

This class of material is again a chemical compound, formed from oxides such as silica (sand), sodium and calcium, as well as silicates such as clay. Glass is an example of a ceramic material, with its main constituent being silica. The oxides and silicates mentioned above have very high melting temperatures and on their own are very difficult to form. They are usually made more manageable by mixing them in powder form, with water, and then hardening them by heating. Ceramics include, brick, earthenware, pots, clay, glasses and refractory (furnace) materials. Ceramics are usually hard and brittle, good electrical and thermal insulators and have good resistance to chemical attack.

Composites

These combine the attractive properties of the other classes of material while avoiding some of their drawbacks. They are light, stiff and strong, and they can be tough.

A composite is a material with two or more distinct constituents, so, for example, we can classify bricks made from mud and reinforced with straw which were used in ancient civilizations, as a composite. A versatile and familiar building material which is also a composite is concrete; concrete is a mixture of stones (aggregate), held together by cement. In the last forty years there has been a rapid increase in the production of synthetic composites, those incorporating fine fibres held in various polymers.

Although not considered as a separate class of material, some *nature materials* exist in the form of a composite. The best known examples are wood, mollusc shells and bone. Wood is an interesting example of a natural fibre composite; the longitudinal hollow cells of wood are made up of layers of spirally wound cellulose fibres with varying spiral angle, bonded together with lignin during the growing of the tree.

The above classification of materials is rather crude and many important subdivisions exist within each category. The natural materials, except for those mentioned above under composites, have been deliberately left out. The study of materials such as wool and cotton is better placed in a course concerned with the textile industry. Here, we will be concentrating on the engineering application of materials and will only mention naturally occurring materials where appropriate.

Activity 4.1

How much do you already know about different materials and their properties? Test your knowledge by trying the exercise set out below. In attempting to tackle this task you might find it helpful to explore the objects that exist within your own home, and ask yourself why they are made from those particular materials. Complete the table by using a grading scheme such as: excellent, good, fair, poor; or high, above average, below average, low, or some other similar scheme.

Material properties	Classes of material			
	Metals	Polymers	Ceramics	Composites
Density				
Stiffness				
Strength				
Toughness				
Ductility				
Shock resistance				
Hardness				
Thermal conductivity				
Electrical conductivity				
Corrosion resistance				
Chemical stability				
Melting temperature				

What you may have discovered from Activity 4.1 was how difficult it is to make valid judgements, even using the rather crude classification of materials provided. You may also not have been entirely clear about the properties listed. For instance, what do you understand by 'chemical stability'? How do we really define 'hardness'?

Properties of materials

To help you answer the questions resulting from Activity 4.1, we can now look at some of the more important properties of materials. These properties are often broken down into two major subdivisions; *mechanical properties* and *physical properties*. The latter includes; *electrical properties*, *magnetic properties*, *thermal properties* and *chemical properties*.

It can be argued that chemical properties are in themselves another major subdivision. To introduce the small amount of physical chemistry necessary to understand the environmental stability of materials, I will present the subject of corrosion and corrosion prevention separately.

We will be looking at all of the above properties but we will leave processing properties until we deal with material processing, where it fits more readily. Also, information on the cost of materials will be found later when we deal with the selection of materials for engineering products.

Mechanical properties

Mechanical properties are the behaviour of materials when subject to forces and include strength, stiffness, hardness, toughness, and ductility to name but a few. For the sake of completeness and precision most of the important mechanical properties are defined below. They make rather tedious reading, but are necessary to help you select appropriate materials for specific engineering functions.

When a material is subject to an external force, then the forces which hold the atoms of the material together (bonding forces), act like springs and oppose these external forces. These external forces may tend to stretch or squeeze the material or make two parts of the material slide over one another in opposite directions, by acting against the bonding forces (Figure 4.1).

When a material is subject to external forces which tend to stretch it, then it is said to be in *tension*. The ability of a material to withstand these tensile (pulling) forces is a measure of its *tensile strength* (Figure 4.2(a)). When a material is subject to forces which squeeze it then it is said to be in *compression*. The ability of a material to withstand these compressive forces is a measure of its *compressive strength* (Figure 4.2(b)). If a material is subject to opposing forces which are offset and cause one face to slide relative to an opposite face, then it is said to be in *shear* and the ability of the material to resist these shearing forces is a measure of its *shear strength* (Figure 4.2(c)).

In discussing the application of forces to materials, it is often desirable to be able to compare one material with another. For this reason we may not be concerned so much with the size of the force,

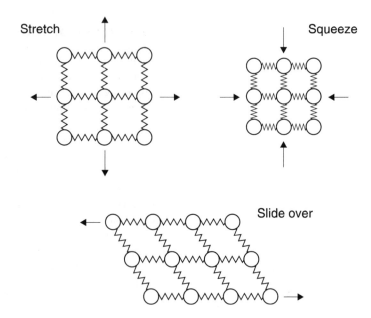

Figure 4.1   *Reaction of atomic bonds to external forces*

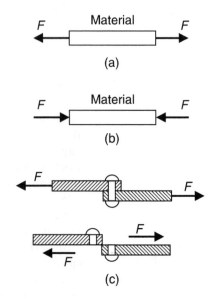

Figure 4.2   *(a) Tensile, (b) compressive and (c) shear forces*

as the force applied per unit area. Thus, for example, if we apply a tensile force F to a length of material over its cross-sectional area A, then the force applied per unit area is F/A. The term stress is used for the force per unit area.

$$\text{Stress} = \frac{\text{Force}}{\text{Area}}$$

The unit in which stress is measured is the pascal (Pa), with 1 Pa being a force of 1 newton per square metre, i.e., $1\,\text{Pa} = 1\,\text{N/m}^2$. Note that, in materials science, it is perhaps more convenient to measure stress in terms of newtons per square millimetre (N/mm^2). This unit, moreover, produces a value which is easier to appreciate, whereas the force necessary to break (for example) a steel bar one square metre in cross-section is so large as to be difficult to visualize in ordinary measurable terms. The Greek letter (sigma σ) is often used to indicate stress.

The stress is said to be *direct stress* when the area being stressed is at right angles to the line of action of the external forces, as when the material is in tension or compression. Shear stresses are not direct stresses since the forces being applied are in the same plane (parallel with) the area being stressed. The area used for calculating the stress is generally the original area that existed before the application of forces, this stress is often referred to as the *engineering stress*. The term *true stress* being used for the force divided by the actual area that exists while the material is in the stressed state.

Strain refers to the proportional change produced in a material as a result of the stress applied. It is measured as the number of millimetres of deformation (change in dimension) suffered per millimetre of original dimension and is a numerical ratio, therefore strain has no units.

When a material is subject to tensile or compressive forces and a change in length results then the material has been strained, this strain is defined as:

$$\text{Strain} = \frac{\text{change in length}}{\text{original length}}$$

For example, if we have a strain of 0.02. This would indicate that the change in length is $0.02 \times$ the original length. However, strain is frequently expressed as a percentage:

$$\text{Strain} = \frac{\text{change in length}}{\text{original length}} \times 100\%$$

Thus the strain of 0.02 as a percentage is 2%, i.e. here the change in length is 2% of the original length.

The Greek letter (epsilon ε) is the symbol normally used to represent strain. The symbol for length is (l) and the symbol for change in length is (δl), where δ is the Greek letter delta.

Example 4.1

A copper bar has a cross-sectional area of 75 mm^2 and is subject to a compressive force of 150 N. What is the compressive stress?
The compressive stress is the force divided by the area that is:

$$\text{compressive stress } (\sigma) = \frac{150}{75} \text{ N/mm}^2 = 2 \text{ N/mm}^2$$

$$\text{or compressive stress } (\sigma) = \frac{150}{75 \times 10^6} = 2 \text{ MN/m}^2 = 2 \text{ MPa}$$

Example 4.2

In a tensile test a specimen of length 140 mm, is subject to a tensile force which increases its length by 0.028 mm. What is the percentage strain?
The strain is the change in length divided by the original length that is

$$\text{Strain } (\varepsilon) = \frac{0.028}{140} \times 100 = 0.02\%$$

We have already mentioned tensile, compressive and shear strength (Figure 4.2) but we did not give the general definition. The *strength* of a material is defined as *the ability of a material to resist the application of a force without fracturing*.

The stress required to cause the material to fracture, i.e. *fracture stress* is a *measure of its strength* and requires careful consideration.

Hooke's Law

Hooke's Law states that *within the elastic limit of a material the change in shape is directly proportional to the applied force producing it*. What this means is that a linear (straight line) relationship exists between the applied force and the corresponding strain while the material is being elastically deformed (in other words, while it is still able to return to its original size when the external load (i.e. force) is removed).

A good example of the application of Hooke's law is the *spring*. A spring balance used for measuring weight force, for instance, where an increase in weight causes a corresponding extension (Figure 4.3).

If the load (weight) is increased sufficiently, there will come a point when the internal forces holding the spring material together start to break or permanently stretch and so, even after the load has been removed, the spring will remain permanently deformed, i.e. *plastically strained*.

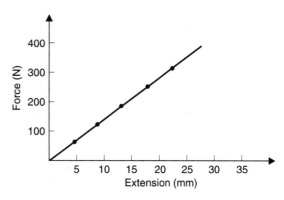

Figure 4.3 *Application of Hookes Law to a spring*

By considering Hooke's law, it follows that *stress* is also directly proportional to strain while the material remains elastic, because stress is no more than force (load) per unit area. The stress required to first cause plastic strain is known as the *yield stress* (Figure 4.4).

For *metals*, the *fracture stress* (i.e. the measure of *strength*) is considered to be identical to the 0.2% yield stress. This is because, for all engineering purposes, metals are only used within their elastic range, so a strength measurement above the yield stress is of little value to engineers when deciding which metal to use. The *0.2% yield stress* is defined as the stress at which the stress–strain curve (Figure 4.4), for tensile loading, deviates by a strain of 0.2% from the linear elastic line. Note here that a permanent change in length (strain) has occurred, the material has been plastically deformed by 0.2% of its original length.

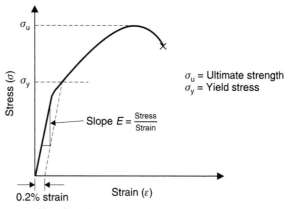

Figure 4.4 *The stress–strain curve for a metal, showing the measure of yield strength*

σ_f is the symbol for fracture stress (units MPa or MN/m^2) and σ_1 is the yield stress (the stress needed to start to plastically deform or permanently strain the material), with the same units as fracture stress. For metals the fracture stress is the same in tension and compression.

For *polymers* the fracture stress is identified as the yield stress at which the stress–strain curve becomes markedly nonlinear, i.e. typically at strains of around 1%. Polymers are a little stronger (approximately 20%) in compression than in tension (Figure 4.5).

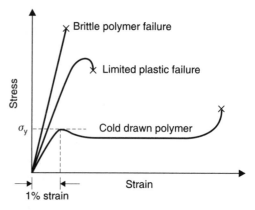

Figure 4.5 *Stress–strain curves for a polymer showing the 1% measure of yield strength*

For ceramics and glasses the strength depends strongly on the mode of loading. In tension, strength means the fracture strength given by the *tensile fracture stress* (symbol σ_f^t). In compression it means the crushing strength, given by the *compressive fracture stress* (symbol σ_f^c) which is much larger than the tensile fracture stress, typically fifeteen times as large. The tensile and compressive fracture stresses for a typical ceramic are shown in figure 4.6.

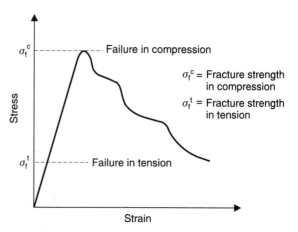

Figure 4.6 *The stress–strain curve for a ceramic showing the large variation in yield strength in tension (low) and compression (high)*

The symbol σ_u is used to indicate the *ultimate tensile strength*, measured by the nominal stress at which a bar of material loaded in tension separates (breaks). For brittle solids – ceramics, glasses and brittle polymers – it is the same as the fracture stress in tension (Figures 4.5 and 4.6). For metals, ductile polymers and most composites, it is larger than the fracture stress (σ_f) by a factor of between 1.1 and 3 because of work hardening (Figure 4.4), or in the case of composites, because of load transfer to the strong reinforcing fibres. More will be said about work hardening and fibre reinforcement of composites latter when we deal with the structure of materials.

Example 4.3

A circular metal rod 10 mm in diameter has a yield stress of 210 MPa. What tensile force is required to cause yielding?

$$\text{Since stress (s)} = \frac{\text{force}}{\text{area}}$$

we must first calculate the cross-sectional area of the metal rod. Thus the area A is given by:

$$A = \pi r^2 = \pi \times 5^2 = 78.54 \, \text{mm}^2$$

Therefore yield force required = yield stress $\times$ area

$$= 210 \times 106 \times 78.54 \times 10^{-6}$$
$$= 16493 \, \text{N}$$

Young's modulus

Stiffness can be defined as the ability of a material to resist deflection when loaded. For example, a material's resistance to bending is a measure of its stiffness. When a material is subject to external bending forces the less it gives, the stiffer it is. Thus stiffness is related to the stress imposed on the material and the amount of movement or strain caused by this stress. We mentioned earlier the linear relationship between stress and strain on the stress–strain graph. A measure of the stiffness of a material when strained in tension can be obtained from the graph by measuring the slope of the linear part of the graph (see Figure 4.4). This slope (stress)/(strain) is known as the elastic modulus or Young's modulus of elasticity.

$$\text{Modulus of elasticity} = \frac{\text{stress}}{\text{strain}}$$

The modulus of elasticity has units of stress (often quoted as GPa), since strain has no units. The symbol for the elastic modulus is E. Figure 4.4 indicates the relationship between, stress, strain and the elastic modulus.

In addition to the elastic modulus E, when dealing with three-dimensional solids, there are two other moduli which are worthy of mention. The *shear modulus*, G, describes the rigidity of a material subject to shear loading; and the *bulk modulus*, K, describes the effect of a material when subjected to external pressure.

So far a fairly rigorous definition of the strength of a material has been given, as well as a definition of stress, strain and material stiffness. You have already met quite a lot of terms with which you may not be completely familiar. To aid your understanding and to refresh your memory, it is time to try the problems and the activity that follow.

Test your knowledge 4.1

Define as accurately as you can the terms listed below and, for each, give (if appropriate) the units and the normal symbol used to identify them.
  engineering stress
  true stress
  tensile strain
  strength
  ultimate strength
  modulus of elasticity

Test your knowledge 4.2

Explain briefly how the fracture strength and yield stress are related with respect to metals, polymers and ceramics. Clearly defining fracture strength and yield stress, as part of your explanation.

Given that the moduli, E, G and K are related in the following ways:

$$E = \frac{3G}{(1 = G/3K)};$$

$$G = \frac{E}{2(1 + 2\nu)};$$

$$K = \frac{E}{3(1 - 2\nu)}$$

determine the shear modulus and bulk modulus for a steel which has an elastic modulus of 210 GN/m^2 and Poisson's ratio ν is 0.3.

Activity 4.2

The abbreviations for a number of well known polymers and elastomers are given below. Find, from appropriate literature, the full chemical name and write this alongside each abbreviation.

Abbreviation	Full chemical name
LDPE	
PP	
PC	
PMMA	
PTFE	
PF	
UF	
PU	
SBR	
PB	

More mechanical properties

Let us now consider a few more mechanical properties, which are presented here with examples of materials that display these properties.

Ductility, the ability to be drawn into threads or wire. Examples include wrought iron, low carbon steels, copper, brass and titanium.

Brittleness, the tendency to break easily or suddenly with no prior extension. Examples include cast iron, high carbon steels, brittle polymers, concrete, and ceramic materials.

Malleability, the ability to plastically deform and shape a material by forging, rolling or by the application of pressure. Examples include gold, copper and lead.

Elasticity, the ability of a material to deform under load and return to its original shape once the external loads have been removed. Internal atomic binding forces are only stretched not broken and act like minute springs to return the material to normal, once the force has been removed. Examples include rubber, mild steel and some plastics.

Plasticity is the readiness to deform to a stretched state when a load is applied. The *plastic deformation* is *permanent* even after the load has been removed. Plasticine exhibits plastic deformation.

Hardness, the ability to withstand scratching (abrasion) or indentation by another body. It is an indication of the wear resistance of a material. Examples of hard materials include diamond, high carbon steel and other materials which have undergone a hardening process.

Fatigue is a phenomenon by which a material can fail at much lower stress levels than normal when subjected to cyclic loading. Failure is generally initiated from micro-cracks on the surface of the material.

Creep may be defined as the time-dependent deformation of a material under load, accelerated by increase in temperature. It is an important consideration where materials are subjected to high temperatures for sustained periods of time, e.g. gas turbine engine blades.

Toughness, in its simplest form, is defined as the ability of a material to withstand sudden loading. It is measured by the total energy that a material can absorb, that just causes fracture. Toughness (symbol, G) must not be confused with strength which is measured in terms of the stress required to break a standard test piece. Toughness has the units of energy per unit area, i.e., MN/m^2.

Fracture toughness (symbol K_c) measures the resistance of a material to the propagation (growth) of a crack. Fracture toughness for a material is established by loading a sample containing a deliberately introduced crack of length $2c$ (Figure 4.7), recording the tensile stress (σ_c) at which the crack propagates.

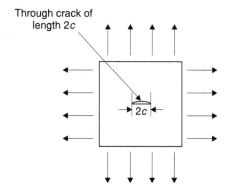

Through crack of
length $2c$

$2c$

Figure 4.7 *Establishment of fracture toughness K_c by loading a sample with a deliberately introduced through-crack of length 2c and recording tensile stress*

The quantity K_c is then calculated from:

$$K_c = Y\sigma_c(\pi c)^{1/2}$$

normal units for K_c being $MPa\,m^{1/2}$ or $MN/m^{3/2}$

The fracture toughness (K_c) is related to the toughness by the relationship:

$$G_c = \frac{K_c^2}{E(1 - \nu^2)}$$

Y is a geometric factor, near unity, which depends on the geometry of the sample under test, ν is known as Poisson's ratio where:

$$\text{Poisson's ratio } (\nu) = \frac{\text{lateral strain}}{\text{axial strain}}$$

of a strained material under load

Note: axial strain is strain along the longitudinal axis of the material.

Physical properties

In the previous section we dealt in some detail with the mechanical properties of materials, it is now time to concentrate on their physical properties, which are subdivided into *electrical* and *magnetic*, *thermal*, *density* and *optical*. With the exception of a brief statement on photoconduction, optical properties will not be considered in this course. We will start by briefly discussing some of the electrical and magnetic properties of materials including *electrical conductivity*, *superconductivity*, *semiconductors*, *magnetization*, and *dielectrics*.

In many applications, the electrical properties of a material are of primary importance. Copper wire is chosen for electrical wiring because of its extremely high electrical conductivity. You may also remember that copper is also a very ductile material and so is easily drawn or extruded into shape. These two properties make copper ideal for electrical wiring.

Conductors are materials having outer electrons that are loosely connected to the nucleus of their atoms and can easily move through the material from one atom to another. *Insulators* are materials whose electrons are held firmly to the nucleus.

For a conducting material the electromotive force (e.m.f.), V, measured in volts, the current, I, measured in amperes, and the resistance, R, measured in ohms, are related by Ohm's law. This states that:

$$V = I R$$

The resistance to current flow in a circuit is proportional to the length, I, and inversely proportional to the cross sectional area, A, of the component. The resistance can be defined as:

$$R = \frac{\rho I}{A} \text{ where } \rho \text{ is the electrical resistivity}$$

or

$$R = \frac{I}{\sigma A} \text{ where } \sigma \text{ is the electrical conductivity}$$

The unit of *resistivity* is the ohm metre (Ωm), and of *conductivity* is the Siemens per metre (S/m). It can be seen that the electrical conductivity is the inverse of the electrical resistivity. Both of these properties, conductivity and resistivity, are inherent in each material. Typical tables of values normally show only the resistivity of a material. Very high values suggest very good resistive characteristics and, conversely very low values indicate good conductivity.

Metals which have many free electrons are very good electrical conductors, their *conductivity* is reduced with increase in temperature. The rate of increase of electrical resistivity is given by the temperature resistivity coefficient. The resistivity for some of the more common materials together with their temperature resistivity coefficients are given in Table 4.1.

Superconductivity – superconducting materials are those where the resistance falls to zero when they are cooled to a critical temperature and any magnetic fields are minimized. At these temperatures the superconducting material offers no resistance to the flow of current

Table 4.1 *Electrical resistivity and temperature resistivity coefficient for some of the more common materials*

Material	Electrical resistivity at 20°C (Ωm)	Temperature resistivity coefficient (10^{-3}/k)
Aluminium	27×10^{-9}	4.2
Brass	69×10^{-9}	1.6
Constantan	490×10^{-9}	0.02
Copper	17×10^{-9}	4.3
Duralumin	50×10^{-9}	2.3
Gold	23×10^{-9}	3.9
Lead	206×10^{-9}	4.3
Mild steel	120×10^{-9}	3.0
Polythene	100×10^{9}	No data found
Rubber	Approx 10×10^{12}	No data found
Silver	16×10^{-9}	4.1
Tungsten	55×10^{-9}	4.6

and so there are no wastages due to heat generation. All pure crystals would act as superconductors at zero Kelvin, the problem of course is to maintain and use them at this temperature!

Serious research into raising the temperature at which selected materials will superconduct, has taken place over the past two decades. By 1986 the critical temperature of a series of ceramic copper oxides had been raised to 77 K. This enabled liquid nitrogen to be used as the cooling medium, rather than liquid helium, the latter being expensive and providing only limited application of these materials. Since this date other compounds based on non rare-earth metal oxides have exhibited temperatures up to about 125 K. There is still a little way to go before we arrive at high temperature superconductors. As superconduction temperatures rise, then more and more industrial applications become feasible. Even today it seems possible that the new materials that are constantly being discovered, could be used to advantage in the electrical power generation industry. Other applications might include the rail transport industry, computing and electronics.

We have already discovered the fact that for metals and most other conductors, the conductivity decreases with increase in temperature. The resistance of insulators remains approximately constant with increase in temperature. *Semiconductors* behave in the opposite way to metals and as the temperature increases the conductivity of a semiconductor increases.

The most important semiconductor materials are *silicon* and *germanium*, both are used commonly in the electronics industry. As the temperature of these materials is raised above room temperature, the resistivity is reduced and ultimately a point is reached where effectly they become conductors. This increase in conductivity with temperature has made semiconductors an essential part of thermistors, where they can be used to sense the temperature and activate a signal when a predetermined temperature is reached. Other uses for semiconductors include, pressure transducers (energy converters), transistors and diodes. The effects of temperature on conductors, insulators and semiconductors is illustrated diagramatically in Figure 4.8. Note that for a specimen of each of these materials it is assumed that they start with the same resistance at say room temperature (20°C). This, of course, implies that each specimen will have completely different physical dimensions (see definition of resistance).

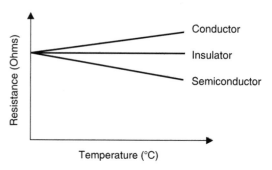

Figure 4.8   *The effect of temperature increase on conductors, insulators and semiconductors*

In order to control the conductivity of semiconductors, small amounts of impurity atoms are introduced and this is called *doping*. If antimony, arsenic or phosphorus are used as a doping agent then an n-type semiconductor is formed, since these doping agents add electrons to the parent semiconductor thus increasing its negative (n) charge. Conversely if gallium, indium or boron are added to the parent material then a p-type semiconductor is formed, with effectively an increased number of absences of electrons or *holes* which act like positive (p) charges.

In *photoconduction* a beam of light can be directed onto a semiconductor positioned in an electrical circuit. This can produce an electric current caused by the increased movement of electrons or holes in the atoms of the semiconductor material. This property is used in photoelectric components such as solar cells where the photo-conductive property of the materials is used to produce power from the rays of light produced by the Sun. Other uses include electronic eyes which trigger the power to open garage doors, or automatic lighting where the photoelectric cell is activated by fading daylight.

Magnetization All substances are magnetized under the effect of a magnet field. A magnet dipole (an atom which has its own minute magnetic field) is formed by the rotation of each electron about its own axis (electron spin) and also its rotation about the nucleus of the atom (Figure 4.9). This induces a magnetic field in the material which is increased in strength when the dipoles are aligned.

Once they are aligned by an external magnetic field, the orientation of the dipoles will dictate what type of magnetism is created within the material being magnetized. Some materials called *paramagnetic*, magnetize with their dipole axis in the direction of the field and others, with their dipole axis perpendicular to the field; these are *diamagnetic* materials. Iron, which shows

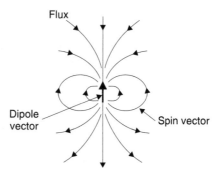

Figure 4.9 *Magnetic dipole moment of an electron which is indicated by direction of arrow*

a very pronounced magnetic effect and retains some residual magnetism when the magnetic field is removed, is *ferromagnetic*. Such materials can be used for permanent magnets.

If a bar of ferromagnetic material is wrapped with a conductor carrying a direct current, the bar will develop a north pole at one end and a south pole at the other (Figure 4.10).

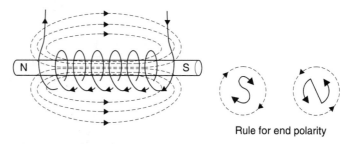

Figure 4.10 *Magnetic flux developed from the current-carrying conductor wrapped around the ferromagnetic material*

The strength of the poles developed depends upon the material used and the magnetizing force. The magnetizing force is the result of the number of turns of conductor per unit length of the bar and the number of turns carried. The magnetic field produced as a result of the current and conductor length is denoted by the symbol H, and is measured in amperes per metre (A/m). The magnetizing force is increased, decreased, or reversed by respectively increasing, decreasing, or reversing the current. The strength of the magnet so produced is called the *magnetic flux density*, which indicates the degree of magnetization that can be obtained. The magnetic flux density is denoted by the symbol B, and is measured in tesla (T); it is related to the applied field H, by:

$$B = \mu H$$

where μ is the magnetic *permeability* and is measured in henry/metre (H/m). The ratio of this magnetic permeability (μ) to the permeability of free space (μ_0) measured in a vacuum, gives an indication of the degree of magnification of the magnetic field and is known as the relative permeability (μ_r).

Magnetization and demagnetization of magnetic materials results in producing a variable magnetic flux density, B, as a result of the magnet field strength, H. A plot of B versus H results in a diagram known as a *hysterisis loop* (Figure 4.11). The area (shown shaded) represents irreversibly lost electromagnetic energy which is converted to heat.

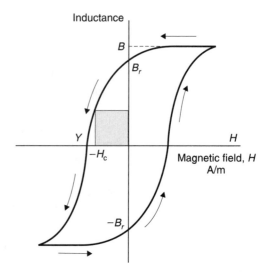

Figure 4.11 *Typical hysteresis curve for a ferromagnetic material. The shaded area indicates the lost electromagnetic energy dissipated as heat*

Soft magnetic materials (temporary magnets) have a relatively small loop, because they are easily magnetized and demagnetized and so little heat is generated during the process. Hard magnetic (permanent magnets) have a large loop, due to the fact that they find difficulty in dissipating their residual magnetism. Thus *remanence* (or residual magnetism, B_r) and the *coercive force*, H_c, necessary to eliminate remanence are large in permanent magnets (Figure 4.12).

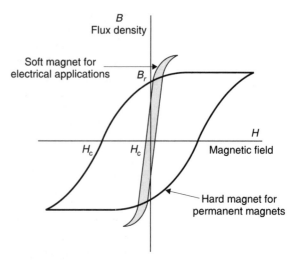

Figure 4.12 *Typical hysteresis curves for magnetically hard and soft materials*

Temporary magnets are soft iron or ferrous alloys; permanent magnets are hard steels, hard alloys, or metal oxides. Temporary magnets are used for alternating current applications such as a.c. motors, electromagnets and transformers.

A *dielectric* is an insulating medium seperating charged surfaces. The most generally useful electric property of nonmetals is their high electrical resistance. Probably, the most common applications of ceramics, apart from their structural uses, depend upon their insulating properties. Breakdown of electrical insulators occurs either along the surface or through the body of the insulator. Surface breakdown is promoted by moisture and other surface contaminants. Water absorption can be minimized by applying a glaze to the surface of a ceramic.

Volume breakdown occurs at voltages high enough to accelerate individual free electrons to energies that will break the bonds holding the atoms of the material together, this causes a large number of electrons to break free at once and become charge carriers. The dielectric strength is the breakdown voltage for volume breakdown, it is measured in units of volts/m. The dielectric constant is the constant of proportionality between the charge stored between two plates of a capacitor separated by a dielectric, when compared with the charge stored when the plates are separated by a vacuum.

The ratio of the charge density, σ, to the electric field strength, E, is called absolute permittivity, ε, of a dielectric. It is measured in farads/metre, F/m. The permittivity of free space measured in a vacuum is a constant, given by:

$$\varepsilon_0 = 8.55 \times 10^{-12}\,\text{F/m}$$

Relative permittivity is a ratio given by:

$$\varepsilon_r = \frac{\text{flux density of the field in the dielectric}}{\text{flux density of the field in a vacuum}}$$

Let us now continue with our discussion on the physical properties of materials by considering their *density*.

The *density*, ρ, of a substance is its mass per unit volume. The basic SI units of mass and volume are, respectively, the kilogram and the metre cubed, so the basic units of density are kilogram per cubic metre (kg/m^3).

The *specific weight*, w, of a substance is its weight per unit volume. Since the weight of a substance is mass multiplied by acceleration due to gravity, g, the relationship between specific weight and density is:

$$\text{specific weight} = \text{density} \times g$$

$$w = \rho g$$

Density is a property of the material which may be subject to small changes by mixing one material with another. Significant changes in density are only accomplished with composite materials where large percentages of each material can be altered. The density of a composite can be calculated from the proportions of the constituent materials. For example, consider a composite which consists by volume of 60% epoxy resin matrix material to which is added 40% by volume carbon fibre. If we assume that the carbon fibre has a

Test your knowledge 4.4

What properties must dielectric materials used in the construction of capacitors possess? Name three materials that possess these properties.

Test your knowledge 4.5

Using the appropriate formula and Table 4.1, determine the resistance of a 50 m length of copper cable having a cross-sectional area of 1.5 mm².

density of 1500 kg/m³ and the epoxy resin has a density of 1100 kg/m³. Then the density of the composite is given by:

$$\rho_c = 0.6\rho_m + 0.4\rho_f = (0.6 \times 1800) + (0.4 \times 1400)$$
$$= 1640 \text{ kg/m}^3$$

where ρ_c = density of the composite, ρ_m = density of the matrix material and ρ_f = the density of the reinforcing carbon fibre.

The above equation is often referred to as an *equation of mixtures*, it has many uses particularly in the study of composite materials.

Activity 4.3

A small engineering company, Thames Magnetic Components, has commissioned you to carry out some research into materials suitable for use in the cores of a new range of large industrial transformers that they intend to manufacture. They have asked you to summarize the essential electromagnetic properties of a suitable core material and explain how these properties differ from those used in the range of permanent magnets that make up their current product range. Write a briefing paper for the Technical Director, present your report in word processed form and include relevant diagrams and technical specifications.

Activity 4.4

An aerospace company, Archer Avionics, are about to manufacture a electronic control system that will be fitted to the propulsion unit of a deep space probe. This device is expected to be subject to extreme variations in temperature (e.g. from −50° to +150°C). Prepare a presentation (using appropriate visual aids) for the Board of Directors of Archer Avionics, explaining the effect of such a wide variation in temperature on the behaviour of the conductors, insulators and semiconductors that will make up the electronic system. Your presentation should last no more than 10 minutes and should include relevant graphs and material specifications. You should allow a further 5 minutes for questions.

Thermal properties

Let us now turn our attention to the *thermal properties* of materials. The way heat is transferred and absorbed by materials is of prime importance to the designer. For instance the walls of a house need to be constructed from materials which retain heat in winter and yet prevent the house from overheating in the summer. In a domestic refrigerator, the aim is to prevent the contents from absorbing heat. The thermal expansion of materials and their ability to withstand extremes of temperature are other characterisitics that must be understood.

We therefore require knowledge of the most important thermal properties of materials, *specific heat capacity*, *thermal conductivity* and *thermal expansion*, as well as information on freezing, boiling and melting temperatures.

The specific heat capacity of a material is the quantity of heat energy required to raise the temperature of 1 kg of the material by one degree. The symbol used for specific heat capacity is *c* and the units are (J/kg°C) or (J/kgK). If we just consider the units of specific heat capacity we can express it in words as:

$$\text{specific heat capacity} = \frac{\text{heat energy supplied}}{\text{mass} \times \text{temperature rise}}$$

Some typical values for specific heat capacity are given in Table 4.2.

Table 4.2 *Typical values for specific heat capacity for some common materials*

Material	Specific heat capacity (c) at 0°C (J/kg K)
Aluminium	880
Copper	380
Brass (65% Cu–35% Zn)	370
Iron	437
Lead	126
Mild steel	450
Silver	232
Tin	140
Brick	800
Concrete	1100
Polystyrene	1300
Porcelain	1100
Rubber	900

Thermal expansion takes place when heat is applied to a material and the energy of the atoms within the material increases, which causes them to vibrate more vigorously and so increase the volume of the material. Conversely, if heat energy is removed from a material contraction occurs in all directions.

The amount by which unit length of a material expands when the temperature is raised by one degree is called the *coefficient of linear expansion* of the material and is represented by the Greek letter (α) alpha. The units of the coefficient of linear expansion are usually quoted as just /K or K^{-1}.

Typical values for the coefficient of linear expansion of some materials are given in Table 4.3.

We can use the value of the coefficient of linear expansion of materials to determine changes in their length, as the temperature

Table 4.3 *Typical values for coefficient of linear thermal expansion for some common materials*

Material	Coefficient of linear thermal expansion (α) (10^{-6}/K)
Aluminium	23
Copper	16.7
Brass (65% Cu–35% Zn)	18.5
Invar	1
Iron	12
Lead	29
Magnesium	25
Mild steel	11
Silver	19
Tin	6
Brick	3–9
Concrete	11
Graphite	2
Polyethylene	300
Polyurethane foam	90
Polystyrene	60–80
Porcelain	2.2
PVC (plasticized)	50–250
Pyrex glass	3
Rubber	670

rises or falls. If a material, has initial length I_1 at a temperature t_1 and has a coefficient of linear expansion α, then if the temperature is increased to t_2, the new length l_2 of the material is given by:

new length = original length + expansion, i.e.,

$$I_2 = I_1 + I_1\alpha(t_2 - t_1)$$

or since $t_2 - t_1$ is often expressed as Δt (change in temperature) we have new length $I_2 = I_1 + I_1\alpha\Delta t$

Example 4.4

In a domestic central heating system a 6 m length of copper pipe contains water at 8°C when the system is off, the temperature of the water in the pipe rises to 65°C when the system is in use. Calculate the linear expansion of the copper pipe.

From Table 4.3 we see that the coefficient of linear expansion for copper is 16.7×10^{-6}K, then using:

linear expansion of pipe = $I_1\alpha\Delta t = 6 \times 16.7 \times 10^{-6} \times (65 - 8)$

= 0.0057 m

we see that the pipe expands by 5.7 mm over the 6 m length.

Thermal conductivity

Conduction is the transfer of energy from faster more energetic molecules to slower adjacent molecules, by direct contact. The ability of a material to conduct heat is measured by its *thermal conductivity, k*. The units of thermal conductivity are watts per metre Kelvin (W/m K or $Wm^{-1}K^{-1}$). Typical values for some common materials are shown in Table 4.4.

Table 4.4 *Typical values for thermal conductivity for some common materials*

Material	Thermal conductivity (k) at 0°C (W/m K)
Aluminium	235
Copper	283
Brass (65% Cu–35% Zn)	120
Invar	11
Iron	76
Lead	35
Magnesium	150
Mild steel	55
Silver	418
Tin	60
Brick	0.4–0.8
Concrete	10.1
Graphite	150
Polyethylene	0.3
Polyurethane foam	0.05
Polystyrene	0.08–0.2
Porcelain	0.8–1.85
PVC (platicized)	0.16–0.19
Pyrex glass	1.2
Rubber	0.15

A metal when left in a cold envronment quickly feels cold to the touch and when brought into contact with heat quickly feels hot to the touch. Generally *metals* are *good conductors* of heat. Often if a material is a good thermal conductor, it is also a good electrical conductor, silver, copper and aluminium are all good conductors of both heat and electricity. Table 4.4 shows the low values of thermal conductivity for brick, porcelain, PVC and rubber, these are all good *insulators*. Air is also an excellent insulator, double glazing requires an airgap between the external and internal panes of glass, this provides good insulation from the cold and also helps prevent condensation forming between the panes. Expanded foams also use the properties of air to provide good insulation, foam cavity wall insulation for example.

Corrosion and the deterioration of materials in service

Corrosion may be defined as a chemical process, where metals are converted back to the oxides, salts and other compounds from which they were first formed. The corrosion of metals is therefore a natural process and in trying to combat it, we are wrestling with the forces of nature! The chemical stability of materials (in particular metals) has long been the subject of much research, since the consequences of premature failure of materials by corrosive influences can be disastrous.

Corrosive attack frequently occurs in combination with other mechanisms of failure, such as corrosion-fatigue, erosion and stress corrosion. Many environmental factors help to promote corrosion including moist air and industrial pollutants such as dirt, acids, dirty water and salts. Corrosion may occur at elevated temperatures in materials that at lower temperatures are inert.

Corrosion then is the chemical means by which metallic materials deteriorate and fail. Two basic mechanisms have been recognized: *direct chemical attack* and *electrochemical attack.*

Direct chemical attack results in a uniform reaction over the entire exposed surface. Usually, a scale or deposit of uniform thickness is produced on the metallic material. This deposit may adhere (stick) to the surface or remain as loose flakes, the rusting of an iron bar left in the open is an example of the latter. An example of a material that is subject to direct chemical attack, where the products of corrosion (the corrosive oxides) adhere strongly to the surface of the metal, is aluminium. When this happens the oxide layer formed protects the metal underneath from further attack by adhering firmly to it. This process is known as *passivation* and we say that aluminium is a *passive* metal.

Electrochemical attack is characterized by the establishment of an electrochemical cell, this is formed when two metals in electrical contact are placed in a conducting liquid, the *electrolyte*. The cell permits electroplating or corrosion, depending on the source of electrical potential.

In *electroplating* the electrochemical cell, consists of two electrodes (which may or may not be of the same material), the electrolyte and an *external* electric source such as a battery. It is found that an oxidation reaction takes place at electrode A (Figure 4.13).

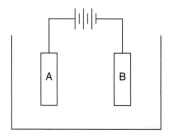

Figure 4.13 *In electroplating (external energy source) it is found that an oxidation reaction takes place at electrode A*

An *oxidation reaction increases the energy of the atom.* In this case by forming an *ion* (an atom with an absence or excess of electrons) and a free electron. This may be represented by using a simple chemical equation:

$$M \rightarrow M^+ + e^-$$

What we are saying is that the metal (M) has been subject to an oxidation reaction and forms a metal ion (M^+), in this case an atom that has lost *one* electron (e^-). The electrode, at which an oxidation reaction takes place is defined as the *anode*. Note that, *corrosion always takes place at the anode.* Then at electrode (A), the ions go into the electrolyte and the electrons go into the external circuit. At electrode (B) a *reduction reaction* takes place. In this case, the ions in the electrolyte combine with electrons from the external circuit and form atoms which are deposited on the electrode. This can again be illustrated using a chemical formula, i.e.

$$M^+ + e^- \rightarrow M$$

The electrode, at which the reduction reaction takes place is known as the *cathode*.

For electroplating, the battery provides the electrical potential to move the electrons, giving rise to an electric current in the external circuit. In practice, corrosion occurs in the absence of a battery. This can be demonstrated by a *galvanic cell*. A galvanic cell may be formed by two dissimilar metals in electrical contact immersed in an electrolyte, with no battery. Figure 4.14 shows a typical arrangement for a zinc–copper galvanic cell. The chemical symbol for zinc is (Zn) and for copper (Cu).

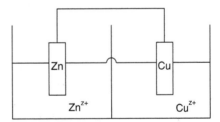

Figure 4.14 *In the copper–zinc galvanic cell an oxidation reaction takes place at the zinc electrode and it preferentially corrodes*

It is found that an oxidation reaction takes place at the Zn electrode. This electrode is thus the anode and it corrodes, i.e.

$$Zn \rightarrow Zn^{2+} + 2e^-$$

At the copper electrode, the cathode, a reduction reaction occurs, i.e.

$$Cu^{2+} + 2e^- \rightarrow Cu$$

The electrons in the external circuit flow between the two electrodes and so there must be an electrical potential difference between them.

Electroplating rarely occurs during electrochemical corrosion. The reduction reaction tends to form either a gas, liquid or solid by-product at the cathode.

A cathodic reaction is a reduction reaction, some possible cathodic reactions are given below.

1 Electroplating $M^+ + e^- \rightarrow M$

2 The hydrogen electrode – here hydrogen gas is liberated at the cathode:

$$2H^+ + 2e^- \rightarrow H_2$$

3 Water decomposition – here water is being broken down by the addition of electrons from the external circuit, to form hydrogen gas and hydroxyl (hydrogen-oxygen) ions

$$2H_2O + 2e^- \rightarrow H_2 + 2(OH)^-$$

Note that *chemical equations balance*. Taking the above equation, for example, two molecules of water plus two electrons form two atoms of hydrogen, diatomically bonded (H_2) and two hydroxyl ions.

4 The oxygen electrode – here oxygen combines with water and the external electrons to form hydroxyl ions:

$$O_2 + 2H_2O + 4e^- \rightarrow 4(OH)^-$$

5 The water electrode – in this case water is formed as a product.

$$O_2 + 4H^+ + 4e^- \rightarrow 2H_2O$$

When hydroxyl ions (OH^-) form as a result of a reaction, they can combine with other available ions to form a solid or sediment, e.g. $Fe(OH)_3$ which is rust.

Note that in all chemical equations the constituents that combine to make up the product, *the reactants*, are always placed at the tail of the arrow, the arrow indicates the direction of the reaction and *the products* (the result of the chemical reaction) are always placed after the head of the arrow.

If the zinc electrode, in the zinc–copper cell, is immersed in a 1 molar* electrolyte and the copper electrode (both at 25°C) is immersed in a 1 molar electrolyte, then a potential difference between the electrodes of 1.1 V occurs. The zinc electrode is at a lower potential than the copper electrode and so electrons flow, via the external circuit, from the zinc to the copper electrode.

The electrode potential of a metal is related to its ability to produce free electrons. As with all potential difference measurements, it is necessary to have a reference. In this case the PD of a metal is measured with respect to the *hydrogen half-cell*, i.e. zero potential is assigned to the oxidation reaction:

$$H_2 \rightarrow 2H^+ + 2e^-$$

The hydrogen half-cell consists of a platinum electrode immersed in a 1 molar solution of hydrogen ions through which hydrogen gas is bubbled. The other half of the galvanic cell consists of a metal electrode immersed in a 1 molar solution of its own ions. Both half cells are at 25°C. For example, if zinc is compared with the hydrogen

---

* A one molar solution of electrolyte is a special measure of the strength of the electrolyte, which is easily reproducible, where the electrolyte contains 1 g atomic mass of zinc ions, i.e. 6×10^{23} ions.

half-cell under the conditions mentioned above, its potential difference is -0.76 V. This implies that the electrons flow via the theoretical circuit, from the zinc electrode to the hydrogen electrode. Zinc is the anode and corrodes, the hydrogen electrode is the cathode.

In the case of silver (Ag), the potential difference, or electrode potential is found to be $+0.8$ V. Thus silver becomes the cathode and corrosion does not occur. The electrode potential of metals have all been measured in this way and a table of values produced. This table is known as the *electrochemical* or *redox series*. Some of the more common metals are listed in Table 4.5 below.

Table 4.5 *The electrochemical (redox) series for some elements*

Element	Potential E (V)
Lithium	−3.05
Potassium	−2.93
Caesium	−2.92
Calcium	−2.87
Sodium	−2.71
Magnesium	−2.37
Aluminium	−1.66
Titanium	−1.63
Zinc	−0.76
Chromium	−0.74
Iron	−0.44
Cadmium	−0.40
Nickel	−0.25
Tin	−0.14
Lead	−0.13
Hydrogen	0.00
Copper	+0.34
Silver	+0.80
Palladium	+0.99
Platinum	+1.20
Gold	+1.50
Cobolt	1.82

The standard conditions under which the electrode potential is measured are, 25°C and electrolytes of 1 molar solution.

Galvanic cells are classified into three groups; *composition cells*, *stress cells* and *concentration cells*.

Composition cells consist of two dissimilar metals in contact. The metal having the lower electrode potential becomes the anode and will corrode. Examples include galvanized steel (often used for manufacturing buckets) and tinplate. Galvanized steel consists of zinc coated mild steel sheet. Since zinc has a lower potential (-0.76 V) than the steel (Fe, -0.44 V), zinc becomes the anode which corrodes and so protects the mild steel. In the case of tinplate, which is a coating of tin (Sn, -0.14 V) on mild steel (Fe, -0.44 V), then iron becomes the anode which corrodes. The layer of tin provides a barrier to the corrosion, but if damaged, corrosion occurs. This is why damaged tin cans are removed from the shelves of shops, because corrosion of the underlying steel can contaminate the contents of the can.

Stress cells are formed where differences in stress within a material give rise to differences in electrode potential. For example regions within a component having different amounts of cold work during its forming process. The regions of strain hardening have a greater energy than annealed material and so become anodic and corrode. Thus stressed components are more likely to corrode than unstressed. More will be said about this when we look at the structure and cold working of materials.

An example where this may be a problem is with crimped metal joints, if the material is not given an appropriate heat-treatment after crimping, then high stress areas are created at the joints which will preferentially corrode.

Concentration cells arise due to differences of the ion concentrate in the electrolyte. The concentration cell accentuates corrosion, but it accentuates it where the concentration of the electrolyte is least. This relationship which occurs in practice can be proved theoretically.

In an oxidation type concentration cell, when the oxygen has access to a moist surface, a cathodic reaction can occur, such as:

$$2H_2O + O_2 + 4e^- \rightarrow 4(OH)^-$$

Thus regions where oxygen concentration is less become anodic and corrosion occurs (see Figure 4.15).

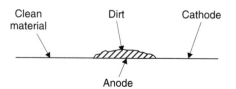

Figure 4.15 *Where the oxygen concentration is least becomes the anode*

An example of this behaviour may occur on a car's bodywork, if a small amount of dirt is left on the bodywork where the surface may have been damaged, the area under the dirt will corrode. The oxygen in this area has been excluded, i.e. it is least when compared to the clean surface adjacent to the dirty area. This is one of the reasons why we try to keep motor vehicles clean!

We have discussed the mechanisms of electrochemical corrosion, so how as engineers, may we prevent it? There are in fact four major ways in which to prevent, or at least help reduce, the effects of corrosion. By protective coatings, cathodic protection, design and materials selection.

Protective coatings, form a barrier layer between the metal and the electrolyte. They must be non-porous and non-conductive. There are many types of coating suitable for this purpose. *Organic coatings* such as polymeric paints, *ceramic coatings* like enamels (these are brittle so care must be taken to avoid damage), *metal coatings* like tinplate and *chemically deposited coatings* such as the formation of a phosphate layer. Phosphating tends to be porous, but forms a keying layer for subsequent metal deposition or paint.

There is also the naturally occurring *protective oxide layer* that is formed by *passive metals*, which provides an excellent barrier against further corrosion. Aluminium, stainless steel, titanium and nickel are all examples of passive metals.

Cathodic protection is the mechanism whereby the anode is made to act as the cathode. It is achieved by use of either a sacrificial anode or an impressed d.c. voltage.

The sacrificial anode is a metal that when connected in the form of a galvanic cell to the component being protected, forms the anode (Figure 4.16). Examples of galvanized steel where zinc is the sacrificial anode are magnesium or zinc plates attached to ships hulls, and buried pipes.

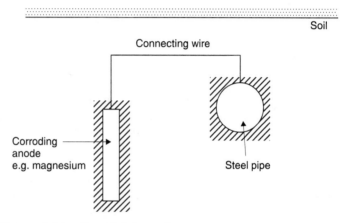

Figure 4.16 *Sacrificial anode*

For the impressed voltage (Figure 4.17), a d.c. source is connected to the metal to be protected and an auxilliary electrode, such that the electrons flow to the metal which then becomes the cathode. The auxiliary electrode has to be replaced from time to time.

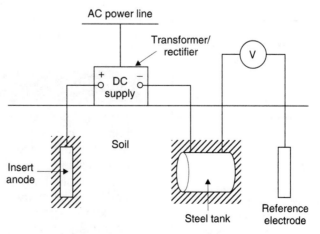

Figure 4.17 *Typical layout for impressed voltage corrosion protection*

There are numerous ways in which the designer can help prevent corrosion. If at all possible avoid the formation of galvanic cells, if dissimilar metals are to be brought into contact, electrically insulate them. Try to ensure that ingress of moisture is avoided.

Make the anodic area much larger than the cathodic area if possible, for example, use copper rivets to fasten steel sheet, not the other way round. When installing fluid systems, try to ensure that system components and plumbing is enclosed to avoid oxygen pick-up. Avoid areas of stagnant liquid. Finally, avoid pipework or components being internally stressed, remember these areas of high stress are more energetic and therefore become anodic and subsequently corrode.

Corrosion can also be minimized by materials selection and appropriate heat treatment, particularly in steels. More will be said later, on the subject in the element concerned with materials selection.

Finally in our discussion on corrosion, a number of the more commonly encountered forms of corrosion are detailed below:

Pitting is a localized form of corrossion resulting in small holes that may completely penetrate some members. It is encountered in aluminium and its alloys, copper and its alloys, stainless steel and high-nickel alloys. Pitting is an electrochemical form of attack involving either galvanic or concentration cells, and sometimes both types of cell.

Intergranular corrosion, a form of galvanic attack, occurs when grain boundaries (see structure of materials) of a metal are selectively corroded. It is the result of composition differences between the grain boundary and the grains themselves.

High-temperature corrosion is accelerated by alternate heating and cooling because brittle protective scales expand and contract at different rates compared to the base metals supporting them. This causes flaking to occur exposing fresh metal to attack.

Stress-corrosion is likely to occur when surface tensile stresses act in combination with a corrosive medium. Failure is believed to start at the high energy grain boundaries, which are anodic when compared to the grains themselves.

Test your knowledge 4.6

Explain the terms concentration cell, composition cell and stress cell, with respect to galvanic corrosion. As part of your explanation give examples where each type of cell may cause corrosion.

Test your knowledge 4.7

Zinc and copper form the electrodes of a galvanic cell.
(a) Which material is the anode and which is the cathode?
(b) Which material will corrode?
(c) Which way will the electrons flow around the external circuit?

Test your knowledge 4.8

Explain the difference between direct chemical attack and electrochemical attack, with respect to corrosion.

Test your knowledge 4.9

Under what conditions are the half-cell reactions of metals measured in order to produce the electrochemical series?

Activity 4.5

A material supplier, Beta Metals, has asked you to assist them in the production of some data sheets on corrosion protection that will be incorporated into the next edition of their catalogue. Identify four principal methods that can be used to protect against corrosion and, for each method, produce a summary that can be used to form the basis of the data sheets required by Beta Metals. Include relevant diagrams and sketches and make sure that your text is suitable for the non-technical reader.

Corrosion-fatigue is caused by the action of a corrosive medium combined with variable cyclic stresses. In this type of failure, a corrosive agent attacks the metal surface, where imperfections produce stress raisers that start a fatigue failure.

This study on the mechanisms and prevention of corrosion, brings to an end our discussion on material properties. We will now look at the structure of materials at the macroscopic (molecular) level and see how this affects their properties.

Structure of materials

The chemical composition and the types of bond that hold atoms and molecules together are the major underlying characteristics that determine the properties of materials described in the previous section. We start therefore, by considering these bonding mechanisms. Then we study the structure of metals and alloys and the ways in which they behave under stress. Next we look at polymers and their various subdivisions, finishing with a discussion on composite materials.

Bonding

As mentioned previously, the way in which atoms join together, or molecules join together, is called *bonding*. In order to fully understand the mechanisms of bonding you will need to be aware of one or two important facts about the atom and the relationship between the type of bond and the *periodic table*.

You may well be aware of the fact that the nucleus of the atom consists of an association of protons and neutrons and that the protons carry a positive charge. Surrounding the nucleus in a series of discreet energy bands, electrons (negative charge) orbit the nucleus. Electrons in the energy bands or shells closest to the nucleus are held tightly by electrostatic attraction. In the outermost shells they are held less tightly to the nucleus.

The *valence* of an atom is related to the ability of the atom to enter into chemical combination with other elements, this is often determined by the number of electrons in the outer most levels, where the binding energy is least. These valence shells are often known as *s* or *p* shells and the letters refer to the shell to which the electrons belong.

So, for example, magnesium which has twelve electrons, aluminium which has thirteen electrons and germanium which has 32 electrons, can be represented as follows:

$$\text{Mg;} \quad 1s^2\ 2s^2\ 2p^6\ \underline{3s^2} \qquad\qquad \text{valence} = 2$$

$$\text{Al;} \quad 1s^2\ 2s^2\ 2p^6\ \underline{3s^2}\ \underline{3p^1} \qquad\qquad \text{valence} = 3$$

$$\text{Ge;} \quad 1s^2\ 2s^2\ 2p^6\ 3s^2\ 3p^6\ 3d^{10}\ \underline{4s^2}\ \underline{4p^2} \qquad \text{valence} = 4$$

The numbers 1s, 2s, 2p, etc., relate to the shell level, the superscript numbers relate to the number of electrons in that shell. Remember the total number of *s* and *p* electrons in the outermost shell (those underlined) often accounts for the valence number. There is an exception to the above rule, the valence may also depend on the nature of the chemical reaction.

If an atom has a valence of zero, no electrons enter into chemical reactions and are all examples of inert elements.

You may be wondering where all this talk about valency is leading us. By studying Table 4.6 (the Periodic Table) you will hopefully be able to see!

The *rows* in the periodic table correspond to the principal energy shells that contain the electrons. The *columns* refer to the number of electrons present in the outermost sp energy level and so correspond to the most common valence. Normally the elements in each column have similar properties and behaviour.

The transition elements are so named because some of their inner shells are being filled progressively as you move from left to right in the table. For instance scandium requires nine electrons to completely fill its 3d shell, while at the other end copper has a filled 3d shell which helps to keep the valence electrons tightly held to the inner core, copper as well as silver and gold are consequently very stable and unreactive. Notice that copper, silver and gold all sit in the same column, so they all have similar properties.

Table 4.6 *Periodic table of the elements*

		s-block															p-block					
Period \ Group	I	II													III	IV	V	VI	VIII	0
1	1 H																			2 He
2	3 Li	4 Be			Transition elements										5 B	6 C	7 N	8 O	9 F	10 Ne
3	11 Na	12 Mg			d-block										13 Al	14 Si	15 P	16 S	17 Cl	18 Ar
4	19 K	20 Ca	21 Sc	22 Ti	23 V	24 Cr	25 Mn	26 Fe	27 Co	28 Ni	29 Cu	30 Zn			31 Ga	32 Ge	33 As	34 Se	35 Br	36 Kr
5	37 Rb	38 Sr	39 Y	40 Zr	41 Nb	42 Mo	43 Tc	44 Ru	45 Rh	46 Pd	47 Ag	48 Cd			49 In	50 Sn	51 Sb	52 Te	53 I	54 Xe
6	55 Cs	56 Ba	57* La	72 Hf	73 Ta	74 W	75 Re	76 Os	77 Ir	78 Pt	79 Au	80 Hg			81 Tl	82 Pb	83 Bi	84 Po	85 At	86 Ru
7	87 Fr	88 Ra	89† Ac	104 –	105 –	106 –														

					f-block											
*Lanthanoids	58 Ce	59 Pr	60 Nd	61 Pm	62 Sm	63 Eu	64 Gd	65 Tb	66 Dy	67 Ho	68 Er	69 Tm	70 Yb	71 Lu		
†Actinoids	90 Th	91 Pa	92 U	93 Np	94 Pu	95 Am	96 Cm	97 Bk	98 Cf	99 Es	100 Fm	101 Md	102 No	103 Lw		

In columns I and II the elements have completed inner shells and, one or two valence electrons. In column III, for example, aluminium has three valence electrons and in column VII chlorine has seven valence electrons. The important point to note is that *it is the number of valence electrons in the outermost shells that determines the reactivity of the element* and therefore the way in which that element will combine with others, i.e. the *type of bond* it will form.

All atoms within the elements try to return or sit in their lowest energy levels, this is achieved if they can obtain the *noble gas configuration*, where their outermost *sp* shells are full or empty and they have no spare electrons to combine with other elements. When atoms bond together they try to achieve this noble gas configuration, as you will see next.

Let us now turn our attention to the ways in which atoms combine or bond together. There are essentially three types of primary bond, *ionic*, *covalent*, and *metallic* as well as secondary bonds such as, *van der Waals*.

When more than one type of atom is present in a material, one atom may donate its valence electrons to a different atom, filling the outer energy shell of the second atom. Both atoms now have full or empty outer energy levels but in the process, both have acquired an electrical charge and behave like ions. These oppositely charged ions are then attracted to one another and produce an *ionic bond*. The ionic bond is also sometimes referred to as the *electrovalent bond*. The combination of a sodium atom with that of a chlorine atom illustrates the ionic bonding process very well, and is shown in Figure 4.18.

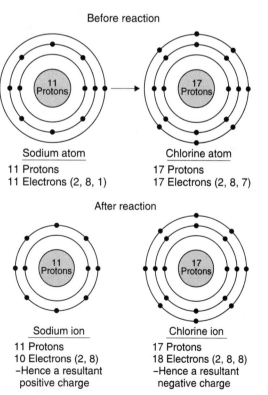

Before reaction

Sodium atom
11 Protons
11 Electrons (2, 8, 1)

Chlorine atom
17 Protons
17 Electrons (2, 8, 7)

After reaction

Sodium ion
11 Protons
10 Electrons (2, 8)
–Hence a resultant
positive charge

Chlorine ion
17 Protons
18 Electrons (2, 8, 8)
–Hence a resultant
negative charge

Figure 4.18 *Illustration of the ionic bonding process between a sodium and chlorine atom*

Note that in the *transfer* of the electron from the sodium atom to the chlorine atom, both the sodium and chlorine ions now have a noble gas configuration, where in the case of sodium the outer valence shell is empty while for chlorine it is full. These two ions in combination, are sitting in their lowest energy level and so readily combine. In this classic example of ionic bonding, the metal sodium has combined with the poisonous gas chlorine to form the sodium chloride molecule, common salt!

In *covalently bonded* materials electrons are *shared* among two or more atoms. This sharing between atoms is arranged in such a way that each atom has its outer *sp* shell filled, so that by forming the molecule each atom sits in its lowest energy level having a noble gas configuration. The covalent bonding of silicon and oxygen to form silica (SiO_2 silicon dioxide) is shown in Figure 4.19.

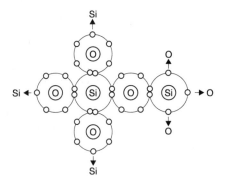

Figure 4.19 *Covalent bond formed between silicon and oxygen atoms*

The metallic elements which have low valence, give up their valence electrons readily to form a sea of electrons which surround the nucleus of the atoms. Thus in giving up their electrons the metallic elements form positive ions which are held together by mutual attraction of the surrounding electrons, producing the strong metallic bond. Figure 4.20 illustrates the *metallic* bond.

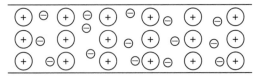

Figure 4.20 *Illustration of the metallic bond*

Van der Waals bonds join molecules or groups of atoms by weak electrostatic attraction. Many polymers, ceramics, water and other molecules tend to form electrical dipoles, that is, some portions of the molecules are positively charged while other portions are negatively charged. The electrostatic attraction between these oppositely charged regions weakly bond the two regions together (Figure 4.21).

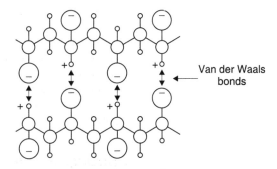

Figure 4.21 *Van der Waals bonds which join molecules or groups of atoms by weak electrostatic attraction*

Van der Waals bonds are *secondary bonds*, but the atoms within the molecules or groups of molecules are held together by strong covalent or ionic bonds. For example when water is boiled the secondary Van der Waals bonds which hold the molecules of water together are broken. Much higher temperatures are then required to break the covalent bonds which combine the oxygen and hydrogen atoms. The ductility of polyvinylchloride (PVC) is attributed to the weak Van der Waals bonds which hold the long chain molecules together. These are easily broken allowing these large molecules to slide over one another.

In many materials bonding between atoms is a mixture of two or more types. Iron for example, is formed from a combination of metallic and covalent bonds. Two or more metals may form a metallic compound, by a mixture of metallic and ionic bonds. Many ceramic and semiconducting compounds which are a combination of metallic and non-metallic elements, have mixtures of covalent and ionic bonds. The energy necessary to break a bond, the binding energy for the bonding mechanisms we have discussed, are shown in Table 4.7.

Table 4.7 *Values of the binding energy for primary and secondary bonds*

Bond	Binding energy (kJ/mol)
Ionic	625–1550
Covalent	520–1250
Metallic	100–800
Van der Waals	<40

The *electronic structure* of an atom may be characterized by the energy levels to which each electron is assigned, in particular to the *valency* of each element. The periodic table of the elements is constructed based on this electronic structure.

The electronic structure plays an important role in determining the bonding between atoms, allowing us to assign general properties to each class of material. Thus metals have good ductility and electrical and thermal conductivity because of the metallic bond. Ceramics, semiconductors and many polymers are brittle and have poor conductivity because of their covalent and ionic bonds. While Van der Waals bonds are responsible for good ductility in certain polymers.

Structure of metals

We have already discussed how metals are formed from their atoms, by metallic bonding. The forces binding the atoms in a metal are non-directional, and since in a pure metal all atoms are of the same kind and therefore are the same size, they will arrange themselves in patterns to give the lowest potential energy. The patterns formed in this process are known as *crystals* or *grains* and the basic building block which replicates itself to form these crystals is known as the *unit lattice* or *unit cell*. Most metals of engineering importance form crystals by using one of three principal types of lattice structure. These are known as *body-centred cubic* (BCC), *face-centred cubic* (FCC) and *close packed hexagonal* (CPH).

The BCC lattice (Figure 4.22) packs the atoms together more loosely than in either the FCC or CPH systems. Since *plastic deformation* in metals is caused by atoms *slipping* over one another. Then the number of ways in which a structure allows this slip to occur, can help determine the degree of ductility of the metal.

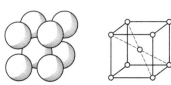

Figure 4.22   *Body-centred cubic cubic unit cell*

The BCC structure has *few planes* over which slip occurs, when compared to either FCC or CPH structures. So metals with this type of structure tend to be less ductile, when compared with the others. This is shown to be true in practice since relatively brittle metals such as chromium, tungsten, molybdenum and vanadium all have a BCC structure.

In contrast metals having the FCC structure (Figure 4.23), where there are more opportunities for slip to occur, are relatively easily deformed and most metals with this structure display good ductility. Copper, gold, silver, alumnium and lead are all good examples of ductile metals with an FCC structure.

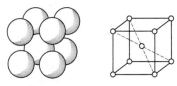

Figure 4.23   *Face-centred cubic unit cell*

Although the CPH structure (Figure 4.24) has a similar number of slip planes to FCC structures, due to the way in which the atoms are packed, relatively few of these planes actually promote slip (plastic deformation). So unexpectedly these metals display far less ductilty than metal formed from the FCC lattice structure. Examples include beryllium, zinc and cadmium.

Figure 4.24   *Close packed hexagon unit cell*

Most metal products, involve, at some stage, melting the metal and casting it into moulds where it solidifies. The process of solidification favours the growth of many crystals (grains), each growing and interlocking as the moulten metal cools and solidifies. The nucleation of these grains is thought to start from specks of dust or other minute impurities in the melt. The growth of an individual crystal (grain) is halted when its extremities come into contact with another grain, thus each grain is separated by a *grain boundary*. The process of grain growth as a metal cools from the melt is illustrated in Figure 4.25, in which the individual squares within each grid, represents the unit lattice or cell from which each grain is formed.

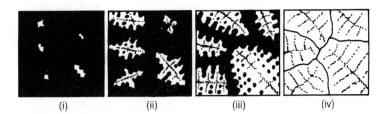

(i)   (ii)   (iii)   (iv)

Figure 4.25   *Grain growth as the metal cools from the melt*

You may remember that when the unit cell is formed it is made up in such a way as to ensure that the individual atoms within the cell are at their lowest energy level. Then any irregularity in the pattern of the lattice that forms the grain, must raise the energy of the atoms. This occurs at grain boundaries where the regular grain structure is distorted, due to the orientation of the grains as they meet. The higher energy at grain boundaries and other imperfections in the lattice structure are important for our understandng of the hardening and strengthenng mechanisms of metals and alloys, as you will observe later.

Metallic alloys

An alloy can be defined as the intimate mixture of two or more metallic elements in solid or liquid form. If we wish to modify the properties of pure metals, in order to meet engineering requirements, then we can alloy that metal with another and produce an alloy which maintains the best attributes of both. For example the alloy duralumin consists mainly of pure aluminium, mixed with about 4% of copper. Aluminium is very ductile but not particularly strong, by adding the copper the tensile strength of the alloy is significantly higher than the pure metal. Also with the appropriate heat treatment the ductility and toughness of the alloy can be made to approach that of pure aluminium. So, within limits, alloying gives us the ability to modify metals to suit our requirements.

Engineering alloys may be divided into two broad categories; ferrous alloys and non-ferrous alloys. As their name suggests the ferrous alloys are alloys of iron with small amounts of other elements added. The iron–carbon alloys or *steels* are very important engineering materials, which have been used successfully for many years. There importance is emphasized by the fact that they are always considered as a separate set of alloys.

Non-ferrous alloys are broken down again into several important subdivisions. These include aluminium alloys, magnesiums alloys, copper alloys, nickel alloys, zinc alloys and titanium alloys. Each sub-set taking its name from the principal alloying element.

Pure iron is an *allotropic* element, i.e. it can exist in more than one physical form or structure. At temperatures below 910°C the crystal structure of iron has a BCC lattice. Between temperatures of 910°C and 1400°C it exists as a FCC structure and above 1400°C it becomes BCC again.

These different physical states have common names. Iron in the BCC form is referred to as *ferrite*. Iron in its intermediate FCC form is referred to as *austinite*. Due to the difference in space between the atoms in the BCC lattice and FCC lattice they can accommodate varying numbers of carbon atoms. The FCC structure has the most room between atoms and so austinite in this form can accommodate more carbon up to around 2%, while, as ferrite, it can only accommodate up to 0.2%.

So as the alloy cools and the structure changes from FCC to BCC, the carbon comes out of the grains and forms a separate very hard and brittle compound known as *cementite*. So iron–carbon alloys having cooled from the solid may consist of pure ferrite grains or grains containing both ferrite and cementite, these mixed grains are often known as pearlite. As already mentioned the cementite is very hard and brittle, pearlite is less brittle, while ferrite is relatively soft and ductile. The properties of iron alloys vary smoothly and continuously with changes in carbon content, because as the carbon content changes so does the structure of the alloy.

Wrought iron, used for making ornamental gates and other items that require a very mallable metal, is an alloy that contains only minute amounts of carbon, hence consists almost exclusively of the very ductile and soft ferrite grains, so is ideal for forging into shape.

Mild steel has around 0.1% carbon and is malleable enough to be formed by pressing or drawing operations (see materials processing), being ductile its used for lightly stressed parts. Commercial tool steels contain from 0.7% to about 1.3% carbon and as their name suggests are used for hand tools like chisels, files, taps and dies, etc. Cast iron which is a particularly brittle material contains from about

2% to 4.5% carbon, it has good machining properties and is extremely hard so is often used for items like surface tables, heavy machine castings, motor vehicle cylinder blocks, etc.

If we add small amounts of other elements, apart from carbon, to iron, we can produce a range of steels with all sorts of useful properties. For example, small amounts of chromium, magnesium, nickel and titanium added to iron and carbon can produce a range of stainless and heat resisting steels. These may be used for kitchen ware, clinical and hospital utensils, and special non-toxic pressure vessels used for example, in the brewing industry.

Example 4.5

Explain why cast iron is an ideal material for the manufacture of engine cylinder blocks.

Engine cylinder blocks need a smooth warp-free precision base on which to place the cylinder head containing the valve gear, as well as being hard enough to withstand the continuous rubbing caused by the piston rings. Cast iron is a dense material that is virtually warp-free, even at elevated temperatures. It is extremely hard and so has good resistance to abrasion. It has excellent machining properties and so is ideal for producing close tolerance precision surfaces, and finally, it is easily cast into complex shapes.

Non-ferrous alloys as their name suggests involve metals other than iron as the primary alloying element. The names of some of these alloys has already been mentioned, one special set of these alloys are known as *light alloys*. These are alloys of beryllium, aluminium, magnesium and titanium where the densities range from $1700 \, \text{kg/m}^3$ to $4500 \, \text{kg/m}^3$ which compare with densities of $7800 \, \text{kg/m}^3$ to $8900 \, \text{kg/m}^3$ for iron and copper.

The property of lightness has led to the association of light metals with transportation and more especially with aerospace which has provided a great stimulus to the development of these alloys during the last 45 years. Their good structural efficiency in terms of strength and stiffness, has been dominant in their choice by designers.

Materials testing

Destructive tests are used to determine certain mechanical properties of materials, for instance the common *tensile test* may be used to check the strength and ductility of a material. Test specimens may be obtained by taking samples from a batch on a production line or, using laboratory specimens that have been especially prepared to check the properties of a new material. Other material properties that can be determined from destructive tests include, hardness (perhaps checking the effectiveness of a heat treatment), creep, fatigue and toughness.

Non-destructive testing can be used to determine the integrity of components in service, or to confim that materials have been processed correctly. Ultrasonics is one method of non-destructive testing which is particularly suitable for determining whether or not the layers of carbon fibre cloth have been fully impregnated by the resin matrix, when manufacturing a carbon fibre reinforced plastic component.

We will now consider some of the more common destructive and non-destructive tests. Later on you will be asked to carry out some of these tests, analysing and comparing the data obtained from them.

Tensile testing

The tensile test is one of the most important materials property tests. It enables us to determine tensile strength, elastic modulus, yield strength, maximum percentage elongation (and thus determine Poisson's ratio) and, it tells us a lot about the ductile behaviour of materials. It is particularly suited for testing metals and many polymers. In order to ensure that the tests are accurate specimen sizes should be of set dimensions which conform to BSEN 10002 or other related standards produced by the British Standards Institute. If tests are to be carried out using non-standard equipment, then the appropriate standard should always be consulted for guidance.

Standard tensile specimens may be rectangular or circular in cross-section, as shown in Figure 4.26. The gauge length should be 5 × (diameter) in the case of round specimens and 5.64 × (cross-sectional area)$^{1/2}$ for rectangular ones.

Tensile testing machines range from small hand-operated bench models known as *tensometers*, to large floor-standing machines which are capable of exerting forces of several hundred kilonewtons

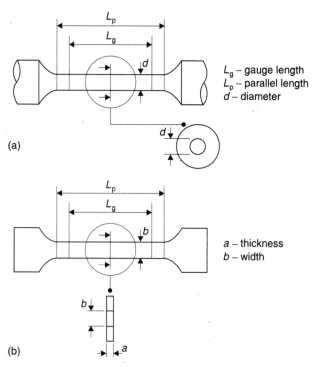

Figure 4.26 *Typical standard tensile test specimens which can have round or rectangular cross-sections which conform to BSEN 10002*

on the specimen As the specimen is loaded, the corresponding extensions are recorded either by taking readings, or graphically by indenting specially prepared graph paper with a pointer which corresponds with the load and extension imposed at the time on the specimen. A typical load–extension graph for a *mild steel* is shown in Figure 4.27.

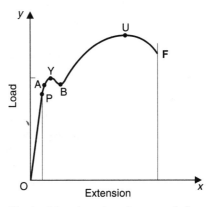

Figure 4.27 *Typical load–extension graph for mild steel*

The graph of Figure 4.27 is typical for a ductile material like mild steel. The key phases resulting from the test are clearly marked on the graph. The point *P* is the *limit of proportionality*. Between *O* and *P* the extension *x* is directly proportional to the applied force *F* and the material obeys Hooke's law, which was defined earlier. *OA* indicates the range in which the specimen extends elastically and will return to its original length the *elastic stage*. The point *A* is the *elastic limit* and may be coincident with *P* for some materials. *OY* marks the region in which the material undergoes internal structural changes before plastic deformation and permanent set occur. The point *Y* is *the yield point*, here the extension suddenly increases with no increase in stress and the material enters the *plastic stage*. At the point *U* the load is greatest. The extension of the test piece has been general up to point *U* but at point *U waisting* occurs (Figure 4.28), and all subsequent extension is local.

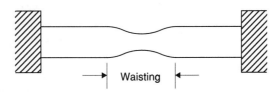

Figure 4.28 *When waisting occurs all subsequent extension occurs locally about the waist*

Since the area at the waist is considerably reduced, then from stress = force/area, stress will increase, resulting in a falling-off of the load, and *fracture* occurs at point *F*.

If the length and diameter of the specimen is taken prior to and after the test, then the percentage elongation and reduction in cross-sectional area (csa) can be determined from the following relationships.

$$\text{percentage elongation} = \frac{\text{increase in gauge length}}{\text{gauge length}} \times 100\%$$

and

$$\text{percentage reduction in area} = \frac{\text{original csa} - \text{final csa}}{\text{original csa}} \times 100\%$$

These values can now be used to calculate Poisson's ratio for the material, remembering our definition! Also from the graph or from the readings taken we are able to determine the elastic modulus (stiffness) of the material.

Figure 4.29 provides some further examples of typical load–extension curves for a variety of materials.

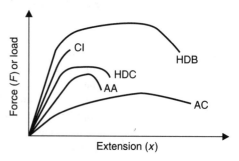

Figure 4.29 *Typical load-extension graphs where HDB = hard drawn brass, CI = cast iron, HDC = hard drawn copper, AA = aluminium alloy, AC = annealed copper*

Figure 4.29 shows that annealed copper is a very ductile material, while hard drawn copper is stronger but less ductile. Hard drawn 70/30 brass (copper–zinc alloy) is both strong and ductile. Cast iron can clearly be seen as brittle and it is for this reason that cast iron is seldom used under tensile load. Aluminium alloy is seen to be fairly strong yet ductile. Although not indicated here aluminium is one of the light alloys (magnesium and titanium being examples of others) which is strong yet light, i.e. it has a very good structural efficiency. Structural efficiency is defined as:

$$\text{Structural efficency} = \frac{\text{yield stress}}{\text{density}}$$

or using symbols

$$\eta = \frac{\sigma_y}{\rho}$$

Some other properties of importance to the engineer are given below, all of which can be determined from the results of the tensile test.

Working stress is the stress imposed on the material as a result of the worst possible load experienced in service and, must be within the elastic limit.

Proof stress is the tensile stress which when applied for a short period of time (often in the region 0 to 15 seconds), produces a permanent set of a specified amount, usually 0.1%. Do not mix this up with the yield stress which has already been defined.

Ultimate tensile stress is given by the relationship:

$$\frac{\text{maximum load}}{\text{original cross-sectional area}}$$

Note that the point *U* on the load–extension graph, shows the maximum load. This must be divided by the original csa not that directly under the point *U*.

Factor of safety It is common design practice to use the tensile strength of a metal which is easily obtained from tensile tests, and a *factor of safety* to ensure that uncertainty is taken into account, so that the stress stays within safe limits. In determining a factor of safety consideration will need to be given to such things as the uniformity of the chosen material; the type of loading-static or dynamic; the likely effect of failure; the effect of wear or corrosion of the material and the environment in which the material is to operate. Factors of safety can vary from about 1.5 to 3 for static loads, to about 15 for impact loads or 20 where fluctuating loads may cause fatigue failure.

Figure 4.30 shows stress–strain curves for four common materials.
(a) Which material has the highest yield stress?
(b) Which material is the stiffest?
(c) Which material is the strongest?
(d) Which material has the greatest ductility?

Define the following terms, with respect to tensile testing:
(a) Elastic deformation
(b) Plastic deformation
(c) Ultimate tensile strength
(d) Proof stress
(e) Percentage elongation
(f) Poisson's ratio.

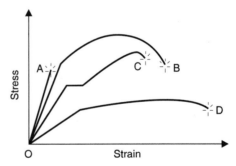

Figure 4.30 *Stress–strain curves for four common materials*

Hardness testing

The hardness test measures the resistance of a material to indentation. A load is gradually applied to an indenter, which is positioned at right angles to the test material. The test causes the material to plastically deform. The properties that affect plastic deformation are identical to those that affect hardness and so the test is a good measure of the hardness of the material. There is also a link between the hardness of a material and its tensile strength, since hardness is measured as the indenter force divided by the projected area of the indenter, i.e.

$$\text{Hardness} = \frac{\text{indenter force}}{\text{surface area of indentation}}$$

$$\frac{F}{A} \text{ (same units as stress)}$$

and for some materials, particularly steels, the tensile strength measured in N/mm^2 is approximately three times the hardness number.

The three most common types of hardness test are the *Brinell*, *Vickers* and *Rockwell* tests.

In the *Brinell* hardness test a steel or tungsten carbide ball is used as the indenter (Figure 4.31). This is forced into the material under load for about fifteen seconds. The average diameter d of the indentation made is then measured in millimetres using a microscope. A ball diameter of 10 mm is often used. The applied loads vary according to the nature of the material under test, but do not normally exceed 3000 kg.

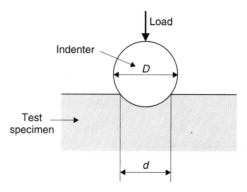

Figure 4.31 *The Brinell hardness test uses a hardened steel ball indenter*

The Brinell hardness number *HB* is then defined as:

$$HB = \frac{\text{load } (F)}{\text{surface area of indentation}} = \frac{2F}{\pi D[D - (D^2 - d^2)^{0.5}]}$$

If the indentation force F is measured in newtons instead of kg force, then the above formula must be multiplied by a factor of 0.102.

In the *Vickers* hardness test the indentation produced is very small and needs to be measured by a microscope. Here the indenter used is a diamond square-based pyramid (Figure 4.32). Test loads will again vary (normally 5 to 100 kg) according to the nature of the material under test. The Vickers hardness number (VHN) for a load F kg is given by:

$$\text{VHN} = \frac{1.854F}{d^2} \quad \text{where } d = \frac{d_1 + d_2}{2}$$

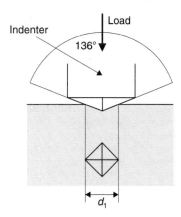

Figure 4.32 *The Vickers hardness test uses a diamond square-based pyramid indenter*

In practice there is no need to calculate the hardness number with either the Brinell or Vickers tests. Tables are provided which can be related to the measurements taken, at the time of the test, which also take into account the load used and the size of the indenter. There are no simple relationships between the hardness scales obtained for the different tests, because different methods are used to obtain a hardness value.

The *Rockwell* test uses either a hardened steel ball for softer material or a diamond cone indenter for harder materials. The depth of the indentation is converted to a hardness reading which is shown on a dial while the material being tested is still under load. This type of test is less accurate than the Vickers test but is still useful for rapid routine checks.

The Brinell, Vickers and Rockwell tests can all be used, quite successfully, for determining the hardness of plastics.

Bending tests

Bending tests are used to estimate the ductility of a material. The material is examined for cracks after it has been bent through some specified angle. There are several forms of bending test, all of which need to comply with the standards given in BS 1639. The tests may be carried out with or without the use of a former. Figure 4.33(a) illustrates a guided bending test where the radius of bend is controlled using a former, Figure 4.33(b) illustrates a free bend test where the material has been bent through 180°.

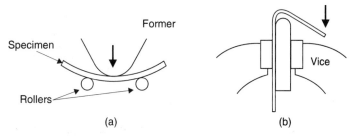

Figure 4.33 *(a) Guided bend test, (b) Free bend test*

Toughness testing

Impact tests are used to measure the energy required to fracture a standard notched bar using a heavy mass which is released at height and allowed to swing freely, in an arc to strike the test piece. The principle of operation of a typical standard impact test machine is illustrated in Figure 4.34.

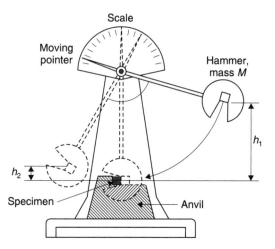

Figure 4.34 *Principle of operation of a typical standard impact test machine*

The potential energy of the mass can be determined mathematically prior to release and compared with the energy of the mass after impact, the difference in these two energies is the amount of energy absorbed by the test specimen and is a direct measure of the toughness of the material.

There are two common types of impact test, the Izod and the Charpy; they differ only in the way in which the test specimen is supported and the test specimen geometry. In the Izod test the specimen used is a circular or square-sectioned cantilever, with a V-notch mounted vertically in the jaws of the anvil as shown in Figure 4.35(a).

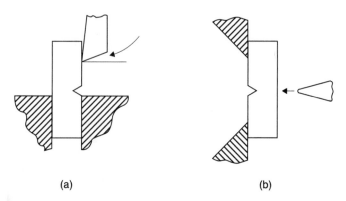

(a)   (b)

Figure 4.35 *(a) Cantilever impact test specimen, (b) Beam impact test specimen*

In the Charpy test a simply supported square sectioned beam is used. Again containing a specially prepared V-notch, but this time the notch is mounted on the far side from the point of impact (Figure 4.35(b)), so that the specimen fractures at the notch.

Impact testing can be used for both metals and polymers, the fracture surface will vary according to whether the material is brittle or ductile. Brittle metals show a clean break, with little change in cross-sectional area and little or no plastic deformation. The fracture surface has a granular structure.

With ductile metals the fracture surface is rough and fibrous. The more ductile a material the more energy is required to cause fracture. The energy of impact is absorbed in causing plastic deformation within the material. Ductile test pieces tend to bend rather than completely break, plastic flow can be identified by noting the corresponding reduction in cross-sectional area.

The results with brittle and ductile polymers is similar to those for metals. With brittle polymers there is a clean break and the fracture surfaces are smooth and glassy in appearance. With ductile polymers there is a significant reduction in cross-sectional area, with little or no fracture having taken place. With polymers that contain a colour pigment, at the point of impact, plastic straining of the material can be seen by a reduction in colour giving a translucent (semi-transparent) effect.

In both the Izod and Charpy tests the energy absorbed at impact is measured to given an indication of toughness of the material under test. For metals this is simply expressed in Joules (J). With polymers the width of the notch or the cross-sectional area of the test piece are also considered, so the toughness of these materials may be expressed in units of (J/m) or (J/m^2), dependent on the type of test.

Other destructive tests

Apart from the forms of destructive testing already mentioned materials can be subjected to *shear* tests. Where the specimen in the form of a thin-walled cylinder is subject to a twisting couple. This twisting moment simulates a shearing action within the walls of the test piece, from which we can determine information on the shear strength (symbol τ) and the shear modulus or modulus of rigidity (symbol G) of the test specimen.

Creep has already been defined as the slow plastic deformation of a material accelerated with increase in temperatures. Metals when subject to loads at elevated temperatures (normally greater than about half their melting point) may continue to deform slowly while the stress is maintained. Polymers can creep at room temperatures.

The creep behaviour of materials can be determined by carrying out standard creep tests on material specimens. Here the creep caused by applying a static tensile load, is determined by measuring the extension with time. The results are plotted and analysed to establish the creep characteristics of the material. A typical creep curve (Figure 4.36) consists of three stages. The first stage shows the creep rate being gradually reduced by strain hardening. During the second stage the creep rate remains approximately constant. Finally in the third stage there is a rapid increase in the strain rate, due to necking, until ultimately fracture occurs.

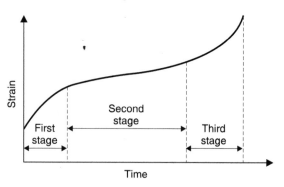

Figure 4.36 *Typical creep curve with specimen subject to constant stress at constant temperature*

In order to establish the fatigue strength of a material, specimens are subjected to some form of dynamic cyclic stressing in a fatigue testing machine. The type of test will depend on the form of the material, i.e. whether in the form of sheet, strip, bars, shafts, etc. Specimens can be pulled and pushed to simulate continuous tensile and compressive loading, or they may be rotated (twisted) backwards and forwards again to set up cyclic loads.

Interpretation of the results of fatigue tests can be complicated, but are necessary because materials may fail at much lower stress levels than when subject to static loads only. The *endurance limit* for steels and the *fatigue* strength for other materials such as light alloys can be determined. The designer can then ensure the life of chosen materials subject to fatigue loads, provided these loads are not exceeded.

Steels subject to cyclic loading will not fail by fatigue, providing this *endurance limit* is not exceeded (Figure 4.37). Other metals such as the light alloys do not have an endurance limit, so no matter how low the cyclic loading is eventually, given enough cycles, the material will fail by fatigue. By knowing the magnitude (size) of the maximum cyclic loads imposed on a material then a fatigue life can be estimated either directly as a number of cycles or, by using statistics, a time in hours or years is established. This technique, which enables a material fatigue life to be estimated, is particularly useful for aircraft designers where the problems created by fatigue are of major importance.

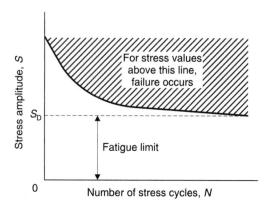

Figure 4.37 *Typical S/N curve for a steel showing that there is a fatigue endurance limiting stress*

We have spent some time discussing destructive testing, and the reasons for such tests have already been mentioned. *Non-destructive tests* will now be considered, remembering that these are useful, not only for checking possible defects produced during manufacture, but also for determining the integrity of materials being used in-service.

The technique used will depend on the nature of the material, whether in-service or being manufactured and the degree of access for inspection. The methods now available for non-destructive testing are numerous and whole fields of research have been set up to look at specialist applications for any one individual method.

It used to be considered that there were five major methods – radiographic, ultrasonic, magnetic, electrical and penetrant. All of these methods having subdivisions. Now, in addition, a range of new techniques have been developed including acoustic emission methods, thermography, and holography. Visual inspections, although not considered separately, are still of great importance, whether using the naked eye or optical aids such as boroscopes. We will not be able to cover all these methods here, so I will concentrate on one or two of the more important conventional methods, listing others and indicating their uses.

Visual inspection

Visual inspection can provide useful information on the surface condition of a material. Boroscopes (low powered microscopes) have been designed with the aid of fibre optics to help see into confined spaces, that are inaccessible to the naked eye. Aircraft engine combustion chambers that need regular inspection for defects, provide us with an example of where use of the boroscope is particularly helpful.

Care must be taken to ensure that no material defects have been overlooked. So this method is limited to detecting defects that are of sufficient size as to be readily seen. In aluminium alloys and low strength steels fatigue cracks do not generally become critical until they exceed about 2 to 3 cm in length, they are therefore capable of being detected visually before they cause failure of the structure. So for these materials visual methods of non-destructing testing are appropriate. This would not be the case when inspecting high-strength steels or other more brittle materials, where the critical crack length can be less than 0.5 mm, here we would need to consider a more sensitive technique such as ultrasonics or radiography.

Holography is a technique that fits broadly under visual inspection. Holographic techniques can be used for the comparison of specimens, or the measurement of small amounts of deformation under stress, or a study of the surface during vibration. As the presence of a defect is likely to cause changes in the deformation or vibration pattern then by definition, holography can be used for defect detection. Normal photographic film is sensitive only to light intensity, although the image being photographed has much more information in it. Holography not only uses the intensity of light, but also its phase information. It is this phase information that provides us with the three-dimensional image, which can be stored after processing and reproduced as a virtual image when illuminated in a particular way.

Radiography

When a beam of X-rays or more energetic gamma-rays are passed through a material onto a photographic plate, an image is obtained. The photographic plate is exposed to the rays for a period of time, which depends on the intensity of the rays, the thickness of the specimen and the characteristics of the film. The film is then processed and placed on an illuminated screen, so that the image can be examined and interpreted. Figure 4.38 shows a typical arrangement for flaw detection using X-ray radiography.

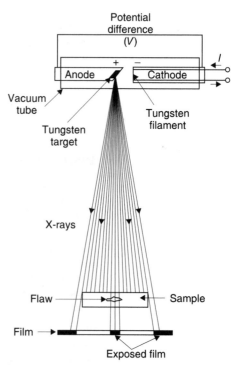

Figure 4.38 *Typical arrangement for flaw detection using X-ray radiography*

X-ray radiography requires a power source so the equipment is rather complex and cumbersome. Radiographical techniques are very useful for examining castings for porosity, blowholes, shrinkage cavities, cracks and other flaws.

Gamma-ray radiography does not need an external power source because the rays are produced directly from a radioactive material such as Caesium-137, Cobalt-60 or Iridium-92, dependent on the intensity of the gamma-rays required. The portable equipment needed is therefore much less cumbersome than that required for X-ray radiography.

Radiography can be used for detecting flaws or defects in metals, and non-metals including composites. All forms of radiography are dangerous and particular care must be exercised when using the equipment, so that nobody is inadvertently exposed to radiation.

Ultrasonic testing

Mechanical vibrations can be made to travel through solids, liquids and gases. The actual particles of matter vibrate. If the frequency of vibration is within the range 16–20 kHz (sixteen to twenty thousand cycles per second) the sound is audible to humans. Above 20 kHz the sound waves are referred to as ultrasound or ultrasonics. Typical frequencies used for ultrasonic testing are in the range 500 kHz to 20 MHz.

There are a number of ways in which ultrasonic waves can be produced but for non-destructive testing, most equipment uses the *piezoelectric effect*, for the test probes. A piezoelectric material has the property that if deformed by external pressure, electric charges are produced and conversely, that if an electrical source is applied to the material it will change shape. By using alternating current a mechanical oscillation is produced in the piezoelectric plate. By coupling the piezoelectric probe to the specimen, sound waves are produced which match the frequency of vibration produced at the probe.

If we couple the probe to the specimen being tested a pulse of ultrasonic energy is generated within the material. This pulse of waves travels through the material with some spreading and will be reflected or scattered at any surface or internal discontinuity, such as an internal flaw in the specimen (Figure 4.39). This reflected or scattered energy can be detected by a suitably placed second piezoelectric disc (receiver) on the material surface and will generate a pulse of electrical energy as a result of the received vibrations. The time interval between the transmitted and reflected pulses is a measure of the distance of the discontinuity from the surface and the size of the return pulse can be a measure of the size of the flaw. This is the simple principle of the ultrasonic flaw detector and ultrasonic thickness gauge.

Ultrasonic examination is particularly suited for the examination of composite materials. Disbonds and delamination (see structure of composite materials) can be identified after manufacture or repair.

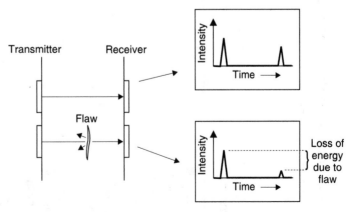

Figure 4.39 *Typical arrangement for ultrasonic flaw detection*

Table 4.8 Some non-destructive testing techniques and their uses with composite materials

Technique	Void content	Fibre content	Resin content	Fibre orientation	Material homogeneity	Mechanical properties	Delaminations	Fatigue damage	Contamination	Disbonds	Cracks	Debris	Condition of internal components
Radiographic													
Low kV, high definition	●			●	●				●		●	●	●
Radio-opaque tracers				●									
Gamma		●	●										
Ultrasonic													
Attenuation measurements	●	●				●	●	●		●			●
Velocity measurement	●	●		●	●	●	●	●					
Spectroscopy	●				●	●							
Holography										●			
Optical													
Optical holography										●			
Speckle photography										●	●		
Laser interferometry										●			
Others													
Acoustic emission		●		●	●	●		●		●	●		
Eddy currents						●		●			●		
Micro waves	●						●						
Mechanical impedance										●		●	●

As mentioned earlier there was simply no time to explain all the methods and techniques that have been developed for the non-destructive testing of materials. So to finish, we have listed some of the more important techniques together with their uses (particularly with respect to composites) in the form of a table (Table 4.8 opposite). You are then asked to investigate some of these methods, as an exercise.

Activity 4.6

Beta Materials has asked you to carry out non-destructive tests on the following materials:

(a) a low carbon steel
(b) a carbon reinforced plastic composite material
(c) an aluminium alloy aircraft skin
(d) a large casting produced from cast iron.

For each material, list two techniques that you consider would be suitable and give reasons for your choice. Present your recommendations in the form of a word processed report.

Activity 4.7

Investigate the acoustic emission and thermographic methods of non-destructive testing. Write short notes describing each method and include:

(a) the physical principles used
(b) their advantages and disadvantages compared to other methods
(c) their industrial uses.

Activity 4.8

Use your library to investigate the procedure for the dye-penetrant method when used to detect possible surface defects on a steel component. Use the information obtained to write a brief explanation of the method and also give an account of how the results of the test may be interpreted.

Materials characteristics and processing methods

In this element we are going to consider the processing of materials and the implications that these processing methods have on their property values. We will concentrate on a selection of metals, polymers and composite materials. Determining how, by modifying their grain structure, composition or by heat treating, we are able to alter their properties.

Metals

Crystal structure, cold working and heat treatment

We have already learnt about how the atoms of metals bond together and form regular *lattice structures*. When a metal cools from the melt these lattice structures repeatedly join together three-dimensionally and grow *dendritically* to form *crystals* or *grains* (Figure 4.40). It is the size and nature of these grains which very much determines the properties of the parent material. Alloying metals also modifies their behaviour; during the manufacture of such alloys the metallurgist will try to maximize the good qualities that the individual elements bring to the alloy being produced.

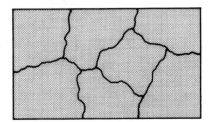

Figure 4.40   *Grains formed on solidification of the metal*

The strength of metals and alloys can be improved by modifying their grain structures. For pure metals an increase in yield stress can be achieved by reduction in grain size or by cold working which not only increases the yield stress but also increases hardness.

A regular structure within the grains of a metal helps to maintain that metal in its lowest energy state (see bonding of materials). When this regular pattern is disturbed by either defects or an increase in grain boundary area, the internal energy of the metal is increased. Thus the energy needed to fracture the material is also increased. This increase in fracture strength is measured by a resulting increase in yield stress.

Therefore an increase in yield stress is achieved by reducing the grain size and so increasing the high energy grain boundary area (Figure 4.41).

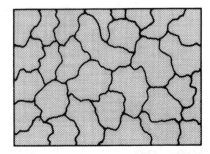

Figure 4.41   *Increase in grain boundary area as a result of reduction in grain size*

If we cold work a metal say by cold-rolling. We increase the dislocation density within the grains. That is we raise the energy of the metal by increasing the amount of line defects (dislocations) present. Further plastic deformation (resulting from lines of atoms slipping over one another) is impeded due to the increase in energy required to overcome the increased density of dislocations (line defects) that are already present due to the cold work. Figure 4.42 illustrates this idea.

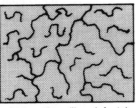 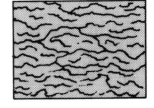

Dislocations (line defects) prior to cold work

Figure 4.42 *The increase in dislocation density as a result of cold-working the material*

As we have already said an increase in cold work produces a subsequent increase in the number of dislocations which results in them becoming entangled with one another. It is these *dislocation tangles* that impedes the progress of further line defects and so plastic deformation only occurs at much higher stress levels. At the same time, for the same reasons, cold-working also produces an increase in hardness.

When a cold-worked metal is heated to about a third of its melting temperature (measured on the Kelvin scale), then there is a marked reduction in tensile strength and hardness. What actually happens is that at this temperature recrystallization takes place (Figure 4.43). Further increase in temperature enables the crystals to grow until the original destorted crystals, resulting from the cold work, are all replaced. The term *annealing* is used for the heat treatment process whereby the material is heated to above the recrystallization temperature and more ductile properties replace those produced by the cold work. The greater the amount of cold work the smaller the grain size produced after heat treatment, with a subsequent increase in yield stress when compared to a metal which has not been cold worked.

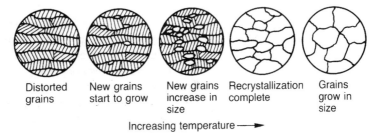

Distorted grains | New grains start to grow | New grains increase in size | Recrystallization complete | Grains grow in size

Increasing temperature ⟶

Figure 4.43 *Illustration of the recrystallization process with increasing temperature*

If copper is cold rolled then the yield stress and hardness will increase. At about 60% cold work the copper becomes so brittle that any further cold work results in fracture. So if further reduction in cross-section is required then the copper needs to be *process annealed*, the original ductility and mallability is restored and the cold-working process may continue.

Cold-working involves plastically deforming the material at temperatures below the recrystallization temperature. Hot-working as you might expect involves deforming the material at temperatures above the recrystallization temperature. So that as the grains deform they immediately recrystallize thus no hardening takes place and processing can continue without difficulty. Thus processing often involves hot-working initially to produce the maximum amount of plastic deformation followed by cold-rolling to improve the surface finish and increase the surface hardness as required. For example aluminium baking foil may be produced from blocks of aluminium in billet form, which are first hot-rolled then cold-rolled to produces thin even sheets.

Increase in yield stress for metal *alloys* is again achieved by modifying the grain structure of the host metal, but in a different way to that described above. Apart from line defects within the grain there may also be *point* defects. The various types of point defect are illustrated in Figure 4.44.

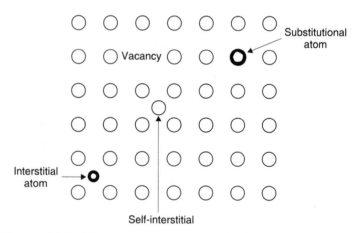

Figure 4.44   *Various types of point defect. A vacancy self interstitial is known as a Frenkel defect. The simple vacancy on its own is known as a Schottky defect*

These point defects may be caused by impurities in the melt or may be deliberately introduced by *alloying*. In either case the net result is to increase the energy within the grains or at the grain boundaries, resulting once again in increases in yield stress and hardness.

The above process is particularly useful in improving the properties of aluminium alloys, and other light alloys. The heat-treatment process involved is known as *precipitation hardening*. The alloy is heated to above its recrystallization temperature, then quenched. The result is a distorted high-energy lattice structure, where the alloying elements initially lodge within the grains. After a time the fine precipitate diffuses toward the grain boundaries where it stays. Once again the grain boundary energy is increased making slip very difficult, hence an increase in yield stress (a measure of strength) and an increase in hardness.

A classic example of this process is found in the Al–Cu alloy *duralumin* (named after the town Duran in Germany where it was first produced). In the annealed state this alloy has a tensile strength in the region of 180–190 MPa and a hardness around 40–50 HB. After precipitation hardening these values may climb to around 420 MPa and 100 HB, respectively. This alloy is often used in aircraft skin construction, where it is clad with pure aluminium to improve its corrosion resistance properties while at the same time increasing its strength and hardness over and above that of pure aluminium.

Steels may be made very hard by heating them to above their recrystallization temperature and then suddenly reducing their temperature by quenching in water or oil. The sudden reduction in temperature does not allow sufficient time for the carbon atom to diffuse to the grain boundaries and form cementite. Instead the excess carbon atoms are trapped within the lattice structure and form a separate very hard phase known as *martensite*. This very hard and brittle substance has the effect of increasing the hardness and brittleness of the steel. The above process is known as *quenching*. Quenched steels may be up to four times as hard as their annealed counterpart, dependent upon the original amount of carbon added to the alloy. For example, for a steel produced from 1% carbon, which in its annealed state has a hardness value of 200 HV, once quenched this figure may be as high as 800 HV.

After hardening a steel by quenching, some of its ductility and resilience may be restored by *tempering*. The steel is reheated so that the carbon atoms can diffuse out and reduce the distortion within the lattice thus reducing the energy stored and so returning some ductility back to the steel. The higher the tempering temperature the more ductile the steel.

Processing metals

Metals may be processed or fabricated by two major methods, either *shaped* or *joined*, to form a component or structure. Metals may be shaped into something approaching the final form by one of several operations including, casting, rolling, drawing, forging, extruding, cutting, grinding and sintering, or fabricated by joining with adhesives, fasteners, soldering, welding or brazing. Space does not permit all of the processes to be covered comprehensively in this text. We will, however, concentrate on a few processing techniques leaving you as an exercise to research further processes.

Casting of metals requires the metal in liquid form to be poured into a mould and then allowed to solidify before breaking the mould open to reveal the cast product. In order to ensure that the liquid metal reaches all parts of the mould, we either choose alloying elements that provide a low viscosity alloy (that is an alloy which easily flows) or, we use some external pressure to force the molten metal into the mould, as in pressure die casting.

The grain structure of the metal, within the mould, is dependent upon the rate of cooling. If the metal is rapidly cooled only small crystals have time to form. As the cooling rate is reduced so the crystal size grows. Metals that cool within a mould may cool quickly near the surface of the mould and due to heat flow may form long crystals which grow towards the centre of the mould (columnar crystals). At the centre of the mould due to thermal convection the molten metal is continually on the move, this results in an even heat distribution, which results in the production of equal-sized round crystals (equiaxed) being formed. The resultant structure of cast product moulded in an ingot is illustrated in Figure 4.45.

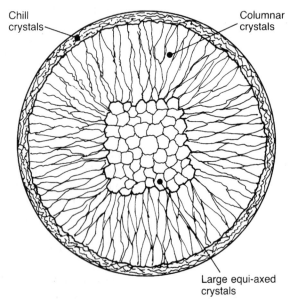

Figure 4.45   *Resultant crystal structure of a casting moulded in an ingot*

The method used for casting metals will depend on the size, number and complexity of the final product. Sand casting is suitable for small batch production of large components. If large numbers of castings are required a far superior product, with better dimensional accuracy, is produced by using a metal mould. In permanent mould casting known as *gravity die casting*, the molten alloy is allowed to run into the mould under gravity, while in *pressure* die casting the charge is forced into the mould under considerable pressure.

The use of die casting is confined mainly to aluminium or zinc based alloys. Metal dies are expensive to produce, so that die casting in all its forms is only economically viable for large-scale production. Pressure die casting produces components with good dimensional accuracy, uniform grain structure and good surface finish. So the metallic components produced by this method require little or no further processing. Sand casting does have the advantage of producing intricate shapes, because of the possibility of using destructable cores.

Since most metals become considerably softer and more malleable as temperature rises less energy is needed to produce a given amount of deformation, this is why *hot-working* is extensively used to shape metals. Drop-forging involves the use of a shaped die, one half being attached to the hammer and other to the anvil (Figure 4.46). When producing complex shapes by this method a series of dies may be used.

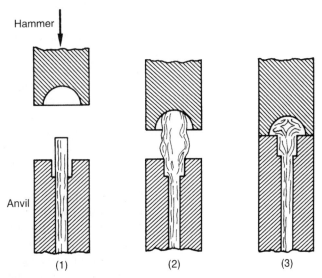

Figure 4.46 *Typical forging process showing resultant structure*

The hammer may be operated mechanically, pneumatically or hydraulically, dependent on the nature of the task.

The *extrusion* process is used for shaping a variety of ferrous and non-ferrous metals and alloys. The metal billet is heated to the required temperature, the ram is then driven hydraulically with sufficient pressure to force the metal through a hardened steel die. The solid metal section exudes from the die in a similar manner to that of toothpaste being squeezed from the tube. Figure 4.47 illustrates this process.

This process is able to produce a wide variety of sections, including round and hexagonal rod, curtain rails, tubes, bearing sections and ordinary wire.

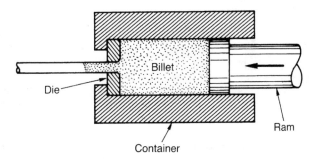

Figure 4.47 *An extrusion process*

Cold-pressing and deep-drawing are closely related to each other and it is difficult to differentiate between them. The operations range from making a suitable pressing in one stage to cupping followed by a number of drawing operations as shown in Figure 4.48. In each case the components are produced from sheet metal. Car-bodies, bullet cases and general metal containers are examples of components that are easily produced using this process.

Sintering from a powder has become an important way of producing metallic structures. The metals to be sintered, in the form of a fine powder, are mixed together and then placed in a hardened steel die and compressed. The pressures used depend upon the metals to be sintered but are usually between 70 and 700 MN/m². At these high pressures a degree of cold welding takes place between the metals. The brittle compressed mass is then heated in a furnace to a temperature at which sintering (grain growth across the cold welds) takes place.

Tungsten is compacted and sintered in this way and the resulting sintered rod may be drawn into a fine wire to produce tungsten filaments for light bulbs. Tungsten carbide products for machine tools are also produced in this way. Cobalt being used with the tungsten carbide to produce a tough, shock resistant bonding agent between the particles.

Sintering may also be used to produce bronze bearings. Here copper, tin and graphite are used in the sintering process to produce self-lubricating bearings.

Let us now turn our attention to just one metal cutting process, that of *machining*. This is essentially a cold-working process in which the cutting edge of the tool forms chips or shavings of the material being machined. Very ductile alloys do not machine well, because local fracture does not occur ahead of the cutting tool edge. Thus brittle materials are considered to have good machining properties. Ideal materials have a suitable concentration of small isolated particles in their microstructure. These particles have the effect of setting up local stress raisers, as the cutting edge approaches them and minute local fractures occur. The graphite in cast iron and particles of a hard compound in bronze are examples of the presence of secondary stress raisers, which improve machinability. Elements may be added to alloys, other than those mentioned above, to improve machinability. These include manganese, molybdenum, zirconium, sulphur, carbon and selenium.

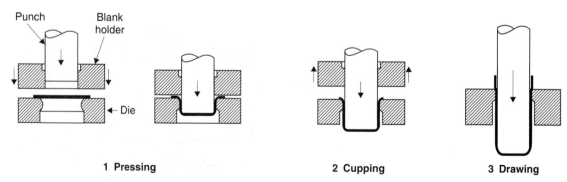

Figure 4.48 *A deep drawing process*

Let us now look briefly at one or two methods of joining materials, in particular welding and soldering. In welding, brazing and soldering fusion takes place at the surfaces of the metals being joined. Soldering and brazing are fundamentally similar processes in that the joining material always melts at a temperature which is lower than the work piece.

Soldering or *soft* soldering as it is often called can be described as a process in which temperatures below 450°C are involved, whereas brazing temperatures are generally between 600 and 900°C. Welding can be achieved by hammering the surfaces in contact together at high temperatures, so that crystal growth takes place.

When *soldering* the solder must be capable of spreading across the surfaces of the metals to be joined, the solder is often assisted in this process by use of a *flux* or *wetting agent*. Solders produced from tin–lead alloys have good flow properties and melt at temperatures 183 to 250°C, which are comfortably below the temperatures of the metals to be joined. Some of the more common solders are listed in Table 4.9 together with their main uses.

Table 4.9 *Some commonly used tin-lead solders*

Composition (%)			Melting range (°C)	Uses
Sn	Pb	Other elements		
64	36	–	183–185	Mass soldering of printed circuits.
60	40	–	183–188	General soldering – sheet metal (steel, copper and tinplate); plumbing (capillary joints); printed circuits; electronics; food cans; electrical (hand soldering).
50	50	–	183–220	'Coarse tinman's solder' – general sheet-metal work (brass and galvanized sheet). Lower quality work in electrical trades.
40	60	–	183–234	Coating and pre-tinning; automobile radiators; refrigerators.
30	70	–	183–255	Electrical cable conductors, heat exchangers; automobile radiators; refrigerators.
15	85	–	227–288	Electric lamp bases.
40	57.6	Sb 2.4	185–277	Heat-exchangers; automobile radiators; refrigerators.
32	66.1	Sb 1.9	188–243	'Wiped joints' in lead-cable sheaths and lead pipes.
–	97.5	Ag 2.5	304	Eutectic alloy – high temperature service; also soldering copper and its alloys.
92	–	Zn 8	200	Eutectic alloy – flux-cored wire for soldering aluminium.
62	36	Ag 2	178–189	Soldering silver-coated surfaces.
48	–	In 52	117	Tin/indium eutectic – soldering glazed surfaces.
50	32	Cd 18	145	Making joints adjacent to other soldered joints which have used higher melting-point solders.

In *fusion welding* processes either thermochemical sources, electric arc or some form of radiant energy can be used to melt the weld metal. In gas welding the surfaces to be joined are melted by a flame from a gas torch, the gases most commonly used being suitable mixtures of oxygen and acetylene.

In gas welding and other fusion welding processes a welding rod, is used to supply the necessary metal for the weld. The weld joint being suitably prepared prior to the commencement of welding. Other fusion welding processes apart from gas welding include electric arc where the arc is struck between a carbon electrode and the work itself.

Solid phase welding processes include smith welding (described earlier), ultrasonic welding, friction welding and diffusion welding. In diffusion welding the sheets to be joined are held together under light pressure in a vacuum chamber. The temperature is then raised sufficiently for diffusion to occur across the interface so that the surfaces become joined by a region of solid solution. Steel can be clad with brass in this way.

Some of the other joining processes such as rivetting, and joining by adhesives you have been asked to investigate as an exercise at the end of this element. It is necessary to say something about the advantages and disadvantages of using *adhesives* to join materials.

Possibly the principal advantage of an adhesive bond is that the adhesive fastens to the entire bonded surface, thereby distributing the load more evenly and thus avoiding high localized stresses. Adhesives may also be used to advantage instead of riveting. Rivets add weight to structures, increase the likelihood of corrosion and can look unsightly on many domestic products. Materials with different coefficients of expansion can be joined by elastomer type adhesives which takes the strain at the adhesive joint, rather than the materials being joined. Adhesives can also be cured at relatively low temperatures, so preventing any uncessary damaged to the materials being joined (adherends).

Adhesive joints also have one or two disadvantages primarily they are very much restricted in use at high temperatures. Also components cannot easily be dismantled for maintenance. Finally, surface cleanliness and process control are very important, this usually requires a considerable amount of equipment.

Polymer adhesives are by far the most commonly used for engineering and industrial applications.

So much then for the processing of metals and metal alloys, let us now focus our attention on the processing of polymers.

Non-metals

Polymer processing

An important attraction of polymer compounds is that they can be readily converted into a variety of useful shapes. Polymer processing is concerned with the technology needed to make articles from polymer compounds. Three common themes underly most of the methods. The first involves making the appropriate compound, usually in liquid form, from the raw ingredients. The second is concerned with transforming the compound into useful shapes. Finally, the third theme is to ensure that once the product has been formed it retains its shape and dimensions.

So the first theme is concerned with mixing the raw ingredients to produce the correct compound. There are two basic stages in the mixing process, dispersing the additives in the polymer and achieving a uniform shapable state. The two main processes used for good dispersion of the polymers ingredients, particularly in the rubber industry, are the two-roll mill and the intensive mixer. In the intensive mixer two rotors counter-rotate within a robust casing. There is only a small clearance between the tips of the rotors and the casing. Ingredients are fed in through an opening in the top of the machine, which may be closed during use. The fully mixed compound being removed through a port in the underside of the casing.

The two-roll mill consists of two heavy horizontal cylindrical polished rollers fitted with water-cooling channels (Figure 4.49). The rollers counter rotate and are separated by a narow gap. The feed is dropped between the two rollers. The sticky rubber substance is dragged down between the two rollers and adheres to them in the form of a band. This band is cut on a helix at an angle to the roll-axis and it is simply folded over.

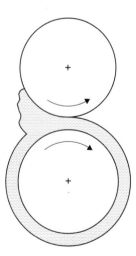

Figure 4.49 *Polymer being processed in a two-roll mill*

Because of the high viscosity of the rubber compound, the power to drive the rollers is high, but because the water-cooled rollers have a large surface area in contact with the thin band of polymer, this prevents excessive temperature rise. It is therefore safe to add the vulcanizing (cross-linking) agents to the mix.

Extrusion processes are used to make continuous products of constant cross-section, usually from thermoplastics or rubber compounds. Two basic types of equipment are commonly used these are the *calender* and the *screw extruder*.

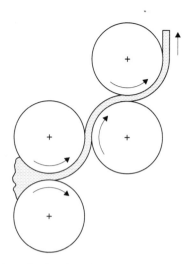

Figure 4.50   *A typical calendering process for a polymer*

The *calender* consists of four heavy rollers which are sometimes known as *bowls* Figure 4.50. The top two bowls act just like the two-roll mill previously described. The compound is drawn through the first two rollers and adheres to them. It is thus transferred to the next pair where its cross-section is further reduced, finally the required surface finish, either plain or embossed is supplied as the polymer mix passes through the final stage rollers.

Sheet up to a few millimetres thick and a metre or so wide can be produced in this way.

The *screw extruder* consists of one or sometimes two screws which rotate inside a close-fitting barrel of constant diameter. The screw is driven by a large electric motor, being connected to the screw by a reduction gearbox. The screw has to deliver a steady stream of molten polymer to the die. The screw acts as a pump, which develops drag flow and thus heat which helps to melt or plasticize the feed. A hopper is used to supply the feed to the screw. A typical screw extruder is shown in Figure 4.51.

Compression moulding of polymers is similar to cold-pressing metals, in that a thermosetting polymer compound known as the charge is fed into the jaws of a moulding die. Pressure is applied

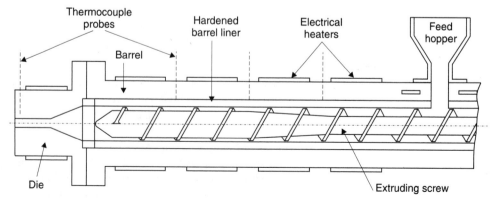

Figure 4.51   *A typical polymer screw extruder*

and the polymer takes up exactly the shape of the die to form a three-dimensional product. The stages of this process are shown in Figure 4.52.

The final product is ejected from the mould after completion of the process.

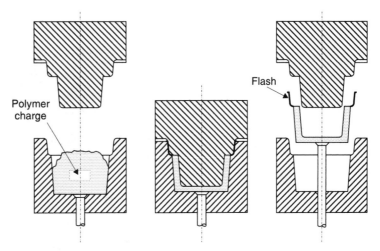

Figure 4.52 *Polymer compression moulding process*

In *extrusion blow moulding* a thick-walled thermoplastic called a *parison* is extruded vertically downwards between the open faces of a cold split mould, which produces a hollow cavity. The mould is then closed and sealed and the still warm parison is inflated with compressed air so that the outside of the tube takes up the shape of the mould (Figure 4.53).

Plastic bottles and other useful containers are often made in this way.

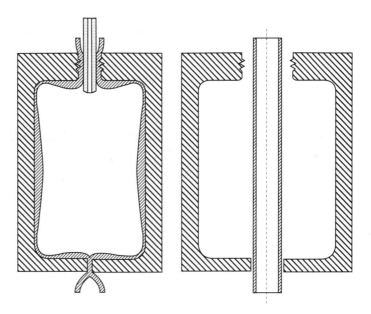

Figure 4.53 *Extrusion blow moulding*

Let us consider one final moulding process, that of *injection moulding*. In this process polymer melt is injected into an impression within a closed split mould which has the dimensions required for the finished product, see Figure 4.54.

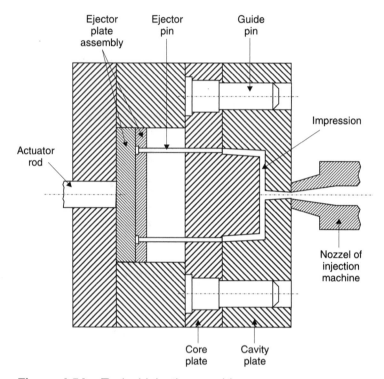

Figure 4.54   *Typical injection moulder*

Thermoplastics, thermosets and elastomers can all be injection moulded. Many aspects of the construction of compression and injection moulds are similar in principle.

We could consider many other pieces of polymer processing equipment, such as hand lay-up techniques, but these are perhaps better covered in the next section, when we deal with composite materials.

Composite materials and their processing

This range of materials has been left to last because *composites* are a mixture of two or more constituents or phases, rather than a distinct class. We have already introduced you to composites when we talked initially about classes of material. However, that definition was not really sufficient and three other criteria have to be satisfied in order to classify a material as a composite. First, both constituents have to be present in reasonable proportions, rather than fractions of a per cent. Secondly, the constituent phases will have different properties, so that the properties of the resulting composite are different from its component parts. Finally, a composite is usually produced by intimately mixing and combining the constituents by various means. So, for example, a metal alloy which has a two-phase microstructure which is produced during solidification from the melt, or by subsequent heat treatment, has not involved intimate mixing and cannot therefore, be classified as a true composite material.

The continuous constituent of a composite is known as the *matrix*; the matrix is often but not always present in the greater quantity. A composite may have a ceramic, metallic or polymeric matrix. The mechanical properties of composites produced from these matrices differ completely, as Table 4.10 shows.

The second constituent within the composite is referred to as the *reinforcing phase*, because this phase strengthens or enhances in some way the properties of the matrix. The reinforcement may take the form of small particles, chopped strand, continuous strand or woven matting. How it is mixed will generally dictate whether or not the composite has uni-directional or multi-directional strength and stiffness characteristics: Figure 4.55 illustrates this point.

Table 4.10 *Some properties of ceramics, metals and polymers*

	Density (Mg/m^3)	Young's modulus (GPa)	Strength[a] (MPa)	Ductility (%)	Toughness K_{IC} (MPa m$^{1/2}$)	Specific modulus [(GPa)/ (Mg/m^3)]	Specific strength [MPa)/ (Mg/m^3)]
Ceramics							
Alumina	3.87	382	332	0	4.9	99	86
Magnesia	3.60	207	230	0	1.2	58	64
Silicon Nitride		166	210	0	4.0		
Zirconia	5.92	170	900	0	8.6	29	152
β-Sialon	3.25	300	945	0	7.7	92	291
Metals							
Aluminium	2.70	69	77	47	~30	26	29
Aluminium alloy	2.83	72	325	18	~25–30	25	115
Brass	8.50	100	550	70	–	12	65
Nickel alloy	8.18	204	1200	26	~50–80	25	147
Steel mild	7.86	210	460	35	~50	27	59
Titanium alloy	4.56	112	792	20	~55–90	24	174
Polymers							
Epoxy	1.12	4	50	4	1.5	4	36
Nylon 6.6	1.14	2	70	60	3–4	18	61
Polyetheretherketone	1.30	4	70		1.0	3	54
Polymethylmethacrylate	1.19	3	50	3	1.5	3	42
Polystyrene	1.05	3	50	2	1.0	3	48
Polyvinylchloride rigid	1.70	3	60	15	4.0	2	35

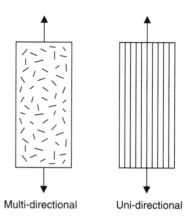

Multi-directional   Uni-directional

Figure 4.55 *Reinforcing fibre orientation dictates whether or not the composite material has multi-directional or uni-directional properties*

In this text we will be concentrating on just one major group of composites; *polymer matrix composites* (PMCs). This group has a wide range of engineering applications and by studying them, the general principles underlying their properties and processing can be extended to other groups of composite such as those with a ceramic or metal matrix. PMCs use all three classes of polymer; thermoplastics, thermosets and elastomers, although thermosetting polymers dominate the market for this type of composite.

Carbon fibre reinforced plastic (CFRP) is a very well known polymer matrix composite, where the reinforcement is carbon fibre. Other reinforcing materials used with PMCs include glass, polyethylene, boron, and Kevlar (a type of aromatic polyamide). A range of reinforcing fibres and matrices, with their mechanical properties is given in Table 4.11.

Let us now concentrate on one or two processing methods for PMCs. In *hand lay-up* the reinforcement is put down to line a mould previously treated with some form of release agent to prevent sticking. The reinforcement can be in many forms, such as chopped strand mat, woven mat, etc. The liquid thermosetting resin is mixed with a curing (setting) agent and applied with a brush or roller, ensuring that the resin is thoroughly worked into the reinforcement. The most commonly used resins are polyesters and curing normally takes place at room temperature. Hand lay-up is labour intensive but requires little capital equipment. For these reasons it is often used to produce one-off specialist articles or large components such as swimming pools and boat hulls.

Another manual method of production is known as *spray-up*. In this method a spray gun charged with the matrix resin, chopped fibres, and curing agent, is used. This method is quick, cheap and efficient, although at suitable intervals the sprayed composite has to be rolled to release trapped air.

Let us consider just two moulding methods for the production of composite components, *die-moulding* and *bag-moulding*. Die-moulding is widely used for long production runs for components ranging in size from small domestic items to large commercial vehical panels. The material to be shaped is pressed between heated

Table 4.11   *Some properties of typical reinforcing fibres and matrix materials*

	Relative density	Young's modulus (GPa)	Tensile Strength (GPa)
Reinforcing fibres			
E Glass	2.55	72	1.5–3.0
S Glass	2.5	87	3.5
Carbon-pitch	2.0	380	2.0–2.4
Carbon-pan Type A high strength (XA)	1.8	220–240	3.0-3.3
Carbon-pan Type A high performance	1.8	220–240	3.3–3.6
Carbon-pan Type A high strain	1.8	220–240	3.7
Carbon-pan Type II high strength	1.8	250	2.7
Carbon-pan Type I high modulus	2.0	330–350	2.3–2.6
SiC whisker	3.2	480	7.0
Kevlar	1.47	130–180	2.6–3.5
Nomex	1.4	17.5	0.7
Polyamide (typical)	1.4	5.0	0.9
Matrix materials			
Steel	7.8	210	0.34–2.1
Aluminium alloys	2.7	70	0.14–0.62
Epoxy resin	1.2	2–3.5	0.05–0.09
Polyester resin	1.4	2–3.0	0.04–0.08

matched dies. The pressure required may be as high as 50 MPa. The feed material flows into the contours of the mould and when the temperature is high enough it rapidly cures. Good dimensional accuracy and detail are possible with this method, depending on the quality of the die used. The feed material, which already contains all necessary ingredients and the curing agent, may be in the form of sheet or simply fed in as a dough.

In the *bag moulding* process only one half of the mould is used to shape the component. In *vacuum-bagging* the laid-up material, which consists of heated pre-impregnated reinforcement, is sealed by a bag over the component. When vacuum pressure is applied to the bag, sufficient pressure is applied to the work piece to cure it (Figure 4.56).

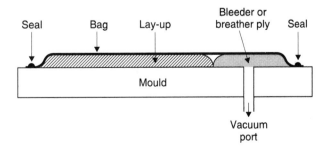

Figure 4.56   *Typical lay-up procedure using the vacuum-bagging process*

Autoclave moulding is a modification of vacuum forming where pressure in excess of atmospheric is used to produce high density products for critical applications, such as racing car and aircraft components. An *autoclave* is a recirculating oven, that is pressurized by an inert gas, often nitrogen. The sealed bag is still used to stabilize the component against the mould (Figure 4.57).

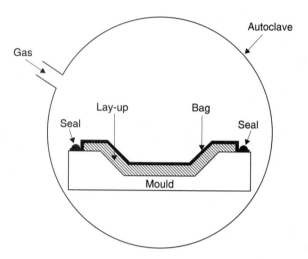

Figure 4.57 *Pressurized autoclave moulding process*

Moulding techniques for PMCs concludes our look at materials processing. There are many methods that we have not mentioned but space prevents us from doing so. The assignment at the end of this unit asks you to investigate some of these processes.

Selecting materials for engineered products

In this final, rather short element, we will attempt to select materials for a variety of engineering applications. On what criteria must we base our assumptions? The following example may help provide the answers:

Example 4.6

Let us imagine that we have been tasked with selecting three possible candidate materials suitable for the manufacture of the fuselage (body) of a passenger airliner.

The argument might go as follows:

An aircraft needs to be as light as possible, yet strong enough to overcome the effects of changing pressure and the constant buffeting cause by the airflow over the aircraft wings and body. The fuselage of an aircraft will be subject to complicated dynamic and static loads, that may cause it to twist and bend, as well as the low frequency cyclic loads imposed on the fuselage by the aircraft's pressurization system. We must also take into account the corrosion resistance of the chosen material and the ease with which it can be fabricated into large sheet which will be attached to the aircraft skeleton.

Thus our material must have good *structural efficiency*, that is good specific stiffness and strength. So we must choose a material with the highest yield stress and highest value of elastic modulus but with the lowest density.

Having selected our material on this basis we must then consider its toughness, that is its resistance to the propagation of cracks. Cracks of a critical length, if not detected, could cause catastrophic failure. If a material is stressed and a crack starts to grow there will come a time when the crack reaches a certain length, that without any further increase in stress the material will fail very rapidly. This certain length is known as the *critical crack length*, the tougher a material the larger the crack that can be tolerated and the greater the stress that may be applied, before a critical situation occurs.

The slow cycling caused by the aircraft's pressurization system and the vibration caused by the engines and environment, can cause premature failure by *fatigue*. Thus the necessity to ensure that our material has good fatigue resistance, this is a complicated subject which will not be dealt with in this text. Fatigue resistance is related to fracture toughness K_c (see earlier definition) of a material, so we will use this as our measure.

What about corrosion resistance? Well you will remember that we discussed the *electrochemical series* earlier and discovered that metals like silver, gold and copper were less likely to corrode when compared to metals at the other end of the table like magnesium. The exception to this rule was the *passive* metals which form a protective oxide layer such as, aluminium, titanium and stainless steel. Gold, silver and platinum are all heavy ductile metals with poor structural efficiency, so could not be considered as serious contenders, never mind the cost!

We will also need to consider the physical properties and the ease with which we can fabricate our candidate materials. Physical properties include thermal and electrical conductivity, how important might this be for a passenger airliner? Well in aircraft design, the fuselage is used as the earth return for electrical supplies, this removes the necessity for return wires and so reduces weight. Therefore electrical conductivity is of some importance!

The ease with which the material can be manufactured and repaired is also of importance. Bearing in mind all that has been said, if we now look at Table 4.12, we should be able to find three candidate materials that meet the criteria discussed above.

Consider first structural efficiency, i.e. low density, high strength and stiffness. Possible candidates include aluminium alloy, magnesium, titanium and carbon fibre. Monel, steel and nickel are all relatively heavy metals, that have relatively high densities.

If we now consider fracture toughness, then from the table, titanium and steel alloys come out well. Although not shown, carbon fibre when combined with a polymer matrix such as epoxy resin, is also relatively tough. Aluminium alloys are also reasonably tough materials. Since we also agreed that fracture toughness K_c was to be our measure of fatigue resistance, then the above materials also meet this criteria.

Lets now consider corrosion resistance, mild steel is not a passive material and has poor corrosion resistance, so at this stage must be rejected remembering that it is also a relatively heavy material. Monel has good anti-corrosive properties, since it is an alloy of nickel and copper but must be rejected because of its relatively high density. Magnesium alloys have excellent structural efficiency but very poor resistance to corrosion, so will be rejected. Aluminium and titanium are passive and if aluminium alloys are clad with a pure aluminium coating they will also possess good anti-corrosive properties. Carbon fibre reinforced plastic materials are also resistant to corrosion and are, therefore, still candidate materials.

The electrical conductivity of aluminium is excellent and titanium has good conductivity, when compared with the non-metals. Carbon fibre reinforced plastics have limited conductivity which is provided by the carbon reinforcing material. However, since CFRPs are composites, the addition of some conducting agent such as aluminium strand can be added to improve their electrical conductivity and this is often done in practice.

Table 4.12 *Selected properties of a range of materials*

Metals

	Density (kg m^{-3})	Melting temp. (K)	Thermal conductivity (Wm^{-1} K^{-1})	Electical resistivity (10^{-8} Ωm)	Tensile strength (MN m^{-2})	Yield stress (MN m^{-2})	Young's modulus (GN m^{-2})
Aluminium, pure	2700	933	201	2.65	80	75	71
Aluminium alloy (duralumin)	2800	800	180	5.00	500	450	71
Brass (70 Cu/30 Zn)	8520	1227	110	6.33	300	85	101
Copper, pure	8960	1356	385	1.67	215	45	130
Gold	19300	1336	296	2.3	125	0	71
Iron, pure	7870	1810	80	9.71	210	120	211
Lead, pure	11340	600	35	20.65	20	0	16
Magnesium	1740	923	150	4.45	185	60	45
Monel (70 Ni/30 Cu)	8800	1600	210	48	515	240	200
Nickel	8900	1726	59	6.84	300	60	219
Nickel alloy (nimonic)	7990	1600	12	132	990	800	219
Nickel-silver	8685	1333	29	24	350	125	133
Silver	10500	1234	419	1.6	140	5	83
Solder, soft (63 Sn/37 Pb)	8420	456	50	40.5	50	35	28
Stainless steel	7930	1800	150	70	570	215	215
Steel, mild	7860	1700	63	12	690	350	212
Tin	7300	505	65	12.8	25	20	50
Titanium	4500	1943	23	55.0	240	100	120
Zinc	7140	693	111	5.92	115	25	105

Non-Metals

	Density (kg m^{-3})	Melting temp. (K)	Thermal conductivity (Wm^{-1}K^{-1})	Electrical resistivity (10^{-8} Ωm)	Ultimate Tensile strength (MN m^{-2})	Young's modulus (GN m^{-2})
Aluminia, ceramic	3800	2300	29	~10^{15}	~150	345
Carbon, graphite	2300	3800	150	~10^{-5}	~20	27
Concrete	2400	–	0.1	–	~5	14
Epoxy resin	1120	–	0.17	–	50	4.5
PTFE	2200	–	0.25	~10^{18}	22	0.34
Glass, plate	2500	1400	1.0	~10^{5}	~100	71
Magnesium oxide	3600	3200	40.0	~10^{7}	~100	207
Nylon	1150	470	0.25	~10^{16}	70	1.5
Perspex	1190	350	0.2	~10^{13}	50	3
Polythene	920	410	0.2	~10^{16}	13	0.2
Polypropene	900	450	0.24	~10^{15}	35	1.2
Polystyrene	1050	510	0.08	~10^{19}	50	3.1
Rubber (polyisoprene)	910	300	0.15	–	17	0.02

What about the fabrication of aluminium alloys, titanium alloys and CFRPs? Well both aluminium alloys and CFRPs, are relatively easy to work. This is not the case with titanium alloys. Never-the-less all three of these materials are used extensively in the production of aircraft. Titanium alloys have the advantage of having high melting points, so can be used anywhere on an aircraft where heat might be a problem, such as around the engines and jetpipes. CFRPs, although relatively expensive are also used extensively for aircraft production. Aluminium alloys have been and still are used for the production of aircraft fuselage skins, since they meet all the criteria given earlier.

We would therefore recommend aluminium alloys, titanium alloys and carbon fibre reinforced plastics as candidate materials.

When you are faced with making choices for suitable materials you should consider their static strength and stiffness, structural efficiency, fatigue resistance, corrosion resistance, as well as their availability, cost and fabrication characteristics. For specialized requirements you may also have to consider their erosion, abrasion and wear characteristics; their compatibility with other materials, and their thermal and electrical properties.

We will now consider another example, which will be much more familiar to you:

Example 4.7

Select suitable candidate materials for the manufacture of a domestic three-pin electrical plug.

We need to first familiarize ourselves with the components that go to make up a plug. There is the plug body, electrical lead connectors, fuse holder, and the three conducting pins.

The plug body will need to be an excellent insulator, if we are to handle the plug safely. It will require some resistance to the heat that may be generated by the electrical wiring, due to the power being carried. It needs to be reasonably tough and resistant to rough handling. The body also needs to be manufactured from a material which can easily be mass produced at a competitive price.

Ceramics are excellent insulators, but are brittle and fragile, so can easily be cracked and broken during use. Polymers are excellent insulators and can be made with a very wide range of properties. So which polymers are best?

We need a relatively tough and resilient material. Rubbers are able to absorb vast quantities of energy and therefore would be resistant to rough handling, they are excellent insulators. The melting temperature of rubbers are in general lower than thermoset polymers such as phenol-formaldehyde (phenolic) and melamine-formaldehyde (melamine). Natural rubbers have poor resistance to the environment, although butyl-rubbers have good resistance to heat and chemicals.

Thermoplastics are in general not suitable for plug bodies and similar applications where heat is a problem, because they tend to soften and lose their shape at elevated temperatures. Thermoplastics, however, in the form of ABS (acrylonitrile-butadiene-styrene) and PVC (polyvinyl chloride) are used for a wealth of domestic applications such as telephone hand-sets, housings for vacuum cleaners and grass mowers, water pipes and guttering, insulation for wire and curtain rails. The decision on which polymer to choose, is not quite as simple as you may have first thought. From the above discussion, a thermoset plastic appears to have the desired properties. In fact phenolics are used predominantly for the manufacture of plugs, switches, sockets and car distributor heads. Various rubbers are often used for plugs and electrical connectors that are required for outdoor applications.

The fuse holder link, terminal screws and conducting pins, all need to be made from a good conducting material. In addition the terminal screws and fittings need to be robust enough to take the torsional loads created by fitting and removing the conducting wires from the appliance. Suitable conductors might include, aluminium, silver and copper. Silver is a relatively soft and weak material and is expensive, so can be eliminated, even though its conductivity is slightly better than copper. The conductivity of both copper and aluminium is excellent, but pure aluminium is weaker than copper, so perhaps we should choose copper. However, copper tends to oxidize (passivate) very easily particularly at elevated temperatures, which might be experienced at the terminals. So pure copper might not be totally appropriate; if we alloy copper with zinc, we produce brass, which becomes much less suceptible to oxidation, but retains the strength characteristics necessary at the terminals. Brass is in fact commonly used for the terminal fittings and screws of electrical plugs, as well as the conducting pins. The fuse links may be pure copper or brass.

All polymer materials can be easily moulded and are very suitable for mass production. Copper, zinc and aluminium are also easy to produce and for the small amounts required in the conducting parts of a plug, they are relatively inexpensive. Note that in our choice of materials for an electrical plug, there are many similiar candidate materials which may be used. It is the job of the materials engineer to make the best choice for each and every engineering application.

For our final example, we will consider materials selection in a slightly different way:

Example 4.8

Compare and contrast the differences in the materials and fabrication techniques necessary for:

(a) a large industrial flywheel used for a crank press, and
(b) a flywheel for a child's clockwork toy.

A flywheel is designed to store energy and use up this stored energy when required. This is achieved by winding up a large mass and rotating it at suitable speed. The rotational kinetic energy produced at the shaft enables further rotation to take place even after the power source has been removed.

In the crank press the flywheel is run up using an electrical motor, the stored energy is then used for the actually pressing operation itself. This avoids the need for a very heavy duty and powerful motor, which would be expensive and less energy efficient. So the flywheel needs to be heavy, tough and resistant to fatigue and creep loads. It must also have sufficient strength to avoid *bursting* at high rotational velocities. Steel alloys and cast irons are often used for flywheel construction.

The size of flywheel necessary for typical pressing operations may be up to two metres in diameter possibly weighing two tons or more, dependent obviously on the speed of operation and the energy required for pressing operations. If we are interested in one-off or very small batch production, we could sand cast the flywheel, and machine the hub to ensure that the flywheel runs true. However, machining operations are time consuming and expensive, especially for such a large structure. An alternative might be to fabricate the flywheel from smaller segmented parts and bolt these together. Another alternative might be to spin the outer, very large rim of the flywheel and weld to the inner flywheel disc and pre-turned flywheel hub. By virtue of the size of the flywheel, it is unlikely that a die casting or forging process would be used.

Now how does this compare with the flywheel of a childs clockwork toy? Well obviously there is the question of scale, the toy flywheel will be very small, able to supply sufficient energy to propel the toy once released, but not too large to prevent the child winding up the toy. Safety must also be considered, the flywheel should not have sharp edges or be manufactured from toxic materials. Metals in this case may not be appropriate; the material will still need to be tough and robust but will not need to be as dense as that used for the industrial version. It will also need to be made from a material capable of mass production. The loads imposed on the flywheel will be minimal and elevated temperatures are not involved. Thus an ideal candidate might be a material from the polymer range. Thermoplastics such as polyethylene, polypropylene and nylon would be suitable. All these polymers can be injection moulded, making them suitable for mass production.

In order to make choices about suitable materials, there are many sources of reference to help you. For example, data on the properties of materials can be found in reference books and technical data books, held in most libraries. Specific information about components and specific materials may be obtained from manufacturers data catalogues. Information on materials testing procedures can be obtained from British Standards Publications

Finally then, try to remember that, when selecting a material, a balance has to be reached between its mechanical and physical properties, its ease of fabrication and availability, as well as its cost!

Activity 4.9

A toy manufacturing company, Micro Models, is about to embark on the manufacture of a working model (1:12) traction engine. They have asked you to advise them on the selection of materials to be used in various component parts of the model traction engine. Suggest, with reasons, materials to be used for each of the following:

(a) engine flywheel
(b) driving wheels
(c) chassis
(d) steam cylinder
(e) water tank
(f) mechanical linkages

Present your recommendations in the form of a briefing pack for the Technical Director and Production Manager of Micro Models. Your briefing pack should be word processed and should contain relevant data and specifications, where appropriate.

Multiple choice questions

1 Thermosetting plastics

   A never cross-link during curing
   B cannot be re-worked or reheated
   C have the ability to be remoulded and reheated
   D are also known as thermoplastics.

2 The structure of a pure metal is

   A crystalline
   B amorphous
   C opaque
   D linear.

3 With respect to an electrochemical corrosion cell

   A an oxidation reaction always reduces the energy of the atom
   B corrosion always takes place at the anode
   C a cathodic reaction is an oxidation reaction
   D in a zinc-copper cell the copper electrode acts as the anode.

4 In order to ensure that tensile tests are carried out accurately, specimen dimensions should be checked in accordance with:

   A catalogue of metals AMC 54
   B Brinell data sheets
   C BSEN 10002
   D engineer's year book.

5 The slope of the linear part of a graph, resulting from a tensile test, is a measure of specimen

   A stiffness
   B toughness
   C Poisson's ratio
   D yield strength.

6 In order to establish the fatigue strength of a material it is subjected to:

   A a constant static load
   B some form of dynamic cyclic stressing
   C cyclic loads above its yield strength
   D a continuous steady increase in load.

7 Ultrasonic testing

   A requires an energy source such as Cobalt-60 to obtain accurate results
   B uses a direct current to activate the piezoelectric transducer
   C is particularly suited for the examination of composite materials
   D uses electromagnetic radio waves.

8 For pure metals an increase in yield stress and hardness can be achieved by

   A heat treating to increase the grain size
   B cold-working to increase the dislocation density

C a reduction in the number of foreign atoms within the lattice structure

D cold-working to reduce the dislocation density.

9 Die casting is confined mainly to

A aluminium or zinc based metals
B ferrous metals
C nickel chromium alloys
D titanium alloys.

10 When selecting a material for its strength and lightness the most important property is its

A specific strength
B specific stiffness
C fracture toughness
D density.

Unit 5 — Design development

Summary

This unit will help you to acquire the skills required to develop and communicate designs, and successfully produce design assignments either alone or as a team. It will also complement your communication skills.

The unit is divided into three elements. The first deals with design briefs for an electromechanical engineered product and an engineering service. The second is concerned with producing and evaluating design solutions for an electromechanical engineered product and an engineering service. The final element deals with the technical drawings used to communicate designs for engineered products and engineering services.

Before we start it is necessary to establish what types of an engineered product and engineering service you should be considering. The engineered product should be an *electromechanical device.* For example, a remote controlled garage door or an electronically activated locking system, or any design that is a combination of electrical or electronic components used with a mechanical device.

The service chosen should involve *installation* or *maintenance.* For the purposes of this unit, maintenance is assumed to include repair. For example a computerized network to control factory production or a distribution service for one of the utilities such as gas, electricity, etc. Try to think of some service that you are familiar with.

Think hard about the types of engineered product and engineering service you choose. In both cases, try considering something not too complicated but at the same time one which satisfies the requirements of your assignments.

We will first look at a description of design, then consider the requirements of a design brief. The principles of a design brief will equally apply to both an engineered product and to an engineering service.

Description of design

We have always designed things, it is a basic characteristic of us all to design to meet our needs. It does not require a special ability to design, as often a craftsman may make an item without the need of drawings or modelling before the completion of his product. In industry, where many items are to be manufactured, the activities of designing and manufacturing are quite separate.

For the purposes of this unit, engineering design and manufacture are considered to be where the process of manufacturing a product cannot proceed until the design of it is complete, this is the usual procedure for the manufacture of the majority of factory made engineering products.

In some cases, e.g. in the automobile industry, the time taken to design a car can be several years, whereas the time to manufacture each individual vehicle may be measured in hours.

If a product cannot be manufactured until design is finished, then at least it is clear what the design process needs to achieve – it must provide a complete description of the product that is to be manufactured, with almost nothing is left to the discretion of the production team. The shape, materials, dimensional tolerances and finishes, etc., will all be specified by the designers.

The essential design activity then, is the producing of a set of drawings which completely satisfy the customers or marketing design requirements, and equally as important, are suitable for communicating the design manufacturing requirements to the production department.

Therefore the drawings will play a very important part in the design and manufacture operations and are controlled by a specification to enable a common standard of presentation to be achieved (British Standard 308, Engineering Drawing Practice, is the usual accepted standard). Later, we will discuss the requirements of the drawing 'design package' required to manufacture a product.

Basically, design is about 'problems finding'. If this seems odd, the design process involves addressing the problems identified by the customer and the marketing department. Problem finding is far more important than problem solving!

Einstein said, *'The formulation of a problem is often more essential than its solution, which may be merely a matter of mathematics or of experimental skill. To raise new questions, new possibilities, to regard old problems from new angles requires creative imagination and a real advance in science'.*

The design brief

Here we will consider what is a design brief, this can only be decided after some thought has been given as to the design changes or requirements. In other words what do you expect the design to achieve, if you have completed the exercise on Einstein's statement, you may have produced a design brief of sorts.

Design problems usually come by a statement to the designer from either a customer requirement or from the company management. These statements are referred to as design 'briefs', they can vary considerably in both content and form.

The normal 'brief' statement from the company management is probably to improve the design of an existing product that is familiar to the company designers, it may be related to performance, size or weight, etc., or maybe as a redesign to reduce manufacturing costs to keep the product competitive on the market.

Other design problems occur by statements such as 'it would be nice if' or 'is it possible to have'. Often this type of comment would be expected from a product user to the marketing department, who in turn would approach the designers to find whether the customer suggestions could be made feasible.

Perhaps the greatest task given to designers in recent times was the brief given by the USA President Kennedy in 1961 whose brief was, *'Before the end of the decade, to land a man on the moon and bring him back safely'.*

The only constraint in this brief being one of time, so in this case the designers had a fixed goal, only one constraint and large resources of money, materials and people to work on the project. Think of all the problems and sub-problems that must have occurred.

It is important to note that a design 'brief' does not specify what the design solution will be, and there is no way of proceeding from the stated 'brief' to a proposed solution without designing.

What is generally expected from a design brief would be certain constraints stated by the customer and legal constraints such as the product safety, also standards and legislation relevant to the product. This is applicable to an engineering service equally as well.

The considerations that should be taken into account to produce a design brief are: (a) customer requirements, (b) standards and legislation, and (c) constraints. We shall consider each of these factors in turn.

Customer requirements

Customer requirements include:

- functional considerations (technical specification)
- ergonomic considerations (including ease of use and adaptability to suit different users)
- aesthetic considerations (details on styling, general appeal, range of colour options, etc.)
- quality (type of materials, reliability and expected life)
- cost (initial purchase price)
- whole life cost (ease and cost of repair, the need for routine maintenance and the cost of spare parts and consumable items, as well as purchase price)
- quantity (prototypes and production costs can be directly related to the quantities involved.
- size and weight (this is often is of prime importance to the customer)
- time-scale (involves creating a realistic planning and development schedule to meet customer requirements)
- tolerance.

Standards and legislation

The considerations that may apply under this heading include:

- Health and Safety legislation
- codes of practice
- conventions
- British Standards.

- European Union directives
- International Standards.

Standards and legislation varies widely according to the type of product or service. You are expected to be aware of any legislation relevant to the product or service you are studying, you are advised to consult the latest BSI *(British Standard Institute)* catalogue for the relevant standards and information you need.

Constraints

The constraints that may impinge on the design brief include:

- technological
- resources (labour, materials, plant)
- environment
- cost.

In most cases it is necessary to work well within the bounds of existing technology while recognizing that some design briefs may demand technological development before implementation.

The brief need not necessarily apply to a new invention, it is quite acceptable to redesign part of a product, for example, to reduce the number of components or take advantage of new materials and technology. Having checked the customer requirements, standards and legislation and the constraints imposed on you, you should now be able to produce a design brief.

A design brief is a description of the customer's needs, so it is vital to get the design brief correct. You should discuss the brief with your 'customer', ideally someone in industry, more likely your lecturer or tutor, using the listed considerations as a 'ticking list'. Make absolutely certain that the brief *clearly and unambiguously* states the customer requirements!

Feasibility studies

The next stage is a feasibility study of the design 'brief'. This entails an in-depth study of the brief to establish whether a feasible design is possible to satisfy all the requirements the customer expects, it is at this stage all sorts of problems need consideration. Sometimes these problems will require a compromised solution agreed between you the design team and the customer.

By the time you and your team have finished the feasibility study and found proposed solutions to satisfy the design brief, many ideas and solutions are experienced, remember though at this stage the task has only been to see whether the design brief is feasible, and probably very little real design work has taken place, apart from investigations and design possibilities.

The problems most generally encountered in engineered products are perhaps those associated with weight or size, and other problems may occur by not being able to keep pace with changes in technology, especially electronic devices, and you could find your design is outdated 'before it has left the ground'.

Test your knowledge 5.2

Acme Tools wish to extend their range of small production tools to include an adjustable jig for holding a Eurocard printed circuit board during inspection and assembly. In use, the jig is to be clamped to a workbench and it should rotate and swivel to allow inspection of the printed circuit board from any angle.

What items would form an initial design brief for this product? What questions would you need to ask Acme Tools?

A client has sent you a fax message concerning your initial design proposals for a product that is to be incoporated within a small yacht.

Fax message:

Thanks for your proposal concerning the A11 project.

Your basic ideas look good however we require the following changes to the design:

50% reduction in external dimensions (essential for bulkhead mounting)

40% reduction in weight (we suggest diecast aluminium alloy rather than pressed steel with PVC coating)

Please advise on feasibility.

List and explain the likely effects of the changes proposed by the customer.

When you are confident that you will be able to further the ideas expressed in the design brief from the customer and you are satisfied your feasibility study shows you would be capable of handling the design, the next stage is to submit to your customer a design proposal.

Design proposals

By proposing solutions, a greater understanding of the overall design problem will be gained which in itself will show many sub-problems. The design proposal can take a considerable amount of time and money to investigate and produce, it will need to convince the customer that you are, as a company, capable of solving the problems of design, and have the expertise and qualified staff to do so.

On an elaborate equipment that requires knowledge that is close to the edge of technology, for instance, a ship's complete radar system, the design proposal can cost thousands of pounds and take months to complete. If the contract demands a competitive tender, as it almost certainly would, then even more time will be spent to estimate the cost of the contract, which is a difficult task as the final design specification has yet to be agreed.

Fortunately your team project need not be as elaborate, but you will still need to analyse your customers design brief and your own feasibility study before any design proposal can be produced.

The design proposal sent to the customer basically consists of:

- a provisional design specification
- proposed overall contract costs
- delivery dates
- servicing and maintenance
- any legal requirements.

The above is very much simplified but you will need to consider each of them to enable you to write the design specification for your own project.

Design specification

Up to this point only a few staff have been fully employed in analysing the customer brief and submitting the design proposal. Very little real detail design has taken place and only a broad view of the customer requirements has been formed. Assuming that the design proposals have been agreed by the customer, your company will then be given the task of producing a detailed design specification.

A basic project design team would be formed to look at the problems in greater detail and write the design specification which will be similar to the proposal but with more detail of the design targets and time-scales that must be achieved.

In the case of your own project, you will probably be working as part of a team of three or four students. Collectively you will act as the project design team. Furthermore, you will have multiple tasks to handle in much the same way as a real team in industry.

Some of the departments and personnel that will form the nucleus of a design team, will have already been involved with the project right from the start (i.e. at the design brief and design proposal stages). These people will therefore have prior knowledge of some of the problems they will encounter and they will thus be ideally suited to producing the design specification, which will hopefully meet with approval of the customer.

We will now briefly look at the team required to handle a design specification in engineering and this may give you an insight into possible career paths.

In small design and manufacturing companies, one person may take responsibility for more than one task (as you will, in working within a team on your project.). As an example, the Company Managing Director may also take on the role of Financial Director and perhaps also be directly responsible for staff recruitment. But for our purpose we will assume the company is of reasonable size each task is allocated to an individual (Figure 5.1).

At the Company Board level, both the Financial and Research and Design Directors will need to agree the necessary costs of the intended specification. The design team, usually headed by a Project Manager, will basically consist of electronic/electrical engineers, mechanical engineers, designers and draughtsmen in the design

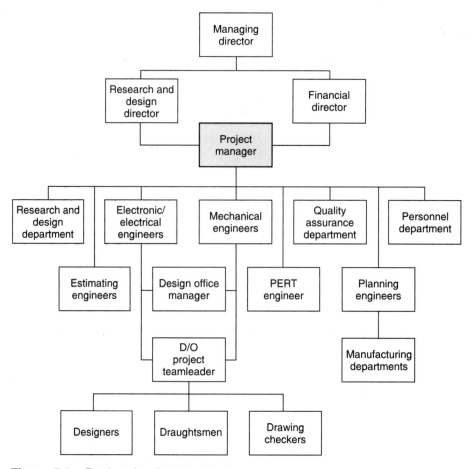

Figure 5.1   *Design development team*

office. In addition, planning engineers will consult with the team and plan a task and time-scales chart, the chart itself will in all probability be generated by a PERT Engineer (programme evaluation and review technique).

Planning and Manufacturing Departments will need to assess available facilities and whether any special machinery or test equipment should be acquired and the Quality Assurance Department should check that the company is capable of dealing with the required standards of the design specification or brief.

The Personnel Department may be tasked to find staff with capable skills, experience and specialized knowledge if the project requires it. When the tasks of all departments have been completed the design specification can then be written. When this specification is agreed with the customer, a contract will then be drawn up, stating the cost to the customer, date of delivery, servicing contract details and any legalities that may apply to the main contract. There may also be a penalty clause (for non-delivery of goods on the agreed date) written into the contract.

As the project develops and unseen problems occur the contract may require 'fine tuning' by both the contractor and the customer. In the electronics industry, the continuous improvements to available devices sometimes make design outdated as the project develops so certain areas may be subject to renegotiation with the customer.

While considering the design proposal, many people were involved and they will almost certainly form the basis of the final project design team. Now each will be responsible for their own department's role in the progress of the project. The main responsibilities of each will be to monitor the allocated costs to their department, to establish time-scales of the different tasks and to formulate the design objectives.

Matrix management

In setting up the project team a 'matrix organization' is often adopted in which the Project Manager is allocated teams from different departments in the organization. The team members report in the normal way to their line managers but have a reporting link to the Project Manager as well. For instance the drawing design office team are responsible to the DO Manager or Chief Draughtsman but report the progress of the drawing package to the Project Manager.

The advantages of adopting a matrix structure are:

1 Flexible deployment of the company resources.
2 Effective availability of specialized knowledge.
3 The ability to run more than one project at a time.
4 Better career paths in the specialist areas.

In Figure 5.2 we can see that the various Project Managers can have access to the expertise of all the other departments needed to execute the research, design and production required, without having the need to set up a unique team for each function of design and manufacture of his own individual project.

It often happens that the Project Manager has staff working in his team that in the company job structure are at a higher level than

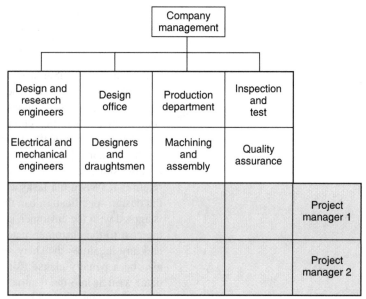

Figure 5.2   *Example of matrix management*

himself, but these staff are usually highly qualified experts in their field and they are available for the needs of any company project.

The design specification can take a considerable amount of time and money to investigate and produce; in industry it would need to convince the customer that you are, as a company, capable of solving the problems of design, and have the expertise and qualified staff to do so.

Before continuing let's assume you have been given your design assignments and that you need to complete them in say, twenty-four weeks, and you have, as a class, been divided into teams of three or four students to produce the assignment. Each of you will need to be tasked to investigate and solve the problems involved with your design, and *all of you will need to meet the time-scales*. You will need to produce an Action Plan.

What is an Action Plan?

Basically, an Action Plan is a chart of tasks that are time related and show the team responsibilities to the design, it will determine how long relative tasks should take. It is a *vitally important* design document and must be produced at the very beginning of your assignment.

You should, of course, design your own Action Plan to suit your requirements, but Figure 5.3 will give you some idea of how it should look. You may of course need to adjust the time-scales and functions to suit your assignments, but in principle the chart will be similar. Planning is an essential part of the success or otherwise of an assignment, without careful planning, you as a team will find

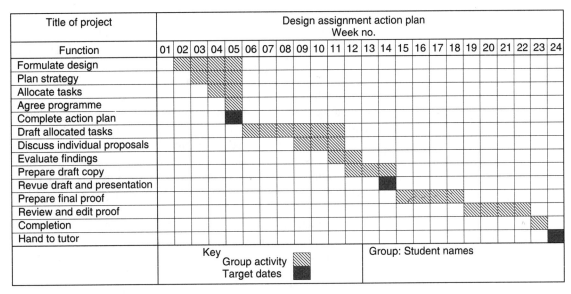

Title of project	Design assignment action plan Week no.																							
Function	01	02	03	04	05	06	07	08	09	10	11	12	13	14	15	16	17	18	19	20	21	22	23	24
Formulate design																								
Plan strategy																								
Allocate tasks																								
Agree programme																								
Complete action plan																								
Draft allocated tasks																								
Discuss individual proposals																								
Evaluate findings																								
Prepare draft copy																								
Revue draft and presentation																								
Prepare final proof																								
Review and edit proof																								
Completion																								
Hand to tutor																								

Key
Group activity
Target dates

Group: Student names

Figure 5.3 *Example of an action plan*

difficulty in achieving the target dates. It will be up to you to interpret the assignment requirements, but of course your tutor is available to assist you, but try to plan your actions first .

It is *very important* to keep the dates you commit yourself to as 'set-out' in the plan, also any dates set by your tutor must be adhered to, such as completion of action plan, revue of draft and verbal presentation and of course the final date to hand the project to your tutor. Failure to achieve these dates could lose you marks.

The Action Plan may look simple enough, but there is need to investigate many areas of design to succeed in your assignment, so seriously consider what you want your design to accomplish and adhere the plan. Before you start on your own design ideas, practice writing a design specification, consider what is required and work as a team, or preferably ask the tutor to involve the whole class as this will help you understand the needs for your own assignment,

Presenting your work

Whether you are individually or as a group presenting your projects and assignments, each of you need to try to observe the following methods of delivery. Your style, mannerisms, speech, gestures, eye-to-eye contact with your listeners, clarity of expression, appearance and 'personality' can make a considerable impact on them.

You will, while presenting your assignments, be the sole focus of attention for most of the time; your style of delivery can result in acceptance and assimilation, or rejection, of your assignment presentation content. Your 'expressiveness', i.e. your obvious enthusiasm for your project, your perceived desire to communicate and your ability to generate listener interest, can 'make or break' your presentation.

Techniques involved are the ability to speak clearly, to modulate voice tone and pitch, use gestures sparingly but effectively, and to speak at a pace that does not prevent assimilation and understanding. It is suggested that 110 words per minute may be the 'normal' rate of delivery and that a rate beyond 200 w.p.m. results in a rapid decline in assimilation.

Your delivery style should be neither too casual nor to much of a boring oratory. The best way would be to first practise until you are able to sound natural, interesting and relaxed.

Timing is important along with the emphasis of key points, these may require an intensity of speech, a pause, a gesture or a visual illustration. A carefully timed pause can serve as a signal for a key statement.

Some mannerisms (e.g. of voice, posture) may cause irritation, even offend and alienate, creating a difficulty in communicating with your listeners, if you are aware of a mannerism that may annoy, try to eradicate it.

It is vital that you should convey a genuine enthusiasm and interest. Non-verbal cues, facial expressions, eye contact (the absence of which can be interpreted by the listeners as nervousness, fear or lack of interest), use of hands is all important.

Where your presentation involves the use of visual aids, they should be prepared in advance and in the order required, so continuity of presentation runs smoothly.

Timing

It is very important to adhere to the time allowed to present your assignment, therefore you individually or as a group need to plan who will be responsible for which part or parts, you may only be given as little as ten to fifteen minutes to complete your presentation, so it necessary to draw up a simple 'plan of action' to ensure the smooth presentation of your assignment.

We would suggest you take into account the following in the sequence shown:

1 Introduction of yourself or group, it may seem unnecessary to do this to a class of colleagues but you may well be a stranger to the over-seeing lecturer.
2 State clearly the objective of your project or assignment and, in the case of a 'design assignment', briefly why or how you finally choose the subject for design.
3 Now talk about how your ideas came to fruition including marketing, costs, manufacturing and customer guarantees, if applicable, these may be split as tasks to be dealt with by other team members, in which case they need to present them individually.
4 Be prepared to answer questions, preferably at the end of your presentation, *think* and *answer carefully.* If you are unable to do so, say that you will investigate further and let the questioner know as soon as possible.
5 Finally, thank your listeners, especially those that may have contributed during question time.
6 Above all, *be confident in yourself.*

Activity 5.1

You have been commissioned by an environmental group to produce a design proposal for a prototype of an environmentally friendly car. Use your library to carry out some reasearch on this topic and produce an initial design proposal for a vehicle that will:

(a) be suitable as a town car
(b) carry one adult and two young children, plus family shopping
(c) must be easy to park
(d) must be inexepnsive to run.

Present your findings to the class using appropriate handouts and visual aids. Allow plenty of time for questions at the end of your presentation.

Design solutions

Having dealt at some length with design briefs and design specifications, we can now consider how you should go about handling a design specification (assuming you are now prepared to go ahead with your proposed design). At this stage, it is worth remembering that the design specification is not a design solution.

The design path

Having established your design team that now has a reasonable insight into the design requirements of the project specification, we can set up a design programme of the project from start to finish. However. before designing begins we need to consider what design strategy should be adopted.

Design strategies

What is a design strategy?. It is basically having a design method and it consists of two things:

1 A *framework of intended actions* within which to work
2 Some form of *management control function* to enable you to adapt your actions as the problem unfolds.

Using a design strategy may seem to divert effort and time from the main task of designing, but this may not be a bad thing, as the purpose of a design strategy will make you think of the way design problems will be dealt with. It also provides you with an awareness as to where the design team is going and how it intends to get there.

The purpose then of having a strategy is to ensure that design activities are realistic with respect to the constraints of both time and resources within which the design team has to work. In a manufacturing company the most used strategy is a sequence of actions that have previously been applied to an already existing product.

For instance, to design a variation of an already designed electromechanical device or engineering service, the strategy most likely to be used for the new variation will be the same tactics and design methods used for the previous design. This would therefore be making use of a 'pre-established' strategy. The relevant tactics would be drawn from conventional techniques and rational methods already familiar to the design team. This type of strategy applies to innovative designs.

It is not always possible to have a design strategy, as would be the case in research design situations but having no particular plan of action would be a type of strategy in itself. This could be referred to as an 'inventive' strategy. The type of final design may be purely inventive, where no previous market exists.

Often the designers may not know when or what the final outcome may be, although hopefully they may achieve some degree of success in designing a material, product or engineering service that can be commercially exploited. The relevant tactics would be mainly creative.

The two strategies mentioned are extreme forms. In all probability, most designs require a compromise between the two, certain parts of the project design may need the inventive strategy if it calls for unknown areas of engineering design.

The 'pre-established' strategy is predominantly a convergent design approach, whereas the 'inventive' strategy is predominantly a 'divergent' approach. Usually the aim of a design strategy is to converge onto a final, evaluated and detailed design.

Sometimes in reaching that final design it may be necessary in some areas of the design to diverge, so as to widen the search for new ideas and solutions. Therefore the overall design process is mainly convergent, but has elements of divergent thinking.

Convergent thinkers are usually good at detail design, and evaluating and choosing the most suitable solution from a range of options. On the other hand, divergent thinkers are best at conceptual design problems and are able to produce a wide range of alternative solutions.

The design team needs both types of thinkers for a successful design, but generally engineering promotes and develops only convergent thinkers.

There are basically six stages in a design action framework that should be adopted right from the start of the design process:

1 Clarifying objectives
2 Establishing functions
3 Setting requirements
4 Generating alternatives
5 Evaluating alternatives
6 Improving details.

Now let us look in more detail at the stages that make up the design process and expand the meaning of each:

1 Clarifying objectives

This stage would in all probability have been dealt with during the design brief and design proposals stages, when the objectives of the design would be stated. But you would still need clarify them before design can commence.

Aim

To clarify the design objectives and sub-objectives, and the relationships between them.

Method

This is best achieved by discussions with the design team and questions to the customer.

2 Establishing functions

Although the customer may have specified the functions expected from the design the designer may find a more radical or innovative solution by reconsidering the level of the problem definition. He or she may be able to offer the customer a better solution to the functional problems of the design in excess to the expected at no extra cost.

Aim

To establish the functions required.

Method

Break down the overall function into sub-functions. The sub-functions will comprise of all the functions expected within the product.

3 Setting requirements

Design problems are usually all set within certain limits, these limits may be cost, weight, size, safety or performance etc., or any combination of them.

Aim

To produce an accurate specification of the performance of the designed product.

Method

Identify the required performance attributes, these may well have been considered at the design feasibility study stage.

4 Generate alternatives

Even if you think you have a good design solution always look further, if time and costs permit for an alternative solution, hopefully better than the one you thought would be an ideal design.

Aim

To have a choice of solutions to allow comparisons of ideas in solving the design requirements.

Method

It would help to draw several design layout drawings to enable discussions to take place with the design team and the customer.

5 Evaluate alternatives

When some alternative design proposals have been thought about and maybe some design layouts have been produced, the evaluation of the alternatives can be discussed.

Aim

To evaluate the alternatives, choose the ones that satisfy the customer requirements and are good value to him.

Method

Compare the value of the alternative design proposals against the original proposal agreed with the customer on the basis of performance.

6 Improving details

There are mainly two reasons improving details, they are either aimed at increasing the product's value to the customer or reducing the cost to the producer.

Aim

To increase or maintain the value of the product to the customer at the same time reducing its cost to the producer.

Method

This can be approached using two methods, one is called Value Engineering and the other Value Analysis.

Value engineering and value analysis

Value engineering

A great deal of design work in practice is concerned not with the creation of radical new design concepts but with making modifications to existing product designs. Value engineering is used for this purpose, but it is difficult to establish without a prototype or model of the design project, as it basically requires listing of all the separate components of the product so that the function of each may be identified and evaluated. For instance, it is often found that further standardization is possible from one unit assembly to another that was not previously obvious from the design drawings. This often results from the complexity of the design break-down and the team not being aware of the different approaches to the solving of problems within the same team. Hence the team leader should keep an eye on the design as it progresses and check that the team tries to standardize parts and components wherever possible, by doing this he will make a valuable contribution to the success of the product.

When carrying out a value engineering exercise, it will often be found that some manufactured parts are over-designed for their required function or, by using different manufacturing techniques, improvements can be made to the reliability of the product. It is important to remember though, any design change due to the value engineering exercise should not diminish the customer requirements of the product and, if anything, should enhance it.

Some manufacturers may purchase a competitor's product to enable them to subject it to the value engineering method, and afterwards design and market an improved competitive version. This is one way of learning without resorting to industrial espionage.

It does not take much imagination to see how this method has been applied to industries concerned with the motor, electronics and domestic appliance markets. So we are looking for ways of reducing costs without reducing value or adding value without adding cost. This design stage requires both critical and creative thinking, it means critically looking at the design as it is and creatively thinking how it could be improved. Care must taken not to change the design concept purely for the sake of change as can sometimes happen.

The aim must always be to achieve high value functions with low cost components. A checklist for cost reduction guidelines can be as follows:

1 Standardize   Can parts be standard rather than special?
2 Modify   Is there a satisfactory cheaper material?
3 Reduce   Can the number of components be reduced?
                 Can several components be combined into one?
4 Simplify   Is there a simpler alternative? Is there an easier assembly sequence? Is there a simpler shape?
5 Eliminate   Can any function and therefore its components, be eliminated altogether? Are any components redundant?

Value analysis

Value analysis can perhaps be best described by a product that meets the needs of the customer at a competitive price. This can be achieved in a similar manner to value engineering but with greater consideration to the customer/market. This does not mean paring the price down to rock bottom, as the product in some cases may be designed to suit popular demand, take for instance a car radio tuner, push button tuning is more popular than knob tuning, although the cost may be considerably higher, the customer may accept this as better value.

No modifications to a product should diminish the customer's requirements. Modifications should seek to:

● improve a product by improving its performance
● reduce its weight
● lower its cost
● enhance its appearance, and so on.

But at all times keep your customer (and hence your market) in mind.

In other words value analysis really means, *'is your designed product meeting the demands of the customer at a reasonable cost?'* Can you enhance your design within a competitive price range?

It can be seen that value engineering and value analysis must go hand in hand as both have an equally important role in manufacturing costs and the product that is delivered to the customer.

We have now looked at a system that could be adopted as a complete 'pre-established' strategy. It consists of a framework covering the design process from customer requirements through to detail design. The other important function of a successful design strategy is that it must be well controlled by good management.

A designer working alone will still require to manage his own design strategy, but if it involves a team of designers, either the team leader or the whole team collectively must review the progress of the design and if necessary amend the strategy, time can be wasted if the design strategy is not organized.

Activity 5.2

From the list given below, choose a product you are familiar with and then:

1 Think of ways of reducing its manufacturing costs without reducing its value. (value engineering)
2 Improve its function to give you more value within a reasonably competitive price. (value analysis)

Present your results in the form of a written memorandum to the product's Design Team Leader.

(a) an electric drill
(b) a garden thermometer
(c) a set-top TV aerial
(d) a battery tester
(e) a cycle lamp
(f) a tyre pump
(g) a battery charger.

These are suggested rules for keeping the design strategy under control:

● Be sure to keep all objectives in mind; in designing it is impossible to have only one set of completely fixed objectives.
● A creative resolution of a design problem often means changing some of the earlier objectives.
● The design strategy should be kept under continuous review, the aim is to solve the design problem in a creative and competent way and not follow a path leading to nowhere. If no progress is being made, review the strategy.
● Involve others in the team, they may see the problem in different ways, and may be able to suggest a different path and change the way of thinking of a solution to the problem.
● Keep all files and sketches throughout the project design stages, jot down any ideas that come to mind to be possibly used at a later stage, even when working on different aspects of the project.
● *Never* throw away any sketch or layout drawings until well after the design is finished and proven.

Communicating designs

Almost certainly you will need to communicate your design by drawing it, as this is by far the easiest way to describe your intention, in fact to verbally describe a design can cause confusion as the persons listening may well imagine something totally different to the idea as you perceive it.

Unit 2 of the Intermediate GNVQ in Engineering deals with Graphical Communication in Engineering, and the following are covered:

Element 2.1   Select graphical methods for communicating engineering information

Element 2.2   Produce scale and schematic drawings for engineering applications

Element 2.3   Interpret information presented in engineering drawings

A knowledge of these elements is essential if you are to successfully submit your design ideas. Generally you will need sufficient drawings to fully explain your design concept, this means an ability to draw the following, if required:

1 Layout drawings	The original sketches and drawings required to show your design proposals.
2 Detail drawings	Dimensioned drawings of manufactured parts.
3 Assembly drawings	Showing how the project should be assembled.
4 Item lists	Listing all drawn and 'bought out' parts required to make the final assembly

Although drawings are preferred to be drawn to British Standard BS 308, you may find sketches drawn in good proportion are acceptable, you will need to ask your tutor. Also note that initial design concepts are often made up from rough sketches.

Remember to state the materials and finishes required on any of the parts to be drawn and be careful with your dimensioning and tolerancing. It is important to ensure that your drawings or sketches can be understood easily and without confusion.

If you have experience in using CAD (computer aided design) you will know how much easier it is to draw the assemblies and details, etc. required in a drawing package.

Activity 5.3

You have been commissioned to write an article for your local paper. The article is to appear within a feature on 'New Technology' and you have been asked to explain, in simple terms and using diagrams, how a computer network can be used within an engineering company to monitor and control the manufacture of a product.

Produce your article in word-processed form (using no more than 1500 words) and use a CAD package to produce original artwork to be used for the diagrams.

To help you understand the requirements of a drawing package for a product, it is good idea to look at what a production engineer may expect from the drawings prior to them being issued for manufacture.

Before design drawings are issued to the production department for manufacture, it is important to obtain approval for each drawing from a qualified production engineer, this can considerably help the cost of manufacture, as he or she will be able to advise as to the suitability of the product for the various methods available to produce the individual machined parts. He or she should also check all aspects of the drawings affecting methods of production, datum's, tolerances, etc.

The following are the guidelines a production engineer would use to view the drawings subsequent to 'signing off':

Material suitability

Is the specification correct?.

Is the material machinable and/or weldable if required?.

Could machining time be saved by using stock sizes? (check raw material tolerances).

Dimensioning

Check that there are sufficient dimensions to manufacture the item and the drawing can be clearly understood.

Dimensioning drawings from left to right is good drawing office practice, check that no dimensions are left to machine shop calculation.

Ensure inside and/or outside radii are stated.

Datums

Datums are preferred if made from vertical and horizontal edges or a datum hole, the fewer datums the better (holes can be used for tooling purposes).

Tolerances

Note the tolerances specified, if in doubt enquire whether any tight tolerances stated are justified. Wider tolerances could save considerably on manufacturing costs (often there can be a misuse of geometric tolerancing).

Machined finishes

Surface texture is often specified on a drawing, check the necessity of any very fine finishes shown, by establishing the function of the component part.

Heat treatments

Check the heat treatment specification if quoted, is correct for the material.

Coated finishes

Check the specified coated finish is applicable to the material used.

Machine processes

Could the shape be slightly changed to allow for easier machining, if the answer is yes, consultation with the designers will be necessary.

Assemblies and sub-assemblies

Check whether the number of parts could be reduced by standardization, re-design or machining from the solid. Check the build up of tolerances on assemblies.

Other points

Do the final assemblies satisfy any interchangeability requirements? Is the item commensurate with the layout or scheme previously vetted in conjunction with the designers?

Notes:

1 *At the layout stage*, agreement must be achieved with regard to the technique and method of manufacture, materials, critical dimensions, environment, conditions of use, etc. These should **all** have been satisfied and agreed.
2 Contentious points that may arise must be solved by arbitration with the Chief Designer and the Chief Production Engineer. Do not fall into a position where design is accepted and becomes a 'challenge' to produce!
3 Log all information where contentious points arise, keep any 'marked up' prints, this is for your own protection at a later date.
4 'Sign off' the drawings only when you are satisfied that all criteria have been covered to the best of your knowledge, practice and experience.

Co-operation between designers and production engineers from the layout stage to the final assembly is essential for a well-made product.

As the production engineer's involvement progresses with knowledge of the detail of a new design, he or she will sometimes need to contact special material suppliers or may require the services of outside contractors for machining purposes, heat treatments or surface finishes, he or she will need to alert the Quality Assurance Department of the requirements so that these outside services can be given quality assurance approval if they are not already listed.

Activity 5.4

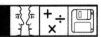

Acme Tools have asked you to produce a set of sketches and detail drawings to support your design proposals (see test your knowledge 5.2 and 5.4). For the Eurocard jig, produce:

(a) a sketch
(b) a layout drawing
(c) a detail drawing
(d) an assembly diagram
(e) an item list.

Present your work in the form of a portfolio of drawings.

Unit 6 Engineering in society and the environment

Summary

This section starts by explaining the different contributions made by engineering to the economy. The terms GNP and GDP are explained at some length. Other aspects such as direct and indirect labour, exports, imports and balance of payments are fully covered. The five major engineering sectors contributing to the economy are identified as the chemical, mechanical, electrical, civil and aeronautical sectors. These and the significance of the different levels of the economy; local, regional, national and European Union are discussed. The section concludes with comments on the positive and negative impact of engineering activities on the social environment. The aspects included are domestic and leisure, health, employment patterns, employee protection and safety.

The influence of engineering on society

The different contributions made by engineering sectors to the economy

The different contributions which we need to consider are as follows:

National product

This is an important term which warrants some explanation. Suppose we first of all consider the 'family' product of a family comprising a husband, a wife, a son and a daughter. Let's imagine the husband to be a skilled cabinet maker who sells his specialist furniture directly to the public. His wife owns a furnished seaside cottage, left to her by her parents, which she rents out as holiday accommodation. Their son is an accountant with a local firm and their daughter is an infant school teacher. All four members of the family have individual saving accounts with local banks or building societies.

The total family 'income' is the sum of the earnings, including savings account interest, of the four individual members of the family. This may be made up as follows:

Husband	sale of furniture	£30 000
	interest from bank savings	£1 000
Wife	rent from holiday cottage	£5 000
	building society interest	£750
Son	accountant's salary	£20 000
	interest from bank savings	£300
Daughter	teacher's salary	£18 000
	building society interest	£500
Therefore the total family income is:		£75 750

Alternatively, we could have produced exactly the same result by adding together the money value of the outputs or 'products' of the family as a whole. The family products are the goods and services which they provide in return for money.

Husband	sale of furniture (goods)	£30 000
Wife	loan of cottage (service)	£5 000
Son	accountancy skills (service)	£20 000
Daughter	teaching skills (service)	£18 000
All four	loans of cash to banks and building societies (service)	£2 550
The total or *gross family product* is:		£75 750

If we added together the total family product of all the families in the UK we would have the 'national' product. This must be the case because it is the members of all the families throughout the land that work in the factories, firms, offices, banks, schools and the like to produce the goods and services which the families themselves consume.

Instead of looking at the money income or the money value of the output of a family, we could undertake a similar exercise by examining the national product of the furniture production process.

Figure 6.1 shows the complete production process for the manufacture and sale of a simple wooden chair. The process is broken down into four stages with the first being the supply of the raw timber, the tree. This supposes that the tree-grower pays his workers their wages and retains a business profit by selling the tree to the timber merchant for a total price of £30. The timber merchant adds to the £30 his costs of sawing the tree into pieces, storing the cut timber and his profit. The added value in this case is £20 making the subsequent sale price to the chair manufacturer of £50.

The chair manufacturer adds a further £30 of production costs and profit making the wholesale value of the chair £80. The furniture shop retailing the chair to the public adds his shop and distribution costs and his profit to the £80 making a high street selling price for the finished chair of £100.

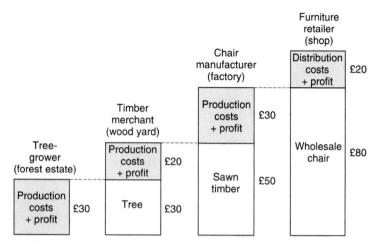

The gross product value of £100 can be calculated by taking the final selling price or adding together the individual 'added values' (shaded) contributed by each of the four production stages.

Figure 6.1 *Diagram showing the national product arising from the production of wooden chairs*

The £100 price of the chair is the money value of the output or product of the chair-making process. The process has contributed £100 to the national product. Note that this £100 can be calculated either by taking the final selling price or by adding together the shaded areas of 'added values' contributed by each of the four different stages of chair production.

Figure 6.2 is a diagram showing how the production of goods and services and their consumption can be regarded as forming a closed

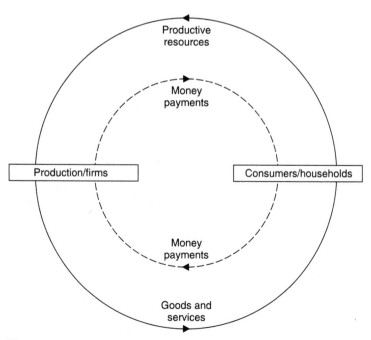

Figure 6.2 *Flow of goods, services and productive resources in an economic system*

circle. The firms make the goods and provide the services consumed by the people living in the households. The people living in the households are the same ones that own and work in the production and service firms. The demand for the goods and services is originated by the households which is satisfied by the production firms that pay the wages of the householders. Hence, the flow of goods and services and production resources are in one direction and is balanced by the flow of money in the other.

Yet another diagram encountered in written articles concerning the economy, the management of the material resources of a community or country, is shown at Figure 6.3.

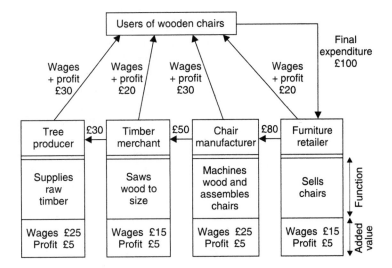

The users of the wooden chairs are the same people that own and provide the labour force for the different stages of production.

Figure 6.3 *An alternative diagrammatic representation of the engineering function of producing wooden chairs*

In many respects it is no more that a combination of Figures 6.1 and 6.2. The diagram again relates to the production of the same wooden chairs as discussed earlier. The four major production functions are shown but this time with the added value element at each stage being sub-divided into wages and profit. The wages are paid to the stage production workers and the profit to its shareholders. Of course, all of these people are themselves buyers of the wooden chairs and hence the arrows in Figure 6.3 showing the wages and profits of each stage of production being passed to the users of the wooden chairs. The horizontal arrows linking the production stages represent the cash payments made for the materials supplied. You will notice how the flow of total output money from each production stage is exactly matched by the money it receives from the previous production stage. For example, in the case of the final production stage, the buyer of a wooden chair pays the furniture retailer £100. Of this amount, the furniture retailer pays the chair manufacturer £80, for the wholesale chair, and pays his shop workers and shareholders the remaining £20 in wages and profit dividend, respectively.

So, the national product for the whole engineering function of wooden chair production, £100, can calculated either by:

- the final expenditure (the retail price of a chair) method, or
- the sum of the added values method.

An information diagram in the form of Figure 6.3 enables both of these methods to be used.

Gross national product (GNP)

The total output of the UK can be measured by adding together the value of all goods and services produced by the UK. This figure is called the gross national product. The word 'gross' implies that no deduction has been made for the loss in value of the country's capital equipment, which helps to make the national product, caused by normal wear and tear.

The word 'national' in this context does not mean that the GNP is the total output produced within the borders of the UK. You see, the gross product of the UK includes some output taking place and produced by resources within the UK but owned by people from other countries. Therefore, this particular element of output cannot be regarded as part of our national income. At the same time, some sources of output are located in other countries but owned by UK citizens. Therefore the GNP is defined as the value of the total output of all resources owned by citizens of the UK wherever the resources themselves may be situated.

Gross domestic product (GDP)

If we measure the value of the total output actually produced 'within' the borders of the UK, it is called the gross domestic product. So, the GDP is defined as the value of the output of all resources situated within the UK wherever the owners of the resources happen to live. In many ways the GDP is a more important measure than the GNP.

The government periodically issues statistical tables showing the performance of the different sectors of the economy. Table 6.1 is a sample of part of such a statistical table. It is an extract the 'Blue Book', issued by the Central Statistics Office, entitled *United Kingdom National Accounts*.

Gross domestic product per head

This is a measure of productivity. It relates output to the number of people employed producing that output. The formula used is:

$$\text{Output per head (or } per\ capita\text{)} = \frac{\text{output produced divided by the number of people producing it}}{}$$

Put another way, we can write,

$$\text{Output per head} = \text{output/employment.}$$

Table 6.1 *Sample extract from the CSO Blue Book United Kingdom National Accounts (1994 Edition)*

	1983	1984	1985	1986	1987	1988	1989	1990	1991	1992	1993
All industries:											
Income from employment	169 847	181 406	196 858	212 380	229 832	255 634	283 454	312 358	329 609	342 215	352 896
Gross profits and other trading income	86 225	92 843	101 904	105 600	121 785	136 220	151 124	154 251	140 013	145 570	162 193
Rent	18 857	19 816	21 875	23 848	26 155	29 904	33 730	38 569	44 707	49 193	52 872
Imputed charge for capital consumption	2 498	2 619	2 830	3 068	3 307	3 634	4 005	4 391	4 363	4 207	3 942
less Stock appreciation	−4 204	−4 513	−2 738	−1 835	−4 727	−6 375	−7 061	−6 131	−2 010	−1 832	−2 359
less Adjustment for financial services	−11 893	−12 688	−12 827	−14 789	−15 677	−17 589	−23 493	−24 552	−20 782	−23 326	−23 741
Statistical discrepancy (income adjustment)	−105	1 170	−	−	−	−	−	−	−	−	317
Gross domestic product	261 225	280 653	307 902	328 272	360 675	401 428	441 759	478 886	495 900	516 027	546 120

Figures are in £ million

Table 6.2 *Output, employment and productivity for the period 1990 to 1997*

Year	Output	Employment	Output per head
1990	100.0	100.0	100.0
1991	100.5	100.1	100.4
1992	100.6	100.0	100.6
1993	100.5	99.5	101.0
1994	99.9	99.4	100.5
1995	90.5	90.0	100.6
1996	89.5	88.9	100.6
1997	89.5	88.8	100.8

Usually both the output and employment figures are index numbers. The government issues tables of statistics covering different industries and a typical format is shown at Table 6.2.

The figures in Table 6.2 are index numbers adjusted to be 100 for both output and employment in the year 1990. The table shows the trend as being a fall in output accompanied by a correspondingly larger fall in employment resulting in improved productivity figures in the last column.

Direct employment

This is the term used to describe the mode of employment of people that are actually working to produce a product. For example, the people working in a factory making furniture could all be regarded a direct labour being directly employed on the manufacture of the furniture.

Indirect employment

Following on from the previous example, the people concerned with the transportation of the production materials to the furniture factory and the finished furniture to the shops which sell the furniture, are regarded as indirect labour and are in indirect employment.

Note however, people may be directly employed by their own trade but indirectly by another. For example, the people felling the trees and producing the raw timber used to make the furniture are directly employed by the timber trade but are indirectly employed by the furniture-making trade.

Exports

Exports are goods and services which we sell to other countries. *Visible* exports are the hard goods which are physically transported abroad and for which we receive payment. *Invisible* exports are those services which we provide for foreigners and for which they pay. Invisible exports include the payments we receive for insurance and financial services, technical or military training and the like. Tourism is also an important part of our invisible export trade. A German tourist in London will spend money that he has earned in Germany. This is provides a useful income to the UK no different from, say, visibly exporting and selling the German a bottle of Scotch whisky in Berlin.

Note that when we take our holidays abroad, the goods and services we buy and consume abroad are in fact imports to the UK.

Imports

Imports flow in the opposite direction to that of exports. Imports are the goods and services which we buy from abroad.

Balance of payments

If we are to remain financially sound, we must ensure that our income exceeds our expenditure. This applies both to our personal domestic lives and to the nation as a whole. On a national basis, the total income we earn from abroad for our exports is balanced against the total payment we must make abroad for our imports. We compare or 'balance' the two figures and hopefully the export figure is at least as large as and preferably larger than the import figure.

Very often the UK balance of visible exports and imports shows an excess of import value over exports. However, we have a relatively healthy sale of our services abroad and our invisibles usually gives us a favourable trading balance. The government lets us know what our overseas trading position is by issuing monthly *balance of payment* figures.

Activity 6.1

Table 6.3 is an extract from the official publication, *Eurostat* for the ten-year period 1977–1986. The table shows the GDPs of each of the 12 European Union (EU) countries together with those for the EU as a whole, the USA and Japan.

Use Table 6.3 to respond to the following requirements.

(a) Draw a histogram showing the relative contribution of each country to the GDP of the EU.
(b) Name the four major and the four minor contributors to the EU economy.
(c) Name two countries whose percentage contribution to the EU has fallen over the ten year period.
(d) State which had the greater output in 1985, America or the EU.

Using Table 6.3 answer the following questions concerning the ten year period covered.

(e) By what percentage did the Danish and Dutch prices increase? (Hint: The British prices increased by 120.2%)
(f) Which EU country suffered the most inflation and which the least?

Table 6.3 *European Union – Relative GDPs. This is an extract from Eurostat (Review 1977–1986)*

	1977	1978	1979	1980	1981	1982	1983	1984	1985	1986	1977	1986
	Price Indices (1980 = 100)										1977 = 100	
Belgique/België	88.3	92.2	96.4	100.0	104.9	112.4	119.0	125.0	131.9	136.7	100.0	154.8
Danmark	78.2	85.9	92.4	100.0	110.1	121.7	131.0	138.5	145.9	153.0	100.0	195.7
BR Deutschland	88.0	91.7	95.4	100.0	104.0	108.6	112.1	114.3	116.8	120.4	100.0	136.9
Ελλάσσ	63.4	71.6	85.0	100.0	119.8	149.8	178.4	214.6	252.7	300.8	100.0	474.4
España	62.0	74.8	87.6	100.0	112.0	127.4	142.2	157.8	171.4	190.2	100.0	306.7
France	74.0	81.5	89.8	100.0	111.4	124.4	136.6	146.7	155.2	162.4	100.0	219.3
Ireland	69.4	76.7	87.2	100.0	117.4	135.3	149.3	160.8	168.8	178.3	100.0	257.0
Italia	62.8	71.5	82.9	100.0	118.5	137.7	158.8	175.0	190.5	205.8	100.0	327.6
Luxembourg	83.2	87.7	93.0	100.0	106.8	117.9	126.0	133.0	137.6	141.1	100.0	169.5
Nederland	86.4	91.1	94.6	100.0	105.5	111.9	114.0	116.1	118.1	118.9	100.0	137.7
Portugal	57.3	69.7	82.9	100.0	115.8	142.1	177.3	218.8	266.2	309.4	100.0	539.8
United Kingdom	65.5	72.9	83.5	100.0	111.5	119.9	126.1	131.4	139.3	144.2	100.0	220.2
EUR 12	**72.2**	**79.7**	**88.5**	**100.0**	**111.0**	**122.4**	**132.9**	**141.6**	**150.1**	**158.4**	**100.0**	**219.5**
USA	78.5	84.2	91.7	100.0	107.9	114.8	118.5	123.0	126.8	130.2	100.0	165.8
Nippon (Japan)	89.2	93.5	96.3	100.0	103.2	105.1	105.9	107.2	108.9	110.8	100.0	124.2

The different engineering sectors

The activities sectors with which we must be familiar are as follows:

Chemical

The products of this sector include such things as fertilizer, pharmaceuticals, plastics, petrol, etc. Companies in this field include Fisons, Glaxo, ICI and British Petroleum.

Mechanical

Typical products are bearings, agricultural machinery, motor vehicles, fasteners, machine tools and the like from companies such as RHP, Rover, GKN and Rolls-Royce.

Electrical

Electric generators and motors, radios, TVs, power cables, computers, etc. are produced by companies such as GEC, BICC and ICL.

Civil

Concrete bridges and fly-overs, docks, factories, power stations, dams etc, from companies like Bovis, Wimpey and Balfour-Beatty.

Aeronautical

Passenger and military aircraft, satellites, space rockets, missiles, etc. from British Aerospace, Westlands and Rolls-Royce.

Activity 6.2

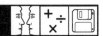

A group of estate agents has asked you to carry out some research for them based on your home town. They are particular interested in the size and scope of local engineering firms with a view to future developments.

(a) Identify the three largest engineering firms in the area of your home town.
(b) Find out who owns these firms and whether they are part of a larger group of companies.
(c) Allocate each firm to the appropriate engineering sector.
(d) Ascertain the annual sales turnover (its output in money terms) of each firm.
(e) Draw a histogram showing the individual engineering sector turnover in your area.

Present your findings in the form of a brief written report and include relevant diagrams and tables. Produce your report in word processed form.

The different economies

We are expected to be familiar with the effects of engineering at four different economic levels: local, regional, national and European. In each of these economies the engineering activities appear to be spread unevenly. This is the case whether we examine a local town or rural area, a larger region of possibly two or three counties, the whole of UK on a national basis or the European Union.

Local economy

For the first half of the twentieth century, engineering was generally located within cities. Since then there has been a tendency for any new engineering enterprise to be located in an industrial estate on the periphery of a town rather in the town itself. Usually this is because

- the town centre is already too congested to allow for additional new industry;
- of the advantages of being located in a ready, purpose-built industrial accommodation on a site having good road links with the national motorway network;
- engineering activities which may involve noise and other pollutants are best kept away from the commercial and domestic centres of towns.

In general, the engineering industries that remained in the city centres have slowly become outdated and, in many cases, have closed down. The impact of this migration from the city centres to the suburbs has been to leave derelict buildings, unemployment and social deprivation for the city residents. For the outer suburbs receiving the new engineering industries, the impact has not always been positive. The decentralization of engineering from the city centres has contributed to urban sprawl, and this has led to conflict for land on the city's boundary between engineering, farming and recreation. Also, it has tended merely to move the problem of engineering pollution from the city centre to its suburbs.

Regional economy

The regional economy comprises many local economies but the change in the engineering pattern is much the same. While there is still a great deal of engineering activity to be found in and around many large cities and conurbations, there is a definite migratory move towards the small town and rural areas. This trend is to be found in most economically developed countries and has been a consistent feature of the last 25 years.

National

At the national level the uneven spread of engineering is between the different regions. The processes that caused this variation are historic. Very often they are directly connected to the availability of natural resources. For example, in the 19th century, regions rich in coal were favoured with engineering expansion because of the local availability of coal to fire boilers to drive the steam engines which powered the factories. The technical skills acquired by the workers in the coal-bearing regions were the same skills required for other industries and enterprises and cumulative expansion took place. This expansion, and the highly paid work it created, attracted labour from the less industrialized regions so exacerbating the regional disparities.

However, over the last 50 years there has been a shift of engineering away from the old industrial regions such as the North-East and Midlands of England and parts of Scotland to more convenient locations such as the Thames Valley along the M4 motorway and along the M11 motorway north of London. The reasons for the regional shift are many and varied and include such factors as:

● because of its cost and pollution-causing record, coal is no longer a popular fuel;
● with natural gas and electrical power being available almost anywhere in the country, new engineering activities can be located in regions having pleasant natural and social environments;
● because of the ubiquitous motor car, good roads and frequent air services, commuter and business communications to most regions are no longer a major problem.

European Union

Within the EU, engineering activities have the usual varied pattern. The favoured countries are those which were the first to industrialize in the 18th and 19th centuries. Britain, Germany, France and Italy are predominant in Europe with the main concentration lying within a rough triangle formed by London, Hamburg and Milan. Ireland, Spain, Southern Italy and Greece lie outside this triangle and tend to be less industrialized.

The past 30 years has seen a shift in some of the major engineering activities which used to be concentrated in Europe, North America and Japan. In particular, much of the electronics and printing industries have migrated to the 'Pacific rim' countries such as Hong Kong, Singapore, Taiwan, Thailand and more recently into Indonesia. The main reason for this shift is the low labour costs to be found in the Far East. Another prime example of the shift of engineering activities out of Europe is that of shipbuilding. Britain's contribution in particular has fallen and is now virtually non-existent except for the manufacture of oil platforms and ships for the Royal Navy.

However, the traffic in engineering activities has not been all negative. The Japanese, wanting to sell their motor cars in Europe, have established several engineering production plants in Britain. The firms of Toyota (Deeside and Burnaston), Nissan (Sunderland) and Honda (Swindon) are three good examples. All occupy rural sites and have access to skilled and well-educated workforces. Road communications are good and, in the case of Nissan, the site is in an assisted area where Government grants are available.

Test your knowledge 6.2

Why do Japanese firms need to manufacture their cars in UK as opposed to Japan?

Activity 6.3

A company based in the Far East has asked you to carry out some research in order to help them investigate some investment opportunities in Europe. They have asked you to produce a broad comparison of the performance of the various countries that comprise the European Union (EU).

(a) Draw a map of Europe (Hint: photocopy or scan this from a suitable atlas).
(b) Mark in the 12 countries that constitute the EU.
(c) Mark in the capital cities of each EU country.
(d) Ascertain the GDP for each EU country then list the countries in descending order of GDP. What is the position of the UK?

Produce your findings in the form of a set of overhead projector transparencies to be used at a board meeting.

The effects of engineering on the social environment

Domestic and leisure

The television set

Perhaps the engineering product which has had the greatest impact on society is the domestic television set. From 1945 the TV began to replace the sound-only radio as the main domestic link with the outside world for daily news and information. The original national TV programmes were transmitted from local sites, only by the BBC and only in black and white. The programmes, mainly news reports, sports commentaries or shows, were not broadcast until 7 pm and closed down altogether at midnight. To watch the evening TV programme assumed the importance of a family visit to the local cinema. As 7 pm approached, many a family would be riveted to their 12 inch TV screen awaiting the first 405 line pictures.

Today we have an ever-increasing choice of programmes to watch. They are broadcast by both the BBC and independent (ITV) television companies. Many programmes are now received live from around the world using satellite relay stations. Also, specialist companies are daily laying cables carrying yet more TV channels beneath our streets for domestic consumption. The now 625 line pictures are invariably clear, in colour and are broadcast 24 hours a day. The TV set can be purchased with a screen size to suit any room.

The viewing pattern in many homes, especially those with young children, is for the TV to be switched on at breakfast time and left running until bedtime. The programmes cover everything from high quality educational programmes and current affairs to the usual family entertainment comprising a mixture of news, sport, comedy and drama together with a contentious amount of sex, horror and violence. Also available is a vast amount of travel, weather, business, statistical and other written information which is shown on the text-only channels, Ceefax (BBC) and Teletext (ITV). Last, but by no means least, are the advertisements which are shown at approximately 15 minute intervals on all the ITV channels. These regularly exhort viewers to buy some product and can be more entertaining than the main TV programmes themselves which are often no more than frequently repeated films.

The more educational or straightforward entertainment programmes which we purposely watch undoubtedly have a beneficial effect upon society. They are interesting, amusing or relaxing. However, the continual aural and visual battering to which we subject ourselves – and others – through the ever-on TV is blamed for many of the shortcomings found in society today. For example, young people in particular are said to be very much influenced by the violent TV scenes frequently shown. The result may be violence being regarded as a normal part of life.

The refrigerator

The domestic refrigerator appeared at the same time as the TV. Today, virtually every household owns a 'fridge. Before the introduction of the refrigerator fresh food had a very limited life, especially in the summer months. Milk and meats in particular, could be kept fresh in a cool cupboard for one or two days only. The refrigerator, with its internal temperature regulated to stay only a little above (+4°C) the freezing point of water (0°C), and its hermetically sealed door has at least doubled the storage time of fresh food and keeps insects away. Two immediate benefits of the refrigerator has been a healthier range of fresh food readily available in the kitchen and the need to go shopping every day reduced to perhaps only once or twice a week. On the negative side, the refrigerator costs money to buy and to run.

The freezer

This is really no more than a super refrigerator which stores food at −18°C and below in a truly solid frozen state. The benefits are an even longer food storage time – between three and six months – and the economy of bulk buying of frozen meats and ready cooked meals.

The microwave oven

This is ideal for the quick meal. The electronic magnetron device inside the oven produces very high frequency electromagnetic waves which heat up any non-conducting material – food in this case. A ready cooked meal, stored for the purpose in the freezer, can be placed straight into the microwave oven. The food is heated from its inside out and can be fully cooked in a matter of two or three minutes. These foods are often called *convenience foods* because of the ease and speed with which the meal is prepared for the table. On the negative side there is the usual purchase and running costs together with, it is said, a need to ensure that there is no leakage from the oven of the microwaves themselves.

Test your knowledge 6.3

What is meant by a 405 line TV picture? Why is a 625 line picture of higher quality? See if you can find out how many lines *actually* appear on the screen (not all of them do!).

Test your knowledge 6.4

Why is the leakage of microwaves undesirable? What is the name of the device that produces the microwaves?

The personal computer

The personal computer (PC) is not so prevalent on the domestic scene as are the previous examples. They tend to be used more as word processors than in any other role. Students and business people are the major domestic users.

Other domestic examples

- Telephone
- Washing machine
- Vacuum cleaner
- Motor car

Activity 6.4

Many households own at least one car. The car has many advantages, the main one being its convenience as a means of personal transport.

(a) Check the number of cars belonging to 50 households in your area. What is the average number of cars per household?
(b) Compare your above results with those obtained by a colleague living in a different area. Discuss the reasons for any meaningful differences.
(c) What negative impact has the motor car had on society?

Present your findings to the class using appropriate visual aids. Your presentation should last no more than 10 minutes and you should allow a further 5 minutes for questions.

Health

Engineered products are playing an increasingly important part in health care. There is a wide range of sophisticated medical diagnostic equipment such as magnetic resonance imaging (MI) and computerized tomography (CAT) scanners which combine engineering and computer technologies. Some of these advanced techniques are used to detect not only the structure of part of a person's body but also whether it is functioning correctly. Basically the techniques involve the examination of the electromagnetic and mechanical properties of the atoms of an organ with the body. It does this by looking at individual sectional slices of the organ, using a computer to analyse the electrical characteristics of the atoms in the slices and finally constructing an image of the whole organ.

A further example of high technology engineering currently under development in the medical field is computer-aided surgery. Existing scanning techniques are to be used accurately to define the position of, say, a brain tumour and the associated pattern of local blood vessels. The operation can then be planned for minimum damage to the area surrounding the tumour. The operation on the tumour would be undertaken through a relatively small hole cut through the skull. When the technique is perfected, the idea is for the surgeon's implement to have three-dimensional positional guidance using computer-aided control. The operating surgeon will need to be specially trained in the new technique.

Also available is a wide range of advanced monitoring and life support equipments for use in hospital operating theatres and intensive care units not to mention exercise machines associated with keep fit programmes.

Activity 6.5

Your local newpaper has commissioned you to write a short article (no more than 1500 words) describing the specialist medical equipment available in your local hospital. The article is to be suitable for the non-technical reader and will appear as part of a feature on the impact of 'New Technology'.

You should aim to describe several of the most important items of equipment and explain, in simple terms, what each is used for and why it is vital to the service that the hospital offers. Hint: It might be worth contacting the Public Relations Officer of your local hospital as he or she may be willing to help in supplying you with information.

Employment

Engineering advancements have, in many cases, had a significant impact upon the need for large numbers of unskilled workers. In many firms, the manually operated moving conveyor belt production line which passes a product along a line of stationary workers, each of whom performs some simple task on the product, is dying out. In the main, this low skilled work has been taken over by automated production lines. Typical of these are the much publicized, robot operated, motor car body assembly lines. Also, in the micro-electronics field, the manufacture of integrated circuits and their subsequent assembly onto printed circuit boards is so detailed and fine that this is possible only by using computer controlled machines.

The new technologies are also bringing about a change in the type of worker required. The concept of each worker having a well defined list of work to perform – a job description – is, in some firms, regarded as counter productive. The job description, it is argued, leads to a 'that's not my job' restrictive approach where work can be passed around but not done. A new approach is that of team work to see the whole work in hand completed properly and on time. While an individual may have a special skill that the team requires, if he or she has other skills which are useful, then they should be used. For example, a secretary may have left her old 'job' of typing for the production manager and instead joined a new firm, ostensibly as the secretary to a project leader. However, her new firm uses the whole team approach to work and not only does she type for the project leader and others, she agrees to undertake certain investigative work which she says she can manage. She finds that her work is more interesting and she is becoming skilled in a management role. Similarly, the project leader may, at times, need to type a letter or report; he or she is acting then as a typist.

Some American firms are well advanced with this team approach to getting the job done. It was recently reported in a Sunday newspaper (*The Independent on Sunday*) that not only is work tackled by a team approach, the time spent doing the work is likewise not rigidly defined between daily start and finish times. Some project teams with a target finish date, if necessary, work 24 hours a days for weeks at a time.

The newspaper quoted the American firm of Microsoft as an example of this new way of employing people. A female software design engineer was quoted as saying 'You won't last at Microsoft if your job is just a job'. She went on to describe what it is like to work for Microsoft. To begin with, people work at any time and all the time, with no one keeping track of their hours, but with everyone watching their output. They are accountable not to conventional managers but to the project teams of which they are a part. Those teams, in turn, are likely to be sub-sets of some larger group, and in a very big project, such as the development of a Windows operating system for PCs, there may be many project-within-larger-project groupings.

Within each team, individuals are always given a little more than they can accomplish on their own, so that there is constant collaboration between team members. New employees, given important responsibilities from the first day, are assigned a 'mentor' to help them learn the team's way of working. 'Microsoft trusts them to do what they already know how to do, turns them loose to solve problems and helps them when they get stuck'.

Workers make regular reports at their team meetings as to how their particular work is progressing. 'It does not take long to straighten out a team member who is not pulling his weight. The next team meeting, in which a developer stands before the group to explain what he has contributed, becomes a strong incentive to have the work done, and done right'.

Not all firms will wish to adopt the Microsoft method of employing people but without doubt the introduction of new technologies will require a change in the old style employment patterns. Perhaps, in some cases, the trouble and cost of re-training existing workers will suffice. The re-training of workers may well be more than off-set by long-term benefits of increased production, efficiency, effectiveness and profitability.

A simple but real case, experienced by the author, of the value of re-training existing workers for multiskilling purposes was as follows. A firm selling both diesel engined and battery electric forklift trucks was required to provide on-site, after sales service on call out. Some clients had a mixed fleet of forklifts. Some were fast, diesel powered for outdoor use, others were electrically driven – no toxic exhaust fumes – predominantly for use indoors. The electric forklifts were fitted with electronic speed controllers using the latest thyristor technology. The existing service engineers were either skilled diesel fitters or electronic technicians. None of them could repair or service both diesel and electric forklifts. Often, this meant that two service engineers had to be sent together up to 20 miles; one to repair an electric control fault; the other to carry out a routine diesel engine check and service.

The problem was solved by asking for the service engineers to volunteer for re-training so that they could undertake both diesel and electrical repair work – and qualify for a higher rate of pay. The volunteers were sent on a one-week diesel or electrical conversion course, as appropriate, and after a little practical experience all were re-graded as being competent to work on both systems. They had become *multiskilled*.

Employee protection and safety

In the seventeenth and eighteenth centuries there seemed to be little regard for the comfort or safety of industrial workers. Children as young as eight years were employed. Workers were paid only for what they produced (piece work) or the time (hourly rate) they attended the workplace. The advent of trades unions, legislation and, in general, a more enlightened society, has resulted in the much improved working conditions of today. Attention is paid to the safety and protection of the employee which is implemented through such measures as published safety procedures, audio and visual alarm systems, safe working practices, maintenance procedures, hygiene procedures and the availability of safety equipment to provide employee protection, for example, first aid equipment and personal safety clothing.

Activity 6.6

(a) List the items you would expect to find in the first aid box supporting an office for between 10 and 20 administrative staff.

(b) Examine a *real* first aid box (e.g. the one that is kept in your school/college office) and compare it with your list at (a).

(c) Explain the reasons for any major differences.

Present your findings in the form of a brief written report for your school/college Safety Officer.

The influence of engineering on the workplace

The salient features of the workplace are identified as being comfort, health, productivity and efficiency. These are discussed in turn with appropriate references made to the relevant legislation. The ergonomics of both office and workshop workplaces are included. The engineering effects of heating, ventilation, lighting and noise on the workplace are mentioned. The section concludes with a detailed coverage of workplace risks and the precautions which can be taken to increase health and safety in the workplace.

Features of the workplace

You are expected to be able to identify the the following main features of the workplace and to give appropriate examples:

Health

Working environments differ in their potential and actual health hazards to employees, e.g. an office environment, while posing minimal machinery hazards to workers, can in some cases give rise to back and eyesight problems associated with work of a sedentary nature, excessive typing and the use of computer screens.

You should also be aware of the role and impact of legislation governing the workplace, such as:

- A Guide to the Health and Safety at Work etc. Act 1974
- The Reporting of Injuries, Diseases and Dangerous Occurrences Regulations 1985
- The Control of Substances Hazardous to Health Regulations 1988
- The Workplace (Health, Safety and Welfare) Regulations 1992
- The Management of Health and Safety at Work Regulations 1992
- The Personal Protective Equipment at Work Regulations 1992
- The Manual Handling Operations Regulations 1992
- The Health and Safety (Display Screen Equipment) Regulations 1992
- The Electricity at Work Regulations 1989
- The Noise at Work Regulations 1989
- The Ionising Radiations Regulations 1985
- The Pressure Systems and Transportable Gas Containers Regulations 1989

You should have an understanding of the main purposes of each set of regulations and its impact upon working conditions. You are not expected to know dates or detailed aspects of the legislation. However, you should be aware of those agencies whose job it is to enforce the legislation, such as the Health and Safety Executive (HSE) and Local Authorities. All these Regulations are published as booklets in non-legal, easy to follow English. Copies are usually kept in main public libraries and most college libraries. You will find it useful to browse through each of these to familiarize yourself with the coverage of each of them. Your knowledge of these regulations will be assessed in the written end test!

Legislation, and common sense, requires workers to work in conditions which are not injurious to their health and safety. For example,

- floors should not be slippery or uneven,
- tools and equipment are to be properly maintained in a safe working condition,
- workers are to be protected from the harmful effects of dust, fumes, smoke and other pollutants,
- the size of the workplace must meet certain minimum limits,
- it must be possible for workers rapidly to leave their workplaces in the event of an emergency such a fire.

Comfort

In order that workers can give of their best they must be comfortable. Not only must they be comfortable in their minds by understanding what they have to do and knowing that they can do it, they must also be physically comfortable. For example, they must be:

● sheltered from adverse weather conditions,
● dry and warm,
● in a clean atmosphere,
● free from excessive noise, and
● sitting down if the nature of the work so permits.

Productivity

As far as the owners, proprietors or shareholders of a firm are concerned, perhaps the most important feature of a workplace is its usefulness in supporting production. Workplace can vary, for example, from being an engineering manager's desk area to a radio repair and test bench in an electronics workshop or even the cockpit of an aircraft. However, all workplaces have a common feature: they are all designed to assist the worker to achieve maximum output with minimum effort.

1 Adequate lighting
2 Adequate contrast, no glare or distracting reflections
3 Distracting noise minimized
4 Leg room and clearances to allow postural changes
5 Window covering
6 Software: appropriate to task, adapted to user, provides feedback on system status, no undisclosed monitoring
7 Screen: stable image, adjustable, readable, glare/reflection free
8 Keyboard: usable, adjustable, detachable, legible
9 Work surface: allow flexible arrangements, spacious, glare free
10 Work chair: adjustable
11 Footrest

Figure 6.4 *Typical office workplace (Source: HSE booklet* The Health and Safety (Display Screen Equipment) Regulations 1992)

The *manager's desk* will be situated in a quiet part of a building, usually in its own office with a secretary in an adjoining office. On the desk, or on an adjacent table, will be a personal computer, telephone, intercom set and the like, all of which the manager can easily reach without having to stand up. In filing cabinets, located conveniently nearby in either the manager's or the secretary's office, will be stored routine correspondence and work records. The whole managerial workplace is tuned for minimum movement, ease of finding things and maximum productivity. Figure 6.4 shows the layout of a typical office workplace.

The *radio repair and test bench* will be situated in a cool, well ventilated room with an extractor fan suitably located for the removal of smoke or fumes caused by soldering. The workbench will be specially fitted with its own low voltage (a safe 24 V) soldering iron supply together with the usual 230 V mains electrical supply for the electronic test equipment. The test equipments will be located within easy reach of the radio repair technician, on shelves around but away from the centre working area of the bench. The technician will be seated on a mobile swivelling stool, complete with footrest and five castored wheels, with all his or her immediate needs to hand from a sitting position. Again, the aim is maximum convenience leading to maximum throughput of repaired and tested radios.

Efficiency

Fortunately, the attributes of the workplace that maximize productivity also maximize its efficiency especially if efficiency is measured as maximum output for minimum input. As seen in the previous section, this is largely brought about by locating people, furniture and machinery in the most convenient places. The aim is to reduce unnecessary movement of people and materials.

Deciding the ideal workplace layout or design can be assisted by a technique called 'work study' or 'time and motion study'. Briefly, this involves measuring and noting the time taken and the distance travelled for every movement the worker makes. The total distance and the total time taken for the whole operation is also measured. The collated operational data is then studied with a view to economizing in both time taken and distance travelled. Surprisingly large savings can be made.

Ergonomic considerations in the workplace

Chambers English Dictionary defines ergonomics as 'the study of man in relationship to his working environment: the adaptation of machines and general conditions to fit the individual so that he may work at maximum efficiency'.

A good example of the use of ergonomics is the driving position in a motor vehicle. Unless the vehicle is a very slow mover, walking pace only, the most secure position for the driver is being strapped into a seat in an upright sitting position. The steering wheel, gear lever and hand-brake, being the most frequently used hand-operated controls, should be the most convenient placed for the driver to reach. Ideally, the driver should not need to move his body, only his arms and hands, to operate these particular controls. Similarly, the three foot-operated control pedals; the foot-brake, the clutch and the accelerator should require no more of the driver than simple leg and foot movements. The remaining controls – such as those for the horn, lights, windscreen wiper, heater and the radio – and the various information displays or indicating instruments – such as the speedometer, petrol gauge, engine temperature gauge – then need compete with each other for the remaining space within an easy arm's reach or eye-shot of the driver.

It is highly desirable, therefore, that the driver's 'workplace' in the motor vehicle is ergonomically laid out. Any reduction in the number and extent of the total body movements required to drive the vehicle must result in reduced driver fatigue and, therefore, increased safety. Also, because the driver can drive longer before feeling the need to rest, his driving productivity and efficiency are increased.

The same principle applies to the office workplace. Figure 6.5 shows an ergonomic layout for a typical office workplace for an operator using a typewriter or word processor.

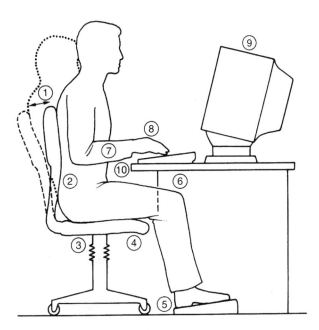

1 Seat back adjustability
2 Good lumbar support
3 Seat height adjustability
4 No excess pressure on underside of thighs and backs of knees
5 Foot support if needed
6 Space for postural change, no obstacles under desk
7 Forearms approximately horizontal
8 Minimal extension, flexion or deviation of wrists
9 Screen height and angle should allow comfortable head position
10 Space in front of keyboard to support hands/wrists during pauses in keying

Figure 6.5 *Seating and posture for typical office tasks (Source: HSE booklet* The Health and Safety (Display Screen Equipment) Regulations 1992)

Precautions against risks in the workplace

'A stitch in time saves nine' is the old saying. Another interpretation could be: 'It is better to prevent the accident than to repair the damage'. If we are to take precautions against accidents we need to know what the risks are. We should examine each workplace for potential accidents. This is called making a *risk analysis*.

Workplace risks

This depends to a large degree on the nature of the workplace. The risks in a high voltage electrical repair workshop can be different from those associated with assembling motor car gearboxes. However, most workplaces have common risks such as:

slips or trips e.g. caused by polished floors, loose or holed carpets, badly placed waste bins, rough floors;

electric shock e.g. from frayed electric flexible cable showing bare wire – also see Figure 6.6;

air-pollution e.g. because of tobacco smoke, hair-spray;

head injury e.g. from falls of badly stacked books, files, printers, VDUs, tools, etc. placed overhead on cupboards and other *ad hoc* storage places.

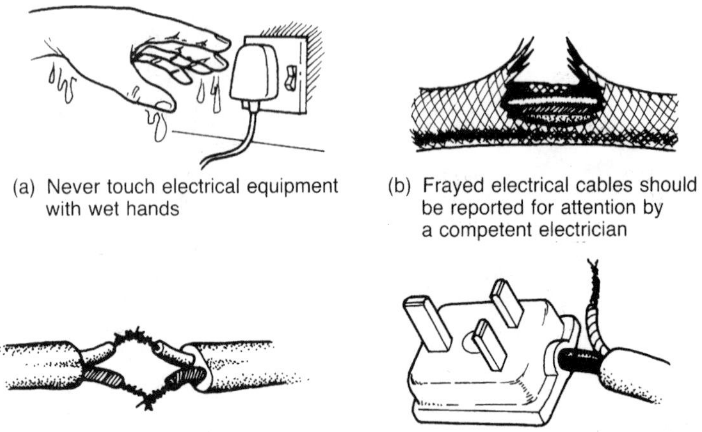

(a) Never touch electrical equipment with wet hands

(b) Frayed electrical cables should be reported for attention by a competent electrician

(c) Amateur connections can be dangerous–use a competent electrician

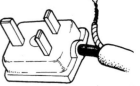

(d) Unearthed plugs (green/yellow wire loose) are dangerous

Figure 6.6 *Electrical danger points*

More specialist engineering operations bring added risks. Workplaces involved with the movement of heavy loads or working with hazardous materials have additional personal risks such as:

crushing e.g. in loading bays from reversing lorries and forklift trucks in particular;

trapped fingers e.g. in unguarded belt or chain drives – also see Figure 6.7;

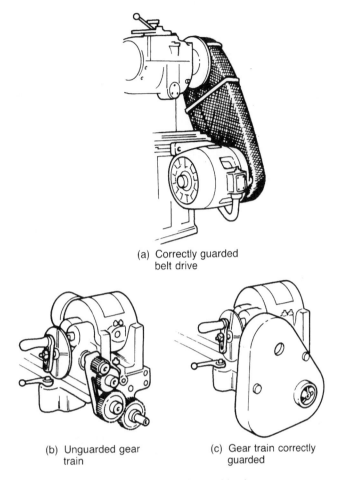

(a) Correctly guarded
belt drive

(b) Unguarded gear
train

(c) Gear train correctly
guarded

All guards must be in place before the machine is
made to run. Guards must not allow finger access
around the sides to any moving parts.

Figure 6.7 *Examples of correct guarding*

dry burns	e.g. from hot workpieces in welding bays and heat treatment ovens;
chemical burns	e.g. from acid splashes when battery charging and copper chloride splash burns from etching plants;
cutting	e.g. from careless operation of machine or hand tools in woodworking or metal fitting shops;
absorption of radio activity	e.g. from radioactive material used to re-luminize instrument dials and X-ray machines;
deafness	e.g. especially for operators of noisy machinery such as metal grinders, wood saws, diesel engined industrial trucks, etc.;
blindness	e.g. from excessively bright lights and ultraviolet rays associated with electric welding operations;
strains	e.g. from lifting too heavy loads manually (see Figure 6.8).

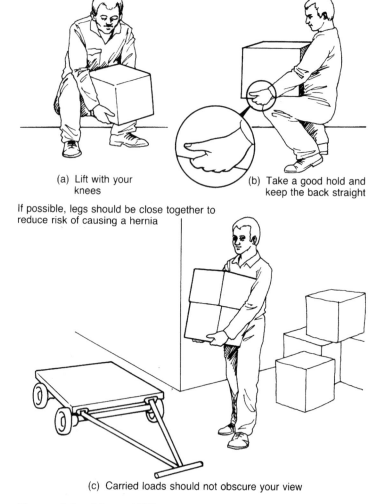

(a) Lift with your knees

(b) Take a good hold and keep the back straight

If possible, legs should be close together to reduce risk of causing a hernia

(c) Carried loads should not obscure your view

Figure 6.8 *Manual lifting*

Prevention and protection

The wearing of appropriate protective clothing and following proper safe operating procedures are obvious ways of reducing workplace risks and subsequent accidents.

Protective clothing includes suitable overalls to protect against dirt and liquid splashes while gloves, goggles, hats and leather aprons are useful protection against flying hot metal welding slag and sparks. Darkened goggles are required for welding processes or where damagingly bright lights are encountered. Boots fitted with protective steel toe-caps are essential wear in workplaces such as engineering fabrication shops where falls of heavy objects are possible. Hard hats are essential wear for workers at risk of receiving knocks to the head (see Figure 6.9).

Loose or torn clothing and long hair can become caught in moving machinery. Sharp tools in pockets can cause cuts. Too long trouser legs can cause a trip. Metal finger rings can catch in moving machinery and if flattened on the finger are difficult to

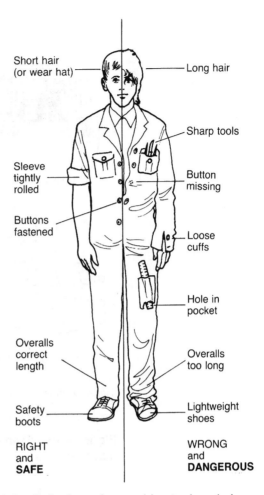

Short hair
(or wear hat)

Long hair

Sharp tools

Sleeve
tightly
rolled

Button
missing

Buttons
fastened

Loose
cuffs

Hole in
pocket

Overalls
correct
length

Overalls
too long

Safety
boots

Lightweight
shoes

RIGHT
and
SAFE

WRONG
and
DANGEROUS

Figure 6.9 *Safe dress for machine tool workplace*

remove. Before starting oily or dirty work, the hands should be rubbed with an anti-dermatitis cream to protect them from sores and rashes.

With regard to the safe operation of powered machinery used in engineering environments, the various acts and regulations previously mentioned provide massive documentation of the precautions which must be taken and who is responsible for their implementation and who their enforcement. Some of the protective measures called for by legislation include:

● proper training of operators,
● provision of operating instructions,
● fitting guards around danger points,
● emergency stops on all machines,
● safety interlocks on removable panels,
● means of isolating machines from sources of energy,
● posting of warning notices,
● regular maintenance of powered machines.

Figure 6.10 shows examples of danger points on unguarded machine tools.

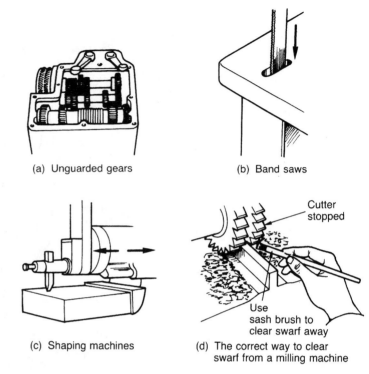

(a) Unguarded gears

(b) Band saws

(c) Shaping machines

(d) The correct way to clear swarf from a milling machine

Cutter stopped

Use sash brush to clear swarf away

Never touch any part of a moving machine. Swarf and other sharp edges are dangerous and should never be touched directly.

Figure 6.10 *Examples of danger points on unguarded machine tools*

Finally, regulations require the safe storage of materials. This includes, for example:

- provision of safe storage shelves or racking for the storage of non-hazardous materials,
- for quantities in excess of 50 litres, the provision of an outdoor, secure storage area for flammable materials such as paints,
- for radio-active materials a secure, lead-lined, concrete store is required as are properly trained people for its periodic checking for dangerous emissions.

How engineering affects the features of different workplaces

The features we are expected to identify in any workplace are:

- efficiency,
- productivity,
- health, and
- comfort.

The engineering effects on these features that we are required to consider are:

- heating,
- ventilation,
- lighting, and
- noise.

Let's now consider the features in more detail.

Workplace efficiency and productivity

In this context we need to consider the following aspects.

Workplace layout If possible a workplace should have a space layout which matches the sequence of work operations to be carried out. For example, if the task of a workshop is to recondition motorcar engines, this main task could be broken down into sub-tasks as follows:

1 Receive worn engines and hold them awaiting their turn for repairs.
2 Dismantle, inspect and order new parts.
3 Store dismantled engines to await receipt of new parts.
4 Assemble engines using new parts.
5 Test completed engines on dynamometer.

Figure 6.11 shows how this sequence of operations can be translated into a workshop layout which minimizes handling and movement.

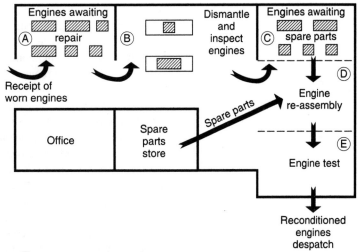

Ⓐ Engines in store awaiting repair.
Ⓑ Engines cleaned, dismantled, inspected and new parts ordered.
Ⓒ Engines in store awaiting receipt of new parts.
Ⓓ Engines fitted with new parts.
Ⓔ Assembled reconditioned engines tested before despatch.

Figure 6.11 *Engine reconditioning line layout to suit the order of repair functions. This allows a progressive clockwise flow of engines around the workshop*

Machinery and equipment   The workplace equipment not only needs to be kept in good working order, it also need to be replaced periodically by more modern and efficient machines. For example, manual typewriters with no letter storage facilities are being replaced by computerized wordprocessors which can store vast numbers of letters any one of which can be recalled and printed as the result of a few keystrokes.

Similarly, in the workshop, manually operated machine tools, such as lathes, grinders and cutting gear are being replaced by computerized numerically controlled machines. These store programs of machining instructions and can rapidly produce accurate repetitive jobs.

Energy usage and costs   In addition to the energy the workplace uses to undertake its designed function, be it office work or an engineering activity, it also uses energy for heating purposes in the winter and cooling in the summer. In the UK, with its temperate climate, the cooling of workplaces is usually confined to being no more than an open window and a fan. Of course, air-conditioning is used in some essential engineering activities such as optical or microelectronic assembly areas.

With regard to the energy used for space heating, engineering technology has moved from the open fire, or solid fuelled boiler, driving large cast-iron manually controlled radiators, to gas-fired boilers driving slim-line radiators that are individually thermostatically controlled. In large public buildings, rooms are often fitted with sensors which detect the presence of people. Energy can then be saved by arranging that the heating is switch off in unoccupied parts of buildings.

Nowadays, large buildings are usually subjected to stringent energy management systems which involve thermal insulation, the selection of the most advantageous method of heating – natural gas or electricity – and are computer controlled. Windows will be double glazed to exclude noise and retain heat. Ventilation can be through open windows, possibly computer controlled – close automatically if noisy aircraft fly overhead – or by an air-conditioning system.

Energy waste   Some engineering workplace processes involve the production of energy that could be let go to waste. For example, the steam used to drive the generator turbines in some electricity power stations can instead be sold off to heat water for use in local public central heating systems. Alternatively, the power station used-steam can be recirculated. It is first condensed back into hot water, using a large cooling tower, before being injected back into the power station water boiler for reprocessing into the dry, superheated steam required by the turbines. The hot coolant water, resulting from the cooling tower operation, can be similarly used for space heating.

Sale of by-products   These are the secondary effects that accompany an engineering process designed for a particular product. Typical of these by-products is the used steam mentioned in the previous section.

Another useful by-product, this time from the coal-fired electricity power station, is the flue dust or breeze which is deposited in the exhaust flues and chimneys. It is also called *fly ash* and is used for making breeze-blocks, a mixture of fly ash and cement, as used by the building trade.

The carbonization of coal, a chemical process involving the heating of coal in the absence of air, which boils off the volatile tars and gases from coal leaving coke, a smokeless solid fuel. The volatile materials have several uses such as the making of benzene, naphthalene and plastic; all by-products of the coking process.

Workplace comfort and health

For comfort and health in the workplace, some of the more important considerations are listed below.

Ventilation Enclosed workplaces should be sufficiently well ventilated so the stale air is replaced at a reasonable rate. The fresh air supply should not normally fall below 5 to 8 litres per second, per occupant. Guidance on the measures necessary to avoid legionnaires' disease, caused by bacteria which can grow in water cooling towers and elsewhere, is covered in special publications issued by the Health and Safety Executive.

Temperature in indoor workplaces Normal enclosed workrooms should normally be at least 16°C and up to 20°C for normal light work such as office work or operating a lathe. For heavier work involving severe physical effort, such as mixing concrete manually, the temperature should be at least 13°C. Thermometers should be available to measure the temperature in any workplace.

Lighting Lighting should be sufficient to enable people to work, use facilities and move from place to place safely and without experiencing eye-strain. Stairs should be well lit in such a way that shadows are not cast over the main part of the treads. Where necessary, local lighting should be provided at workplaces, and at places of particular risk such as pedestrian crossing points an vehicular traffic routes.

Cleanliness and waste materials The standard of cleanliness depends upon the use to which the workplace is put. For example, an area in which workers take meals would be expected to be cleaner than a factory floor, and a factory floor would be expected to be cleaner than an animal house. Floors and indoor traffic routes should be cleaned at least once a week. In workplaces where dirt and refuse accumulates, any dirt and refuse not in a suitable receptacle should be removed at least daily.

Room dimensions and space A workshops and offices should have sufficient free space between individual workplaces to allow people to move around safely and with ease. The number of workers allowed in a particular workroom at any one time will depend upon the size of the room and the amount of space consuming furniture in it. It is also important that the ceiling of a workroom is sufficiently high over most of the room to allow safe access to workplaces.

The method of calculating the number of people permitted to work in a particular room is to divide the volume of the empty room by 11 cubic metres. For the purposes of this calculation, any ceiling height greater than 3.0 m should also be taken as being 3.0 m. The figure of 11 cubic metres per person is the minimum and if, for example, there is much furniture in the room, it may need to be increased. Further, the figure of 11 cubic metres does not apply to very small workplaces, such as sales kiosks and vehicle driving cabs, nor to large rooms used for lectures and meetings.

Activity 6.7

A room measures 3.5 m × 4.5 m and has a ceiling height of 2.5 m and is to be used as an office. What is the maximum number of people permitted to work in the room? If the ceiling were raised by 1.5 m what then would be the maximum permitted number of workers?

Workplaces and seating Workplaces should be organized so that each task can be undertaken safely and comfortably. The worker should be at a suitable height in relation to the work surface. Work materials and frequently used tools and controls without undue bending and stretching. There should be sufficient space to allow the safe handling and manoeuvring of long pieces of material, such as large sheets of metal in an engineering fabrication shop.

If the nature of the work permits, a suitable seat with lower back support should be provided. If the seat is mobile on castored wheels these should be five in number in order to give safe stability.

There are special HSE publications dealing with seating and ergonomic considerations.

Falls or falling objects Because the consequences of falling from heights or into dangerous substances can be so serious, a high degree of protection is necessary. Substantial fencing is required to prevent people from falling over edges and 'kick-boards' are required to prevent heavy objects from being knocked off high platforms onto people below. Dangerous substances in pits and open tanks should be securely fenced or covered.

Windows and see-through doors Transparent or translucent surfaces in doors, gates, walls and partitions should, in general, be made from safety material or be adequately protected from being damaged. Further, windows and doors should not be positioned such that when open a person can accidentally be injured by falling through the opening.

Traffic routes These are covered in great detail by workplace legislation. Examples of points to be considered are:

- pedestrian and vehicular routes to be kept separate where possible and be properly signed;
- large reversing vehicles should be fitted with an audible alarm or there should be people on foot to supervise its safe movement;

- vehicle loading bays and pedestrian crossings require special attention to prevent personal injury;
- allowance should be made for people in wheelchairs;
- pedestrian access between floors should normally be by stairs rather than fixed ladders.

Sanitary and washing facilities These must be provided within easy distance of the workplace and be maintained in a hygienic condition. Workplace regulations give guidance regarding the numbers of wash-basins, showers, water closets and urinals which must be provided. The precise scale of provision depends not only upon the numbers of male and female workers but also upon the nature of the work and how dirty it is.

Drinking water This should normally be provided from a public or private water supply through a pipe and tap connected directly to the water main. Drinking cups or beakers should be available. The drinking water supply point should be labelled as such and, if possible, not located in the same area as toilets.

Facilities for storing and changing clothing These are particularly required where workers are required to change into special clothing. If appropriate, they should ensure the privacy of the user.

Facilities for rest and to eat meals Rest facilities are in particular required for people that normally stand to do their work. It may be simply the provision of a chair or it may extend to a special room. Meals are usually taken in a canteen provided the number of workers is sufficiently large to warrant one. Otherwise a simple seat in a clean area will suffice together the facilities for obtaining a hot drink using a kettle or vending machine.

First-aid kit and training In case of injury at work, there should at least be a first-aid kit available. One or more of the people in the workplace, or the accommodation in which it is located, should have had formal certified first-aid training. An Accident Report Book should also be available in which any reportable accidents and injuries can be logged.

Fire precautions and instructions Fire extinguishers of suitable type for the workplace should be readily available. Instructions should be posted in a prominent position informing all workers of the action expected of them in the event of a fire.

The effects of engineering activities on the physical environment

This section first identifies the engineering activities with which we are concerned as being production, servicing and materials handling. Each of these is then defined. The social and economic effects of using engineering materials is briefly investigated. Next follows a detailed description of some of the waste products from engineering activities and their effects on the environment. Finally, there is a discussion about the effects of the environmental rules and regulations which engineering companies are expected to observe.

Definitions

In the context of the GNVQ in Engineering we are to take term *physical environment* as meaning the physical world in which we live. This is to include people, all animals and plant wildlife, the land masses, the rivers and seas, the atmosphere surrounding the earth and all man-made creations such as built up areas and cultivated regions.

We shall take the term *engineering activities* as including all production, servicing and materials handling processes that use engineering equipment in any part of the activity. Perhaps we should take a closer look at these last three terms:

Production The manufacture of any man-made item including the extraction of natural resources by mining, quarrying, fishing and the like.

Servicing The after sales care given to a piece of equipment in order to keep it in good working order.

Materials handling The movement of raw material or partly finished products between stages of production. This may involve only simple manual handling but also includes the use of hand carts, dump trucks, fork lift trucks, lorries, conveyer belts, cranes and the like.

Engineering materials used

Most materials are used, one way or another, in engineering activities. They appear in the product itself or in its manufacturing process. Some of the materials occur naturally and, after extraction from the ground, require only minimal treatment before being used for some engineering purpose. Examples are, timber, copper, iron, silicon, water and air. Other engineering materials need to be manufactured. Examples are steel, brass, plastic, glass, gallium arsenide and ceramics. The use of these materials produces effects; some beneficial; some not.

Economic and social effects stem from the regional wealth that is generated by the extraction of the raw material and its subsequent processing or manufacture into useful engineering materials. For example, the extraction of iron-ore in Cleveland and its processing into pure iron and steel has brought great benefit to the Middlesbrough region. The work has attracted people to live in the area and the money they earn tends to be spent locally. This benefits trade at the local shops and entertainment centres and local builders must provide more homes and schools and so on. The increased numbers of people produces a growth in local services which includes a wider choice of different amenities, better roads and communications and arguably, in general, a better quality of life.

On the debit side, the extraction of raw materials can leave the landscape untidy. Heaps of slag around coal mines and steelworks together with holes left by disused quarries are not a pretty sight. In recent years much thought and effort has been expended on improving these eyesores. Slag heaps have been remodelled to become part of golf courses and disused quarries filled with water to become centres for water sports or fishing. Disused mines and quarries can also be used for taking engineering waste in what is known as a landfill operation prior to the appropriate landscaping being undertaken.

Activity 6.8

Find our what happens to the domestic waste in your locality.

What items are recycled?

Is any of it burnt to produce useful heat?

Present your findings in the form of a brief written report. Illustrate your report with the aid of a simple flow chart.

The effects of waste products from engineering activities

Engineering activities are a major source of many types of *pollution*. Air, soil, rivers, lakes and seas are all, some where or other, polluted by waste gases, liquids and solids discarded by the engineering industry. Because engineering enterprises tend to be concentrated in and around towns and other built-up areas, these tend to be common sources of pollutants.

Electricity is a common source of energy and its generation very often involves the burning of *fossil fuels*: coal, oil and natural gas. In so doing, each year, billions of tonnes of carbon dioxide, sulphur dioxide, smoke and toxic metals are released into the air to be distributed by the wind. The release of hot gases and hot liquids also produces another pollutant; heat. Some electricity generating stations use nuclear fuel which produces a highly radioactive solid waste rather than the above gases.

The generation of electricity is by no means the only source of toxic or biologically damaging pollutants. The exhaust gases from motor vehicles, oil refineries, chemical works and industrial furnaces are other problem areas. Also, not all pollutants are graded as *toxic*. For example, plastic and metal scrap dumped on waste tips, slag heaps around mining operations, old quarries, pits and derelict land are all *non-toxic*. Finally, pollutants can be further defined as *degradable* or *non-degradable*. These terms simply indicate whether the pollutant will decomposes or disperses itself with time. For example, smoke is degradable but dumped plastic waste is not.

Carbon dioxide in the air absorbs some of the long-wave radiation emitted by the earth's surface and in so doing is heated. The more carbon dioxide there is in the air, the greater the heating or greenhouse effect. This is suspected as being a major cause of global warming causing average seasonal temperatures to increase. In addition to causing undesirable heating effects, the increased quantity of carbon dioxide in the air, especially around large cities, may lead to people developing respiratory problems.

Oxides of nitrogen are produced in most exhaust gases and nitric oxide is prevalent near industrial furnaces. Fortunately, most oxides of nitrogen are soon washed out of the air by rain. But if there is no rain, the air becomes increasingly polluted and unpleasant.

Sulphur dioxide is produced by the burning of fuels that contain sulphur. Coal is perhaps the major culprit in this respect. High concentrations of this gas cause the air tubes in peoples' lungs to constrict and breathing becomes increasingly difficult. Sulphur dioxide also combines with rain droplets eventually to form sulphuric acid or *acid rain*. This is carried by the winds and can fall many hundreds of miles from the sulphur dioxide source. Acid rain deposits increase the normal weathering effect on buildings and soil, corrode metals and textiles and damage trees and other vegetation.

Smoke is caused by the incomplete burning of the fossil fuels. It is a health hazard on its own but even more dangerous if combined with fog. This poisonous combination, called *smog*, was prevalent in the early 1950s. It formed in its highest concentrations around the large cities where many domestic coal fires were then in use. Many deaths were recorded, especially among the elderly and those with respiratory diseases. This lead to the first Clean Air Act which prohibited the burning of fuels that caused smoke in areas of high population. So-called smokeless zones were established.

Dust and grit (ash) are very fine particles of solid material that are formed by combustion and other industrial processes. These are released into the atmosphere where they are dispersed by the wind before falling to the ground. The lighter particles may by held in the air for a many hours. They form a mist, which produces a weak, hazy sunshine and less light.

Toxic metals, such as lead and mercury are released into the air by some engineering processes and especially by motor vehicle exhaust gases. Once again the lead and mercury can be carried over hundreds of miles before falling in rainwater to contaminate the soil and the vegetation it grows. Motor vehicles are now encouraged to use lead-free petrol in an attempt to reduce the level of lead pollution.

Ozone is a gas that exists naturally in the upper layers of the earth's atmosphere. At that altitude it is one of the earth's great protectors but should it occur at ground level it is linked to pollution.

Stratospheric ozone shields us from some of the potentially harmful excessive ultra-violet radiation from the sun. In the 1980s it was discovered that emissions of gases from engineering activities were causing a 'hole' in the ozone layer. There is concern that this will increase the risk of skin cancer, eye cataracts and damage to crops and marine life.

At ground level, sunlight reacts with motor vehicle exhaust gases to produce ozone. Human lungs cannot easily extract oxygen (O_2) from ozone (O_3) so causing breathing difficulties and irritation to the respiratory channels. It can also damage plants.

This ground level or 'tropospheric' ozone is a key constituent of what is called photochemical smog or 'summer' smog. In the UK it has increased by about 60% in the last 40 years.

Note: 0800 556677 is the UK free-phone number of an air quality information line which gives details of the regional pollutant levels in the air.

Heat is a waste product of many engineering activities. A typical example being the dumping of hot coolant water from electricity generating stations into rivers or the sea. This is not so prevalent today as increasingly stringent energy saving measures are applied. However, where it does happen, river and sea temperatures can be raised sufficiently in the region of the heat outlet to destroy natural aquatic life.

Chemical waste dumped directly into rivers and the sea, or on to land near water, can cause serious pollution which can wipe out aquatic life in affected areas. There is also the long-term danger that chemicals dumped on soil will soak through the soil into the ground water which we use for drinking purposes and which will therefore require additional purification.

Radioactive waste from nuclear power stations or other engineering activities which use radioactive materials poses particular problems. Not only is it extremely dangerous to people – a powerful cause of cancer – its effects do not degrade rapidly with time and remain dangerous for scores of years. Present methods of disposing of radioactive waste, often very contentious however, include their encasement in lead and burial underground or at sea.

Derelict land is an unfortunate effect of some engineering activities. The term derelict land may be taken to mean land so badly damaged that it cannot be used for other purposes without further treatment. This includes disused or abandoned land requiring restoration works to bring it into use or to improve its appearance. Land may be made derelict by mining and quarrying operations, the dumping of waste or by disused factories from by-gone engineering activities.

Test your knowledge 6.5

Name a pollutant which fits each of the following categories:

(a) toxic and degradable,
(b) toxic and non-degradable,
(c) non-toxic and degradable,
(d) non-toxic and non-degradable.

The effect of environmental legislation on engineering activities

Engineering activities can have harmful effects on the physical environment and therefore on people. In order to minimize these effects, there is a range of legislation (rules and regulations) which engineering companies must observe.

The appropriate United Kingdom Acts of Parliament include Deposit of Poisonous Wastes Act, Pollution of Rivers Act, Clean Air Act, Environmental Protection Act, Health and Safety at Work, etc. Act and the like. Additionally, not only are there local by-laws to be observed there are also European Union (EU) directives that are activated and implemented either through existing UK legislation in the form of Acts of Parliament or mandatory instructions called Statutory Instruments (Sis).

New Acts and directives are introduced from time to time and industry needs to be alert to and keep abreast of these changes. Typical of these new initiatives is the European Electromagnetic Compatibility (EMC) legislation. This states that with effect from 1st January 1996 it is a requirement that all products marketed must conform with the new legislation. This new EMC legislation, at last, officially recognizes the well known problem of unwanted electromagnetic wave radiation that emanates from most pieces of electrical equipment. The unwanted radiation can interfere with adjacent electronic equipments causing them damage or to malfunction.

In the case of UK Acts of Parliament, the above legislation is implemented by judgement in UK Courts of Justice in the normal manner but based on EU legislation, if more appropriate, or by judgement of the European Court of Justice.

The purpose of the of this legislation is to provide the following functions:

- *prevent* the environment being damaged in the first place;
- *regulate* the amount of damage by stating limits, for example, the maximum permitted amount of liquid pollutant that a factory may discharge into the sea;
- *compensate* people for damage caused, for example, from a chemical store catching fire and spreading wind borne poisonous fumes across the neighbourhood;
- *impose sanctions* on those countries or other lesser parties that choose to ignore the legislation;
- *define who is responsible* for compliance with legislation to persons who can be named and their precise area of responsibility documented.

Note: For the purposes of showing understanding of the above, you are *not* expected to have a detailed understanding of the various Acts however you *should be aware of the general provisions* of the legislation and what it is trying to achieve. Your school, college or local town library will be able to provide you with more details.

The effects of the above legislation on engineering activities has, in general, made them more difficult and more expensive to implement. A few simple examples of this follow.

- *Chemical factories* can no longer discharge their dangerous waste effluent straight into the river or sea without first passing it through some form of purification.
- *Coal fuelled power stations* must ensure that their chimney stacks do not pollute the neighbourhood with smoke containing illegal limits of grit, dust, toxic gases and other pollutants. A system of smoke filtration and purification must be (expensively) incorporated.
- *Motor car* exhaust gases must be sufficiently free of oxides of nitrogen, carbon monoxide and other toxic gases. This can only be achieved by, among other things, replacing the crude petrol carburettor with a more sophisticated petrol injection system and fitting a catalyser in the exhaust pipe. All this has added to the price of the motor car and has made it more difficult for the DIY motorist to service his vehicle.
- *All Electrical equipments* including TVs, PCs, power hand tools, electromedical machines, lighting and the like, must be tested and certified that they comply with the EMC legislation. So, in addition to the cost of reducing any excessive radiation from the product itself, the purchase or hire of expensive EMC test equipment and the training of people to use it must also be taken into account. Further, because of delays in obtaining an official EMC examination and supporting certificate (EC), the introduction of new product designs can be delayed and this may have adverse marketing effects.

Activity 6.9

Write a report based on your investigations into the effects of ONE engineering activity from EACH category in the range, *production*, *servicing* and *materials handling*, on the physical environment to include *human*, *natural* and *built*.

Examples of engineering production activities are:

- motor car manufacture,
- steel manufacture,
- coal mining.

Examples of engineering servicing activities are:

- motor car dealership garages,
- local council road maintenance depots,
- maintenance of electricity and gas supplies.

Examples of materials handling activities are:

- container handling terminals,
- moving cargo by rail and road,
- conveying goods on moving belts.

For the engineering activity you have chosen, your report should include a brief description of:

- the environmental effects of the materials used,
- the short-term and long-term environmental effects of any waste products,
- any environmental legislation effects giving specific examples.

Hints:

Make sure that your selected engineering activity gives you the opportunity to produce the necessary amount of evidence to demonstrate your competence and understanding.

You should approach this activity through case studies (e.g., those highlighted by court cases concerning failure to comply with legislation).

Finally, it is important to be clear about the difference *waste products* and *by-products*. The by-products from one process can be sold as the raw materials for other processes. For example, natural gas is a by-product of oil extraction and a useful fuel used in the generation of electricity. Waste products are those that cannot be sold and may attract costs in their disposal. Nuclear power station waste is a typical example.

Multiple choice questions

1 The gross national product (GNP) of a country is the total value of all goods and services produced

A by the citizens of the country
B within the borders of the country
C by the resources owned by the citizens of the country, no matter in which country the resources may be situated
D by all the citizens and foreigners living in the country.

2 The gross domestic product per head is a measure of a country's

A population
B number of unemployed workers
C productivity
D flexibility.

3 With regard to the production of an aircraft engine, the direct labour element is provided by the people who

A are to use the completed engine
B are sub-contracted to supply the engine parts
C deliver the engine to the end user
D assemble the engine ready for delivery.

4 Exports are goods that we sell abroad and are divided into 'visible' and 'invisible' exports. These two classifications respectively mean

A hard goods transported abroad and their transport costs
B goods shipped loose and containerized goods
C hard goods shipped abroad and services sold to foreigners
D firm export orders and anticipated export orders.

5 Which ONE of the following best describes why computer controlled robots are used in many motor car assembly lines?

A Increased speed, reliability and accuracy of the assembly process
B Reduced cost of assembly
C The cars are more robust
D The assembly line can work 24 hours per day.

6 A crane operator's internal cab layout is ergonomically designed in order to

A reduce the number of controls available
B position the controls in the most accessible position for the operator to reach
C improve operator access to and from the cab
D to reduce the cost of the cab.

7 The main objective of work study in the workplace is to

A increase productivity
B determine the work done in watts
C interface the worker's physical size with the workplace layout
D introduce incentive payments.

8 The purpose of risk analysis in the workplace is to

A determine the number of unreported workplace accidents
B to check all tools and equipment for correct working
C that all doors and windows can be properly secured at night
D identify work areas, tasks and substances that are likely to be the cause of an accident unless preventive measures are taken.

9 Smog is the name given to air which is heavily polluted with

A motor vehicle exhaust gases
B gases from coal fires and water vapour
C cigarette smoke
D dust.

10 A by-product from an engineering process is

A the main purpose of the process
B an undesirable waste product which may cost money in its disposal
C a pollutant
D a further product from the process which can be put to some use.

Unit 7 Science for engineering

Summary

This section aims to develop in the reader an understanding of fundamental science concepts and to give a basic mechanical, thermal and electrical engineering systems background for student engineers.

More specifically, the aims are to describe engineering systems in terms of basic scientific laws and principles, to investigate the behaviour of simple linear systems in engineering, to calculate the response of engineering systems to changes in variables, and to determine the response of such engineering systems to changes in parameters.

SI Units

The system of units used in engineering and science is the *Système Internationale d'Unités* (international system of units), usually abbreviated to SI units, and is based on the metric system. This was introduced in 1960 and is now adopted by the majority of countries as the official system of measurement.

The basic units in the SI system are listed below with their symbols:

Quantity	*Unit and symbol*
length	metre, m
mass	kilogram, kg
time	second, s
electric current	ampere, A
thermodynamic temperature	Kelvin, K
luminous intensity	candela, cd
amount of substance	mole, mol

SI units may be made larger or smaller by using *prefixes* which denote multiplication or division by a particular amount. The eight most common multiples, with their meaning, are listed below:

Prefix	Name	Meaning
T	tera	multiply by 1 000 000 000 000 (i.e. $\times 10^{12}$)
G	giga	multiply by 1 000 000 000 (i.e. $\times 10^{9}$)
M	mega	multiply by 1 000 000 (i.e. $\times 10^{6}$)
k	kilo	multiply by 1 000 (i.e. $\times 10^{3}$)
m	milli	divide by 1 000 (i.e. $\times 10^{-3}$)
μ	micro	divide by 1 000 000 (i.e. $\times 10^{-6}$)
n	nano	divide by 1 000 000 000 (i.e. $\times 10^{-9}$)
p	pico	divide by 1 000 000 000 000 (i.e. $\times 10^{-12}$)

Length is the distance between two points. The standard unit of length is the *metre*, although the *centimetre* (cm), *millimetre* (mm) and *kilometre* (km), are often used.

$$1\,cm = 10\,mm; \ 1\,m = 100\,cm = 1000\,mm; \ 1\,km = 1000\,m$$

Area is a measure of the size or extent of a plane surface and is measured by multiplying a length by a length. If the lengths are in metres then the unit of area is the *square metre*, m^2.

$$1\,m^2 = 1\,m \ x \ 1\,m = 100\,cm \times 100\,cm = 10\,000\,cm^2$$
$$\text{or } 10^2\,cm^2$$

$$= 1000\,mm \times 1000\,mm = 1\,000\,000\,mm^2$$
$$\text{or } 10^6\,mm^2$$

Conversely, $1\,cm^2 = 10^{-4}\,m^2$ and $1\,mm^2 = 10^{-6}\,m^2$.

Volume is a measure of the space occupied by a solid and is measured by multiplying a length by a length by a length. If the lengths are in metres then the unit of volume is in *cubic metres*, m^3.

$$1\,m^3 = 1\,m \times 1\,m \ x \ 1 \ m$$

$$= 100\,cm \times 100\,cm \times 100\,cm = 10^6\,cm^3$$

$$= 1000\,mm \times 1000\,mm \times 1000\,mm$$

$$= 10^9\,mm^3$$

Conversely, $1\,cm^3 = 10^{-6}\,m^3$ and $1\,mm^3 = 10^{-9}\,m^3$

Another unit used to measure volume, particularly with liquids, is the litre, l, where $1\,l = 1000\,cm^3$.

Mass is the amount of matter in a body and is measured in *kilograms*, kg.

$$1\,kg = 1000\,g \text{ (or conversely, } 1\,g = 10^{-3}\,kg)$$

and

$$1 \text{ tonne (t)} = 1000\,kg$$

Example 7.1

Express (a) a length of 36 mm in metres, (b) 32 400 mm² in square metres, and (c) 8 540 000 mm³ in cubic metres.

(a) $1\,m = 10^3\,mm$ or $1\,mm = 10^{-3}\,m$.

Hence $36\,mm = 36 \times 10^{-3}\,m = \dfrac{36}{10^3}\,m = \dfrac{36}{1000}\,m = \mathbf{0.036\,m}$

(b) $1\,m^2 = 10^6\,mm^2$ or $1\,mm^2 = 10^{-6}\,m^2$.

Hence $32\,400\,mm^2 = 32\,400 \times 10^{-6}\,m^2 = \dfrac{32\,400}{10^6} = \mathbf{0.0324\,m^2}$

(c) $1\,m^3 = 10^9\,mm^3$ or $1\,mm^3 = 10^{-9}\,m^3$.

Hence $8\,540\,000\,mm^3 = 8\,540\,000 \times 10^{-9}\,m^3$

$$= \dfrac{8\,540\,000}{10^9}\,m^3$$

$$= 8.54 \times 10^{-3}\,m^3 \text{ or } \mathbf{0.00854\,m^3}$$

Test your knowledge 7.1

1 Determine the area of a room 15 m long by 8 m wide in (a) m², (b) cm² and (c) mm²
2 A bottle contains 4 litres of liquid. Determine the volume in (a) cm³, (b) m³ and (c) mm²

Example 7.2

A cube has sides each of length 50 mm. Determine the volume of the cube in cubic metres.

Volume of cube $= 50\,mm \times 50\,mm \times 50\,mm = 125\,000\,mm^3$

$1\,mm^3 = 10^{-9}\,m$, thus volume $= 125\,000 \times 10^{-9}\,m^3$

$$= \mathbf{0.125 \times 10^{-3}\,m^3}$$

Density

Density is the mass per unit volume of a substance. The symbol used for density is ρ and its units are kg/m^3.

$$\text{Density} = \frac{\text{mass}}{\text{volume}}, \text{ i.e. } = \frac{m}{V} \text{ or } m = V\rho \text{ or } V = \frac{m}{d}$$

where m is the mass in kg, V is the volume in m³ and ρ is the density in kg/m^3

Some typical values of densities include:

Aluminium	2700 kg/m³	Steel	7800 kg/m³
Cast iron	7000 kg/m³	Petrol	700 kg/m³
Cork	2500 kg/m³	Lead	11 400 kg/m³
Copper	8900 kg/m³	Water	1000 kg/m³

The *relative density* of a substance is the ratio of the density of the substance to the density of water, i.e.

$$\text{relative density} = \frac{\text{density of substance}}{\text{density of water}}$$

Relative density has no units, since it is the ratio of two similar quantities. Typical values of relative densities can be determined from above (since water has a density of $1000 \, \text{kg/m}^3$), and include:

Aluminium	2.7	Steel	7.8
Cast iron	7.0	Petrol	0.7
Cork	0.25	Lead	11.4
Copper	8.9		

The relative density of a liquid may be measured using a *hydrometer.*

Example 7.3

Determine the density of $50 \, \text{cm}^3$ of copper if its mass is $445 \, \text{g}$.

Volume $= 50 \, \text{cm}^3 = 50 \times 10^{-6} \, \text{m}^3$; mass $= 445 \, \text{g} = 445 \times 10^{-3} \, \text{kg}$

$$\text{Density} = \frac{\text{mass}}{\text{volume}} = \frac{445 \times 10^3 \, \text{kg}}{50 \times 10^{-6} \, \text{m}^3}$$

$$= \frac{445}{50} \times 10^3$$

$$= 8.9 \times 10^3 \, \text{kg/m}^3 \text{ or } \mathbf{8900 \, kg/m^3}$$

Test your knowledge 7.2

1 Determine the density of $80 \, \text{cm}^3$ of cast iron if its mass is $560 \, \text{g}$.
2 Determine the volume, in litres, of $35 \, \text{kg}$ of petrol of density $700 \, \text{kg/m}^3$.
3 A piece of metal $200 \, \text{mm}$ long, $150 \, \text{mm}$ wide and $10 \, \text{mm}$ thick has a mass of $2700 \, \text{g}$. What is the density of the metal?

Example 7.4

The density of aluminium is $2700 \, \text{kg/m}^3$. Calculate the mass of a block of aluminium which has a volume of $100 \, \text{cm}^2$.

Density $\rho = 2700 \, \text{kg/m}^3$; volume $V = 100 \, \text{cm}^3 = 100 \times 10^{-6} \, \text{m}^3$

Since density $=$ mass/volume, then mass $=$ density $\times$ volume.

Hence $m = \rho V = 2700 \, \text{kg/m}^3 \times 100 \times 10^{-6} \, \text{m}^3$

$$= \frac{2700 \times 100}{10^6} \, \text{kg} = 0.270 \, \text{kg} \text{ or } \mathbf{270 \, g}$$

Scalar and vector quantities

Quantities used in engineering and science can be divided into two groups:

(a) *Scalar quantities* have a size (or magnitude) only and need no other information to specify them. Thus, 10 centimetres, 50 seconds, 7 litres and 3 kilograms are all examples of scalar quantities.

(b) *Vector quantities* have both a size or magnitude and a direction, called the line of action of the quantity. Thus, a velocity of 50 kilometres per hour due east, an acceleration of 9.81 metres per second squared vertically downwards and a force of 15 newtons at an angle of 30 degrees are all examples of vector quantities.

Force

When forces are all acting in the same plane, they are called *coplanar*. When forces act at the same time and at the same point, they are called *concurrent forces*.

Force is a *vector quantity* and thus has both a magnitude and a direction. A vector can be represented graphically by a line drawn to scale in the direction of the line of action of the force. Vector quantities may be shown by using bold, lower case letters, thus *ab* in Figure 7.1 represents a force of 5 newtons acting in a direction due east.

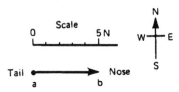

Figure 7.1

The resultant of two coplanar forces

For two forces acting at a point, there are three possibilities.

(a) For forces acting in the same direction and having the same line of action, the single force having the same effect as both of the forces, called the *resultant force* or just the *resultant*, is the arithmetic sum of the separate forces. Forces of F_1 and F_2 acting at point P, as shown in Figure 7.2(a), have exactly the same effect on point P as force F shown in Figure 7.2(b), where $F = F_1 + F_2$ and acts in the same direction as F_1 and F_2. Thus F is the resultant of F_1 and F_2.

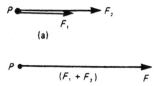

Figure 7.2

(b) For forces acting in opposite directions along the same line of action, the resultant force is the arithmetic difference between the two forces. Forces of F_1 and F_2 acting at point P as shown in Figure 7.3(a) have exactly the same effect on point P as force F shown in Figure 7.3(b), where $F = F_2 - F_1$ and acts in the direction of F_2, since F_2 is greater than F_1. Thus F is the resultant of F_1 and F_2.

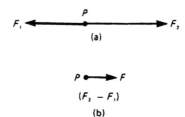

Figure 7.3

Example 7.5

Determine the resultant force of two forces of 5 kN and 8 kN,

(a) acting in the same direction and having the same line of action,
(b) acting in opposite directions but having the same line of action.

(a) The vector diagram of the two forces acting in the same direction is shown in Figure 7.4(a) which assumes that the line of action is horizontal, although since it is not specified, could be in any direction. From above, the resultant force F is given by:

$$F = F_1 + F_2, \text{ i.e. } F = (5 + 8)\,\text{kN} = \textbf{13 kN}$$

in the direction of the original forces.

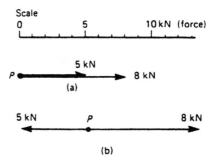

Figure 7.4

(b) The vector diagram of the two forces acting in opposite directions is shown in Figure 7.4(b), again assuming that the line of action is in a horizontal direction. From above, the resultant force F is given by:

$$F = F_2 - F_1, \text{ i.e. } F = (8 - 5)\,\text{kN} = \textbf{3 kN}$$

in the direction of the 8 kN force.

(c) When two forces do not have the same line of action, the magnitude and direction of the resultant force may be found by a procedure called vector addition of forces. There are two graphical methods of performing *vector addition*, known as the *triangle of forces* method and the *parallelogram of forces* method.

Triangle of forces method

A simple procedure for the triangle of forces method of vector addition is as follows:

(i) Draw a vector representing one of the forces, using an appropriate scale and in the direction of its line of action.

(ii) From the *nose* of this vector and using the same scale, draw a vector representing the second force in the direction of its line of action.

(iii) The resultant vector is represented in both magnitude and direction by the vector drawn from the tail of the first vector to the nose of the second vector.

Example 7.6

Determine the magnitude and direction of the resultant of a force of 15 N acting horizontally to the right and a force of 20 N, inclined at an angle of 60° to the 15 N force. Use the triangle of forces method.

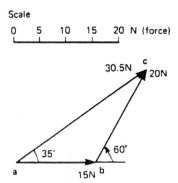

Figure 7.5

Using the procedure given above and with reference to Figure 7.5

(i)   **ab** is drawn 15 units long horizontally.
(ii) From b, **bc** is drawn 20 units long, inclined at an angle of 60° to **ab**. (Note, in angular measure, an angle of 60° from **ab** means 60° is in an anticlockwise direction.)
(iii) By measurement, the resultant **ac** is 30.5 units long inclined at an angle of 35° to **ab**. That is, the resultant force is **30.5 N**, inclined at an angle of **35°** to the 15 N force.

The parallelogram of forces method

A simple procedure for the parallelogram of forces method of vector addition is as follows:

(i)   Draw a vector representing one of the forces, using an appropriate scale and in the direction of its line of action.

(ii) From the *tail* of this vector and using the same scale draw a vector representing the second force in the direction of its line of action.

(iii) Complete the parallelogram using the two vectors drawn in (i) and (ii) as two sides of the parallelogram.

(iv) The resultant force is represented in both magnitude and direction by the vector corresponding to the diagonal of the parallelogram drawn from the tail of the vectors in (i) and (ii).

Example 7.7

Use the parallelogram of forces method to find the magnitude and direction of the resultant of a force of 250 N acting at an angle of 135° and a force of 400 N acting at an angle of −120°.

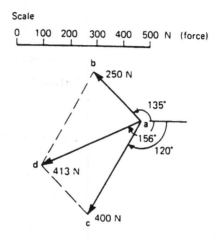

Figure 7.6

From the procedure given above and with reference to Figure 7.6:

(i)   ***ab*** is drawn at an angle of 135° and 250 units in length
(ii) ***ac*** is drawn at an angle of −120° and 400 units in length
(iii) ***bd*** and ***cd*** are drawn to complete the parallelogram
(iv) ***ad*** is drawn. By measurement, ***ad*** is 413 units long at an angle of −156°. That is, the resultant force is **413 N** at an angle of **−156°**.

Test your knowledge 7.3

1 Find the magnitude and direction of the two forces given, using the triangle of forces method.
First force: 1.5 kN acting at an angle of 30°
Second force: 3.7 kN acting at an angle of −45°

2 Determine the magnitude and direction of the resultant of forces of 23.8 N at −50° and 14.4 N at 215° using the parallelogram of forces method.

Resultant of coplanar forces by calculation

An alternative to the graphical methods of determining the resultant of two coplanar forces is by *calculation*. This can be achieved by trigonometry using the cosine rule and the sine rule, as shown in Example 7.8, or by resolution of forces (see later).

Example 7.8

Use the cosine and sine rules to determine the magnitude and direction of the resultant of a force of 8 kN acting at an angle of 50° to the horizontal and a force of 5 kN acting at an angle of −30° to the horizontal.

The space diagram is shown in Figure 7.7(a). A sketch is made of the vector diagram in Figure 7.7(b), ***oa*** representing the 8 kN force in magnitude and direction and ***ab*** representing the 5 kN force in magnitude and direction. The resultant is given by length ***ob***.

By the cosine rule,

$$ob^2 = oa^2 + ab^2 - 2(oa)(ab)\cos oab$$

$$= 8^2 + 5^2 - 2(8)(5)\cos 100°$$
$$(\text{since } oab = 180° - 50° - 30° = 100°)$$

$$= 64 + 25 - (-13.892) = 102.892$$

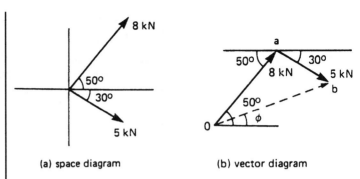

(a) space diagram   (b) vector diagram

Figure 7.7

Hence ob = $\sqrt{(102.892)}$ = 10.14 kN
  By the sine rule,

$$\frac{5}{\sin aob} = \frac{10.14}{\sin 100°}$$

from which,

$$\sin aob = \frac{5 \sin 100°}{10.14} = 0.4856$$

Hence aob = arcsin (0.4856) = 29° 3′. Thus angle θ in Figure 8.10(b) is 50° − 29° 3′ = 20° 57′.
  Hence the resultant of the two forces is **10.14 kN** acting at an angle of 20° 57′ to the horizontal.

Resultant of more than two coplanar forces

For the three coplanar forces F_1, F_2 and F_3 acting at a point as shown in Figure 7.8, the vector diagram is drawn using the nose-to-tail method. The procedure is:

(i)   Draw *oa* to scale to represent force F_1 in both magnitude and direction (see Figure 7.9).
(ii) From the nose of *oa*, draw *ab* to represent force F_2.
(iii) From the nose of *ab*, draw *bc* to represent force F_3.
(iv) The resultant vector is given by length *oc* in Figure 7.9. The direction of resultant *oc* is from where we started, i.e. point o, to where we finished, i.e. point c. When acting by itself, the resultant force, given by *oc*, has the same effect on the point as forces F_1, F_2 and F_3 have when acting together. The resulting vector diagram of Figure 7.9 is called the *polygon of forces*.

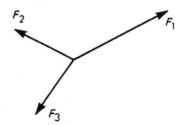

Figure 7.8

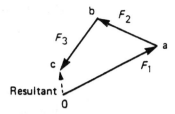

Figure 7.9

Example 7.9

Determine graphically the magnitude and direction of the resultant of these three coplanar forces, which may be considered as acting at a point. Force A, 12 N acting horizontally to the right; force B, 7 N inclined at 60° to force A; force C, 15 N inclined at 150° to force A.

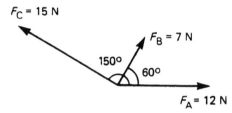

Figure 7.10

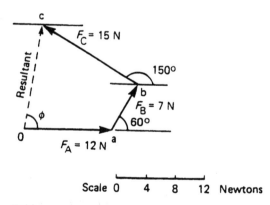

Figure 7.11

The space diagram is shown in Figure 7.10. The vector diagram (Figure 7.11) is produced as follows:

(i)   *oa* represents the 12 N force in magnitude and direction
(ii) From the nose of *oa, ab* is drawn inclined at 60° to *oa* and 7 units long.
(iii) From the nose of *ab, bc* is drawn 15 units long inclined at 150° to *oa* (i.e. 150° to the horizontal).
(iv) *oc* represents the resultant. By measurement, the resultant is 13.8 N inclined at 80° to the horizontal.

Thus the resultant of the three forces, F_A, F_B and F_C is a force of **13.8 N** at **80°** to the horizontal.

Coplanar forces in equilibrium

When three or more coplanar forces are acting at a point and the vector diagram closes, there is no resultant. The forces acting at the point are in *equilibrium*.

Example 7.10

A load of 200 N is lifted by two ropes connected to the same point on the load, making angles of 40° and 35° with the vertical. Determine graphically the tensions in each rope when the system is in equilibrium.

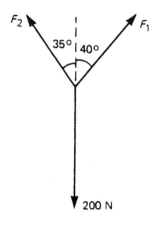

Figure 7.12

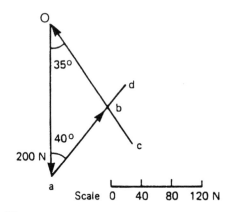

Scale

Figure 7.13

The space diagram is shown in Figure 7.12. Since the system is in equilibrium, the vector diagram must close. The vector diagram (Figure 7.13) is drawn as follows:

(i)   The load of 200 N is drawn vertically as shown by *oa*.
(ii) The direction only of force F_1 is known, so from point a, *ad* is drawn 40° to the vertical.
(iii) The direction only of force F_2 is known, so from point o, *oc* is drawn at 35° to the vertical.
(iv) Lines *ad* and *oc* cross at point b. Hence the vector diagram is given by triangle oab. By measurement, *ab* is 119 N and *ob* is 133 N.

Thus the tensions in the ropes are F_1 = **119 N** and F_2 = **133 N**.

1 Calculate the magnitude and direction of the resultant of the two forces 1.7 N at 45° and 2.4 N at −60°.
2 Determine the magnitude and direction of the resultant of the following coplanar forces:
   force 1, 23 kN acting at 80° to the horizontal,
   force 2, 30 kN acting at 37° to force 1,
   force 3, 15 kN acting at 70° to force 2.

Resolution of forces

A vector quantity may be expressed in terms of its *horizontal* and *vertical components*. For example, a vector representing a force of 10 N at an angle of 60° to the horizontal is shown in Figure 7.14. If the horizontal line *oa* and the vertical line *ab* are constructed as shown, then *oa* is called the horizontal component of the 10 N force and *ab* the vertical component of the 10 N force.

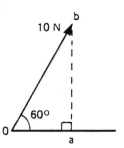

Figure 7.14

By trigonometry, cos 60° = oa/ob. Hence the horizontal component, oa = 10 cos 60°. Also, sin 60° = ab/ob. Hence the vertical component ab = 10 sin 60°.

This process is called finding the horizontal and vertical components of a vector or the resolution of a vector, and can be used as an alternative to graphical methods for calculating the resultant of two or more coplanar forces acting at a point. For example, to calculate the resultant of a 10 N force acting at 60° to the horizontal and a 20 N force acting at −30° to the horizontal (see Figure 7.15) the procedure is as follows:

(i) Determine the horizontal and vertical components of the 10 N force, i.e. horizontal component, oa = 10 cos 60° = 5.0 N, and vertical component, ab = 10 sin 60° = 8.66 N.

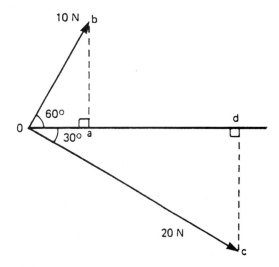

Figure 7.15

(ii) Determine the horizontal and vertical components of the 20 N force, i.e. horizontal component, od = $20 \cos(-30°)$ = 17.32 N, and vertical component, cd = $20 \sin(-30°)$ = −10.0 N.

(iii) Determine the total horizontal component, i.e.

$$oa + od = 5.0 + 17.32 = 22.32 \text{ N}$$

(iv) Determine the total vertical component, i.e.

$$ab + cd = 8.66 + (-10.0) = -1.34 \text{ N}$$

(v) Sketch the total horizontal and vertical components as shown in Figure 7.16. The resultant of the two components is given by length *or* and, by Pythagoras' theorem *or* = $\sqrt{[(22.32)^2 + (1.34)^2]}$ = 22.36 N and using trigonometry,

$$\text{angle } \theta = \arctan \frac{1.34}{22.32} \quad 3° \, 26'$$

Hence the resultant of the 10 N and 20 N forces shown in Figure 7.15 is 22.36 N at an angle of −3° 26′ to the horizontal.

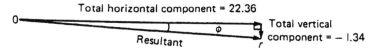

Total horizontal component = 22.36
Resultant
Total vertical component = −1.34

Figure 7.16

This example demonstrates the use of resolution of forces for calculating the resultant of two coplanar forces acting at a point. However, the method may be used for more than two forces acting at a point.

Example 7.11

Forces of 5.0 N at 25° and 8.0 N at 112° act at a point. By resolving these forces into horizontal and vertical components, determine their resultant.

The space diagram is shown in Figure 7.17.

(i) The horizontal component of the 5.0 N force,

$$oa = 5.0 \cos 25° = 4.532;$$

the vertical component of the 5.0 N force, ab = $5.0 \sin 25°$ = 2.113.

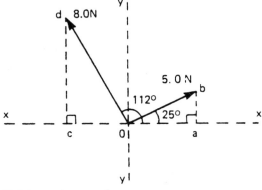

Figure 7.17

(ii) The horizontal component of the 8.0 N force,

$$oc = 8.0 \cos cod = 8.0 \cos 68° = 2.997.$$

However, in the second quadrant, the cosine of an acute angle is negative, hence the horizontal component of the 8.0 N force is −2.997.

The vertical component of the 8.0 N force,

$$cd = 8.0 \sin cod = 8.0 \sin 68° = 7.417.$$

Since, in the second quadrant, the sine of an acute angle is positive, the vertical component of the 8.0 N force is +7.417.

Figure 7.18

(A useful check is that the vertical components ab and cd are both above the XX axis and are thus both positive; horizontal component oa is positive since it is to the right of axis YY and the horizontal component oc is negative since it is to the left of axis YY.)

(iii) Total horizontal component = oa + oc

$$= 4.532 + (-2.997) = +1.535$$

(iv) Total vertical component $= ab + dc = 2.113 + 7.417 = +9.530$

(v) The components are shown sketched in figure 7.18. By Pythagoras' theorem, $r = \sqrt{[(1.535)^2 + (9.530)^2]} = 9.653$, and by trigonometry, angle = arctan (9.530/1.535) = 80° 51′.

Hence the resultant of the two forces shown in figure 7.17 is a force of **9.653 N** acting at **80° 51′** to the horizontal.

Summary

(a) To determine the resultant of two coplanar forces acting at a point, four methods are commonly used. They are:

by drawing: (1) triangle of forces method, and
              (2) parallelogram of forces method, and
by calculation: (3) use of cosine and sine rules, and
              (4) resolution of forces.

(b) To determine the resultant of more than two coplanar forces acting at a point, two methods are commonly used. They are:

by drawing: (1) polygon of forces method, and
by calculation: (2) resolution of forces.

Test your knowledge 7.5

1 Determine by resolution of forces the resultant of the following three coplanar forces acting at a point:
   200 N acting at 20° to the horizontal;
   400 N acting at 165° to the horizontal;
   500 N acting at 250° to the horizontal.

2 The following coplanar forces act at a point:
   force A is 18 kN at 15° to the horizontal;
   force B is 25 kN at 126° to the horizontal;
   force C is 10 kN at 197° to the horizontal;
   force D is 15 kN at 246° to the horizontal;
   force E is 30 kN at 331° to the horizontal.
   Determine the resultant of the five forces by resolution of forces.

Speed

Speed is the rate of covering distance and is given by:

$$\text{speed} = \frac{\text{distance travelled}}{\text{time taken}}$$

The usual units for speed are metres per second (m/s or m s^{-1}), or kilometres per hour (km/h or km h^{-1}). Thus if a person walks 5 kilometres in 1 hour, the speed of the person is 5/1, that is, 5 kilometres per hour. The symbol for the SI unit of speed (and velocity) is written as m s^{-1}, called the 'index notation'. However, engineers usually use the symbol m/s, called the 'oblique notation'.

Example 7.12

A man walks 600 metres in 5 minutes. Determine his speed in (a) metres per second and (b) kilometres per hour.

(a) Speed $= \dfrac{\text{distance travelled}}{\text{time taken}} = \dfrac{600\,\text{m}}{5\,\text{min}}$

$$= \frac{600\,\text{m}}{5\,\text{min}} \times \frac{1\,\text{min}}{60\,\text{s}} = \mathbf{2\,m/s}$$

(b) $\dfrac{2\,\text{m}}{1\,\text{s}} = \dfrac{2\,\text{m}}{1\,\text{s}} \times \dfrac{1\,\text{km}}{1000\,\text{m}} \times \dfrac{3600\,\text{s}}{1\,\text{h}} = \mathbf{7.2\,km/h}$

(Note: to change from m/s to km/h, multiply by 3.6)

Distance/time graph

One way of giving data on the motion of an object is graphically. A graph of distance travelled (the scale on the vertical axis of the graph) against time (the scale on the horizontal axis of the graph) is called a *distance/time graph*. Thus if an aeroplane travels 500 kilometres in its first hour of flight and 750 kilometres in its second hour of flight, then after 2 hours, the total distance travelled is (500 + 750) kilometres, that is, 1250 kilometres. The distance/time graph for this flight is shown in Figure 7.19.

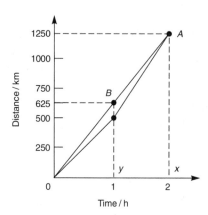

Figure 7.19

The *average speed* is given by

$$\frac{\text{total distance travelled}}{\text{total time taken}}$$

Thus, the average speed of the aeroplane is:

$$\frac{(500 + 750)\,\text{km}}{(1 + 1)\,\text{h}}, \text{ i.e. } \frac{1250}{2} \text{ or } 625\,\text{km/h}$$

If points 0 and A are joined in Figure 7.19, the slope of line 0A is defined as

$$\frac{\text{change in distance (vertical)}}{\text{change in time (horizontal)}}$$

for any two points on line 0A. For point A, the change in distance is AX, that is, 1250 kilometres, and the change in time is 0X, that is, 2 hours. Hence the average speed is 1250/2, i.e. 625 kilometres per hour.

Alternatively, for point B on line 0A, the change in distance is BY, that is, 625 kilometres and the change in time is 0Y, that is 1 hour, hence the average speed if 625/1, i.e. 625 kilometres per hour.

In general, the average speed of an object travelling between points M and N is given by the slope of line MN on the distance/time graph.

Example 7.13

A person travels from point 0 to A, then from A to B and finally from B to C. The distances of A, B and C from 0 and the times, measured from the start to reach points A, B and C are as shown:

	A	B	C
Distance (m)	100	200	250
Time (s)	40	60	100

Plot the distance/time graph and determine the speed of travel for each of the three parts of the journey.

The vertical scale of the graph is distance travelled and the scale is selected to span 0 to 250 m, the total distance travelled from the start. The horizontal scale is time and spans 0 to 100 seconds, the total time taken to cover the whole journey. Coordinates corresponding to A, B and C are plotted and 0A, AB and BC are joined by straight lines. The resulting distance/time graph is shown in Figure 7.20.

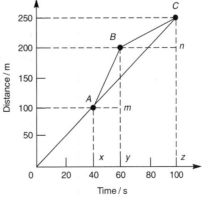

Figure 7.20

The speed is given by the slope of the distance/time graph. Speed for part OA of the journey = slope of OA = AX/OX

$$= \frac{100\,\text{m}}{40\,\text{s}} = 2\tfrac{1}{2}\,\text{m/s}$$

Speed for part AB of the journey = slope of AB = B m/A m

$$= \frac{(200 - 100)\,\text{m}}{(60 - 40)\,\text{s}} = \frac{100\,\text{m}}{20\,\text{s}} = \mathbf{5\,m/s}$$

Speed for part BC of the journey = slope of BC = Cn/Bn

$$= \frac{(250 - 200)\,\text{m}}{(100 - 60)\,\text{s}} = \frac{50\,\text{m}}{40\,\text{s}} = 1\tfrac{1}{4}\,\text{m/s}$$

Example 7.14

Determine the average speed (both in m/s and km/h) for the whole journey for the information given in Example 7.13.

$$\text{Average speed} = \text{(total distance travelled)/(total time taken)}$$

$$= \text{slope of line OC.}$$

From figure 7.20,

$$\text{slope of line OC} = \frac{Cz}{Oz} = \frac{250\,\text{m}}{100\,\text{s}} = \mathbf{2.5\,m/s}$$

$$2.5\,\text{m/s} = \frac{2.5\,\text{m}}{1\,\text{s}} \times \frac{1\,\text{km}}{1000\,\text{m}} \times \frac{3600\,\text{s}}{1\,\text{h}}$$

$$= 2.5 \times 3.6\,\text{km/h} = \mathbf{9\,km/h}$$

Speed/time graph

If a graph is plotted of speed against time, *the area under the graph gives the distance travelled.* This is demonstrated in Example 7.15.

Example 7.15

The motion of an object is described by the speed/time graph given in Figure 7.21. Determine the distance covered by the object when moving from 0 to B.

The distance travelled is given by the area beneath the speed/time graph, shown shaded in Figure 7.21.

Area of triangle OAC

$$= \frac{1}{2} \times \text{base} \times \text{perpendicular height}$$

$$= \frac{1}{2} \times 5\,\text{s} \times 10\,\frac{\text{m}}{\text{s}} = 25\,\text{m}$$

Area of rectangle AEDC = base × height

$$= (12 - 5)\,\text{s} \times (10 - 0)\,\frac{\text{m}}{\text{s}} = 70\,\text{m}$$

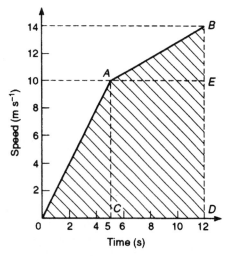

Figure 7.21

Area of triangle ABE

$$= \frac{1}{2} \times \text{base} \times \text{perpendicular height}$$

$$= \frac{1}{2} \times (12 - 5)\,\text{s} \times (14 - 10)\,\frac{\text{m}}{\text{s}}$$

$$= \frac{1}{2} \times 7\,\text{s} \times 4\,\frac{\text{m}}{\text{s}} = 14\,\text{m}$$

Hence the distance covered by the object moving from 0 to B is $(25 + 70 + 14)\,\text{m}$, i.e. **109 m**

Velocity

The *velocity* of an object is the speed of the object *in a specified direction*. Thus if a plane is flying due south at 500 kilometres per hour, its speed is 500 kilometres per hour, but its velocity is 500 kilometres per hour *due south*. It follows that if the plane had flown in a circular path for one hour at a speed of 500 kilometres per hour, so that one hour after taking off it is again over the airport, its average velocity in the first hour of flight is zero.

The average velocity is given by:

$$\frac{\text{distance travelled in a specific direction}}{\text{time taken}}$$

If a plane flies from place 0 to place A, a distance of 300 kilometres in one hour, A being due north of 0, then 0A in Figure 7.22 represents the first hour of flight. It then flies from A to B, a distance of 400 kilometres during the second hour of flight, B being due east of A, thus AB in Figure 7.22 represents its second hour of flight. Its average velocity for the two hour flight is

$$\frac{\text{distance 0B}}{\text{2 hours}} \quad \text{i.e.} \quad \frac{500\,\text{km}}{2\,\text{h}}$$

or 250 km/h in direction 0B.

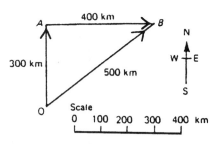

Figure 7.22

A graph of velocity (scale on the vertical axis) against time (scale on the horizontal axis) is called a *velocity/time graph*. The graph shown in Figure 7.23 represents a plane flying for 3 hours at a constant speed of 600 kilometres per hour in a specified direction. The shaded area represents velocity (vertically) multiplied by time (horizontally), and has units of

$$\frac{\text{kilometres}}{\text{hours}} \times \text{hours}$$

i.e. kilometres, and represents the distance travelled in a specified direction. In this case,

$$\text{distance} = 600 \ \frac{\text{km}}{\text{h}} \times (3 \, \text{h}) = 1800 \, \text{km}$$

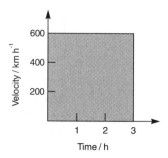

Figure 7.23

Another method of determining the distance travelled is from:

$$\text{distance travelled} = \text{average velocity} \times \text{time}$$

Thus if a plane travels due south at 600 kilometres per hour for 20 minutes, the distance covered is

$$\frac{600 \, \text{km}}{1 \, \text{h}} \times \frac{20}{60} \, \text{h, i.e. } 200 \, \text{km}$$

Introduction to acceleration

Acceleration is the rate of change of velocity with time. The average acceleration, a, is given by:

$$a = \frac{\text{change in velocity}}{\text{time taken}}$$

Test your knowledge 7.7

A coach travels from town A to town B, a distance of 40 kilometres at an average speed of 55 kilometres per hour. It then travels from town B to town C, a distance of 25 kilometres in 35 minutes. Finally, it travels from town C to town D at an average speed of 60 kilometres per hour in 45 minutes. Determine:

(a) the time taken to travel from A to B,
(b) the average speed of the coach from B to C,
(c) the distance from C to D, and
(d) the average speed of the whole journey from A to D.

The usual units are metres per second squared (m/s^2 or m s^{-2}). If u is the initial velocity of an object in metres per second, v is the final velocity in metres per second and t is the time in seconds elapsing between the velocities of u and v, then

$$\text{average acceleration, } a = \frac{v - u}{t} \text{ m/s}^2$$

Velocity/time graph

A graph of velocity (scale on the vertical axis) against time (scale on the horizontal axis) is called a *velocity/time graph*, as introduced above. From the velocity/time graph shown in Figure 7.24, the slope of line 0A is given by AX/0X. AX is the change in velocity from an initial velocity u of zero to a final velocity, v, of 4 metres per second. 0X is the time taken for this change in velocity, thus

$$\frac{AX}{0X} = \frac{\text{change in velocity}}{\text{time taken}}$$

$$= \text{the acceleration in the first two seconds}$$

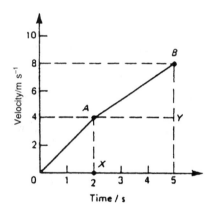

Figure 7.24

From the graph:

$$\frac{AX}{0X} = \frac{4 \text{ m/s}}{2 \text{ s}} = 2 \text{ m/s}^2$$

i.e. the acceleration is 2 m/s^2. Similarly, the slope of line AB in Figure 7.24 is given by BY/AY, i.e. the acceleration between 2 s and 5 s is

$$\frac{8 - 4}{5 - 2} = \frac{4}{3} = 1\tfrac{1}{3} \text{ m/s}^2$$

In general, the slope of a line on a velocity/time graph gives the acceleration.

The words 'velocity' and 'speed' are commonly interchanged in everyday language. Acceleration is a vector quantity and is correctly defined as the rate of change of velocity with respect to time. However, acceleration is also the rate of change of speed with respect to time in a certain specified direction.

Free-fall and equation of motion

If a dense object such as a stone is dropped from a height, called *free-fall*, it has a constant acceleration of approximately 9.81 m/s². In a vacuum, all objects have this same constant acceleration, vertically downwards, that is, a feather has the same acceleration as a stone. However, if free-fall takes place in air, dense objects have the constant acceleration of 9.81 m/s² over short distances, but objects which have a low density, such as feathers, have little or no acceleration.

For bodies moving with a constant acceleration, the average acceleration is the constant value of the acceleration, and since from earlier:

$$a = \frac{v - u}{t}$$

then $a \times t = v - u$ or $v = u + at$

where u is the initial velocity in m/s,
           v is the final velocity in m/s,
           a is the constant acceleration in m/s²,
           t is the time in s.

When symbol 'a' has a negative value, it is called *deceleration* or *retardation*. The equation $v = u + at$ is called an *equation of motion*.

Test your knowledge 7.8

1 A ship changes velocity from 15 km/h to 20 km/h in 25 min. Determine the average acceleration in m/s² of the ship during this time.
2 Determine how long it takes an object, which is free-falling, to change its speed from 100 km/h to 150 km/h, assuming all other forces, except that due to gravity, are neglected.
3 A car travelling at 50 km/h applies its brakes for 6 s and decelerates uniformly at 0.5 m/s. Determine its velocity in km/h after the 6 s braking period.

Example 7.16

A stone is dropped from an aeroplane. Determine (a) its velocity after 2 s and (b) the increase in velocity during the third second, in the absence of all forces except that due to gravity.
   The stone is free-falling and thus has an acceleration, a, of approximately 9.81 m/s² (taking downward motion as positive).
   From above:

   final velocity, $v = u + at$

(a) The initial downward velocity of the stone, u, is zero. The acceleration, a, is 9.81 m/s² downwards and the time during which the stone is accelerating is 2 s. Hence, final velocity, $v = 0 + 9.81 \times 2 = 19.62$ m/s, i.e. the velocity of the stone after 2 s is approximately **19.62 m/s**.
(b) From part (a), the velocity after two seconds, u, is 19.62 m/s. The velocity after 3 s, applying $v = u + at$, is

        $v = 19.62 + 9.81 \times 3 = 49.05$ m/s.

Thus, the change in velocity during the third second is:

   (49.05 − 19.62) m/s, that is **29.43 m/s**

Introduction to force, mass and acceleration

When an object is pushed or pulled, a force is applied to the object. This force is measured in newtons (N). The effects of pushing or pulling an object are:

(i)   to cause a change in the motion of the object, and
(ii)   to cause a change in the shape of the object.

If a change in the motion of the object, that is, its velocity changes from u to v, then the object accelerates. Thus, it follows that acceleration results from a force being applied to an object. If a force is applied to an object and it does not move, then the object changes shape, that is, deformation of the object takes place. Usually the change in shape is so small that it cannot be detected by just watching the object. However, when very sensitive measuring instruments are used, very small changes in dimensions can be detected.

A force of attraction exists between all objects. The factors governing the size of this force F are the masses of the objects and the distances between their centres. Thus, if a person is taken as one object and the earth as a second object, a force of attraction exists between the person and the earth. This force is called the *gravitational force* and is the force which gives a person a certain weight when standing on the earth's surface. It is also this force which gives freely falling objects a constant acceleration in the absence of other forces.

Newton's laws of motion

To make a stationary object move or to change the direction in which the object is moving requires a force to be applied externally to the object. This concept is known as *Newton's first law of motion* and may be stated as:

An object remains in a state of rest, or continues in a state of uniform motion in a straight line, unless it is acted on by an externally applied force

Since a force is necessary to produce a change of motion, an object must have some resistance to a change in its motion. The force necessary to give a stationary pram a given acceleration is far less than the force necessary to give a stationary car the same acceleration. The resistance to a change in motion is called the *inertia* of an object and the amount of inertia depends on the mass of the object. Since a car has a much larger mass than a pram, the inertia of a car is much larger than that of a pram. Newton's second law of motion may be stated as:

The acceleration of an object acted upon by an external force is proportional to the force and is in the same direction as the force

Thus, force $\propto$ acceleration, or force = a constant $\times$ acceleration, this constant of proportionality being the mass of the object, i.e.

force = mass $\times$ acceleration

The unit of force is the newton (N) and is defined in terms of mass and acceleration. One newton is the force required to give a mass of 1 kilogram an acceleration of 1 metre per second squared. Thus

$F = ma$

where F is the force in newtons (N), m is the mass in kilograms (kg) and a is the acceleration in metres per second squared (ms^2), i.e.

$$1\,\text{N} = \frac{1\,\text{kg m}}{\text{s}^2}$$

It follows that $1 \text{ m/s}^2 = 1 \text{ N/kg}$. Hence a gravitational acceleration of 9.81 m/s^2 is the same as a gravitational field of 9.81 N/kg. *Newton's third law of motion* may be stated as:

For every force, there is an equal and opposite reacting force

Thus, an object on, say, a table, exerts a downward force on the table and the table exerts an equal upward force on the object, known as a *reaction force* or just a *reaction*.

Example 7.17

Calculate the force needed to accelerate a boat of mass 20 tonne uniformly from rest to a speed of 21.6 km/h in 10 minutes.

The mass of the boat, m, is 20 t, that is 20 000 kg. The law of motion, $v = u + at$ can be used to determine the acceleration a. The initial velocity, u, is zero. The final velocity, v is 21.6 km/h, that is, 21.6/3.6 or 6 m/s. The time, t, is 10 min, that is, 600 s.

$$\text{Thus} \quad 6 = 0 + a \times 600 \text{ or } a = \frac{6}{600} = \mathbf{0.01 \text{ m/s}^2}$$

From Newton's second law, $F = ma$, i.e.

$$\text{Force} = 20\,000 \times 0.01 \text{ N}$$

$$= \mathbf{200 \text{ N}}$$

Test your knowledge 7.9

1 A lorry of mass 1350 kg accelerates uniformly from 9 km/h to reach a velocity of 45 km/h in 18 s. Determine (a) the acceleration of the lorry, (b) the uniform force needed to accelerate the lorry.
2 The tension in a rope lifting a crate vertically upwards is 2.8 kN. Determine its acceleration if the mass of the crate is 270 kg.

Example 7.18

The moving head of a machine tool requires a force of 1.2 N to bring it to rest in 0.8 s from a cutting speed of 30 m/min. Find the mass of the moving head.

From Newton's second law, $F = ma$, thus $m = F/a$, where force is given as 1.2 N. The law of motion $v = u + at$ can be used to find acceleration a, where $v = 0$, $u = 30$ m/min, that is 30/60 or 0.5 m/s, and $t = 0.8$ s. Thus, $0 = 0.5 + a \times 0.8$,

$$\text{i.e. } a = -\frac{0.5}{0.8} = -0.625 \text{ m/s}^2$$

or a retardation of 0.625 m/s².

Thus the mass, m = 1.2/0.625 = **1.92 kg**

Centripetal acceleration

When an object moves in a circular path at constant speed, its direction of motion is continually changing and hence its velocity (which depends on both magnitude *and* direction) is also continually changing. Since acceleration is the (change in velocity)/(time taken) the object has an acceleration.

If the tangential velocity is v and r is the radius of the circular path then the acceleration a is v^2/r and is towards the centre of the circle of motion. It is called the *centripetal acceleration*. If the mass of the rotating object is m, then by Newton's second law, the *centripetal force* is mv^2/r, and its direction is towards the centre of the circle of motion.

An object is suspended by a thread 250 mm long and both object and thread move in a horizontal circle with a constant angular velocity of 2.0 rad/s. If the tension in the thread is 12.5 N, determine the mass of the object.

Example 7.19

An aircraft is turning at constant altitude, the turn following the arc of a circle of radius 1.5 km. If the maximum allowable acceleration of the aircraft is $2.5\,g$, determine the maximum speed of the turn in km/h. Take g as $9.8\,\text{m/s}^2$. The acceleration of an object turning in a circle is v^2/r. Thus, to determine the maximum speed of turn, $v^2/r = 2.5\,g$.

$$v = \sqrt{(2.5\,gr)} = \sqrt{(2.5 \times 9.8 \times 1500)} = \sqrt{36\,750}$$

$$= 191.7\,\text{m/s}$$

$191.7\,\text{m/s} = 191.7 \times 3.6\,\text{km/h} = 690\,\text{km/h}$

The moment of a force

When using a spanner to tighten a nut, a force tends to turn the nut in a clockwise direction. This turning effect of a force is called the *moment of a force* or more briefly, just a *moment*. The size of the moment acting on the nut depends on two factors:

(a) the size of the force acting at right angles to the shank of the spanner, and
(b) the perpendicular distance between the point of application of the force and the centre of the nut.

In general, with reference to Figure 7.25, the moment M of a force acting about a point P is force $\times$ perpendicular distance between the line of action of the force and P, i.e.

$$M = F \times d$$

The unit of a moment is the newton metre (N m). Thus, if force F in Figure 7.25 is 7 N and distance d is 3 m, then the moment M is 7 N $\times$ 3 m, i.e. 21 N m.

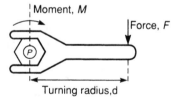

Figure 7.25

Example 7.20

A force of 15 N is applied to a spanner at an effective length of 140 mm from the centre of a nut. Calculate (a) the moment of the force applied to the nut, (b) the magnitude of the force required to produce the same moment if the effective length is reduced to 100 mm.

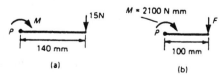

Figure 7.26

From above, $M = F \times d$, where M is the turning moment, F is the force applied at right angles to the spanner and d is the effective length between the force and the centre of the nut. Thus, with reference to Figure 7.26(a):

(a) Turning moment,

$$M = 15\,N \times 140\,mm = 2100\,N\,mm$$

$$= 2100\,N\,mm \times \frac{1\,m}{1000\,mm} = \mathbf{2.1\,N\,m}$$

(b) Turning moment, M is 2100 N mm and the effective length d becomes 100 mm (see Figure 7.26(b)). Applying $M = F \times d$ gives:

$$2100\,N\,mm = F \times 100\,mm$$

from which,

$$\text{force } F = \frac{2100\,N\,mm}{100\,mm} = \mathbf{21\,N}$$

Equilibrium and the principle of moments

If more than one force is acting on an object and the forces do not act at a single point, then the turning effect of the forces, that is, the moment of the forces, must be considered.

Figure 7.27 shows a beam with its support (known as its *pivot* or *fulcrum*) at P, acting vertically upwards, and forces F_1 and F_2 acting vertically downwards at distances a and b respectively, from the fulcrum.

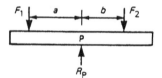

Figure 7.27

A beam is said to be in *equilibrium* when there is no tendency for it to move. There are two conditions for equilibrium:

(i) The sum of the forces acting vertically downwards must be equal to the sum of the forces acting vertically upwards, i.e. for Figure 7.27,

$$R_P = F_1 + F_2$$

(ii) The total moment of the forces acting on a beam must be zero; for the total moment to be zero:

the sum of the clockwise moments about any point must be equal to the sum of the anticlockwise moments about that point

This statement is known as the *principle of moments*. Hence, taking moments about P in Figure 7.27,

$$F_2 \times b = \text{the clockwise moment, and}$$

$$F_1 \times a = \text{the anticlockwise moment.}$$

Thus for equilibrium:

$$F_1 a = F_2 b$$

Example 7.21

A system of forces is as shown in Figure 7.28.

(a) If the system is in equilibrium find the distance d.
(b) If the point of application of the 5 N force is moved to point P, distance 200 mm from the support, find the new value of F to replace the 5 N force for the system to be in equilibrium.

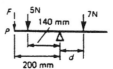

Figure 7.28

(a) From above, the clockwise moment M_1 is due to a force of 7 N acting at a distance d from the support, called the fulcrum, i.e.

$$M_1 = 7\,N \times d$$

The anticlockwise moment M_2 is due to a force of 5 N acting at a distance of 140 mm from the fulcrum, i.e.

$$M_2 = 5\,N \times 140\,mm$$

Applying the principle of moments, for the system to be in equilibrium about the fulcrum: clockwise moment = anticlockwise moment, i.e.

$$7\,N \times d = 5 \times 140\,N\,mm$$

Hence

$$\text{distance, } d = \frac{5 \times 140\,N\,mm}{7\,N} = \textbf{100 mm}$$

(b) When the 5 N force is replaced by force F at a distance of 200 mm from the fulcrum, the new value of the anticlockwise moment is $F \times 200$. For the system to be in equilibrium: clockwise moment = anticlockwise moment, i.e.

$$(7 \times 100)\,N\,mm = F \times 200\,mm$$

Hence,

$$\text{new value of force, } F = \frac{700\,N\,mm}{200\,mm} = \textbf{3.5 N}$$

1 A moment of 7.5 N m is required to turn a wheel. If a force of 37.5 N is applied to the rim of the wheel, calculate the effective distance from the rim to the hub of the wheel.
2 For the centrally supported uniform beam shown in Figure 7.29 determine the values of forces F_1 and F_2 when the beam is in equilibrium.

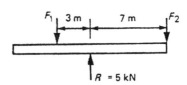

Figure 7.29

Simply supported beams having point loads

A *simply supported beam* is one which rests on two supports and is free to move horizontally.

Two typical simply supported beams having loads acting at given points on the beam (called *point loading*) are shown in Figure 7.30.

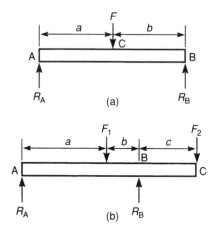

Figure 7.30

A man whose mass exerts a force F vertically downwards, standing on a wooden plank which is simply supported at its ends, may, for example, be represented by the beam diagram of Figure 7.29(a) if the mass of the plank is neglected.

The forces exerted by the supports on the plank, R_A and R_B, act vertically upwards, and are called *reactions*.

When the forces acting are all in one plane, the algebraic sum of the moments can be taken about *any* point.

For the beam in Figure 7.29(a) at equilibrium:

(i) $R_A + R_B = F$, and
(ii) taking moments aboout A, $Fa = R_B(a + b)$.
      (Alternatively, taking moments about C, $R_A a = R_B b$.)

For the beam in Figure 7.30(b), at equilibrium

(i) $R_A + R_B = F_1 + F_2$, and
(ii) taking moments about B, $R_A(a + b) + F_2 c = F_1 b$.

Typical *practical applications* of simply supported beams with point loadings include bridges, beams in buildings, and beds of machine tools.

Example 7.22

A beam is loaded as shown in Figure 7.31.

Determine (a) the force acting on the beam support at B, (b) the force acting on the beam support at A, neglecting the mass of the beam.

A beam supported as shown in Figure 7.31 is called a simply supported *beam.*

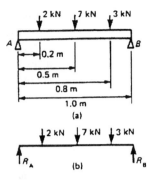

Figure 7.31

(a) Taking moments about point A and applying the principle of moments gives: clockwise moments = anticlockwise moments

$$(2 \times 0.2) + (7 \times 0.5) + (3 \times 0.8)\, \text{kN m} = R_B \times 1.0\,\text{m}$$

where R_B is the force supporting the beam at B, as shown in Figure 7.31(b).

Thus $(0.4 + 3.5 + 2.4)\,\text{kN m} = R_B \times 1.0\,\text{m}$, i.e.

$$R_B = \frac{6.3\,\text{kN m}}{1.0\,\text{m}} = \textbf{6.3 kN}$$

(b) For the beam to be in equilibrium, the forces acting upwards must be equal to the forces acting downwards, thus

$$R_A + R_B = (2 + 7 + 3)\,\text{kN}$$

$$R_B = 6.3\,\text{kN, thus } R_A = 12 - 6.3 = \textbf{5.7 kN}$$

Test your knowledge 7.12

1 A metal bar AB is 4.0 m long and is supported at each end in a horizontal position. It carries loads of 2.5 kN and 5.5 kN at distances of 2.0 m and 3.0 m, respectively, from A, Neglecting the mass of the beam, determine the reactions of the supports when the beam is in equilibrium.

2 A simply supported beam AB is loaded as shown in Figure 7.32. Determine the load *F* in order that the reaction at A is zero.

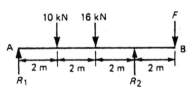

Figure 7.32

Linear and angular velocity

Linear velocity v is defined as the rate of change of linear displacement *s* with respect to time *t*, and for motion in a straight line:

$$\text{Linear velocity} = \frac{\text{change of displacement}}{\text{change of time}}$$

i.e.

$$v = \frac{s}{t} \tag{7.1}$$

The unit of linear velocity is metres per second (m/s).

Angular velocity. The speed of revolution of a wheel or a shaft is usually measured in revolutions per minute or revolutions per second but these units do not form part of a coherent system of units. The basis used in SI units is the angle turned through in one second.

Angular velocity is defined as the rate of change of angular displacement θ, with respect to time t, and for an object rotating about a fixed axis at a constant speed:

$$\text{Angular velocity} = \frac{\text{angle turned through}}{\text{time taken}}$$

i.e.

$$\omega = \frac{\theta}{t} \qquad (7.2)$$

The unit of angular velocity is radians per second (rad/s).

An object rotating at a constant speed of n revolutions per second subtends an angle of $2\pi n$ radians in one second, that is, its angular velocity

$$\omega = 2\pi n \text{ rad/s} \qquad 7.3)$$

$s = r\theta$ and from equation (7.2), $\theta = t$, hence $s = r\omega t$, or $s/t = \omega r$. However, from equation (7.1), $v = s/t$, hence

$$v = \omega r \qquad (7.4)$$

Equation (7.4) gives the relationship between linear velocity, v, and angular velocity, ω.

Example 7.23

A wheel of diameter 540 mm is rotating at $(1500/\pi)$ rev/min. Calculate the angular velocity of the wheel and the linear velocity of a point on the rim of the wheel.

From equation (7.3), angular velocity $\omega = 2\pi n$, where n is the speed of revolution in revolutions per second, i.e.

$n = 1500/60\pi$ revolutions per second. Thus

$$\omega = 2\pi \frac{1500}{60\pi} = \textbf{50 rad/s}$$

The linear velocity of a point on the rim, $v = \omega r$, where r is the radius of the wheel, i.e. 0.54/2 or 0.27 m. Thus

$$v = 50 \times 0.27 = \textbf{13.5 m/s}$$

Test your knowledge 7.13

A pulley driving a belt has a diameter of 360 mm and is turning at $2700/\pi$ revolutions per minute. Find the angular velocity of the pulley and the linear velocity of the belt assuming that no slip occurs.

Linear and angular acceleration

Linear acceleration, a, is defined as the rate of change of linear velocity with respect to time (as introduced earlier). For an object whose linear velocity is increasing uniformly:

$$\text{linear acceleration} = \frac{\text{change of linear velocity}}{\text{time taken}}$$

i.e.

$$a = \frac{v_2 - v_1}{t} \qquad (7.5)$$

The unit of linear acceleration is metres per second squared (m/s^2). Rewriting equation (7.5) with v_2 as the subject of the formula gives:

$$v_2 = v_1 + at \tag{7.6}$$

Angular acceleration, α, is defined as the rate of change of angular velocity with respect to time. For an object whose angular velocity is increasing uniformly:

$$\text{angular acceleration} = \frac{\text{change of angular velocity}}{\text{time taken}}$$

that is,

$$\alpha = \frac{\omega_2 - \omega_1}{t} \tag{7.7}$$

The unit of angular acceleration is radians per second squared (rad/s^2).

Rewriting equation (7.7) with ω_2 as the subject of the formula gives:

$$\omega_2 = \omega_1 + \alpha t \tag{7.8}$$

From equation (7.8), $v + \omega r$. For motion in a circle having a constant radius r, $v_2 = \omega_2 r$ and $v_1 = \omega_1 r$, hence equation (7.5) can be rewritten as

$$a = \frac{\omega_2 r - \omega_1 r}{t} = \frac{r(\omega_2 - \omega_1)}{t}$$

But from equation (7.7),

$$\frac{\omega_2 - \omega_1}{t} = \alpha$$

Hence

$$a = r\alpha \tag{7.9}$$

Example 7.24

The speed of a shaft increases uniformly from 300 revolutions per minute to 800 revolutions per minute in 10 s. Find the angular acceleration, correct to four significant figures.

From equation 7.8, $\omega_2 = \omega_1 + \alpha t$, hence $\alpha = \dfrac{\omega_2 - \omega_1}{t}$

Initial angular velocity, $\omega_1 = 300$ revolutions per minute

$$= \frac{300}{60} \text{ revolutions per second} = \frac{300 \times 2\pi}{60} \text{ rad/s}$$

Final angular velocity, $\omega_2 = \dfrac{800 \times 2\pi}{60}$ rad/s

Hence,

$$\text{angular acceleration } \alpha = \frac{\dfrac{800 \times 2\pi}{60} - \dfrac{300 \times 2\pi}{60}}{10} \text{ rad/s}^2$$

$$= \frac{500 \times 2\pi}{60 \times 10} = \mathbf{5.236 \text{ rad/s}^2}$$

Example 7.25

If the diameter of the shaft in Example 7.38 is 50 mm, determine the linear acceleration of the shaft, correct to three significant figures.

From equation 7.9, $a = r\alpha$

The shaft radius is 0.05/2 m and the angular acceleration α is 5.236 rad/s^2, thus the linear acceleration,

$$a = \frac{0.05}{2} \times 5.236 = \mathbf{0.131\ m/s^2}$$

Further equations of motion

From equation (7.1), $s = vt$, and if the linear velocity is changing uniformly from v_1 to v_2, then s = mean linear velocity × time, i.e.

$$s = \frac{(v_1 + v_2)}{2} t \tag{7.10}$$

From equation (7.6), $\theta = \omega t$, and if the angular velocity is changing uniformly from ω_1 to ω_2, *then* θ = mean angular velocity × time, i.e.

$$\theta = \frac{(\omega_1 + \omega_2)}{2} t \tag{7.11}$$

Two further equations of linear motion may be derived from equations (7.6) and (7.9):

$$s = v_1 t + \frac{1}{2} at^2 \tag{7.12}$$

and

$$v_2^2 = v_1^2 + 2\,as \tag{7.13}$$

Two further equations of angular motion may be derived from equations (7.8) and (7.10):

$$\theta = \omega_1 t = \frac{1}{2} \alpha t^2 \tag{7.14}$$

and

$$\omega_2^2 = \omega_1^2 + 2\alpha\theta \tag{7.15}$$

Test your knowledge 7.14

A disc accelerates uniformly from 300 revolutions per minute to 600 revolutions per minute in 25 s. Determine (a) its angular acceleration and (b) the linear acceleration of a point on the rim of the disc, if the radius of the disc is 250 mm. (c) Calculate the number of revolutions the disc makes during the 25 s acceleration period.

Example 7.26

The shaft of an electric motor, initially at rest, accelerates uniformly for 0.4 s at 15 rad/s^2. Determine the angle turned through by the shaft, in radians, in this time.

From equation (7.14), $\theta = \omega_1 t + \frac{1}{2}\alpha t^2$. Since the shaft is initially at rest, $\omega_1 = 0$ and $\theta = \frac{1}{2}\alpha t^2$. The angular acceleration, α, is 15 rad/s^2 and time t is 0.4 s, hence angle turned through,

$$\theta = \frac{1}{2} \times 15 \times 0.4^2 = \mathbf{1.2\ rad}$$

Introduction to friction

When an object, such as a block of wood, is placed on a floor and sufficient force is applied to the block, the force being parallel to the floor, the block slides across the floor. When the force is removed, motion of the block stops; thus there is a force which resists sliding. This force is called *dynamic* or *sliding friction*. A force may be applied to the block which is insufficient to move it. In this case, the force resisting motion is called the *static friction* or *striction*. Thus there are two categories into which a frictional force may be split:

(i)   dynamic or sliding friction force which occurs when motion is taking place, and
(ii) static friction which occurs before motion takes place.

There are three factors which affect the size and direction of frictional forces.

(i)   The size of the frictional force depends on the type of surface (a block of wood slides more easily on a polished metal surface than on a rough concrete surface).
(ii) The size of the frictional force depends on the size of the force acting at right angles to the surfaces in contact, called the *normal force*. Thus, if the weight of a block of wood is doubled, the frictional force is doubled when it is sliding on the same surface.
(iii) The direction of the frictional force is always opposite to the direction of motion. Thus the frictional force opposes motion, as shown in Figure 7.33.

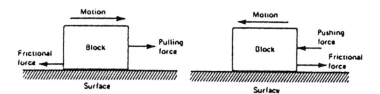

Figure 7.33

Coefficient of friction

The coefficient of friction μ, is a measure of the amount of friction existing between two surfaces. A low value of coefficient of friction indicates that the force required for sliding to occur is less than the force required when the coefficient of friction is high. The value of the coefficient of friction is given by

$$\mu = \frac{\text{frictional force (F)}}{\text{normal force (N)}}$$

Transposing gives: frictional force = $\mu \times$ normal force, i.e.

$$F = \mu N$$

The direction of the forces given in this equation is as shown in Figure 7.34.

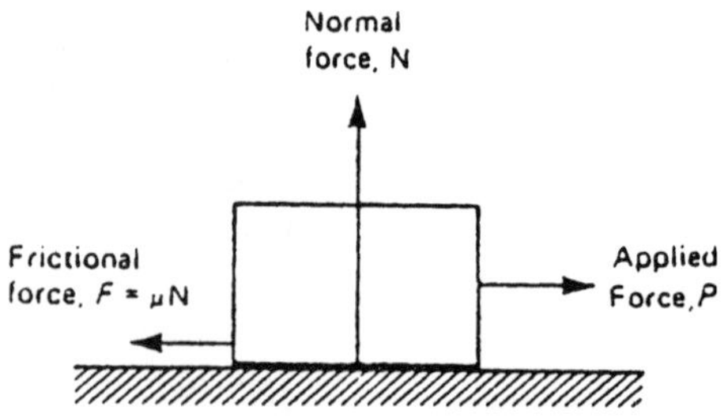

Figure 7.34

The coefficient of friction is the ratio of a force to a force, and hence has no units. Typical values for the coefficient of friction when sliding is occurring, i.e. the dynamic coefficient of friction, are:

for polished oiled metal surfaces   less than 0.1
for glass on glass   0.4
for rubber on tarmac   close to 1.0

Example 7.27

A block of steel requires a force of 10.4 N applied parallel to a steel plate to keep it moving with constant velocity across the plate. If the normal force between the block and the plate is 40 N, determine the dynamic coefficient of friction.

As the block is moving at constant velocity, the force applied must be that required to overcome frictional forces, i.e.

frictional force, $F = 10.4$ N

The normal force is 40 N, and since $f = \mu N$,

$$\mu = \frac{F}{N} = \frac{10.4}{40} = 0.26$$

i.e. the dynamic coefficient of friction is **0.26**

Applications of friction

In some applications, a low coefficient of friction is desirable, for example, in bearings, pistons moving within cylinders, on ski runs, and so on. However, for such applications as force being transmitted by belt drives and braking systems, a high value of coefficient is necessary. Instances where frictional forces are an advantage include:

(i)   Almost all fastening devices rely on frictional forces to keep them in place once secured, examples being screws, nails, nuts, clips and clamps.

(ii)   Satisfactory operation of brakes and clutches rely on frictional forces being present.

(iii)   In the absence of frictional forces, most accelerations along a horizontal surface are impossible. For example, a person's shoes just slip when walking is attempted and the tyres of a car just rotate with no forward motion of the car being experienced.

Disadvantages of frictional forces include:

(i) Energy is wasted in the bearings associated with shafts, axles and gears due to heat being generated.
(ii) Wear is caused by friction, for example, in shoes, brake lining materials and bearings.
(iii) Energy is wasted when motion through air occurs (it is much easier to cycle with the wind rather than against it).

Work

If a body moves as a result of a force being applied to it, the force is said to do work on the body. The amount of work done is the product of the applied force and the distance, i.e.

work done = force × distance moved in the direction of the force

The unit of work is the joule, J, which is defined as the amount of work done when a force of 1 newton acts for a distance of 1 m in the direction of the force. Thus,

$$1\,J = 1\,Nm$$

If a graph is plotted of experimental values of force (on the vertical axis) against distance moved (on the horizontal axis) a force/distance graph or work diagram is produced. *The area under the graph represents the work done.*

For example, a constant force of 20 N used to raise a load a height of 8 m may be represented on a force/distance graph as shown in Figure 7.35(a). The area under the graph, shown shaded, represents the work done. Hence

$$\text{work done} = 20\,N \times 8\,m = 160\,J$$

Similarly, a spring extended by 20 mm by a force of 500 N may be represented by the work diagram shown in Figure 7.35(b).

$$\text{work done} = \text{shaded area}$$
$$= \frac{1}{2} \times \text{base} \times \text{height}$$
$$= \frac{1}{2} \times (20 \times 10^{-3})\,m \times 500\,N = \mathbf{5\,J}$$

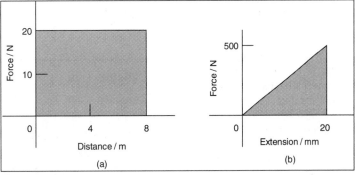

Figure 7.35

Example 7.28

Calculate the work done when a force of 40 N pushes an object a distance of 500 m in the same direction as the force.

work done = force × distance moved in the direction of the force

= 40 N × 500 m = 20 000 J (since 1 J = 1 N m)

i.e.

work done = **20 kJ**

Example 7.29

A motor supplies a constant force of 1 kN which is used to move a load a distance of 5 m. The force is then changed to a constant 500 N and the load is moved a further 15 m. Draw the force/distance graph for the operation and from the graph determine the work done by the motor.

The force/distance graph of work diagram is shown in Figure 7.36.

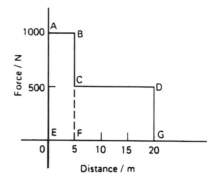

Figure 7.36

Between points A and B a constant force of 1000 N moves the load 5 m; between points C and D a constant force of 500 N moves the load from 5 m to 20 m.

Total work done = area under the force/distance graph

= area ABFE + area CDGF

= (1000 N × 5 m) + (500 N × 15 m)

= 5000 J + 7500 J = 12500 J = **12.5 kJ**

1 Calculate the work done when a mass is lifted vertically by a crane to a height of 5 m, the force required to lift the mass being 98 N.
2 A spring requires a force of 50 N to cause an extension of 100 mm. Determine the work done in extending the spring (a) from 0 to 100 mm, and (b) from 40 mm to 100 mm.
3 Calculate the work done when a mass of 50 kg is lifted vertically through a distance of 30 m.

Example 7.30

Calculate the work done when a mass of 20 kg is lifted vertically through a distance of 5.0 m.

The force to be overcome when lifting a mass of 20 kg vertically upwards is mg, i.e. 20 × 9.81 = 196.2 N

Work done = force × distance = 196.2 × 5.0 = **981 J**

Energy

Energy is the capacity, or ability, to do work. The unit of energy is the joule, the same as for work. Energy is expended when work is done. There are several forms of energy and these include:

(i)   Mechanical energy
(ii)   Heat or thermal energy
(iii) Electrical energy
(iv)   Chemical energy
(v)   Nuclear energy
(vi)   Light energy
(vii) Sound energy

Energy may be converted from one form to another. The principle of *conservation of energy* states that the total amount of energy remains the same in such conversions, i.e. energy cannot be created or destroyed. An example of energy conversion is the conversion of mechanical energy to electrical energy by a generator.

Efficiency is defined as the ratio of the useful output energy to the input energy. The symbol for efficiency is η. Hence

$$\text{efficiency} = \frac{\text{useful output energy}}{\text{input energy}}$$

Efficiency has no units and is often stated as a percentage. A perfect machine would have an efficiency of 100%. However, all machines have an efficiency lower than this due to friction and other losses. Thus, if the input energy to a motor is 1000 J and the output energy is 800 J then the efficiency is

$$\frac{800}{1000} \; 100\%, \text{ i.e. } 80\%$$

Example 7.31

A machine exerts a force of 200 N in lifting a mass through a height of 6 m. If 2 kJ of energy are supplied to it, what is the efficiency of the machine?

$$\text{Work done in lifting mass} = \text{force} \times \text{distance moved}$$
$$= \text{weight of body} \times \text{distance moved}$$
$$= 200 \, \text{N} \times 6 \, \text{m} = 1200 \, \text{J}$$
$$= \text{useful energy output}$$

Energy output = 2 kJ = 2000 J

$$\text{Efficiency} = \frac{\text{useful output energy}}{\text{input energy}}$$

$$= \frac{1200}{2000} = 0.6 \text{ or } \mathbf{60\%}$$

Example 7.32

A hoist exerts a force of 500 N in raising a load through a height of 20 m. The efficiency of the hoist gears is 75% and the efficiency of the motor is 80%. Calculate the input energy to the hoist.

The hoist system is shown diagrammatically in figure 7.43.

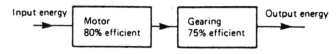

Figure 7.37

$$\text{Output energy} = \text{work done}$$
$$= \text{force} \times \text{distance} = 500\,\text{N} \times 20\,\text{m}$$
$$= 10\,000\,\text{J}$$

For the gearing,

$$\text{efficiency} = \frac{\text{output energy}}{\text{input energy}}$$

i.e.

$$\frac{75}{100} = \frac{10\,000}{\text{input energy}}$$

from which, the input energy to the gears = $10\,000 \times (100/75)$ = 13 333 J.

The input energy to the gears is the same as the output energy of the motor.

Thus, for the motor,

$$\text{efficiency} = \frac{\text{output energy}}{\text{input energy}}$$

$$= \frac{80}{100} = \frac{13\,333}{\text{input energy}}$$

Hence,

$$\text{input energy to the system} = 13\,333 \times \frac{100}{80} = 16\,670\,\text{J} = \mathbf{16.67\,kJ}$$

Test your knowledge 7.17

1 Calculate the useful output of energy of an electric motor which is 70% efficient if it uses 600 J of electrical energy.
2 A machine which is used for lifting a particular mass is supplied with 5 kJ of energy. If the machine has an efficiency of 65% and exerts a force of 812.5 N, to what height will it lift the mass?

Power

Power is a measure of the rate at which work is done or at which energy is converted from one form to another.

$$\text{Power } P = \frac{\text{energy used}}{\text{time taken}}$$

or

$$P = \frac{\text{work done}}{\text{time taken}}$$

The unit of power is the watt, W, where 1 watt is equal to 1 joule per second. The watt is a small unit for many purposes and a larger unit called the kilowatt, kW, is used, where 1 kW = 1000 W. The power output of a motor which does 120 kJ of work in 30 s is thus given by

$$P = \frac{120\,\text{kJ}}{30\,\text{s}} = 4\,\text{kW}$$

Since work done = force × distance, then

$$\text{Power} = \frac{\text{work done}}{\text{time taken}} = \frac{\text{force} \times \text{distance}}{\text{time taken}}$$

$$= \text{force} \times \frac{\text{distance}}{\text{time taken}}$$

However,

$$\frac{\text{distance}}{\text{time taken}} = \text{velocity}$$

Hence

$$\text{power} = \text{force} \times \text{velocity}$$

1 10 kJ of work is done by a force in moving a body uniformly through 125 m in 50 s. Determine (a) the value of the force and (b) the power.

2 A planing machine has a cutting stroke of 2 m and the stroke takes 4 seconds. If the constant resistance to the cutting tool is 900 N calculate for each cutting stroke (a) the power consumed at the tool point, and (b) the power input to the system if the efficiency of the system is 75%.

3 An electric motor provides power to a winding machine. The input power to the motor is 2.5 kW and the overall efficiency is 60%. Calculate (a) the output power of the machine, (b) the rate at which it can raise a 300 kg load vertically upwards.

Example 7.33

The output power of a motor is 8 kW. How much work does it do in 30 s?

Power = (work done)/(time taken), from which,

work done = power × time

$$= 8000\,\text{W} \times 30\,\text{s} = 240\,000\,\text{J}$$

$$= \mathbf{240\,kJ}$$

Example 7.34

Calculate the power required to lift a mass through a height of 10 m in 20 s if the force required is 3924 N.

Work done = force × distance moved = 3924 N × 10 m = 39 240 J

$$\text{Power} = \frac{\text{work done}}{\text{time taken}} = \frac{39\,240\,\text{J}}{20\,\text{s}} = \mathbf{1962\,W}\ \text{or}\ \mathbf{1.962\,kW}$$

Potential and kinetic energy

Mechanical energy is concerned principally with two kinds of energy, potential energy and kinetic energy.

Potential energy is energy due to the position of the body. The force exerted on a mass of m kilograms is mg newtons (where $g = 9.81$ m/s², the acceleration due to gravity). When the mass is lifted vertically through a height h metres above some datum level, the work done is given by: force × distance = $(mg)(h)$J. This work done is stored as potential energy in the mass. Hence,

$$\text{potential energy} = mgh \text{ joules}$$

(the potential energy at the datum level being taken as zero).

Kinetic energy is the energy due to the motion of a body. Suppose a force acts on an object of mass m originally at rest and accelerates it to a velocity v. Then

$$\text{kinetic energy} \; = \; \frac{1}{2}\, mv^2 \; \text{joules}$$

As stated earlier, energy may be converted from one form to another. The principle of conservation of energy states that the total amount of energy remains the same in such conversions, i.e. energy cannot be created or destroyed.

In mechanics, the potential energy possessed by a body is frequently converted into kinetic energy, and vice versa. When a mass is falling freely, its potential energy decreases as it loses height, and its kinetic energy increases as its velocity increases.

1 An object of mass 400 g is thrown vertically upwards and its maximum increase in potential energy is 32.6 J. Determine the maximum height reached, neglecting air resistance.

2 A lorry having a mass of 1.5 t is travelling along a level road at 72 km/h. When the brakes are applied, the speed decreases to 18 km/h. Determine how much the kinetic energy of the lorry is reduced.

3 Supplies of mass 300 kg are dropped from a helicopter flying at an altitude of 60 m. Determine the potential energy of the supplies relative to the ground at the instant of release, and its kinetic energy as it strikes the ground.

Example 7.35

A car of mass 800 kg is climbing an incline at 10° to the horizontal. Determine the increase in potential energy of the car as it moves a distance of 50 m up the incline.

With reference to Figure 7.44, $\sin 10° = h/50$, from which,

$h = 50 \sin 10° = 8.682\,\text{m}$

Hence

increase in potential energy $= mgh$

$\qquad\qquad\qquad\qquad\quad = 800\,\text{kg} \times 9.81\,\text{m/s}^2 \times 8.682\,\text{m}$

$\qquad\qquad\qquad\qquad\quad = \mathbf{69\,140\,J}$ or $\mathbf{68.14\,kJ}$

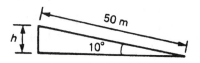

Figure 7.38

The effects of forces on materials

A force exerted on a body can cause a change in either the shape or the motion of the body. The unit of force is the newton, N.

No solid body is perfectly rigid and when forces are applied to it, changes in dimensions occur. Such changes are not always perceptible to the human eye since they are so small. For example, the span of a bridge will sag under the weight of a vehicle and a spanner will bend slightly when tightening a nut. It is important for engineers and designers to appreciate the effects of forces on materials, together with their mechanical properties.

The three main types of mechanical force that can act on a body are (i) tensile, (ii) compressive, and (iii) shear.

Tensile force

Tension is a force which tends to stretch a material, as shown in Figure 7.39(a). Examples include:

(i)   the rope or cable of a crane carrying a load is in tension;
(ii) rubber bands, when stretched, are in tension;
(iii) a bolt; when a nut is tightened, a bolt is under tension.

A tensile force, i.e. one producing tension, increases the length of the material on which it acts.

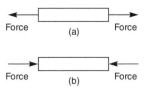

Figure 7.39

Compressive force

Compression is a force which tends to squeeze or crush a material, as shown in figure 7.39(b). Examples include:

(i)   a pillar supporting a bridge is in compression;
(ii) the sole of a shoe is in compression;
(iii) the jib of a crane is in compression.

A compressive force, i.e. one producing compression, will decrease the length of the material on which it acts.

Shear force

Shear is a force which tends to slide one face of the material over an adjacent face. Examples include:

(i)   a rivet holding two plates together is in shear if a tensile force is applied between the plates (as shown in Figure 7.40);
(ii) a guillotine cutting sheet metal, or garden shears, each provide a shear force;
(iii) a horizontal beam is subject to shear force;
(iv) transmission joints on cars are subject to shear forces.

A shear force can cause a material to bend, slide or twist.

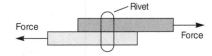

Figure 7.40

Example 7.36

Figure 7.41(a) represents a crane and Figure 7.41(b) a transmission joint. State the types of forces acting labelled A to F.

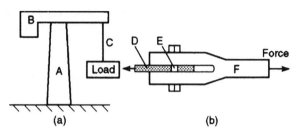

Figure 7.41

(a) For the crane, A, a supporting member, is in compression, B, a horizontal beam, is in shear, and C, a rope, is in tension.
(b) For the transmission joint, parts D and F are in tension, and E, the rivet or bolt, is in shear.

Stress

Forces acting on a material cause a change in dimensions and the material is said to be in a state of *stress*. Stress is the ratio of the applied force F to cross-sectional area A of the material. The symbol used for tensile or compressive stress is σ. The unit of stress is the pascal, Pa, where $1 \text{ Pa} = 1 \text{ N/mm}^2$. Hence

$$\sigma = \frac{F}{A} \text{ Pa}$$

where F is the force in newtons and A is the cross-sectional area in square metres. For tensile and compressive forces, the cross-sectional area is that which is at right angles to the direction of the force. For a shear force the shear stress is equal to F/A, where the cross-sectional area A is that which is parallel to the direction of the force. The symbol used for shear stress is the Greek letter tau, τ.

Example 7.37

A rectangular bar having a cross-sectional area of 75 mm^2 has a tensile force of 15 kN applied to it. Determine the stress in the bar.

Cross-sectional area $A = 75 \text{ mm}^2 = 75 \times 10^{-6} \text{ m}^2$; force $F = 15 \text{ kN} = 15 \times 10^3 \text{ N}$.
  Stress in bar,

$$\sigma = \frac{F}{A} = \frac{15 \times 10^3 \text{ N}}{75 \times 10^{-6} \text{ m}^2} = 0.2 \times 10^9 \text{ Pa} = \mathbf{200 \, MPa}$$

1 A rectangular bar having a cross-sectional area of 80 mm² has a tensile force of 20 kN applied to it. Determine the stress in the bar.
2 A circular cable has a tensile force of 1 kN applied to it and the force produces a stress of 7.8 MPa in the cable. Calculate the diameter of the cable.

Example 7.38

A circular wire has a tensile force of 60.0 N applied to it and this force produces a stress of 3.06 MPa in the wire. Determine the diameter of the wire.

Force F = 60.0 N; stress σ = *3.06 MPa = 3.06 × 10⁶ Pa*.
Since σ = F/A, then

$$\text{area } A = \frac{F}{\sigma} = \frac{60.0 \, \text{N}}{3.06 \times 10^6 \, \text{Pa}} = 19.61 \times 10^{-6} \, \text{m}^2 = 19.61 \, \text{mm}^2$$

Cross-sectional area $A = \pi d^2/4$. Hence $19.61 = \pi d^2/4$, from which,

$$d^2 = \frac{4 \times 19.61}{\pi} \text{ and } d = \sqrt{\frac{4 \times 19.61}{\pi}}$$

i.e. diameter of wire = **5.0 mm**

Strain

The fractional change in a dimension of a material produced by a force is called the *strain*. For a tensile or compressive force, strain is the ratio of the change of length to the original length. The symbol used for strain is ε (Greek epsilon). For a material of length l metres which changes in length by an amount x metres when subjected to stress

$$\varepsilon = \frac{x}{l}$$

Strain is dimensionless and is often expressed as a percentage, i.e.

$$\text{percentage strain} = \frac{x}{l} \times 100$$

For a shear force, strain is denoted by the symbol γ (Greek letter gamma) and, with reference to figure 7.42, is given by:

$$\gamma = \frac{x}{l}$$

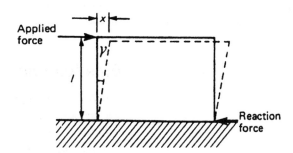

Figure 7.42

Example 7.39

A bar 1.60 m long contracts by 0.1 mm when a compressive load is applied to it. Determine the strain and the percentage strain.

$$\text{Strain } \varepsilon = \frac{\text{contraction}}{\text{original length}} = \frac{0.1\,\text{mm}}{1.60 \times 10^3\,\text{mm}} = \frac{0.1}{1600}$$

$$= 0.000\,062\,5$$

Percentage strain $= 0.000\,062\,5 \times 100 = \mathbf{0.006\,25\%}$

Example 7.40

A rectangular block of plastic material 500 mm long by 20 mm wide by 300 mm high has its lower face glued to a bench and a force of 200 N is applied to the upper face and in line with it. The upper face moves 15 mm relative to the lower face. Determine (a) the shear stress, and (b) the shear strain in the upper face, assuming the deformation is uniform.

(a) Shear stress $\tau = \dfrac{\text{force}}{\text{area parallel to the force}}$

Area of any face parallel to the force $= 500\,\text{mm} \times 20\,\text{mm}$

$$= (0.5 \times 0.02)\,\text{m}^2 = 0.01\,\text{m}^2$$

Hence shear stress $\tau = \dfrac{200\,\text{N}}{0.01\,\text{m}^2} = \mathbf{20\,000\,Pa}$ or $\mathbf{20\,kPa}$

(b) Shear strain $= \dfrac{x}{l}$ (see side view of Figure 7.43)

$$= \frac{15}{300} = \mathbf{0.05}\ (\text{or } \mathbf{5\%})$$

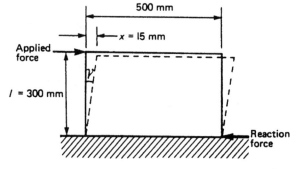

Figure 7.43

Elasticity and elastic limit

Elasticity is the ability of a material to return to its original shape and size on the removal of external forces.

Plasticity is the property of a material of being permanently deformed by a force without breaking. Thus if a material does not return to the original shape, it is said to be plastic.

Within certain load limits, mild steel, copper, polythene and rubber are examples of elastic materials; lead and plasticine are examples of plastic materials.

If a tensile force applied to a uniform bar of mild steel is gradually increased and the corresponding extension of the bar is measured, then provided the applied force is not too large, a graph depicting these results is likely to be as shown in Figure 7.44. Since the graph is a straight line, *extension is directly proportional to the applied force.*

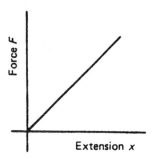

Figure 7.44

If the applied force is large, it is found that the material no longer returns to its original length when the force is removed. The material is then said to have passed its elastic limit and the resulting graph of force/extension is no longer a straight line. Stress = $\sigma = F/A$, and since, for a particular bar, A can be considered as a constant, then $F \propto \sigma$. Strain $\varepsilon = x/l$, and since for a particular bar l is constant, then $x \propto \varepsilon$. Hence for stress applied to a material below the elastic limit a graph of stress/strain will be as shown in Figure 7.45, and is a similar shape to the force/extension graph of Figure 7.44.

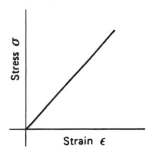

Figure 7.45

Hooke's Law

Hooke's law states:

Within the elastic limit, the extension of a material is proportional to the applied force.

It follows that:

Within the elastic limit of a material, the strain produced is directly proportional to the stress producing it.

Young's modulus of elasticity

Within the elastic limit, stress $\propto$ strain, hence stress = (a constant) $\times$ strain. This constant of proportionality is called *Young's modulus of elasticity* and is given the symbol E. The value of E may be determined from the gradient of the straight line portion of the stress/strain graph. The dimensions of E are pascals (the same as for stress, since strain is dimensionless).

$$E = \frac{\sigma}{\varepsilon} \text{ Pa}$$

Some typical values for Young's modulus of elasticity, E, include:

Aluminium	70 GPa (i.e. 70 $\times$ 10^9 Pa)		
Brass	100 GPa	Copper	96 GPa
Diamond	1200 GPa	Mild Steel	210 GPa
Lead	18 GPa	Tungsten	410 GPa
Cast Iron	110 GPa	Zinc	85 GPa

Stiffness

A material having a large value of Young's modulus is said to have a high value of stiffness, where stiffness is defined as:

$$\text{stiffness} = \frac{\text{force } F}{\text{extension } x}$$

For example, mild steel is much stiffer than lead.

Since $E = \sigma/\varepsilon$ and $\sigma = F/A$ and $\varepsilon = x/l$, then

$$E = \frac{F/A}{x/l}$$

i.e.

$$E = \frac{Fl}{Ax} = \frac{F}{x}\frac{l}{A}$$

i.e.

$$E = (\text{stiffness}) \times \frac{l}{A}$$

Stiffness ($= F/x$) is also the gradient of the force/extension graph, hence

$$E = (\text{gradient of force/extension graph}) \frac{l}{A}$$

Since l and A for a particular specimen are constant, the greater Young's modulus the greater the stiffness.

Example 7.41

A wire is stretched 2 mm by a force of 250 N. Determine the force that would stretch the wire 5 mm, assuming that the elastic limit is not exceeded.

Hooke's law states that extension x is proportional to force F, provided that the elastic limit is not exceeded, i.e. $x \propto F$ or $x = kF$ where k is a constant.

When $x = 2$ mm, $F = 250$ N, thus $2 = k(250)$,

from which, constant $k = (2/250) = (1/125)$.

When $x = 5$ mm, then $5 = kF$, i.e. $5 = (1/125)F$,

from which, force $F = 5(125) =$ **625 N.**

Thus to stretch the wire 5 mm a force of **625 N** is required.

Example 7.42

In an experiment to determine the modulus of elasticity of a sample of mild steel, a wire is loaded and the corresponding extension noted.

The results of the experiment are as shown:

Load (N)	0	40	110	160	200	250	290	340
Extension (mm)	0	1.2	3.3	4.8	6.0	7.5	10.0	16.2

Draw the load/extension graph. The mean diameter of the wire is 1.3 mm and its length is 8.0 m. Determine the modulus of elasticity E of the sample, and the stress at the elastic limit.

A graph of load/extension is shown in Figure 7.46.

$$E = \frac{\sigma}{\varepsilon} = \frac{F/A}{x/l} = \frac{F}{x}\frac{l}{A}$$

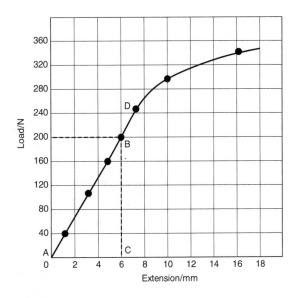

Figure 7.46

(F/x) is the gradient of the straight line part of the load/extension graph.

$$\text{Gradient} = \frac{F}{x} = \frac{BC}{AC} = \frac{200 \, N}{6 \times 10^{-3} \, m}$$

$$= 33.33 \times 10^3 \, N/m$$

Modulus of elasticity = (gradient of graph) (l/A)
  Length of specimen, $l = 8.0 \, m$

$$\text{Cross-sectional area } A = \frac{\pi d^2}{4} = \frac{\pi (0.0013)^2}{4}$$

$$= 1.327 \times 10^{-6}$$

Hence

$$\text{modulus of elasticity} = (33.33 \times 10^3) \frac{8.0}{1.327 \times 10^{-6}}$$

$$= 201 \, GPa$$

The elastic limit is at point D in Figure 7.46 where the graph no longer follows a straight line. This point corresponds to a load of 250 N as shown.

$$\text{Stress at elastic limit} = \frac{\text{force}}{\text{area}} = \frac{250}{1.327 \times 10^{-6}}$$

$$= 188.4 \times 10^6 \, Pa = \mathbf{188.4 \, MPa}$$

Ductility, brittleness and malleability

Ductility is the ability of a material to be plastically deformed by elongation, without fracture. This is a property which enables a material to be drawn out into wires. For ductile materials such as mild steel, copper and gold, large extensions can result before fracture occurs with increasing tensile force. Ductile materials usually have a percentage elongation value of about 15% or more.

Brittleness is the property of a material manifested by fracture without appreciable prior plastic deformation. Brittleness is a lack of ductility, and brittle materials such as cast iron, glass, concrete, brick and ceramics, have virtually no plastic stage, the elastic stage being followed by immediate fracture. Little or no 'waist' occurs before fracture in a brittle material undergoing a tensile test.

Malleability is the property of a material whereby it can be shaped when cold by hammering or rolling. A malleable material is capable of undergoing plastic deformation without fracture. Examples of malleable materials include lead, gold, putty and mild steel.

Example 7.43

Sketch typical load/extension curves for (a) an elastic non-metallic material, (b) a brittle material and (c) a ductile material. Give a typical example of each type of material.

(a) A typical load/extension curve for an elastic non-metallic material is shown in Figure 7.47(a), and an example of such a material is polythene.

1 A rubber band extends 50 mm when a force of 300 N is applied to it. Assuming the band is within the elastic limit, determine the extension produced by a force of 60 N.

2 A copper rod of diameter 20 mm and length 2.0 m has a tensile force of 5 kN applied to it. Determine (a) the stress in the rod, (b) by how much the rod extends when the load is applied. Take the modulus of elasticity for copper as 96 GPa.

3 An aluminium rod has a length of 200 mm and a diameter of 10 mm. When subjected to a compressive force the length of the rod is 199.6 mm. Determine (a) the stress in the rod when loaded, and (b) the magnitude of the force. Take the modulus of elasticity for aluminium as 70 GPa.

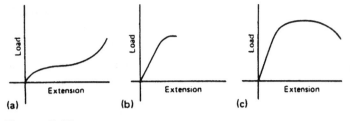

Figure 7.47

(b) A typical load/extension curve for a brittle material is shown in Figure 7.47(b), and an example of such a material is cast iron.

(c) A typical load/extension curve for a ductile material is shown in Figure 7.47(c), and an example of such a material is mild steel.

Linear momentum

The *momentum* of a body is defined as the product of its mass and its velocity, i.e. momentum = mu, where m = mass (in kg) and u = velocity (in m/s). The unit of momentum is kg m/s.

Since velocity is a vector quantity, *momentum is a vector quantity*, i.e. it has both magnitude and direction.

Newton's first law of motion states:

a body continues in a state of rest or in a state of uniform motion in a straight line unless acted on by some external force.

Hence the momentum of a body remains the same provided no external forces act on it.

The principle of conservation of momentum for a closed system (i.e. one on which no external forces act) may be stated as:

the total linear momentum of a system is a constant.

The total momentum of a system before collision in a given direction is equal to the total momentum of the system after collision in the same direction.

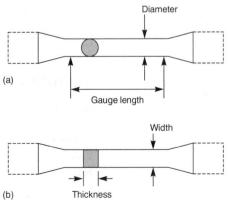

Figure 7.48

In Figure 7.48, masses m_1 and m_2 are travelling in the same direction with velocity $u_1 > u_2$. A collision will occur, and applying the principle of conservation of momentum:

$$\begin{array}{c} \text{total momentum} \\ \text{before impact} \end{array} = \begin{array}{c} \text{total momentum} \\ \text{after impact} \end{array}$$

i.e.

$$m_1 u_1 + m_2 u_2 = m_1 v_1 + m_2 v_2$$

where v_1 and v_2 are the velocities of m_1 and m_2 after impact.

Example 7.44

Determine the momentum of a piledriver of mass 400 kg when it is moving downwards with a speed of 12 m/s.

$$\begin{aligned} \text{Momentum} &= \text{mass} \times \text{velocity} \\ &= 400 \text{ kg} \times 12 \text{ m/s} \\ &= \mathbf{4800\ kg\ m/s}\ \text{downwards} \end{aligned}$$

---

1 A milling machine and its component have a combined mass of 400 kg. Determine the momentum of the table and component when the feed rate is 360 mm/min. [2.4 kg m/s]
2 The momentum of a body is 160 kg m/s when the velocity is 2.5 m/s. Determine the mass of the body. [64 kg]
3 A body has a mass of 30 g and is moving with a velocity of 20 m/s. It collides with a second body which has a mass of 20 g and which is moving with a velocity of 15 m/s. Assuming that the bodies both have the same velocity after impact, determine this common velocity, (a) when the initial velocities have the same line of action and the same sense, and (b) when the initial velocities have the same line of action but are opposite in sense.

Example 7.45

A wagon of mass 10 t is moving at a speed of 6 m/s and collides with another wagon of mass 15 t, which is stationary. After impact, the wagons are coupled together. Determine the common velocity of the wagons after impact.

Mass m_1 = 10 t = 10 000 kg, m_2 = 15 000 kg.
Velocity u_1 = 6 m/s, u_2 = 0

$$\begin{aligned} \text{Total momentum before impact} &= m_1 u_1 + m_2 u_2 \\ &= (10\,000 \times 6) + (15\,000 \times 0) \\ &= 60\,000 \text{ kg m/s} \end{aligned}$$

Let the common velocity of the wagons after impact be v metres per second. Since total momentum before impact = total momentum after impact:

$$60\,000 = m_1 v = m_2 v$$
$$= v(m_1 = m_2) = v(25\,000)$$

Hence

$$v = \frac{60\,000}{25\,000} = 2.4 \text{ m/s}$$

i.e. the common velocity after impact is **2.4 m/s** in the direction in which the 10 t wagon is initially travelling.

Couple and torque

When two equal forces act on a body as shown in Figure 7.49, they cause the body to rotate, and the system of forces is called a *couple*.

The turning moment of a couple is called a *torque*, T. In Figure 7.49, torque = magnitude of either force $\times$ perpendicular distance between the forces, i.e.

$$T = Fd$$

The unit of torque is the newton metre, N m.

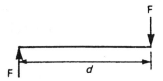

Figure 7.49

When a force F newtons is applied at a radius r metres from the axis of, say, a nut to be turned by a spanner (as shown in Figure 7.50), the torque T applied to the nut is given by $T = Fr$ N m.

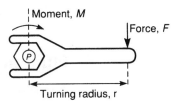

Figure 7.50

Test your knowledge 7.24

1 Determine the torque developed when a force of 200 N is applied tangentially to a spanner at a distance of 350 mm from the centre of the nut.

2 During a machining test on a lathe, the tangential force on the tool is 150 N. If the torque on the lathe spindle is 12 N m, determine the diameter of the workpiece.

Example 7.46

Determine the torque when a pulley wheel of diameter 300 mm has a force of 80 N applied at the rim.

Torque $T = Fr$, where force $F = 80$ N and radius $r = (300/2) = 150$ mm = 0.15 m.

Hence torque $T = (80)(0.15) =$ **12 N m**

Example 7.47

Determine the force applied tangentially to a bar of a screwjack at a radius of 800 mm, if the torque required is 600 N m.

Torque T = force $\times$ radius, from which

$$\text{force} = \frac{\text{torque}}{\text{radius}} = \frac{600 \text{ N m}}{800 \times 10^{-3} \text{ m}} = \textbf{750 N}$$

Pressure

The pressure acting on a surface is defined as the perpendicular force per unit area of surface. The unit of pressure is the pascal, Pa, where 1 pascal is equal to 1 newton per square metre. Thus pressure,

$$p = \frac{F}{A} \text{ pascals}$$

where F is the force in newtons acting at right angles to a surface of area A square metres.

When a force of 20 N acts uniformly over, and perpendicular to, an area of 4 m^2, then the pressure on the area, p, is given by

$$p = \frac{20 \text{ N}}{4 \text{ m}^2} = 5 \text{ Pa}$$

Example 7.48

A table loaded with books has a force of 250 N acting in each of its legs. If the contact area between each leg and the floor is 50 mm², find the pressure each leg exerts on the floor.

From above, pressure p = (force)(area). Hence

$$p = \frac{250\,\text{N}}{50\,\text{mm}^2} \times \frac{10^6\,\text{mm}^2}{1\,\text{m}^2}$$

$$= 5 \times 10^6\,\text{N/m}^2 = 5\,\text{MPa}$$

That is, the pressure exerted by each leg on the floor is **5 MPa**.

Fluid pressure

A fluid is either a liquid or a gas and there are four basic factors governing the pressure within fluids.

(a) The pressure at a given depth in a fluid is equal in all directions, see Figure 7.51(a).
(b) The pressure at a given depth in a fluid is independent of the shape of the container in which the fluid is held. In Figure 7.51(b), the pressure at X is the same as the pressure at Y.
(c) Pressure acts at right angles to the surface containing the fluid. In Figure 7.51(c), the pressures at points A to F all act at right angles to the container.
(d) When a pressure is applied to a fluid, this pressure is transmitted equally in all directions. In Figure 7.51(d), if the mass of the fluid is neglected, the pressures at points A to D are all the same.

The pressure, p, at any point in a fluid depends on three factors:

(a) the density of the fluid, in kg/m³;
(b) the gravitational acceleration, g, taken as approximately 9.8 m/s² (or the gravitational field force in N/kg); and
(c) the height of fluid vertically above the point, h metres. The relationship connecting these quantities is:

$$p = gh \text{ pascals}$$

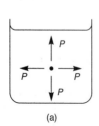

(a)

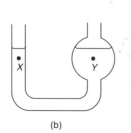

(b)

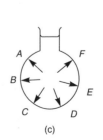

(c)

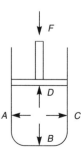

(d)

Figure 7.51

When the container shown in Figure 7.52 is filled with water of density 1000 kg/m³, the pressure due to the water at a depth of 0.03 m below the surface is given by:

$$p = gh$$

$$= (1000 \times 9.8 \times 0.03)\,\text{Pa}$$

$$= 294\,\text{Pa}$$

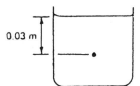

Figure 7.52

Test your knowledge 7.25

1 Determine the pressure acting at the base of a dam, when the surface of the water is 35 m above base level.

2 Calculate the force exerted by the atmosphere on a pool of water which is 30 m long by 10 m wide, when the atmospheric pressure is 100 kPa.

3 A vertical tube is partly filled with mercury of density 13 600 kg/m³. Find the height, in millimetres, of the column of mercury, when the pressure at the base of the tube is 101 kPa. Take the gravitational field force as 9.8 m/s².

Example 7.49

A tank contains water to a depth of 600 mm. Calculate the water pressure (a) at a depth of 350 mm and (b) at the base of the tank. Take the density of water as 1000 kg/m³ and the gravitational acceleration as 9.8 m/s².

From above, pressure p at any point in a fluid is given by $p = gh$ pascals, where p is the density in kg/m³, g is the gravitational acceleration in m/s² and h is the height of fluid vertically above the point.

(a) At a depth of 350 mm, i.e. 0.35 m

$$p = 1000 \times 9.8 \times 0.35 = \textbf{3430 Pa} = \textbf{3.43 kPa}$$

(b) At the base of the tank, the vertical height of the water is 600 mm, that is, 0.6 m. Hence

$$p = 1000 \times 9.8 \times 0.6 = \textbf{5880 Pa} = \textbf{5.88 kPa}$$

Atmospheric pressure

The air above the earth's surface is a fluid, having a density, ρ, which varies from approximately 1.225 kg/m³ at sea level to zero in outer space.

Since $p = \rho gh$, where height h is several thousands of metres, the air exerts a pressure on all points on the earth's surface. This pressure, called *atmospheric pressure*, has a value of approximately 100 kilopascals. Two terms are commonly used when measuring pressures:

(a) *absolute pressure*, meaning the pressure above that of an absolute vacuum (i.e. zero pressure); and

(b) *gauge pressure*, meaning the pressure above that normally present due to the atmosphere. Thus:

absolute pressure = atmospheric pressure + gauge pressure

Thus, a gauge pressure of 50 kPa is equivalent to an absolute pressure of (100 + 50) kPa, i.e. 150 kPa, since the atmospheric pressure is approximately 100 kPa.

Example 7.50

Calculate the absolute pressure at a point on a submarine at a depth of 30 m below the surface of the sea, when the atmospheric pressure is 101 kPa. Take the density of sea water as 1030 kg/m^3 and the gravitational acceleration as 9.8 m/s^2.

The pressure due to the sea, that is, the gauge pressure (p_g) is given by $p_g = gh$ pascals, i.e.

$$p_g = 1030 \times 9.8 \times 30 = 302\,820\,\text{Pa} = 302.82\,\text{kPa}$$

From above,

absolute pressure = atmospheric pressure + gauge pressure

$$= (101 + 302.82)\,\text{kPa} = 403.82\,\text{kPa}$$

That is, the absolute pressure at a depth of 30 m is **403.82 kPa**.

Test your knowledge 7.26

State the most suitable pressure indicating device for the following:
(a) A robust device to measure high pressures in the range 0–30 MPa.
(b) Calibration of a Pirani gauge.
(c) Measurement of gas pressures comparable with atmospheric pressure.
(d) To measure pressures of the order of 200 kPa.
(e) Measurement of atmospheric pressure to a high degree of accuracy.

Measurement of pressure

Pressure indicating instruments are made in a wide variety of forms because of their many different applications. Apart from the obvious criteria such as pressure range, accuracy and response, many measurements also require special attention to material, sealing and temperature effects. The fluid whose pressure is being measured may be corrosive or may be at high temperatures. Pressure indicating devices used in science and industry include:

(i) barometers – Fortin and aneroid types,
(ii) manometers – U-tube and inclined types,
(iii) Bourdon pressure gauge, and
(iv) McLeod and Pirani vacuum gauges

Archimedes' principle

Archimedes' principle states that:

If a solid body floats, or is submerged in a liquid, the liquid exerts an upthrust on the body equal to the gravitational force on the liquid displaced by the body.

In other words, if a solid body is immersed in a liquid, the apparent loss of weight is equal to the weight of liquid displaced.

If V is the volume of the body below the surface of the liquid, then the apparent loss of weight W is given by:

$$W = V\omega = V \rho g$$

where ω is the specific weight (i.e. weight per unit volume) and ρ is the density.

If a body floats on the surface of a liquid all of its weight appears to have been lost. The weight of liquid displaced is equal to the weight of the floating body.

Example 7.51

A body weighs 2.760 N in air and 1.925 N when completely immersed in water of density 1000 kg/m³. Calculate (a) the volume of the body and (b) the density of the body. Take the gravitational acceleration as 9.81 m/s².

(a) The apparent loss of weight is 2.760 N − 1.925 N = 0.835 N.

This is the weight of water displaced, i.e. $V\rho g$, where V is the volume of the body and ρ is the density of water, i.e.

$$0.835\,\text{N} = V \times 1000\,\text{kg/m}^3 \times 9.81\,\text{m/s}^2$$

$$= V \times 9.81\,\text{kN/m}^3$$

Hence

$$V = \frac{0.835}{9.81 \times 10^3}\,\text{m}^3 = 8.512 \times 10^{-5}\,\text{m}^3$$

$$= \mathbf{8.512 \times 10^4\,mm^3}$$

(b) The density of the body $= \dfrac{\text{mass}}{\text{volume}} = \dfrac{\text{weight}}{g \times V}$

$$= \frac{2.760\,\text{N}}{9.81\,\text{m/s}^2 \times 8.512 \times 10^{-5}\,\text{m}^3}$$

$$= \frac{\dfrac{2.760}{9.81}\,\text{kg} \times 10^5}{8.512\,\text{m}^3}$$

$$= \mathbf{3305\,kg/m^3} = \mathbf{3.305\,tonne/m^3}$$

Test your knowledge 7.27

1 A Bourdon pressure gauge shows a pressure of 1.151 MPa. If the absolute pressure is 1.25 MPa, find the atmospheric pressure in millimetres of mercury.
2 A body of weight 27.4 N and volume 1240 cm³ is completely immersed in water of specific weight 9.81 kN/m³. What is its apparent weight?

Heat energy

Heat is a form of energy and is measured in joules.

Temperature is the degree of hotness or coldness of a substance. Heat and temperature are thus *not* the same thing. For example, twice the heat energy is needed to boil a full container of water than half a container – that is, different amounts of heat energy are needed to cause an equal rise in the temperature of different amounts of the same substance.

Temperature is measured either (i) on the *Celsius* (°C) *scale* (formerly Centigrade), where the temperature at which ice melts, i.e. the freezing point of water, is taken as 0°C and the point at which water boils under normal atmospheric pressure is taken as 100°C, or (ii) on the *thermodynamic scale*, in which the unit of temperature is the Kelvin (K). The Kelvin scale uses the same temperature interval as the Celsius scale but its zero takes the 'absolute zero of temperature' which is at about −273°C. Hence,

Kelvin temperature = degree Celsius + 273

i.e.

$$K = (°C) + 273$$

Thus, for example, 0°C = 273 K, 25°C = 298 K and 100° = 373 K.

Example 7.52

Convert the following temperatures into the Kelvin scale: (a) 37°C (b) −28°C

From above, Kelvin temperature = degree Celsius + 273

(a) 37°C corresponds to a Kelvin temperature of 37 + 273, i.e. **310 K**
(b) −28°C corresponds to a Kelvin temperature of −28 + 273, i.e. **245 K.**

Example 7.53

Convert the following temperatures into the Celsius scale: (a) 365 K (b) 213 K

From above, K = (°C) + 273

Hence, degree Celsius = Kelvin temperature −273

(a) 365 K corresponds to 365 − 273, i.e. **92°C**
(b) 213 K corresponds to 213 − 273, i.e. **−60°C.**

Specific heat capacity

The *specific heat capacity* of a substance is the quantity of heat energy required to raise the temperature of 1 kg of the substance by 1°C. The symbol used for specific heat capacity is c and the units are J/(kg °C) or J(kg K). (Note that these units may also be written as $J\,kg^{-1}\,°C^{-1}$ or $J\,kg^{-1}\,K^{-1}$.)

Some typical values of specific heat capacity for the range of temperature 0°C to 100°C include:

Water	4190 J/(kg °C)	Ice	2100 J/(kg °C)
Aluminium	950 J/(kg °C)	Copper	390 J/(kg °C)
Iron	500 J/(kg °C)	Lead	130 J/(kg °C)

Hence to raise the temperature of 1 kg of iron by 1°C requires 500 J of energy, to raise the temperature of 5 kg of iron by 1°C requires (500×5) J of energy, and to raise the temperature of 5 kg of iron by 40°C requires $(500 \times 5 \times 40)$ J of energy, i.e. 100 kJ.

In general, the quantity of heat energy, Q, required to raise a mass m kg of a substance with a specific heat capacity c J/(kg°C) from temperature t_1°C to t_2°C is given by:

$$Q = mc(t_2 - t_1) \text{ joules}$$

Example 7.54

Calculate the quantity of heat required to raise the temperature of 5 kg of water from 0°C to 100°C. Assume the specific heat capacity of water is 4200 J/(kg°C)

Quantity of heat energy, $Q = mc(t_2 - t_1)$

$= 5\,\text{kg} \times 4200\,\text{J/(kg°C)} \times (100 - 0)°\text{C}$

$= 5 \times 4200 \times 100$

$= \mathbf{2\,100\,000\,J}$ or **2100 kJ** or **2.1 MJ**

Test your knowledge 7.28

1 (a) Convert −63°C into the Kelvin scale.
  (b) Change 225 K into the Celsius scale.
2 20.8 kJ of heat energy is required to raise the temperature of 2 kg of lead from 16°C to 96°C. Determine the specific heat capacity of lead.
3 5.7 MJ of heat energy are supplied to 30 kg of aluminium which is initially at a temperature of 20°C. If the specific heat capacity of aluminium is 950 J/(kg °C), determine its final temperature.

Change of state

A material may exist in any one of three states – solid, liquid or gas. If heat is supplied at a constant rate to some ice initially at, say, –30°C, its temperature rises as shown in Figure 7.53. Initially the temperature increases from –30°C to 0°C as shown by the line AB. It then remains constant at 0°C for the time BC required for the ice to melt into water.

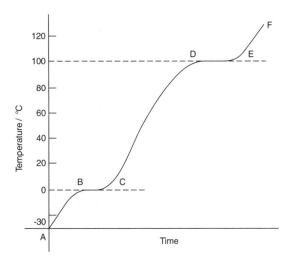

Figure 7.53

When melting commences the energy gained by continual heating is offset by the energy required for the change of state and the temperature remains constant even though heating is continued. When the ice is completely melted to water, continual heating raises the temperature to 100°C, as shown by CD in Figure 7.53. The water then begins to boil and the temperature again remains constant at 100°C, shown as DE, until all the water has vaporized.

Continual heating raises the temperature of the steam as shown by EF in the region where the steam is termed superheated.

Changes of state from solid to liquid or liquid to gas occur without change of temperature and such changes are reversible processes. When heat energy flows to or from a substance and causes a change of temperature, such as between A and B, between C and D and between E and F in Figure 7.53, it is called *sensible heat* (since it can be 'sensed' by a thermometer).

Heat energy which flows to or from a substance while the temperature remains constant, such as between B and C and between D and E in Figure 7.53, is called *latent heat* (latent means concealed or hidden).

Latent heats of fusion and vaporization

The *specific latent heat of fusion* is the heat required to change 1 kg of a substance from the solid state to the liquid state (or vice versa) at constant temperature.

The *specific latent heat of vaporization* is the heat required to change 1 kg of a substance from a liquid to a gaseous state (or vice versa) at constant temperature. The units of the specific latent heats of fusion and vaporization are J/kg, or more often kJ/kg, and some typical values are shown in Table 7.1. The quantity of heat Q supplied or given out during a change of state is given by:

$$Q = mL$$

where m is the mass in kilograms and L is the specific latent heat. Thus, for example, the heat required to convert 10 kg of ice at 0°C to water at 0°C is given by 10 kg × 335 kJ/kg, i.e., 3350 kJ or 3.35 MJ.

Table 7.1

	Latent heat of fusion (kJ/kg)	Melting point (°C)
Mercury	11.8	−39
Lead	22	327
Silver	100	957
Ice	335	0
Aluminium	387	660

	Latent heat of vaporization (kJ/kg)	Boiling point (°C)
Oxygen	214	−183
Mercury	286	357
Ethyl alcohol	857	79
Water	2257	100

Besides changing temperature, the effects of supplying heat to a material can involve changes in dimensions, as well as in colour, state and electrical resistance. Most substances expand when heated and contract when cooled, and there are many practical applications and design implications of thermal movement.

Example 7.55

How much heat is needed to melt completely 12 kg of ice at 0°C? Assume the latent heat of fusion of ice is 335 kJ/kg.

Quantity of heat required, $Q = mL$

$$= 12 \text{ kg} \times 335 \text{ kJ/kg}$$

$$= \mathbf{4020 \text{ kJ} \text{ or } 4.02 \text{ MJ}}$$

1 Determine the heat energy required to change 8 kg of water at 100°C to superheated steam at 100°C. Assume the specific latent heat of vaporization of water is 2260 kJ/kg.
2 Calculate the heat energy required to convert completely 10 kg of water at 50°C into steam at 100°C, given that the specific heat capacity of water is 4200 J/(kg°C) and the specific latent heat of vaporization of water is 2260 kJ/kg.

Example 7.56

Calculate the heat required to convert 5 kg of water at 100°C to superheated steam at 100°C. Assume the latent heat of vaporization of water is 2260 kJ/kg.

Quantity of heat required, $Q = mL$

$$= 5\,kg \times 2260\,kJ/kg$$

$$= \mathbf{11\,300\,kJ}\ \text{or}\ \mathbf{11.3\,MJ}$$

A simple refrigerator

The boiling point of most liquids may be lowered if the pressure is lowered. In a simple refrigerator a working fluid, such as ammonia or freon, has the pressure acting on it reduced. The resulting lowering of the boiling point causes the liquid to vaporize. In vaporizing, the liquid takes in the necessary latent heat from its surroundings, i.e. the freezer, which thus becomes cooled. The vapour is immediately removed by a pump to a condenser which is outside of the cabinet, where it is compressed and changed back into a liquid, giving out latent heat. The cycle is repeated when the liquid is pumped back to the freezer to be vaporized.

Measurement of temperature

A change in temperature of a substance can often result in a change in one or more of its physical properties. Thus, although temperature cannot be measured directly, its effects can be measured. Some properties of substances used to determine changes in temperature include changes in dimensions, electrical resistance, state, type and volume of radiation and colour.

Temperature measuring devices available are many and varied. Those most often used in science and industry are:

1 Liquid-in-glass thermometer (mercury and alcohol)
2 Thermocouples
3 Resistance thermometers
4 Thermistors
5 Pyrometers (total radiation and optical)
6 Temperature indicating paints
7 Temperature sensitive crayons
8 Bimetallic thermometers
9 Mercury-in-steel thermometer
10 Gas thermometer

Activity 7.1

For each of these measuring devices listed below,

(a) explain their principle of operation
(b) describe their construction with appropriate sketches
(c) state their characteristics and range

State which device would be most suitable to measure the following:

(a) metal in a furnace, in the range 50°C to 1600°C
(b) the air in an office in the range 0°C to 40°C
(c) boiler flue gas in the range 15°C to 300°C
(d) a metal surface, where a visual indication is required when it reaches 425°C
(e) materials in a high-temperature furnace in the range 2000°C to 2800°C
(f) to calibrate a thermocouple in the range −100°C to 500°C
(g) brick in a kiln up to 900°C
(h) an inexpensive method for food processing applications in the range −25°C to −75°C

(d) discuss their limitations, advantages and disadvantages
(e) describe typical applications where they may be used.

Present your findings in the form of a brief word processed report and include relevant sketches and diagrams.

Measuring devices:

(i) a thermocouple sensor
(ii) a bimetallic thermometer.

Thermal Expansion

When heat is applied to most materials, *expansion* occurs in all directions. Conversely, if heat energy is removed from a material (i.e. the material is cooled) *contraction* occurs in all directions. The effects of expansion and contraction each depend on the *change of temperature* of the material.

Practical applications of thermal expansion

Some practical applications where expansion and contraction of solid materials must be allowed for include:

(i) Overhead electrical transmission lines are hung so that they are slack in summer, otherwise their contraction in winter may snap the conductors or bring down pylons.

(ii) Gaps need to be left in lengths of railway lines to prevent buckling in hot weather (except where these are continuously welded).

(iii) Ends of large bridges are often supported on rollers to allow them to expand and contract freely.

(iv) Fitting a metal collar to a shaft or a steel tyre to a wheel is often achieved by first heating them so that they expand, fitting them in position, and then cooling them so that the contraction holds them firmly in place. This is known as a 'shrink-fit'. By a similar method hot rivets are used for joining metal sheets.

(v) The amount of expansion varies with different materials. Figure 7.54(a) shows a bimetallic strip at room temperature (i.e., two different strips of metal riveted together). When heated, brass expands more than steel, and since the two metals are riveted together the bimetallic strip is forced into an arc as shown in Figure 7.54(b). Such a movement can be arranged to make or break an electric circuit and bimetallic strips are used, in particular, in thermostats (which are temperature-operated switches) to control central heating systems, cookers, refrigerators, toasters, irons, hot-water and alarm systems.

(vi) Motor engines use the rapid expansion of heated gases to force a piston to move.

(vii) Designers must predict, and allow for, the expansion of steel pipes in a steam-raising plant so as to avoid damage and consequent danger to health.

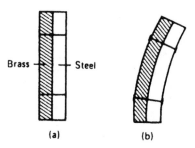

(a) **(b)**

Figure 7.54

Expansion and contraction of water

Water is a liquid which at low temperature displays an unusual effect. If cooled, contraction occurs until, at about 4°C, the volume is at a minimum. As the temperature is further decreased from 4°C to 0°C expansion occurs, i.e. the volume increases. When ice is formed, considerable expansion occurs and it is this expansion which often causes frozen water pipes to burst.

A practical application of the expansion of a liquid is with thermometers, where the expansion of a liquid, such as mercury or alcohol, is used to measure temperature.

Coefficient of linear expansion

The amount by which unit length of a material expands when the temperature is raised one degree is called the *coefficient of linear expansion* of the material and is represented by α (Greek alpha).

The units of the coefficient of linear expansion are m/(mK), although it is usually quoted as just /K or K^{-1}. For example, copper has a coefficient of linear expansion value of $17 \times 10^{-6} K^{-1}$, which means that a 1 m long bar of copper expands by $0.000\,017$ m if its temperature is increased by 1 K (or 1°C). If a 6 m long bar of copper is subjected to a temperature rise of 25 K then the bar will expand by $(6 \times 0.000\,017 \times 25)$ m, i.e. $0.002\,55$ m or 2.55 mm. (Since the Kelvin scale uses the same temperature interval as the Celsius scale, a *change* of temperature of, say, 50°C, is the same as a change of temperature of 50 K.) If a material, initially of length l_1 and at a temperature of t_1 and having a coefficient of linear expansion α, has its temperature increased to t_2, then the new length l_2 of the material is given by:

New length = original length + expansion i.e.

$$l_2 = l_1 + l_1\,\alpha(t_2 - t_1)$$

i.e.

$$l_2 = l_1[1 + \alpha(t_2 - t_1)]$$

Some typical values for the coefficient of linear expansion include:

Aluminium	$23 \times 10^{-6} K^{-1}$	Brass	$18 \times 10^{-6} K^{-1}$
Concrete	$12 \times 10^{-6} K^{-1}$	Copper	$17 \times 10^{-6} K^{-1}$
Gold	$14 \times 10^{-6} K^{-1}$	Invar (nickel-	
Iron	$11\text{–}12 \times 10^{-6} K^{-1}$	steel alloy)	$0.9 \times 10^{-6} K^{-1}$
Steel	$15\text{–}16 \times 10^{-6} K^{-1}$	Nylon	$100 \times 10^{-6} K^{-1}$
Zinc	$31 \times 10^{-6} K^{-1}$	Tungsten	$4.5 \times 10^{-6} K^{-1}$

1 A length of lead piping is 50.0 m long at a temperature of 16°C. When hot water flows through it the temperature of the pipe rises to 80°C. Determine the length of the hot pipe if the coefficient of linear expansion of lead is $29 \times 10^{-6}\,\text{K}^{-1}$.

2 A measuring tape made of copper measures 5.0 m at a temperature of 288 K. Calculate the percentage error in measurement when the temperature has increased to 313 K. Take the coefficient of linear expansion of copper as $17 \times 10^{-6}\,\text{K}^{-1}$.

3 The copper tubes in a boiler are 4.20 m long at a temperature of 20°C. Determine the length of the tubes (a) when surrounded only by feed water at 10°C, (b) when the boiler is operating and the mean temperature of the tubes is 320°C. Assume the coefficient of linear expansion of copper to be $17 \times 10^{-6}\,\text{K}^{-1}$.

Example 7.57

An electrical overhead transmission line has a length of 80.0 m between its supports at 15°C. Its length increases by 92 mm at 65°C. Determine the coefficient of linear expansion of the material of the line.

Length $l_1 = 80.0$ m; $l_2 = 80.0 + 92$ mm $= 80.092$ m; temperature $t_1 = 15$°C; temperature $t_2 = 65$°C.
Length $l_2 = l_1[1 + \alpha(t_2 - t_1)]$, i.e.,

$$80.092 = 80.0[1 + \alpha(65 - 15)]$$

$$80.092 = 80.0 + (80.0)(\alpha)(50)$$

i.e. $80.092 - 80.0 = (80.0)(\alpha)(50)$

Hence the coefficient of linear expansion,

$$\alpha = \frac{0.092}{(80.0)(50)} = 0.000\,023$$

i.e. $\alpha = 23 \times 10^{-6}\,\text{K}^{-1}$ (which is aluminium – see above).

Coefficient of superficial expansion

The amount by which unit area of a material increases when the temperature is raised by one degree is called the *coefficient of superficial* (i.e. *area*) *expansion* and is represented by β (Greek letter beta).

If a material having an initial surface area A_1 at temperature t_1 and having a coefficient of superficial expansion β, has its temperature increased to t_2, then the new surface area A_2 of the material is given by:

New surface area = original surface area + increase in area

i.e. $A_2 = A_1 + A_1\beta(t_2 - t_1)$

i.e. $A_2 = A_1[1 = \beta(t_2 - t_1)]$ (7.17)

It may be shown that the coefficient of superficial expansion is twice the coefficient of linear expansion, i.e. $\beta = 2\alpha$, to a very close approximation.

Coefficient of cubic expansion

The amount by which unit volume of a material increases for a one degree rise of temperature is called the *coefficient of cubic* (or *volumetric*) *expansion* and is represented by γ (Greek gamma).

If a material having an initial volume V_1 at temperature t_1 and having a coefficient of cubic expansion, has its temperature raised to t_2, then the new volume V_2 of the material is given by:

New volume = initial volume + increases in volume

i.e. $V_2 = V_1 + V_1\gamma(t_2 - t_1)$

i.e. $V_2 = V_1[1 + \gamma(t_2 - t_1)]$ (7.18)

It may be shown that the coefficient of cubic expansion is three times the coefficient of linear expansion, i.e. $\gamma = 3\alpha$, to a very close approximation. A liquid has no definite shape and only its cubic or volumetric expansion need be considered. Thus with expansions in liquids, equation (7.18) is used.

Some typical values for the coefficient of cubic expansion measured at 20°C (i.e., 293 K) include:

Ethyl alcohol	$1.1 \times 10^{-3}\,K^{-1}$	Mercury	$1.82 \times 10^{-4}\,K^{-1}$
Paraffin oil	$9 \times 10^{-2}\,K^{-1}$	Water	$2.1 \times 10^{-4}\,K^{-1}$

The coefficient of cubic expansion is only constant over a limited range of temperature.

Example 7.58

A brass sphere has a diameter of 50 mm at a temperature of 289 K. If the temperature of the sphere is raised to 789 K, determine the increase in (a) the diameter, (b) the surface area, (c) the volume of the sphere. Assume the coefficient of linear expansion for brass is $18 \times 10^{-6}\,K^{-1}$.

(a) Initial diameter, $l_1 = 50$ mm; initial temperature, $t_1 = 289$ K;

final temperature, $t_2 = 789$ K; $\alpha = 18 \times 10^{-6}\,K^{-1}$.

New diameter at 789 K is given by $l_2 = l_1[1 + \alpha(t_2 - t_1)]$

from equation 7.16, i.e. $l_2 = 50[1 + (18 \times 10^{-6})(789 - 289)]$

$$= 50[1 + 0.009] = 50.45\,mm$$

Hence the increase in the diameter is **0.45 mm**.

(b) Initial surface area of sphere is given by

$$A_1 = 4\pi r^2 = 4\pi \frac{50^2}{2} = 2500\pi\,mm^2$$

New surface area at 789 K is given by $A_2 = A_1[1 + \beta(t_2 - t_1)]$

from equation (7.17), i.e. $A_2 = A_1[1 + 2\alpha(t_2 - t_1)]$

since $\beta = 2\alpha$, to a very close approximation.

Thus $A_2 = 2500\pi[1 + 2(18 \times 10^{-6})(500)]$

$$= 2500\pi[1 + 0.018]$$

$$= 2500\pi + 2500\pi(0.018)$$

Hence increase in surface area $= 2500\pi(0.018) = $ **141.4 mm²**

(c) Initial volume of sphere is given by

$$V_2 = \frac{4}{3}\pi r^3 = \frac{4}{3}\pi \frac{50^3}{2}\,mm^3$$

New volume at 789 K is given by $V_2 - V_1[1 + (t_2 - t_1)]$

from equation (7.18), i.e. $V_2 = V_1[1 + 3\alpha(t_2 - t_1)]$

since $\gamma = 3\alpha$, to a very close approximation.

1 A block of cast iron has dimensions of 50 mm by 30 mm by 10 mm at 15°C. Determine the increase in volume when the temperature of the block is raised to 75°C. Assume the coefficient of linear expansion of cast iron to be $11 \times 10^{-6}\,K^{-1}$

2 A rectangular glass block has a length of 100 mm, width 50 mm and depth 20 mm at 293 K. When heated to 353 K its length increases by 0.054 mm. What is the coefficient of linear expansion of the glass? Find also (a) the increase in surface area, (b) the change in volume resulting from the change of length.

Thus $V_2 = \dfrac{4}{3}\pi(25)^3[1 + 3(18 \times 10^{-6})(500)]$

$= \dfrac{4}{3}\pi(25)^3[1 + 0.027]$

$= \dfrac{4}{3}\pi(25)^3 + \dfrac{4}{3}\pi(25)^3(0.027)$

Hence the increase in volume $= \dfrac{4}{3}\pi(25)^3(0.027) =$ **1767 mm³**

The gas laws

The relationships which exist between pressure, volume and temperature in a gas are given in a set of laws called the *gas laws*.

Boyle's law

Boyle's law states:

> *the volume V of a fixed mass of gas is inversely proportional to its absolute pressure p at constant temperature.*

i.e. $p \propto 1/V$ or $p = k/V$ or $pV = k$,

at constant temperature, where p = absolute pressure in pascals (Pa), V = volume in m³, and k = a constant.

Changes which occur at constant temperature are called *isothermal* changes. When a fixed mass of gas at constant temperature changes from pressure p_1 and volume V_1 to pressure p_2 and volume V_2 then:

$$p_1V_1 = p_2V_2$$

Example 7.59

A gas occupies a volume of 0.10 m³ at a pressure of 1.8 MPa. Determine (a) the pressure if the volume is changed to 0.06 m³ at constant temperature, and (b) the volume if the pressure is changed to 2.4 MPa at constant temperature.

(a) Since the change occurs at constant temperature (i.e. an isothermal change), Boyle's law applies, i.e. $p_1V_1 = p_2V_2$, where p_1 = 1.8 MPa, V_1 = 0.10 m³ and V_2 = 0.06 m³.
  Hence $(1.8)(0.10) = p_2(0.06)$ from which,

$$\text{pressure } p_2 = \frac{1.8 \times 0.10}{0.06} = \textbf{3 MPa}$$

(b) $p_1V_1 = p_2V_2$ where p_1 = 1.8 MPa, V_1 = 0.10 m³, p_2 = 2.4 MPa.
  Hence $(1.8)(0.10) = (2.4)V_2$ from which

$$\text{volume } V_2 = \frac{(1.8)(0.10)}{2.4} = \textbf{0.075 m}^3$$

Charles' law

for a given mass of gas at constant pressure, the volume V is directly proportional to its thermodynamic temperature T,

i.e. $V \propto T$ or $V = kT$ or

$$\frac{V}{T} = k,$$

at constant pressure, where T = thermodynamic temperature in Kelvin (K). A process which takes place at constant pressure is called an *isobaric* process.

The relationship between the Celsius scale of temperature and the thermodynamic or absolute scale is given by:

Kelvin – degrees Celsius + 273

i.e. K = °C + 273 or °C = K – 273

If a given mass of gas at a constant pressure occupies a volume V_1 at a temperature T_1 and a volume V_2 at temperature T_2, then

$$\frac{V_1}{T_1} = \frac{V_2}{T_2}$$

1 Some gas occupies a volume of 1.5 m³ in a cylinder at a pressure of 250 kPa. A piston, sliding in the cylinder, compresses the gas isothermally until the volume is 0.5 m³. If the area of the piston is 300 cm², calculate the force on the piston when the gas is compressed.

2 Gas at a temperature of 150°C has its volume reduced by one-third in an isobaric process. Calculate the final temperature of the gas.

Example 7.60

A gas occupies a volume of 1.2 litres at 20°C. Determine the volume it occupies at 130°C if the pressure is kept constant.

Since the change occurs at constant pressure (i.e., an isobaric process), Charles' law applies, i.e.

$$\frac{V_1}{T_1} = \frac{V_2}{T_2}$$

where V_1 = 1.2l, T_1 = 20°C = (20 + 273) K = 293 K

and T_2 = (130 + 273) K = 403 K.

Hence $\dfrac{1.2}{293} = \dfrac{V_2}{403}$

from which, volume at 130°C, $V_2 = \dfrac{(1.2)(403)}{293}$ = **1.65 litres**

The pressure law

The *pressure law* states:

the pressure p *of a fixed mass of gas is directly proportional to its thermodynamic temperature* T *at constant volume*

i.e. $p \propto T$ or $p = kT$ or

$$\frac{P}{T} = k$$

When a fixed mass of gas at constant volume changes from pressure p_1 and temperature T_1, to pressure p_2 and temperature T_2 then:

$$\frac{p_1}{T_1} = \frac{p_2}{T_2}$$

Example 7.61

Gas initially at a temperature of 17°C and pressure 150 kPa is heated at constant volume until its temperature is 124°C. Determine the final pressure of the gas, assuming no loss of gas.

Since the gas is at constant volume, the pressure law applies, i.e.,

$$\frac{p_1}{T_1} = \frac{p_2}{T_2}$$

where $T_1 = (17 + 273)\text{K} = 290\,\text{K},$
$T_2 = (124 + 273)\,\text{K} = 397\,\text{K}$ and
$p_1 = 150\,\text{kPa}.$

Hence $\dfrac{150}{290} = \dfrac{p_2}{397}$

from which, final pressure, $p_2 = \dfrac{(150)(397)}{290} = \textbf{205.3 kPa}$

Dalton's law of partial pressure

Dalton's law of partial pressure states:

the total pressure of a mixture of gases occupying a given volume is equal to the sum of the pressures of each gas, considered separately, at constant temperature.

The pressure of each constituent gas when occupying a fixed volume alone is known as the *partial pressure* of that gas.

An *ideal gas* is one which completely obeys the gas laws. In practice no gas is an ideal gas, although air is very close to being one. For calculation purposes the difference between an ideal and an actual gas is very small.

Test your knowledge 7.34

1 Gas, initially at a temperature of 27°C and pressure 100 kPa, is heated at constant volume until its temperature is 150°C. Assuming no loss of gas, determine the final pressure of the gas.

2 A gas A in a container exerts a pressure of 120 kPa at a temperature of 20°C. Gas B is added to the container and the pressure increases to 300 kPa at the same temperature. Determine the pressure which gas B alone exerts at the same temperature.

Example 7.62

A gas R in a container exerts a pressure of 200 kPa at a temperature of 18°C. Gas Q is added to the container and the pressure increases to 320 kPa at the same temperature. Determine the pressure that gas Q alone exerts at the same temperature.

Initial pressure $p_R = 200$ kPa and pressure of gases R and Q together, $p = p_R + p_Q = 320$ kPa. By Dalton's law of partial pressure, the pressure of gas Q alone is

$$p_Q = p - p_R = 320 - 200 = \textbf{120 kPa}$$

Characteristic gas equation

Frequently, when a gas is undergoing some change, the pressure, temperature and volume all vary simultaneously. Provided there is no change in the mass of a gas, the above gas laws can be combined, giving

$$\frac{p_1 V_1}{T_1} = \frac{p_2 V_2}{T_2} = k$$

where k is a constant.

For an ideal gas, constant $k = mR$, where m is the mass of the gas in kg, and R is the *characteristic gas constant*, i.e.

$$\frac{pV}{T} = mR \quad \text{or} \quad pV = mRT$$

This is called the *characteristic gas equation*. In this equation, p = absolute pressure in pascals, V = volume in m^3, m = mass in kg, R = characteristic gas constant in J/(kg K), and T = thermodynamic temperature in Kelvin.

Some typical values of the characteristic gas constant R include: air, 287 J/(kg K), hydrogen 4160 J/(kg K), oxygen 260 J/(kg K) and carbon dioxide 184 J/(kg k).

Standard temperature and pressure (STP) refers to a temperature of 0°C, i.e. 273 K, and normal atmospheric pressure of 101.325 kPa.

Test your knowledge 7.35

1 A quantity of gas in a cylinder occupies a volume of 0.05 m^3 at a pressure of 400 kPa and a temperature of 27°C. It is compressed according to Boyle's law until its pressure is 1 MPa, and then expanded according to Charles' law until its volume is 0.03 m^3. Determine the final temperature of the gas.

2 A spherical vessel has a diameter of 1.2 m and contains oxygen at a pressure of 2 bar and a temperature of −20°C. Determine the mass of oxygen in the vessel. Take the characteristic gas constant for oxygen to be 0.260 kJ/(kg K).

3 Determine the characteristic gas contant of a gas which has a specific volume of 0.5 m^3/kg at a temperature of 20°C and pressure 150 kPa.

Example 7.63

A gas occupies a volume of 2.0 m^3 when at a pressure of 100 kPa and a temperature of 120°C. Determine the volume of the gas at 15°C if the pressure is increased to 250 kPa.

Using the combined gas law

$$\frac{p_1 V_1}{T_1} = \frac{p_2 V_2}{T_2}$$

where $V_1 = 2.0$ m^3, $p_1 = 100$ kPa, $p_2 = 250$ kPa, $T_1 = (120 + 273)$ K $= 383$ K and $T_2 = (15 + 273)$ K $= 288$ K, gives:

$$\frac{(100)(2.0)}{393} = \frac{(250) V_2}{288}$$

from which,

$$\text{volume at 15°C, } V_2 = \frac{(100)(2.0)(288)}{(393)(250)} = \textbf{0.586 m}^3$$

Standard symbols for electrical components

Symbols are used for components in electrical circuit diagrams and some of the more common ones are shown in Figure 7.55.

Electrical current and quantity of electricity

All *atoms* consist of *protons*, *neutrons* and *electrons*. The protons, which have positive electrical charges, and the neutrons, which have no electrical charge, are contained within the *nucleus*. Removed from the nucleus are minute negatively charged particles called electrons. Atoms of different materials differ from one another by having different numbers of protons, neutrons and electrons. An equal number of protons and electrons exist within an atom and it is said to be electrically balanced, as the positive and negative charges

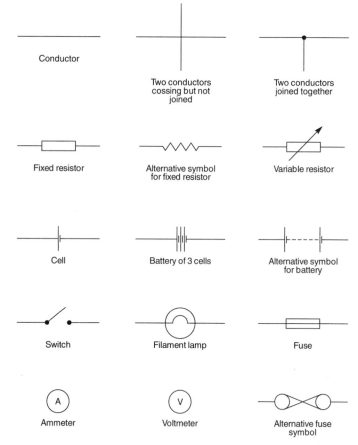

Figure 7.55

cancel each other out. When there are more than two electrons in an atom the electrons are arranged into *shells* at various distances from the nucleus.

All atoms are bound together by powerful forces of attraction existing between the nucleus and its electrons. Electrons in the outer shell of an atom, however, are attracted to their nucleus less powerfully than are electrons whose shells are nearer the nucleus.

It is possible for an atom to lose an electron; the atom, which is now called an *ion*, is not now electrically balanced, but is positively charged and is thus able to attract an electron to itself from another atom. Electrons that move from one atom to another are called free electrons and such random motion can continue indefinitely. However, if an electric pressure or *voltage* is applied across any material there is a tendency for electrons to move in a particular direction. This movement of free electrons, known as *drift*, constitutes an electric current flow. Thus

current is the rate of movement of charge

Conductors are materials that have electrons that are loosely connected to the nucleus and can easily move through the material from one atom to another.

Insulators are materials whose electrons are held firmly to their nucleus. The unit used to measure the *quantity of electrical charge Q* is called the *coulomb C* (where 1 coulomb = 6.24×10^{18} electrons).

If the drift of electrons in a conductor takes place at the rate of one coulomb per second the resulting current is said to be a current of one ampere. Thus

$$1 \text{ ampere } = 1 \text{ coulomb per second}$$

or

$$1 \text{ A } = 1 \text{ C/s}$$

Hence

$$1 \text{ coulomb } = 1 \text{ ampere second} \quad \text{or} \quad 1 \text{ C } = 1 \text{ A s}$$

Generally, if I is the current in amperes and t the time in seconds during which the current flows, then $I \times t$ represents the quantity of electrical charge in coulombs, i.e. quantity of electrical charge transferred.

$$Q = I \times t \text{ coulombs}$$

Example 7.64

If a current of 10 A flows for four minutes, find the quantity of electricity transferred.

Quantity of electricity, $Q = It$ coulombs. $I = 10$ A, $t = 4 \times 60 = 240$ s.

Hence $\quad Q = 10 \times 240 = 2400$ C

Potential difference and resistance

For a continuous current to flow between two points in a circuit a *potential difference* (p.d.) or *voltage*, V, is required between them; a complete conducting path is necessary to and from the source of electrical energy. The unit of p.d. is the volt, V.

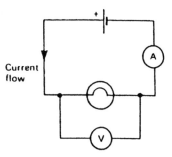

Figure 7.56

Figure 7.56 shows a cell connected across a filament lamp. Current flow, by convention, is considered as flowing from the positive terminal of the cell around the circuit to the negative terminal.

The flow of electric current is subject to friction. This friction, or opposition, is called *resistance R* and is the property of a conductor that limits current. The unit of resistance is the ohm Ω. 1 ohm is defined as the resistance which will have a current of 1 ampere flowing through it when 1 volt is connected across it, i.e.

$$\text{resistance} = \frac{\text{potential difference}}{\text{current}}$$

Basic electrical measuring instruments

An *ammeter* is an instrument used to measure current and must be connected in *series* with the circuit. Figure 7.56 shows an ammeter connected in series with the lamp to measure the current flowing through it. Since all the current in the circuit passes through the ammeter it must have a very *low resistance*.

A *voltmeter* is an instrument used to measure p.d. and must be connected in *parallel* with the part of the circuit whose p.d. is required. In Figure 7.56, a voltmeter is connected in parallel with the lamp to measure the p.d. across it. To avoid a significant current flowing through it a voltmeter must have a very *high resistance*.

An *ohmmeter* is an instrument for measuring resistance.

A *multimeter*, or universal instrument, may be used to measure voltage, current and resistance. An 'Avometer' is a typical example.

The *cathode ray oscilloscope* (CRO) may be used to observe waveforms and to measure voltages and currents. The display of a CRO involves a spot of light moving across a screen. The amount by which the spot is deflected from its initial position depends on the p.d. applied to the terminals of the CRO and the range selected. The displacement is calibrated in 'volts per cm'. For example, if the spot is deflected 3 cm and the volts/cm switch is on 10 V/cm then the magnitude of the p.d. is 3 cm $\times$ 10 V/cm, i.e. 30 V.

Ohm's law

Ohm's law states that the current I flowing in a circuit is directly proportional to the applied voltage V and inversely proportional to the resistance R, provided the temperature remains constant. Thus,

$$I = \frac{V}{I} \quad \text{or} \quad V = IR \quad \text{or} \quad R = \frac{V}{I}$$

1 What current must flow if 0.24 coulombs is to be transferred in 15 ms?
2 A p.d. of 50 V is applied across a heating element. If the resistance of the element is 12.5 Ω, find the current flowing through it.

Example 7.65

The current flowing through a resistor is 0.8 A when a p.d. of 20 V is applied. Determine the value of the resistance.

From Ohm's law,

$$\text{resistance } R = \frac{V}{I} = \frac{20}{0.8} = \frac{200}{8} = \mathbf{25\,\Omega}$$

Multiples and sub-multiples

Currents, voltages and resistances can often be very large or very small. Thus *multiples* and *sub-multiples* of units are often used. The most common ones, with an example of each, are listed in Table 7.2.

Example 7.66

Determine the p.d. which must be applied to a 2 kΩ resistor in order that a current of 10 mA may flow.

Resistance $R = 2\,k\Omega = 2 \times 10^3 = 2000\,\Omega$

Current $I = 10\,mA = 10 \times 10^{-3}\,A$ or $\dfrac{10}{10^3}\,A$ or $\dfrac{10}{1000}\,A = 0.01\,A$.

From Ohm's law, potential difference, $V = IR = (0.01)(2000) =$ **20 V**

Test your knowledge 7.37

1 A 100 V battery is connected across a resistor and causes a current of 5 mA to flow. Determine the resistance of the resistor. If the voltage is now reduced to 25 V, what will be the new value of the current flowing?

2 What is the resistance of a coil which draws a current of (a) 50 mA and (b) 200 µA from a 120 V supply?

Example 7.67

A coil has a current of 50 mA flowing through it when the applied voltage is 12 V. What is the resistance of the coil?

$$\text{Resistance, } R = \frac{V}{I} = \frac{12}{50 \times 10^{-3}} = \frac{12 \times 10^3}{50} = \frac{12000}{50}$$

$$= \mathbf{240\ \Omega}$$

Table 7.2

Prefix	Name	Meaning	Example
M	mega	multiply by 1 000 000 (i.e. $\times 10^6$)	$2\,M\Omega = 2\,000\,000$ ohms
k	kilo	multiply by 1000 (i.e. $\times 10^3$)	$10\,kV = 10\,000$ volts
m	milli	divide by 1000 (i.e. by 10^{-3})	$25\,mA = \dfrac{25}{1000}\,A$ $= 0.025$ amperes
µ	micro	divide by 1 000 000 (i.e. $\times 10^{-6}$)	$50\,\mu V = \dfrac{50}{1\,000\,000}\,V$ $= 0.00005$ volts

Conductors and insulators

A *conductor* is a material having a low resistance which allows electric current to flow in it. All metals are conductors and some examples include copper, aluminium, brass, platinum, silver, gold and also carbon.

An *insulator* is a material having a high resistance which does not allow electric current to flow in it. Some examples of insulators include plastic, rubber, glass, porcelain, air, paper, cork, mica, ceramics and certain oils.

Electrical power

Power P in an electrical circuit is given by the product of potential difference V and current I. The unit of power is the watt, W. Hence

$$P = V \times I \text{ watts} \tag{7.19}$$

From Ohm's law, $V = IR$. Substituting for V in equation (7.19) gives:

$$P = (IR) \times I$$

i.e.

$$P = I^2R \text{ watts}$$

Also, from Ohm's law, $I = V/R$. Substituting for I in equation (7.19) gives:

$$P = V \times \frac{V}{R}$$

i.e.

$$P = \frac{V^2}{R} \text{ watts}$$

There are thus three possible formulae which may be used for calculating power.

Example 7.68

A 100 W electric light bulb is connected to a 250 V supply. Determine (a) the current flowing in the bulb, and (b) the resistance of the bulb.

Power $P = V \times I$, from which, current $I = P/V$

(a) Current $I = \dfrac{100}{250} = \dfrac{10}{25} = \dfrac{2}{5} = \mathbf{0.4\,A}$

(b) Resistance $R = \dfrac{V}{I} = \dfrac{250}{0.4} = \dfrac{2500}{4} = \mathbf{625\,\Omega}$

Example 7.69

The current/voltage relationship for two resistors A and B is as shown in Figure 7.57. Determine the value of the resistance of each resistor.

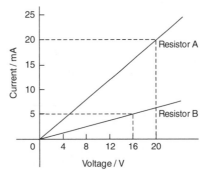

Figure 7.57

For resistor A,

$$R = \frac{V}{I} = \frac{20 \text{ A}}{20 \text{ mA}} = \frac{20}{0.02} = \frac{2000}{2} = \textbf{1000 } \Omega \textbf{ or 1 k} \Omega$$

For resistor B,

$$R = \frac{V}{I} = \frac{16 \text{ V}}{5 \text{ mA}} = \frac{16}{0.005} = \frac{16\,000}{5} = \textbf{3200 } \Omega \textbf{ or 3.02 k} \Omega$$

Example 7.70

The hot resistance of a 240 V filament lamp is 960 Ω. Find the current taken by the lamp and its power rating.

From Ohm's law,

$$\text{current } I = \frac{V}{R} = \frac{240}{960} = \frac{24}{96} = \frac{\textbf{1}}{\textbf{4}} \textbf{ A or 0.25 A}$$

$$\text{Power rating } P = VI = (240) \frac{1}{4} = \textbf{60 W}$$

Electrical Energy

Electrical energy = power × time

If the power is measured in watts and the time in seconds then the unit of energy is watt-seconds or joules. If the power is measured in kilowatts and the time in hours then the unit of energy is kilowatt-hours, often called the 'unit of electricity'. The 'electricity meter' in the home records the number of kilowatt-hours used and is thus an energy meter.

1 Calculate the power dissipated when a current of 4 mA flows through a resistance of 5 kΩ.
2 A current of 5 A flows in the winding of an electric motor, the resistance of the winding being 100 Ω. Determine (a) the p.d. across the winding, and (b) the power dissipated by the coil.
3 Determine the power dissipated by the element of an electric fire of resistance 20 Ω when a current of 10 A flows through it. If the fire is on for 6 hours determine the energy used and the cost if 1 unit of electricity costs 7p.
4 A business uses two 3 kW fires for an average of 20 hours each per week, and six 150 W lights for 30 hours each per week. If the cost of electricity is 7p per unit, determine the weekly cost of electricity to the business.

Example 7.71

A 12 V battery is connected across a load having a resistance of 40 Ω. Determine the current flowing in the load, the power consumed and the energy dissipated in 2 minutes.

$$\text{Current } I = \frac{V}{R} = \frac{12}{40} = \textbf{0.3 A}$$

Power consumed, $P = VI = (12)(0.3) = \textbf{3.6 W}$.

Energy dissipated = power $\times$ time = $(3.6\,\text{W})(2 \times 60\,\text{s})$ = **432 J** (since 1 J = 1 W s).

Example 7.72

Electrical equipment in an office takes a current of 13 A from a 240 V supply. Estimate the cost per week of electricity if the equipment is used for 30 hours each week and 1 kWh of energy costs 7p.

Power = VI watts = $240 \times 13 = 3120\,\text{W} = 3.12\,\text{kW}$.

Energy used per week = power $\times$ time

$$= (3.12\,\text{kW}) \times (30\,\text{h}) = 93.6\,\text{kW h}.$$

Cost at 7p per kWh = $93.6 \times 7 = 655.2\,\text{p}$. Hence

weekly cost of electricity = **£6.55**

Main effects of electric current

The three main effects of an electric current are:

(a) magnetic effect
(b) chemical effect
(c) heating effect.

Some practical applications of the effects of an electric current include:

Magnetic effect: bells, relays, motors, generators, transformers, telephones, car ignition and lifting magnets

Chemical effect: primary and secondary cells and electroplating

Heating effect: cookers, water heaters, electric fires, irons, furnaces, kettles and soldering irons.

Fuses

A *fuse* is used to prevent overloading of electrical circuits. The fuse, which is made of material having a low melting point, utilizes the heating effect of an electric current. A fuse is placed in an electrical circuit and if the current becomes too large the fuse wire melts and so breaks the circuit. A circuit diagram symbol for a fuse is shown in Figure 7.55.

If 5 A, 10 A and 13 A fuses are available, state which is most appropriate for the following appliances which are both connected to a 240 V supply.
(a) Electric toaster having a power rating of 1 kW
(b) Electric fire having a power rating of 3 kW.

Resistance and resistivity

The resistance of an electrical conductor depends on four factors, these being: (a) the length of the conductor, (b) the cross-sectional area of the conductor, (c) the type of material and (d) the temperature of the material.

Resistance, R, is directly proportional to length, l, of a conductor, i.e. $R \propto l$. Thus, for example, if the length of a piece of wire is doubled, then the resistance is doubled.

Resistance, R, is inversely proportional to cross-sectional area, a, of a conductor, i.e. $R \propto 1/a$. Thus, for example, if the cross-sectional area of a piece of wire is doubled then the resistance is halved.

Since $R \propto l$ and $R \propto 1/a$ then $R \propto l/a$. By inserting a constant of proportionality into this relationship the type of material used may be taken into account. The constant of proportionality is known as the *resistivity* of the material and is given the symbol ρ (rho). Thus

$$\text{resistance } R = \frac{\rho l}{a} \text{ ohms}$$

ρ is measured in ohm metres (Ω m). The value of the resistivity is that resistance of a unit cube of the material measured between opposite faces of the cube.

Resistivity varies with temperature and some typical values of resistivities measured at about room temperature are given below:

Copper	$1.7 \times 10^{-8}\,\Omega\,\text{m}$	(or $0.017\,\mu\Omega\,\text{m}$)
Aluminium	$2.6 \times 10^{-8}\,\Omega\,\text{m}$	(or $0.026\,\mu\Omega\,\text{m}$)
Carbon (graphite)	$10 \times 10^{-8}\,\Omega\,\text{m}$	($0.10\,\mu\Omega\,\text{m}$)
Glass	$1 \times 10^{10}\,\Omega\,\text{m}$	
Mica	$1 \times 10^{13}\,\Omega\,\text{m}$	

Note that good conductors of electricity have a low value of resistivity and good insulators have a high value of resistivity.

Test your knowledge 7.40

1 A wire of length 8 m and cross-sectional area 3 mm² has a resistance of 0.16 Ω. If the wire is drawn out until its cross-sectional area is 1 mm², determine the resistance of the wire.
2 The resistance of 1.5 km of wire of cross-sectional area 0.17 mm² is 150 Ω. Determine the resistivity of the wire.
3 Determine the resistance of 1200 m of copper cable having a diameter of 12 mm if the resistivity of copper is $1.7 \times 10^{-8}\,\Omega\,\text{m}$.

Example 7.73

The resistance of a 5 m length of wire is 600 Ω. Determine (a) the resistance of an 8 m length of the same wire, and (b) the length of the same wire when the resistance is 420 Ω.

(a) Resistance, R, is directly proportional to length, l, i.e., $R \propto l$. Hence, $600\,\Omega \propto 5$ m or $600 = (k)(5)$, where k is the coefficient of proportionality. Hence

$$k = \frac{600}{5} = 120$$

When the length l is 8 m, then

$$\text{resistance } R = kl = (120)(8) = \textbf{960}\,\boldsymbol{\Omega}$$

(b) When the resistance is 420 Ω, $420 = kl$, from which

$$\text{length } l = \frac{420}{k} = \frac{420}{120} = \textbf{3.5 m}$$

Temperature coefficient of resistance

In general, as the temperature of a material increases, most conductors increase in resistance, insulators decrease in resistance, while the resistance of some special alloys remain almost constant.

The *temperature coefficient of resistance* of a material is the increase in the resistance of a $1\,\Omega$ resistor of that material when it is subjected to a rise of temperature of $1°C$. The symbol used for the temperature coefficient of resistance is α (alpha). Thus, if some copper wire of resistance $1\,\Omega$ is heated through $1°C$ and its resistance is then measured as $1.0043\,\Omega$ then $\alpha = 0.0043\,\Omega/\Omega\ °C$ for copper. The units are usually expressed only as 'per °C', i.e. $\alpha = 0.0043/°C$ for copper. If the $1\,\Omega$ resistor of copper is heated through $100°C$ then the resistance at $100°C$ would be $1 + (100 \times 0.0043) = 1.43\,\Omega$.

Some typical values of temperature coefficient of resistance measured at $0°C$ are given below:

Copper	0.0043/°C	Aluminium	0.0038/°C
Nickel	0.0062/°C	Carbon	−0.00048/°C
Constantan	0	Eureka	0.00001/°C

(Note that the negative sign for carbon indicates that its resistance falls with increase of temperature.)

If the resistance of a material at $0°C$ is known the resistance at any other temperature can be determined from:

$$R_\theta = R_0(1 + \alpha_0\theta)$$

where R_0 = resistance at $0°C$
R_θ = resistance at temperature $\theta°C$
α_0 = temperature coefficient of resistance at $0°C$

Example 7.74

A coil of copper wire has a resistance of $100\,\Omega$ when its temperature is $0°C$. Determine its resistance at $100°C$ if the temperature coefficient of resistance of copper at $0°C$ is $0.0043/°C$.

Resistance $R_\theta = R_0(1 + \alpha_0\theta)$.

Hence resistance at $100°C$ is given by

$$R_{100} = 100[1 + (0.0043)(100)]$$
$$= 100[1 + 0.43] = 100(1.43) = \mathbf{143\,\Omega}$$

Example 7.75

A carbon resistor has a resistance of $1\,k\Omega$ at $0°C$. Determine its resistance at $80°C$. Assume that the temperature coefficient of resistance for carbon at $0°C$ is -0.0005.

Resistance at temperature $\theta°C$ is given by

$$R_\theta = R_0(1 + \alpha_0\theta)$$

i.e.

$$R_\theta = 1000[(1 + (-0.0005)(80)]$$
$$= 1000(1 - 0.040) = 1000(0.96) = \mathbf{960\,\Omega}$$

1 An aluminium cable has a resistance of 27 Ω at a temperature of 35°C. Determine its resistance at 0°C. Take the temperature coefficient of resistance at 0°C to be 0.0038/°C.

2 The resistance of a coil of aluminium wire at 18°C is 200 Ω. The temperature of the wire is increased and the resistance rises to 240 Ω. If the temperature coefficient of resistance of aluminium is 0.0039/°C at 18°C determine the temperature to which the coil has risen.

If the resistance of a material at room temperature (approximately 20°C), R_{20}, and the temperature coefficient at 20°C, α_{20}, are known then the resistance R_θ at temperature θ°C is given by:

$$R_\theta = R_{20}[1 + \alpha_{20}(\theta - 20)]$$

The simple cell

The purpose of an *electric cell* is to convert chemical energy into electrical energy.

A *simple cell* comprises two dissimilar conductors (electrodes) in an electrolyte. Such a cell is shown in Figure 7.58, comprising copper and zinc electrodes. An electric current is found to flow between the electrodes. Other possible electrode pairs exist, including zinc–lead and zinc–iron. The electrode potential (i.e. the p.d. measured between the electrodes) varies for each pair of metals. By knowing the e.m.f. of each metal with respect to some standard electrode the e.m.f. of any pair of metals may be determined.

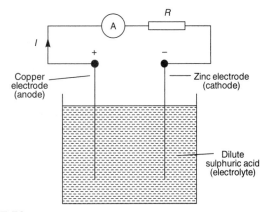

Figure 7.58

E.m.f. and internal resistance of a cell

The *electromotive force* (e.m.f.), *E*, of a cell is the p.d. between its terminals when it is not connected to a load (i.e. the cell is on 'no-load').

The e.m.f. of a cell is measured by using a *high resistance voltmeter* connected in parallel with the cell. The voltmeter must have a high resistance otherwise it will pass current and the cell will not be on no-load. For example, if the resistance of a cell is 1 Ω and that of a voltmeter 1 MΩ then the equivalent resistance of the circuit is 1 MΩ + 1 Ω, i.e. approximately 1 MΩ, hence no current flows and the cell is not loaded.

The voltage available at the terminals of a cell falls when a load is connected. This is caused by the *internal resistance* of the cell which is the opposition of the material of the cell to the flow of current. The internal resistance acts in series with other resistances in the circuit. Figure 7.59 shows a cell of e.m.f. *E* volts and internal resistance, *R*, and *XY* represents the terminals of the cell.

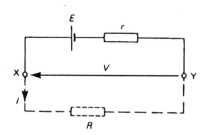

Figure 7.59

When a load (shown as resistance *R*) is not connected, no current flows and the terminal p.d., *V* = *E*. When *R* is connected a current *I* flows which causes a voltage drop in the cell, given by *Ir*. The p.d. available at the cell terminals is less than the e.m.f. of the cell and is given by:

$$V = E - Ir$$

Thus if a battery of e.m.f. 12 volts and internal resistance $0.1 \, \Omega$ delivers a current of 100 A, the terminal p.d. is given by:

$$V = 12 - (100)(0.01)$$

$$= 12 - 1 = 11 \, \text{V}$$

When a current is flowing in the direction shown in Figure 7.59 the cell is said to be *discharging* (*E* > *V*).

When a current flows in the opposite direction to that shown in Figure 7.59 the cell is said to be *charging* (*V* > *E*).

A battery is a combination of more than one cell. The cells in a battery may be connected in series or in parallel.

(i)   For cells connected in series:

Total e.m.f. = sum of cell's e.m.f.s

Total internal resistance = sum of cell's internal resistance

(ii) For cells connected in parallel:

If each cell has the same e.m.f. and internal resistance:

Total e.m.f. = e.m.f. of one cell

Total internal resistance of *n* cells

$$= \frac{1}{n} \times \text{internal resistance of one cell}$$

Example 7.76

Eight cells, each with an internal resistance of $0.2 \, \Omega$ and an e.m.f. of 2.2 V are connected (a) in series, (b) in parallel. Determine the e.m.f. and the internal resistance of the batteries so formed.

(a) When connected in series, total e.m.f. = sum of cell's e.m.f.

$$= 2.2 \times 8 = \textbf{17.6 V}$$

Total internal resistance = sum of cell's internal resistance

$$= 0.2 \times 8 = \textbf{1.6} \, \boldsymbol{\Omega}$$

(b) When connected in parallel, total e.m.f. = e.m.f. of one cell

$$= \textbf{2.2 V}$$

$$\text{Total internal resistance of 8 cells} = \frac{1}{8} \times \text{internal resistance of one cell}$$

$$= \frac{1}{8} \times 0.2 = \textbf{0.025 } \Omega$$

1 A cell has an internal resistance of 0.03 Ω and an e.m.f. of 2.2 V. Calculate its terminal p.d. if it delivers (a) 1 A, (b) 20 A, (c) 50 A.

2 Ten 1.5 V cells, each having an internal resistance of 0.2 Ω, are connected in series to a load of 58 Ω. Determine (a) the current flowing in the circuit and (b) the p.d. at the battery terminals.

Example 7.77

A cell has an internal resistance of 0.02 Ω and an e.m.f. of 2.0 V. Calculate its terminal p.d. if it delivers (a) 5 A, (b) 50 A.

(a) Terminal p.d., $V = E - Ir$ where E = e.m.f. of cell, I = current flowing and r = internal resistance of cell. E = 2.0 V, I = 5 A and r = 0.02 Ω, hence $V = 2.0 - (5)(0.2) = 2.0 - 0.1 = \textbf{1.9 V}$

(b) When the current is 50 A, terminal p.d. is given by

$$V = E - Ir = 2.0 - 50(0.02)$$

i.e. $V = 2.0 - 1.0 = \textbf{1.0 V}$

Thus the terminal p.d. decreases as the current drawn increases.

Primary cells

Primary cells cannot be recharged, that is, the conversion of chemical energy to electrical energy is irreversible and the cell cannot be used once the chemicals are exhausted. Examples of primary cells include the Leclanché cell and the mercury cell.

Activity 7.2

Briefly describe, with a diagram,

(a) a Leclanché cell
(b) a mercury cell

Give typical applications of each, together with their advantages and disadvantages.

Secondary cells

Secondary cells can be recharged after use, that is, the conversion of chemical energy to electrical energy is reversible and the cell may be used many times. Examples of secondary cells include the lead–acid cell and alkaline cells. Practical applications of such cells include car batteries, telephone circuits and for traction purposes – such as milk delivery vans and fork lift trucks.

Activity 7.3

A small engineering company, Alpha Power Tools, is about to embark on the design and manufacture of a range of portable electrically powered tools. You have been asked to advise the company about the available types of battery cell and make recommendations about the type that should be used as the low-voltage power source that will become integral within each tool. Furthermore, the company wishes to standardize on only one type of battery cell. Which type would you recommend and why?

Prepare a briefing pack for the board of directors and include appropriate visual aids, charts, diagrams and handouts. Present your recommendations in the form of a verbal presentation lasting no more than 10 minutes.

Series circuits

Figure 7.60 shows three resistors, R_1, R_2 and R_3 connected end to end, i.e. in series, with a battery source of V volts. Since the circuit is closed a current I will flow and the p.d. across each resistor may be determined from the voltmeter readings V_1, V_2 and V_3.

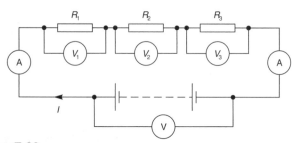

Figure 7.60

In a series circuit:

(a) the current I is the same in all parts of the circuit and hence the same reading is found on each of the ammeters shown, and
(b) the sum of the voltages V_1, V_2 and V_3 is equal to the total applied voltage, V, i.e.

$$V = V_1 + V_2 + V_3$$

From Ohm's law:

$$V_1 = IR_1, V_2 = IR_2, V_3 = IR_3 \text{ and } V = IR$$

where R is the total circuit resistance.

Since $V = V_1 + V_2 + V_3$, then $IR = IR_1 + IR_2 + IR_3$. Dividing throughout by I gives

$$R = R_1 + R_2 + R_3$$

Thus for a series circuit, the total resistance is obtained by adding together the values of the separate resistances.

Example 7.78

For the circuit shown in Figure 7.61, determine (a) the battery voltage V, (b) the total resistance of the circuit, and (c) the values of resistance of resistors R_1, R_2 and R_3, given that the p.d.s across R_1, R_2 and R_3 are 5 V, 2 V and 6 V, respectively.

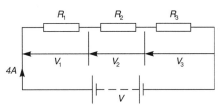

Figure 7.61

(a) Battery voltage $V = V_1 + V_2 + V_3$

$$= 5 + 2 + 6 = \textbf{13 V}$$

(b) Total circuit resistance $R = \dfrac{V}{I} = \dfrac{13}{4} = \textbf{3.25 }\boldsymbol{\Omega}$

(c) Resistance $R_1 = \dfrac{V_1}{I} = \dfrac{5}{4} = \textbf{1.25 }\boldsymbol{\Omega}$

Resistance $R_2 = \dfrac{V_2}{I} = \dfrac{2}{4} = \textbf{0.5 }\boldsymbol{\Omega}$

Resistance $R_3 = \dfrac{V_3}{I} = \dfrac{6}{4} = \textbf{1.5 }\boldsymbol{\Omega}$

(Check: $R_1 + R_2 + R_3 = 1.25 + 0.5 + 1.5 = 3.25\,\Omega = R$)

Example 7.79

For the circuit shown in Figure 7.62, determine the p.d. across resistor R_3. If the total resistance of the circuit is 100 Ω, determine the current flowing through resistor R_1. Find also the value of resistor R_2.

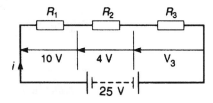

Figure 7.62

p.d. across R_3, $V_3 = 25 - 10 - 4 = \textbf{11 V}$

$$\text{Current } I = \frac{V}{R} = \frac{25}{100} = \textbf{0.25 A}$$

which is the current flowing in each resistor.

$$\text{Resistance } R_2 = \frac{V_2}{I} = \frac{4}{0.25} = \textbf{16 }\boldsymbol{\Omega}$$

Test your knowledge 7.43

A 12 V battery is connected in a circuit having three series-connected resistors having resistance of 4 Ω, 9 Ω and 11 Ω. Determine the current flowing through, and the p.d. across, the 9 Ω resistor. Find also the power dissipated in the 11 Ω resistor.

Potential divider

The voltage distribution for the circuit shown in Figure 7.63 is given by:

$$V_1 = \frac{R_1}{R_1 + R_2} V \qquad V_2 = \frac{R_2}{R_1 + R_2} V$$

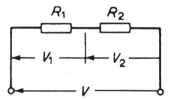

Figure 7.63

The circuit shown in Figure 7.64 is often referred to as a *potential divider* circuit. Such a circuit can consist of a number of similar elements in series connected across a voltage source, voltages being taken from connections between the elements. Frequently the divider consists of two resistors as shown in Figure 7.64, where

$$V_{OUT} = \frac{R_2}{R_1 + R_2} V_{IN}$$

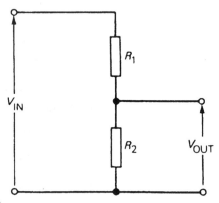

Figure 7.64

Example 7.80

Determine the value of voltage *V* as shown in Figure 7.65.

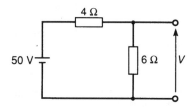

Figure 7.65

Two resistors are connected in series across a 24 V supply and a current of 3 A flows in the circuit. If one of the resistors has a resistance of 2 Ω determine (a) the value of the other resistor, and (b) the p.d. across the 2 Ω resistor. If the circuit is connected for 50 hours, how much energy is used?

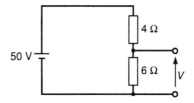

Figure 7.66

Figure 7.65 may be redrawn as shown in Figure 7.66, and

$$\text{voltage } V = \frac{6}{6 + 4} \ (50) = \mathbf{30\,V}$$

Parallel networks

Figure 7.67 shows three resistors, R_1, R_2 and R_3 connected across each other, i.e. in parallel, across a battery source of V volts.

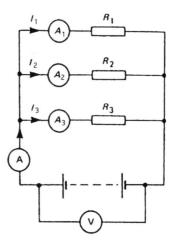

Figure 7.67

In a parallel circuit:

(a) the sum of the currents I_1, I_2 and I_3 is equal to the total circuit current, I, i.e.

$$I = I_1 + I_2 + I_3 \qquad \text{and}$$

(b) the source p.d., V volts, is the same across each of the resistors.

From Ohm's law:

$$I_3 = \frac{V}{R_1}, \quad I_2 = \frac{V}{R_2}, \quad I_3 = \frac{V}{R_3} \quad \text{and} \quad I = \frac{V}{R}$$

where R is the total circuit resistance.

Since

$$I = I_1 + I_2 + I_3$$

then

$$\frac{V}{R} = \frac{V}{R_1} + \frac{V}{R_2} + \frac{V}{R_3}$$

Dividing throughout by V gives

$$\frac{1}{R} = \frac{1}{R_1} + \frac{1}{R_2} + \frac{1}{R_3}$$

This equation must be used when finding the total resistance R of a parallel circuit. For the special case of *two resistors in parallel*

$$\frac{1}{R} = \frac{1}{R_1} + \frac{1}{R_2} = \frac{R_2 + R_1}{R_1 R_2}$$

Hence

$$R = \frac{R_1 R_2}{R_1 + R_2} \quad \text{i.e.} \quad \frac{\text{product}}{\text{sum}}$$

Example 7.81

For the circuit shown in Figure 7.68, determine (a) the reading on the ammeter, and (b) the value of resistor R_2

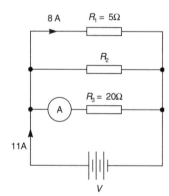

Figure 7.68

P.d. across R_1 is the same as the supply voltage V.

Hence supply voltage, $V = 8 \times 5 = 40\,V$.

(a) Reading on ammeter

$$I = \frac{V}{R_3} = \frac{40}{20} = \textbf{2 A}$$

(b) Current flowing through $R_2 = 11 - 8 - 2 = 1\,A$, hence

$$R_2 = \frac{V}{I_2} = \frac{40}{1} = \textbf{40 } \Omega$$

Example 7.82

For the circuit shown in Figure 7.69, find (a) the value of the supply voltage V and (b) the value of current I.

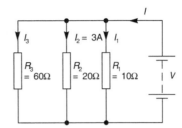

Figure 7.69

(a) P.d. across $20\,\Omega$ resistor = $I_2 R_2 = 3 \times 20 = 60\,\text{V}$, hence supply voltage **$V = 60\,\text{V}$** since the circuit is connected in parallel.

(b) Current $I_1 = \dfrac{V}{R_1} = \dfrac{60}{10} = 6\,\text{A};$ **$I_2 = 3\,\text{A}$**

$$I_3 = \frac{V}{R_3} = \frac{60}{60} = 1\,\text{A}$$

Current $I = I_1 + I_2 + I_3$ and hence $I = 6 + 3 + 1 = \textbf{10 A}$

Alternatively $\dfrac{1}{R} = \dfrac{1}{60} + \dfrac{1}{20} + \dfrac{1}{10} = \dfrac{1 + 3 + 6}{60} = \dfrac{10}{60}$

Hence total resistance $R = \dfrac{60}{10} = 6\,\Omega$

Current $I = \dfrac{V}{R} = \dfrac{60}{6} = \textbf{10 A}$

Test your knowledge 7.45

1 Two resistors, of resistance $3\,\Omega$ and $6\,\Omega$, are connected in parallel across a battery having a voltage of 12 V. Determine (a) the total circuit resistance and (b) the current flowing in the $3\,\Omega$ resistor.

2 Given four $1\,\Omega$ resistors, state how they must be connected to give an overall resistance of (a) $\frac{1}{4}\,\Omega$, (b) $1\,\Omega$, (c) $\frac{1}{3}\,\Omega$, (d) $2\frac{1}{2}\,\Omega$, all four resistors being connected in each case.

3 Resistances of $10\,\Omega$, $20\,\Omega$ and $30\,\Omega$ are connected (a) in series and (b) in parallel to a 240 V supply. Calculate the supply current in each case.

Example 7.83

Find the equivalent resistance for the circuit shown in Figure 7.70.

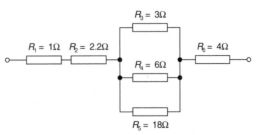

Figure 7.70

R_3, R_4 and R_5 are connected in parallel and their equivalent resistance R is given by:

$$\frac{1}{R} = \frac{1}{3} + \frac{1}{6} + \frac{1}{18} = \frac{6 + 3 + 1}{18} = \frac{10}{18}$$

Hence $R = (18/10) = 1.8\,\Omega$. The circuit is now equivalent to four resistors in series and the equivalent circuit resistance = $1 + 2.2 + 1.8 + 4 = \textbf{9}\,\Omega$.

Current division

For the circuit shown in Figure 7.71, the total circuit resistance, R_T, is given by:

$$R_T = \frac{R_1 R_2}{R_1 + R_2}$$

and

$$V = IR_T = I\frac{R_1 R_2}{R_1 + R_2}$$

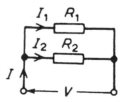

Figure 7.71

$$\text{Current } I_1 = \frac{V}{R_1} = \frac{I}{R_1}\frac{R_1 R_2}{R_1 + R_2}$$

$$= \frac{R_2}{R_1 + R_2}(I)$$

Similarly

$$\text{Current } I_2 = \frac{V}{R_2} = \frac{I}{R_2}\frac{R_1 R_2}{R_1 + R_2}$$

$$= \frac{R_1}{R_1 + R_2}(I)$$

Summarizing, with reference to Figure 7.71

$$I_1 = \frac{R_2}{R_1 + R_2}(I) \quad \text{and} \quad I_2 = \frac{R_1}{R_1 + R_2}(I)$$

Example 7.84

For the series-parallel arrangement shown in Figure 7.72, find (a) the supply current, (b) the current flowing through each resistor and (c) the p.d. across each resistor.

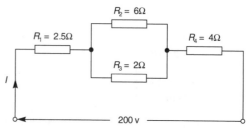

Figure 7.72

(a) The equivalent resistance R_x of R_2 and R_3 in parallel is:

$$R_x = \frac{6 \times 2}{6 + 2} = \frac{12}{8} = 1.5\,\Omega$$

The equivalent resistance R_T of R_1, R_x and R_4 in series is:

$$R_T = 2.5 + 1.5 + 4 = 8\,\Omega$$

Supply current

$$I = \frac{V}{R_T} = \frac{200}{8} = \textbf{25 A}$$

(b) The current flowing through R_1 and R_4 is 25 A

The current flowing through R_2 is

$$\frac{R_3}{R_2 + R_3}\,I = \frac{2}{6 + 2}\,25 = \textbf{8.25 A}$$

The current flowing through R_3 is

$$\frac{R_3}{R_2 + R_3}\,I = \frac{6}{6 + 2}\,25 = \textbf{18.75 A}$$

(Note that the currents flowing through R_2 and R_3 must add up to the total current flowing into the parallel arrangement, i.e. 25 A.)

(c) The equivalent circuit of Figure 7.72 is shown in Figure 7.73.

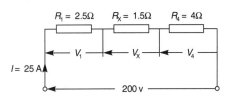

Figure 7.73

p.d. across R_1, i.e. $V_1 = IR_1 = (25)(2.5) = \textbf{62.5 V}$
p.d. across R_x, i.e. $V_x = IR_x = (25)(1.5) = \textbf{37.5 V}$
p.d. across R_4, i.e. $V_4 = IR_4 = (25)(4) = \textbf{100 V}$
Hence the p.d. across R_2 = p.d. across R_3 = **37.5 V**

For the circuit shown in Figure 7.74 calculate (a) the value of resistor R_x such that the total power dissipated in the circuit is 2.5 kW, (b) the current flowing in each of the four resistors.

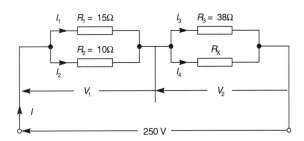

Figure 7.74

Wiring lamps in series and in parallel

Series connection

Figure 7.75 shows three lamps, each rated at 240 V, connected in series across a 240 V supply.

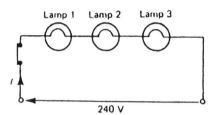

Figure 7.75

(i)   Each lamp has only (240/3) V, i.e. 80 V across it and thus each lamp glows dimly.

(ii) If another lamp of similar rating is added in series with the other three lamps, then each lamp now has (240/4) V, i.e. 60 V across it and each now glows even more dimly.

(iii) If a lamp is removed from the circuit or if a lamp develops a fault (i.e. an open circuit) or if the switch is opened then the circuit is broken, no current flows, and the remaining lamps will not light up.

(iv) Less cable is required for a series connection than for a parallel one.

The series connection of lamps is usually limited to decorative lighting such as for Christmas tree lights.

Parallel connection

Figure 7.76 shows three similar lamps, each rated at 240 V, connected in parallel across a 240 V supply.

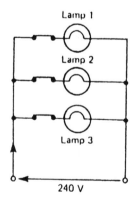

Figure 7.76

(i)   Each lamp has 240 V across it and thus each will glow brilliantly at their rated voltage.

(ii) If any lamp is removed from the circuit or develops a fault (open circuit) or a switch is opened, the remaining lamps are unaffected.

(iii) The addition of further similar lamps in parallel does not affect the brightness of the other lamps.

(iv) More cable is required for parallel connection than for a series one. The parallel connection of lamps is the most widely used in electrical installations.

Example 7.85

If three identical lamps are connected in parallel and the combined resistance is 150 Ω, find the resistance of one lamp.

Let the resistance of one lamp be R, then

$$\frac{1}{150} = \frac{1}{R} + \frac{1}{R} + \frac{1}{R} = \frac{3}{R}$$

from which, $R = 3 \times 150 = \textbf{450 Ω}$

Introduction to Kirchhoff's laws

More complex d.c. circuits cannot be solved by Ohm's law and the formulae for series and parallel resistors alone. Kirchhoff (a German physicist) developed two laws which further help the determination of unknown currents and voltages in d.c. series/parallel networks.

Kirchhoff's current and voltage laws

Current law

At any junction in an electric circuit the total current flowing towards that junction is equal to the total current flowing away from the junction, i.e. $\Sigma I = 0$.

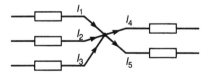

Figure 7.77

Thus referring to Figure 7.77

$$I_1 + I_2 + I_3 = I_4 + I_5$$

or

$$I_1 + I_2 + I_3 - I_4 - I_5 = 0$$

Voltage law

In any closed loop in a network, the algebraic sum of the voltage drops (i.e. products of current and resistance) taken around the loop is equal to the resultant e.m.f. acting in that loop.

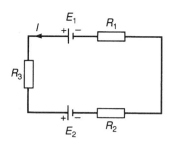

Figure 7.78

Thus referring to Figure 7.78:

$$E_1 - E_2 = IR_2 + IR_2 + IR_3$$

(Note that if current flows away from the positive terminal of a source, that source is considered by convention to be positive. Thus moving anticlockwise around the loop of Figure 7.78, E_1 is positive and E_2 is negative.)

Example 7.86

Determine the value of the unknown currents marked in Figure 7.79.

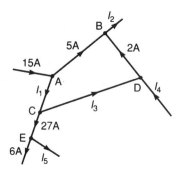

Figure 7.79

Applying Kirchhoff's current law to each junction in turn gives:

For junction A: $15 = 5 + I_1$

Hence $I_1 = \mathbf{10\,A}$

For junction B: $5 + 2 = I_2$

Hence $I_2 = \mathbf{7\,A}$

For junction C: $I_1 = 27 + I_3$

i.e. $10 = 27 + I_3$

Hence $I_3 = 10 - 27 = \mathbf{-17\,A}$

(i.e. in the opposite direction to that shown in Figure 7.79).

For junction D: $I_3 + I_4 = 2$

i.e. $-17 + I_4 = 2$

Hence $I_4 = 17 + 2 = \mathbf{19\,A}$

For junction E: $27 = 6 + I_5$

Hence $I_5 = 27 - 6 = \mathbf{21\,A}$

Example 7.87

Determine the value of e.m.f. E in Figure 7.80.

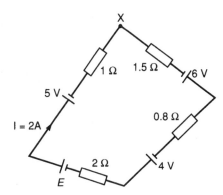

Figure 7.80

Applying Kirchhoff's voltage law and moving clockwise around the loop of Figure 7.80 starting at point X gives:

$$6 + 4 + E - 5 = I(1.5) + I(0.8) + I(2) + I(1)$$
$$5 + E = I(5.3) = 2(5.3)$$

since current I is 2 A.

Hence

$$5 + E = 10.6$$

and

$$\textbf{e.m.f. } E = 10.6 - 5 = \textbf{5.6 V}$$

Example 7.88

Use Kirchhoff's laws to determine the current flowing in the $4\,\Omega$ resistance of the network shown in Figure 7.81.

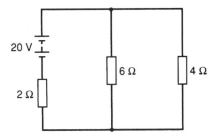

Figure 7.81

Step 1

Label current I_1 flowing from the positive terminal of the 20 V source and current I_2 flowing through the $6\,\Omega$ resistance as shown in Figure 7.82.

By *Kirchhoff's current law*, the current flowing in the $4\,\Omega$ resistance must be $(I_1 - I_2)$.

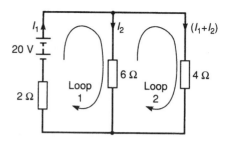

Figure 7.82

Step 2
Label loops 1 and 2 as shown in Figure 7.82 (both loops have been shown clockwise, although they do not need to be in the same direction). *Kirchhoff's voltage law* is now applied to each loop in turn:

$$\text{For loop 1:} \quad 20 = 2I_1 + 6I_2 \tag{1}$$

$$\text{For loop 2:} \quad 0 = 4(I_1 - I_2) - 6I_2 \tag{2}$$

Note the zero on the left-hand side of equation (2) since there is no voltage source in loop 2. Note also the minus sign in front of $6I_2$. This is because loop 2 is moving through the $6\,\Omega$ resistance in the opposite direction to current I_2.
Equation (2) simplifies to:

$$0 = 4I_1 - 10I_2 \tag{3}$$

Step 3
Solve the *simultaneous equations* (1) and (3) for currents I_1 and I_2

$$20 = 2I_1 + 6I_2 \tag{1}$$

$$0 = 4I_1 - 10I_2 \tag{3}$$

$2 \times$ equation (1) gives:

$$40 = 4I_1 + 12I_2 \tag{4}$$

Equation (4) − equation (3) gives:

$$40 = 0 + (12I_2 - -10I_2)$$

i.e. $40 = 22I_2$

Hence

$$\text{current } I_2 = \frac{40}{22} = \mathbf{1.818\,A}$$

Substituting $I_2 = 1.818$ into equation (1) gives:

$$20 = 2I_1 + 6(1.818)$$

$$20 = 2I_1 + 10.908$$

and

$$20 - 10.908 = 2I_1$$

from which

$$I_1 = \frac{20 - 10.908}{2} = \frac{9.092}{2} = \mathbf{4.546\,A}$$

Hence the current flowing in the $4\,\Omega$ resistance is $I_1 - I_2$,

i.e. $(4.546 - 1.818)\,A = \mathbf{2.728\,A}$

The currents and their directions are as shown in Figure 7.83.

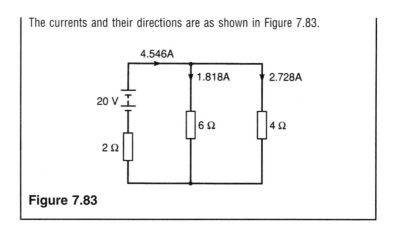

Figure 7.83

Use Kirchhoff's laws to determine the current flowing in each branch of the network shown in Figure 7.84.

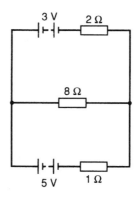

Figure 7.84

Magnetic fields

A *permanent magnet* is a piece of ferromagnetic material (such as iron, nickel or cobalt) which has properties of attracting other pieces of these materials. The area around a magnet is called the *magnetic field* and it is in this area that the effects of the *magnetic force* produced by the magnet can be detected. The magnetic field of a bar magnet can be represented pictorially by the 'lines of force' (or lines of 'magnetic flux' as they are called) as shown in Figure 7.85. Such a field pattern can be produced by placing iron filings in the vicinity of the magnet.

The field direction at any point is taken as that in which the north-seeking pole of a compass needle points when suspended in the field. External to the magnet the direction of the field is north to south.

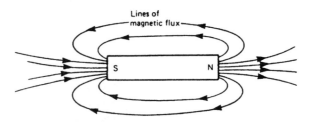

Figure 7.85

The laws of magnetic attraction and repulsion can be demonstrated by using two bar magnets. In Figure 7.86(a), with *unlike pole* adjacent, *attraction* occurs.

In Figure 7.86(b), with *like poles* adjacent, *repulsion* occurs.

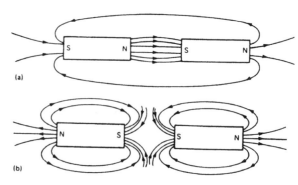

Figure 7.86

Magnetic fields are produced by electric currents as well as by permanent magnets. The field forms a circular pattern with the current-carrying conductor at the centre. The effect is portrayed in Figure 7.87 where the convention adopted is:

(a) current flowing *away* from the viewer is shown by X and can be thought of as the feathered end of a shaft of an arrow;
(b) current flowing *towards* the viewer is shown by • and can be thought of as the tip of an arrow.

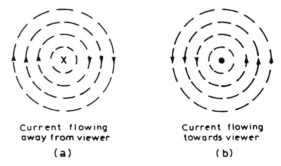

Figure 7.87

The direction of the fields in Figure 7.87 is remembered by the *screw rule* which states: 'If a normal right-hand thread screw is screwed along the conductor in the direction of the current, the direction of rotation of the screw is in the direction of the magnetic field.'

A magnetic field produced by a long coil, or *solenoid*, is shown in Figure 7.88 and is seen to be similar to that of a bar magnet shown in Figure 7.85. If the solenoid is wound on an iron bar an even stronger field is produced. The *direction* of the field produced by current I is determined by a compass and is remembered by either:

(a) the *screw rule*, which states that if a normal right-hand thread screw is placed along the axis of the solenoid and is screwed in the direction of the current it moves in the direction of the solenoid (i.e. points in the direction of the north pole); or

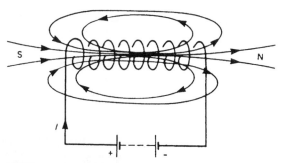

Figure 7.88

(b) the *grip rule*, which states that if the coil is gripped with the right hand with the fingers pointing in the direction of the current, then the thumb, outstretched parallel to the axis of the solenoid, points in the direction of the magnetic field inside the solenoid (i.e. points in the direction of the north pole).

Example 7.89

Figure 7.89 shows a coil of wire wound on an iron core connected to a battery. Sketch the magnetic field pattern associated with the current-carrying coil and determine the polarity of the field.

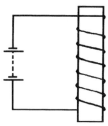

Figure 7.89

The magnetic field associated with the solenoid in Figure 7.89 is similar to the field associated with a bar magnet and is shown in Figure 7.90. The polarity of the field is determined either by the screw rule or by the grip rule. Thus the north pole is at the bottom and the south pole at the top.

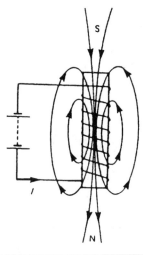

Figure 7.90

Electromagnets

An *electromagnet*, which is a solenoid wound on an iron core, provides the basis of many items of electrical equipment, examples including an electric bell, relays, lifting magnets and telephone receivers.

Activity 7.4

Describe briefly, with the aid of sketches, the principle of operation of

(a) an electric bell
(b) a relay
(c) a lifting magnet
(d) a telephone receiver.

Magnetic flux and flux density

Magnetic flux is the amount of magnetic field (or the number of lines of force) produced by a magnetic source. The symbol for magnetic flux is φ (Greek letter phi). The unit of magnetic flux is the weber, Wb.

Magnetic flux density is the amount of flux passing through a defined area that is perpendicular to the direction of the flux.

$$\text{Magnetic flux density} = \frac{\text{magnetic flux}}{\text{area}}$$

The symbol for magnetic flux density is B. The unit of magnetic flux density is the tesla, T, where $1\,\text{T} = 1\,\text{Wb/m}^2$. Hence

$$B = \frac{\phi}{A} \text{ tesla}$$

where A is the area in square metres.

---

1 Determine the flux density in a magnetic field of cross-sectional area $20\,\text{cm}^2$ having a flux of 3 mWb.

2 The maximum working flux density of a lifting electromagnetic is 1.8 T and the effective area of a pole face is circular in cross-section. If the total magnetic flux produced is 353 mWb, determine the radius of the pole face.

Example 7.90

A magnetic pole face has a rectangular section having dimensions 200 mm by 100 mm. If the total flux emerging from the pole is 150 μWb, calculate the flux density.

Flux $\phi = 150\,\mu\text{Wb} = 150 \times 10^{-6}\,\text{Wb}$.

Cross-sectional area $A = 200 \times 100 = 20\,000\,\text{mm}^2$

$$= 20\,000 \times 10^{-6}\,\text{m}^2.$$

Flux density $B = \dfrac{\phi}{A} = \dfrac{150 \times 10^{-6}}{20\,000 \times 10^{-6}}$

$$= \textbf{0.0075 T or 7.5 mT}$$

Force on a current-carrying conductor

If a current-carrying conductor is placed in a magnetic field produced by permanent magnets, then the fields due to the current-carrying conductor and the permanent magnets interact and cause a force to be exerted on the conductor. The force on the current-carrying conductor in a magnetic field depends upon:

(a) the flux density of the field, B teslas,
(b) the strength of the current, I amperes,
(c) the length of the conductor perpendicular to the magnetic field, l metres, and
(d) the directions of the field and the current.

When the magnetic field, the current and the conductor are mutually at right angles then:

Force $F = BIl$ newtons

When the conductor and the field are at an angle $\Theta°$ to each other then:

Force $F = BIl \sin \Theta$ newtons

Since when the magnetic field, current and conductor are mutually at right angles, $F = BIl$, the magnetic flux density B may be defined by $B = F/Il$, i.e. the flux density is 1 T if the force exerted on 1 m of a conductor when the conductor carries a current of 1 A is 1 N.

Example 7.91

A conductor carries a current of 20 A and is at right angles to a magnetic field having a flux density of 0.9 T. If the length of the conductor in the field is 30 cm, calculate the force acting on the conductor. Determine also the value of the force if the conductor is inclined at an angle of 30° to the direction of the field.

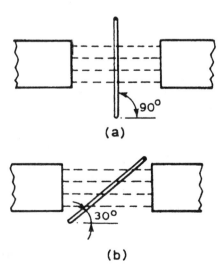

(a)

(b)

Figure 7.91

$B = 0.9\,T$; $I = 20\,A$; $l = 30\,cm = 0.30\,m$. Force $F = BIl = (0.9)(20)(0.30)$ newtons when the conductor is at right angles to the field, as shown in Figure 7.91(a), i.e. $F = 5.4\,N$. When the conductor is inclined at 30° to the field, as shown in Figure 7.91(b), then

Force $F = BIl \sin \Theta$

$F = (0.9)(20)(0.30) \sin 30°$

$F = \textbf{2.7\,N}$

If the current-carrying conductor shown in Figure 7.87(a) is placed in the magnetic field shown in Figure 7.92(a), then the two fields interact and cause a force to be exerted on the conductor as shown in Figure 7.92(b). The field is strengthened above the conductor and weakened below, thus tending to move the conductor downwards. This is the basic principle of operation of the *electric motor* and the *moving-coil instrument*.

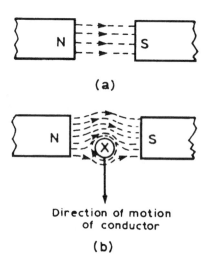

Figure 7.92

The direction of the force exerted on a conductor can be predetermined by using Fleming's left-hand rule (often called the motor rule) which states:

Let the thumb, first finger and second finger of the left hand be extended such that they are all at right-angles to each other [as shown in Figure 7.93]. If the first finger points in the direction of the magnetic field, the second finger points in the direction of the current, then the thumb will point in the direction of the motion of the conductor.

Summarizing:

First finger – Field

SeCond finger – Current

ThuMb – Motion

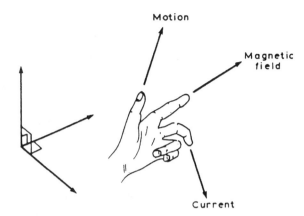

Figure 7.93

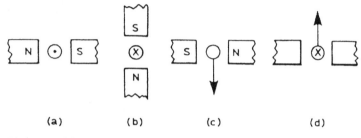

(a)   (b)   (c)   (d)

Figure 7.94

Introduction to electromagnetic induction

When a conductor is moved across a magnetic field so as to cut through the lines of force (flux), an electromotive force (e.m.f.) is produced in the conductor. If the conductor forms part of a closed circuit then the e.m.f. produced causes an electric current to flow round the circuit. Hence an e.m.f. (and thus current) is 'induced' in the conductor as a result of its movement across the magnetic field. This effect is known as *'electromagnetic induction'*.

Figure 7.95(a) shows a coil of wire connected to a centre-zero galvanometer, which is a sensitive ammeter with a zero-current position in the centre of the scale.

(a) When the magnet is moved at constant speed towards the coil (Figure 7.95(a)), a deflection is noted on the galvanometer showing that a current has been produced in the coil.

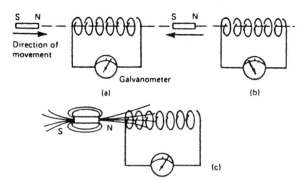

Figure 7.95

(b) When the magnet is moved at the same speed as in (a) but away from the coil the same deflection is noted but is in the opposite direction (see Figure 7.95(b).

(c) When the magnet is held stationary even within the coil no deflection is recorded.

(d) When the coil is moved at the same speed as in (a) and the magnet held stationary the same galvanometer deflection is noted.

(e) When the relative speed is, say, doubled, the galvanometer deflection is doubled.

(f) When a stronger magnet is used, a greater galvanometer deflection is noted.

(g) When the number of turns of wire of the coil is increased, a greater galvanometer deflection is noted.

Figure 7.95(c) shows the magnetic field associated with the magnet. As the magnet is moved towards the coil, the magnetic flux of the magnet moves across, or cuts, the coil. *It is the relative movement of the magnetic flux and the coil that causes an e.m.f. and thus current to be induced in the coil.* This effect is known as *electromagnetic induction*. The laws of electromagnetic induction evolved from experiments such as those described above.

Laws of electromagnetic induction

Faraday's laws of electromagnetic induction state:

(i)   An induced e.m.f. is set up whenever the magnetic field linking that circuit changes.

(ii) The magnitude of the induced e.m.f. in any circuit is proportional to the rate of change of the magnetic flux linking the circuit.

Lenz's law states:

> *The direction of an induced e.m.f. is always such that it tends to set up a current opposing the motion or the change of flux responsible for inducing that e.m.f.*

An alternative method to Lenz's law of determining relative directions is given by *Fleming's Right-hand rule* (often called the geneRator rule) which states:

Let the thumb, first finger and second finger of the right hand be extended such that they are all at right angles to each other [as shown in Figure 7.96]. If the first finger points in the direction of the magnetic field, the thumb points in the direction of motion of the conductor relative to the magnetic field, then the second finger will point in the direction of the induced e.m.f.

Summarizing:

First finger – Field

ThuMb – Motion

SEcond finger – E.m.f.

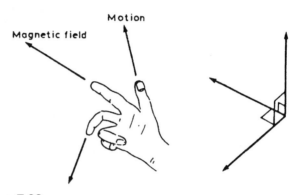

Figure 7.96

In a generator, conductors forming an electric circuit are made to move through a magnetic field. By Faraday's law an e.m.f. is induced in the conductors and thus a source of e.m.f. is created. A generator converts mechanical energy into electrical energy.

The induced e.m.f. E set up between the ends of the conductor shown in Figure 7.97 is given by:

$$E = Blv \text{ volts}$$

where B the flux density is measured in teslas, l the length of conductor in the magnetic field is measured in metres, and v the conductor velocity is measured in metres per second.

If the conductor moves at an angle $\Theta°C$ to the magnetic field (instead of at 90° as assumed above) then

$$E = Blv \sin \Theta$$

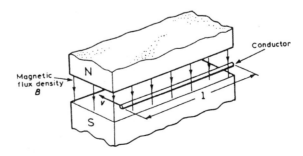

Figure 7.97

Example 7.92

A conductor 300 mm long moves at a uniform speed of 4 m/s at right angles to a uniform magnetic field of flux density 1.25 T. Determine the current flowing in the conductor when (a) its ends are open-circuited, (b) its ends are connected to a load of 20 Ω resistance.

When a conductor moves in a magnetic field it will have an e.m.f. induced in it but this e.m.f. can only produce a current if there is a closed circuit.

$$\text{Induced e.m.f. } E = Blv = (1.25)\,\frac{300}{1000}\,(4) = 1.5\,\text{V}$$

(a) If the ends of the conductor are open-circuited *no current* will flow even though 1.5 V has been induced.
(b) From Ohm's law

$$I = \frac{E}{R} = \frac{1.5}{20} = \textbf{0.075 A or 75 mA}$$

Example 7.93

The diagram shown in Figure 7.98 represents the generation of e.m.f.s. Determine (i) the direction in which the conductor has to be moved in Figure 7.98(a), (ii) the direction of the induced e.m.f. in Figure 7.98(b), (iii) the polarity of the magnetic system in Figure 7.98(c).

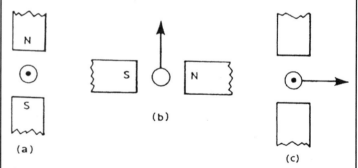

Figure 7.98

The direction of the e.m.f. and thus the current due to the e.m.f. may be obtained by either Lenz's rule or Fleming's <u>R</u>ight-hand rule (i.e. Gene<u>R</u>ator rule).

(i) Using Lenz's law: The field due to the magnet and the field due to the current-carrying conductor are shown in Figure 7.99(a) and are seen to reinforce to the left of the conductor. Hence the force on the conductor is to the right. However Lenz's law says that the direction of the induced e.m.f. is always such as to oppose the effect producing it. *Thus the conductor will have to be moved to the left.*

(ii) Using Fleming's right-hand rule:

<u>F</u>irst finger – <u>F</u>ield, i.e. N → S, or right to left;

Thu<u>M</u>b – <u>M</u>otion, i.e. upwards;

S<u>E</u>cond finger – <u>E</u>.m.f., i.e. *towards the viewer or out of the paper,*
as shown in Figure 7.99(b).

1 At what velocity must a conductor 75 mm long cut a magnetic field of flux density 0.6 T if an e.m.f. of 9 V is to be induced in it? Assume the conductor, the field and the direction of motion are mutually perpendicular.

2 A conductor moves with a velocity of 15 m/s at an angle of (a) 90°, (b) 60°, and (c) 30° to a magnetic field produced between two square-faced poles of side length 2 cm. If the flux leaving a pole face is 5 μWb, find the magnitude of the induced e.m.f. in each case.

(iii) The polarity of the magnetic system of Figure 7.98(c) is shown in Figure 7.99(c) and is obtained using Fleming's right-hand rule.

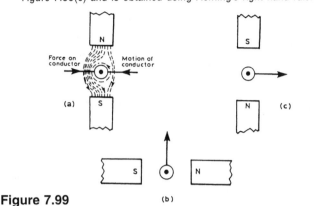

Figure 7.99

Inductance

Inductance is the name given to the property of a circuit whereby there is an e.m.f. induced into the circuit by the change of flux linkages produced by a current change.

When the e.m.f. is induced in the same circuit as that in which the current is changing, the property is called *self-inductance, L*.

When the e.m.f. is induced in a circuit by a change of flux due to current changing in an adjacent circuit, the property is called *mutual inductance, M*. The unit of inductance is the *henry, H*.

A circuit has an inductance of one henry when an e.m.f. of one volt is induced in it by a current changing at the rate of one ampere per second. Induced e.m.f. in a coil of N turns is

$$E = N\left(\frac{\Delta\phi}{t}\right) \text{ volts}$$

where ϕ is the change in flux in webers, and t is the time taken for the flux to change in seconds. Induced e.m.f. in a coil of inductance L henries is

$$E = L\left(\frac{\Delta I}{t}\right) \text{ volts}$$

where I is the change in current in amperes and t is the time taken for the current to change in seconds.

The above equations for e.m.f. E are often stated as $E = -N(\Delta\phi/t)$ and $E = -L(\Delta I/t)$, the minus sign reminding us of its direction (given by Lenz's law). In the following problems the direction of the e.m.f. is assumed.

Example 7.94

Determine the e.m.f. induced in a coil of 200 turns when there is a change of flux of 25 mWb linking with it in 50 ms.

$$\text{Induced e.m.f. } E = N\frac{\Delta\phi}{t} = (200)\frac{25 \times 10^{-3}}{50 \times 10^{-3}} = \textbf{100 volts}$$

1 Calculate the e.m.f. induced in a coil of inductance 12 H by a current changing at the rate of 4 A/s.
2 An e.m.f. of 1.5 kV is induced in a coil when a current of 4 A collapses uniformly to zero in 8 ms. Determine the inductance of the coil.
3 An average e.m.f. of 40 V is induced in a coil of inductance 150 mH when a current of 6 A is reversed. Calculate the time taken for the current to reverse.

Example 7.95

A flux of 400 Wb passing through a 150-turn coil is reversed in 40 ms. Find the average e.m.f. induced.

Since the flux reverses, the flux changes from +400 µWb to −400 µWb, a total change of flux of 800 µWb.

$$\text{Induced e.m.f. } E = N\left(\frac{\Delta\phi}{t}\right) = (150)\,\frac{800 \times 10^{-6}}{40 \times 10^{-3}} =$$

$$\frac{800 \times 150 \times 10^3}{40 \times 10^6}$$

Hence the average e.m.f. induced $E = $ **3 volts**.

Inductance of a coil

If a current changing from 0 to I amperes, produces a flux change from 0 to ϕ webers, then $\Delta I = I$ and $\Delta\phi = \phi$. Then, from above, induced e.m.f.

$$E = \frac{N\phi}{t} = \frac{LI}{t}$$

from which inductance of coil $L = \dfrac{N\phi}{I}$ henrys

Example 7.96

Calculate the coil inductance when a current of 4 A in a coil of 800 turns produces a flux of 5 mWb linking with the coil.

$$\text{For a coil, inductance } L = \frac{N\phi}{I} = \frac{(800)(5 \times 10^{-3})}{4} = \textbf{1 H}$$

Example 7.97

When a current of 1.5 A flows in a coil the flux linking with the coil is 90 µWb. If the coil inductance is 0.60 H calculate the number of turns of the coil.

$$\text{For a coil, } L = \frac{N\phi}{I}. \text{ Thus } N = \frac{LI}{\phi} = \frac{(0.6)(1.5)}{90 \times 10^{-6}} = \textbf{10 000 turns}$$

Mutual inductance

Mutually induced e.m.f. in the second coil is given by

$$E_2 = M\left(\frac{\Delta I_1}{t}\right) \text{ volts}$$

where M is the mutual inductance between two coils in henrys, I_1 is the change in current in the first coil in amperes, and t is the time the current takes to change in the first coil in seconds.

Example 7.98

Calculate the mutual inductance between two coils when a current changing at 200 A/s in one coil induces an e.m.f. of 1.5 V in the other.

Induced e.m.f. $E_2 = M(\Delta I_1/t)$,   or $1.5 = M(200)$.

Thus mutual inductance, $M = \left(\dfrac{1.5}{200}\right) = $ **0.0075 H or 7.5 mH**

Example 7.99

The mutual inductance between two coils is 18 mH. Calculate the steady rate of change of current in one coil to induce an e.m.f. of 0.72 V in the other.

Induced e.m.f. $E_2 = M\dfrac{I_1}{t}$

Hence rate of change of current, $\dfrac{I_1}{t} = \dfrac{E_2}{M} = \dfrac{0.72}{0.018} = $ **40 A/s**

Activity 7.6

A transformer is a device which uses the phenomenon of mutual inductance. Describe briefly its principle of operation. Also derive the relationship between the primary and secondary turns (i.e. the *turns ratio*) and the primary and secondary voltages and currents. Illustrate your answer with typical figures that relate to a small mains transformer.

Introduction to alternating voltages and currents

Electricity is produced by generators at power stations and then distributed by a vast network of transmission lines (called the National Grid system) to industry and for domestic use. It is easier and cheaper to generate *alternating current* (a.c.) than direct current (d.c.) and a.c. is more conveniently distributed than d.c. since its voltage can be readily altered using transformers. Whenever d.c. is needed in preference to a.c., devices called rectifiers are used for conversion.

The a.c. generator

Let a single turn coil be free to rotate at constant angular velocity symmetrically between the poles of a magnet system as shown in Figure 7.100. An e.m.f. is generated in the coil (from Faraday's law)

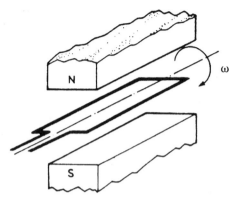

Figure 7.100

which varies in magnitude and reverses its direction at regular intervals. The reason for this is shown in Figure 7.101.

In positions (a), (e) and (i) the conductors of the loop are effectively moving along the magnetic field, no flux is cut and hence no e.m.f. is induced. In position (c) maximum e.m.f. is induced. In position (g), maximum flux is cut and hence maximum e.m.f. is again induced. However, using Fleming's right-hand rule, the induced e.m.f. is in the opposite direction to that in position (c) and is thus shown as $-E$. In positions (b), (d), (f) and (h) some flux is cut and hence some e.m.f. is induced. If all such positions of the coil are considered, in one revolution of the coil, one cycle of alternating e.m.f. is produced as shown. This is the principle of operation of the *a.c. generator* (i.e. the *alternator*).

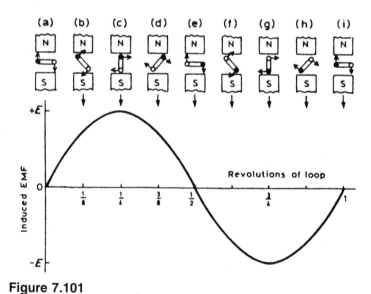

Figure 7.101

Waveforms

If values of quantities which vary with time t are plotted to a base of time, the resulting graph is called a *waveform*. Some typical waveforms are shown in Figure 7.102. Waveforms (a) and (b) are *unidirectional waveforms*, for, although they vary considerably with

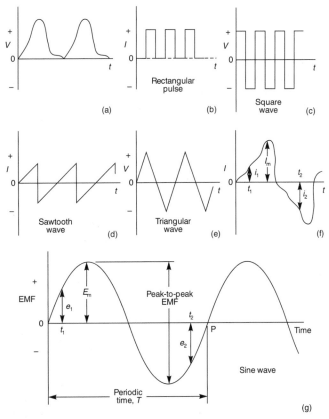

Figure 7.102

time, they flow in one direction only (i.e. they do not cross the time axis and become negative). Waveforms (c) to (g) are called *alternating waveforms* since their quantities are continually changing in direction (i.e. alternately positive and negative).

A waveform of the type shown in Figure 7.102(g) is called a *sine wave*. It is the shape of the waveform of e.m.f. produced by an alternator and thus the mains electricity supply is of 'sinusoidal' form. One complete series of values is called a *cycle* (i.e. from O to P in Figure 7.102(g). The time taken for an alternating quantity to complete one cycle is called the *period* or the *periodic time*, T, of the waveform. The number of cycles completed in one second is called the *frequency*, f, of the supply and is measured in hertz, Hz. The standard frequency of the electricity supply in the UK is 50 Hz.

$$T = \frac{1}{f} \text{ or } f = \frac{1}{T}$$

Example 7.100

Determine the periodic time for frequencies of (a) 50 Hz and (b) 20 kHz.

(a) Periodic time $T = \dfrac{1}{f} = \dfrac{1}{50} = $ **0.02 s** or **20 ms**

(b) Periodic time $T = \dfrac{1}{f} = \dfrac{1}{20\,000} = $ **0.000 05 s** or **50 μs**

---

1 Determine the periodic times
   for the following frequencies:
   (a) 2.5 Hz, (b) 100 Hz,
   (c) 40 kHz
2 An alternating current
   completes 5 cycles in 8 ms.
   What is its frequency?

Example 7.101

Determine the frequencies for periodic times of (a) 4 ms, (b) 4 µs.

(a) Frequency $f = \dfrac{1}{T} = \dfrac{1}{4 \times 10^{-3}} = \dfrac{1000}{4} =$ **250 Hz**

(b) Frequency $f = \dfrac{1}{T} = \dfrac{1}{4 \times 10^{-6}} = \dfrac{1\,000\,000}{4}$

= **250 000 Hz** or **250 kHz** or **0.25 MHz**

A.c. values

Instantaneous values are the values of the alternating quantities at any instant of time. They are represented by small letters, i, v, e, etc. (see Figure 7.102(f) and (g)).

The largest value reached in a half cycle is called the *peak value* or the *maximum value* or the *crest value* or the *amplitude* of the waveform. Such values are represented by V_m, I_m E_m, etc. (see Figure 7.102(f) and (g)). A *peak-to-peak* value of e.m.f. is shown in Figure 7.102(g) and is the difference between the maximum and minimum values in a cycle.

The *average* or *mean value* of a symmetrical alternating quantity (such as a sine wave) is the average value measured over a half cycle (since over a complete cycle the average value is zero.

$$\text{average or mean value} = \frac{\text{area under the curve}}{\text{length of base}}$$

Average values are represented by V_{AV}, I_{AV}, etc.

For a sine wave,

$$\text{average value} = 0.637 \times \text{maximum value}$$
$$\text{(i.e. } 2/\pi \times \text{maximum value)}$$

The *effective value* of an alternating current is that current which will produce the same heating effect as an equivalent direct current. The effective value is called the *root mean square (r.m.s.) value* and whenever an alternating quantity is given, it is assumed to be the r.m.s. value. For example, the domestic mains supply in Great Britain is 240 V and is assumed to mean '240 V r.m.s.'. The symbols used for r.m.s. values are I, V, E, etc. For a non-sinusoidal waveform as shown in Figure 7.103 the r.m.s. value is given by:

$$I = \sqrt{\frac{i_1^2 + i_2^2 + \ldots + i_n^2}{n}}$$

where n is the number of intervals used.

For a sine wave,

$$\text{r.m.s. value} = 0.707 \times \text{maximum value}$$
$$\text{(i.e. } 1/\sqrt{2} \times \text{maximum value)}$$

$$\text{Form factor} = \frac{\text{r.m.s. value}}{\text{average value}}$$

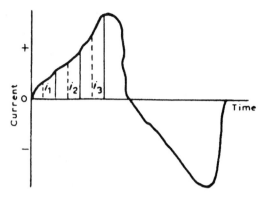

Figure 7.103

For a sine wave, form factor = 1.11.

$$\text{Peak factor} = \frac{\text{maximum value}}{\text{r.m.s. value}}$$

For a sine wave, peak factor = 1.41.

The values of form and peak factors give an indication of the shape of waveforms.

Example 7.102

For the periodic waveform shown in Figure 7.104 determine (i) frequency, (ii) average value over half a cycle, (iii) r.m.s. value, (v) form factor, and (v) peak factor.

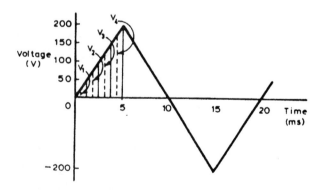

Figure 7.104

(i)   Time for 1 complete cycle = 20 ms = periodic time T,

hence frequency $F = \dfrac{1}{T} = \dfrac{1}{20 \times 10^{-3}} = \dfrac{1000}{20} = $ **50 Hz**

(ii) Area under the triangular waveform for a half cycle

$$= \frac{1}{2} \times \text{base} \times \text{height} = \frac{1}{2} \times (10 \times 10^{-3}) \times 200$$

$$= 1 \text{ volt second}$$

Average value of waveform

$$= \frac{\text{area under curve}}{\text{length of base}} = \frac{1 \text{ volt second}}{10 \times 10^{-3} \text{ second}} = \frac{1000}{10} = \textbf{100 V}$$

(iii)   In Figure 7.104 the first $\frac{1}{4}$ cycle is divided into 4 intervals. Thus

$$\text{r.m.s. value} = \sqrt{\frac{v_1^2 + v_2^2 + v_3^2 + v_4^2}{4}}$$

$$= \sqrt{\frac{25^2 + 75^2 + 125^2 + 175^2}{4}}$$

$$= \textbf{114.6 V}$$

(Note that the greater the numbere of intervals chosen, the greater the accuracy of the result. For example, if twice the number of ordinates as that chosen above are used, the r.m.s. value is found to be 115.6 V.)

(iv)   Form factor $= \dfrac{\text{r.m.s. value}}{\text{average value}} = \dfrac{114.6}{100} = 1.15$

(v)   Peak factor $= \dfrac{\text{maximum value}}{\text{r.m.s. value}} = \dfrac{200}{114.6} = 1.75$

Example 7.103

Calculate the r.m.s. value of a sinusoidal current of maximum value 20 A.

For a sine wave,

$$\text{r.m.s. value} = 0.707 \times \text{maximum value}$$

$$= 0.707 \times 20 = \textbf{14.14 A}$$

Example 7.104

Determine the peak and mean values for a 240 V mains supply.

For a sine wave, r.m.s. value of voltage V = 0.707 $\times$ V_m. A 240 V mains supply means that 240 V is the r.m.s. value. Hence

$$V_m = \frac{V}{0.707} = \frac{240}{0.707} = \textbf{339.5 V} = \text{peak value}$$

Mean value, $V_{AV} = 0.637\ V_M = 0.637 \times 339.5 = \textbf{216.3 V}$

---

1 For the period waveform shown in Figure 7.105 determine (i) its frequency, (ii) average value over half a cycle, (iii) r.m.s. value, (iv) form factor, and (v) peak factor.

2 A supply voltage has a mean value of 150 V. Determine its maximum value and its r.m.s. value.

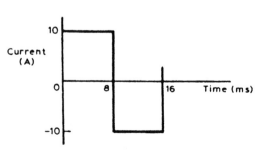

Figure 7.105

Capacitors and capacitance

A *capacitor* is a device capable of storing electrical energy. Figure 7.106 shows a capacitor consisting of a pair of parallel metal plates X and Y separated by an insulator, which could be air. Since the plates are electrical conductors each will contain a large number of mobile electrons. Because the plates are connected to a d.c. supply the electrons on plate X, which have a small negative charge, will be attracted to the positive pole of the supply and will be repelled from the negative pole of the supply on to plate Y. X will become positively charged due to its shortage of electrons whereas Y will have a negative charge due to its surplus of electrons.

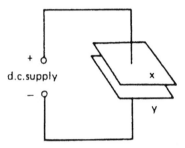

Figure 7.106

The difference in charge between the plates results in a p.d. existing between them, the flow of electrons dying away and ceasing when the p.d. between the plates equals the supply voltage. The plates are then said to be *charged* and there exists an *electric field* between them. Figure 7.107 shows a side view of the plates with the field represented by 'lines of electrical flux'. If the plates are disconnected from the supply and connected together through a resistor the surplus of electrons on the negative plate will flow through the resistor to the positive plate. This is called *discharging*. The current flow decreases to zero as the charges on the plates reduce. The current flowing in the resistor causes it to liberate heat showing that *energy is stored in the electric field*.

A *dielectric* is an insulating medium separating charged surfaces.

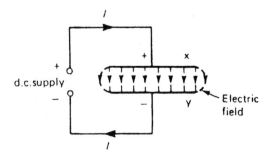

Figure 7.107

Electric field strength, electric force, or voltage gradient,

$$E = \frac{\text{p.d. across dielectric}}{\text{thickness of dielectric}}$$

i.e.

$$E = \frac{V}{d} \text{ volts/m}$$

Charge density

$$\sigma = \frac{\text{charge}}{\text{area of one plate}}$$

i.e.

$$\sigma = \frac{Q}{A} \text{ C/m}^2$$

Charge Q on a capacitor is proportional to the applied voltage, *V*, i.e. $Q \propto V$

$$Q = CV \text{ or } C = \frac{Q}{V}$$

where the constant of proportionality, *C* is the *capacitance*.

The unit of capacitance is the farad, F (or more usually $\mu F = 10^{-6}$ F or $pF = 10^{-12}$ F), which is defined as the capacitance of a capacitor when a p.d. of one volt appears across the plates when charged with one coulomb.

Every system of electrical conductors possesses capacitance. For example, there is capacitance between the conductors of overhead transmission lines and also between the wires of a telephone cable. In these examples the capacitance is undesirable but has to be accepted, minimized or compensated for. There are other situations, such as in capacitors, where capacitance is a desirable property.

The ratio of charge density, σ, to electric field strength, *E*, is called absolute permittivity, ε, of a dielectric. Thus

$$\frac{\sigma}{E} = \varepsilon$$

Permittivity of free space is a constant, given by

$$\varepsilon_o = 8.85 \times 10^{-12} \text{ F/m}$$

Relative permittivity,

$$\varepsilon_r = \frac{\text{flux density of the field in the dielectric}}{\text{flux density of the field in the vacuum}}$$

(ε_r has no units). Examples of the values of ε_r include: air = 1, polythene = 2.3, mica = 3–7, glass = 5–10, ceramics = 6–1000.

Absolute permittivity, $\varepsilon = \varepsilon_0 \varepsilon_r$, thus

$$\frac{\sigma}{E} = \varepsilon_0 \varepsilon_r$$

Example 7.105

Two parallel rectangular plates measuring 20 cm by 40 cm carry an electric charge of 0.2 µC. Calculate the charge density on the plates. If the plates are spaced 5 mm apart and the voltage between them is 0.25 kV, determine the electric field strength.

Charge, $Q = 0.2 \, \mu C = 0.2 \times 10^{-6} \, C$;

area $A = 20 \, cm \times 40 \, cm = 800 \, cm^2 = 800 \times 10^{-4} \, m^2$

$$\text{Charge density, } \sigma = \frac{Q}{A} = \frac{0.2 \times 10^{-6}}{800 \times 10^{-4}}$$

$$= \frac{0.2 \times 10^4}{800 \times 10^6} = \frac{2000}{800} \times 10^{-6}$$

$$= \mathbf{2.5 \, \mu C/m^2}$$

Voltage $V = 0.25 \, kV = 250 \, V$; plate spacing, $d = 5 \, mm = 5 \times 10^{-3} \, m$

$$\text{Electric field strength, } E = \frac{V}{d} = \frac{250}{5 \times 10^{-3}} = \mathbf{50 \, kV/m}$$

Test your knowledge 7.56

1 Two parallel plates having a p.d. of 200 V between them are spaced 0.8 mm apart. What is the electric field strength? Find also the charge density when the dielectric between the plates is (a) air and (b) polythene of relative permittivity 2.3.
2 A direct current of 4 A flows into a previously uncharged 20 µF capacitor for 3 ms. Determine the p.d. between the plates.
3 A 5 µF capacitor is charged so that the p.d. between its plates is 800 V. Calculate how long the capacitor can provide an average discharge current of 2 mA.

Example 7.106

(a) Determine the p.d. across a 4 µF capacitor when charged with 5 mC.
(b) Find the charge on a 50 pF capacitor when the voltage applied to it is 2 kV.

(a) $C = 4 \, \mu F = 4 \times 10^{-6} \, F$; $Q = 5 \, mC = 5 \times 10^{-3} \, C$.

$$\text{Since } C = \frac{Q}{V} \text{ then}$$

$$V = \frac{Q}{C} = \frac{5 \times 10^{-3}}{4 \times 10^{-6}} = \frac{5 \times 10^6}{4 \times 10^3} = \frac{5000}{4}$$

Hence p.d. = **1250 V** or **1.25 kV**

(b) $C = 50 \, pF = 50 \times 10^{-12} \, F$; $V = 2 \, kV = 2000 \, V$;

$$Q = CV = 50 \times 10^{-12} \times 2000 = 0.1 \times 10^{-6}$$

Hence charge = **0.1 µC.**

Energy stored

The energy, W, stored by a capacitor is given by

$$W = \frac{1}{2} CV^2 \text{ joules}$$

1 When a capacitor is connected across a 200 V supply the charge is 4 µC. Find (a) the capacitance, and (b) the energy stored.
2 A capacitor is charged with 10 mC. If the energy stored is 1.2 J find (a) the voltage, and (b) the capacitance.

Example 7.107

(a) Determine the energy stored in a 3 µF capacitor when charged to 400 V. (b) Find also the average power developed if this energy is dissipated in a time of 10 µs.

(a) Energy stored $W = \dfrac{1}{2} CV^2$ joules

$$= \frac{1}{2} \times 3 \times 10^{-6} \times 400^2 = \frac{3}{2}\,16 \times 10^{-2} = \mathbf{0.24\,J}$$

(b) Power $= \dfrac{\text{energy}}{\text{time}} = \dfrac{0.24}{10 \times 10^{-6}}$ watts $= \mathbf{24\,kW}$

Activity 7.7

Briefly describe the construction and operation of a variable capacitor. Illustrate your answer with relevant sketches and diagrams. Obtain the specifications (including maximum and minimum capacitance and working voltage) for a typical variable capacitor. Present your findings in the form of a brief written report.

Effects of capacitance in d.c. circuits

When a d.c. voltage is applied to a capacitor C and resistor R connected in series, there is a short period of time immediately after the voltage is connected during which the current flowing in the circuit and the voltage across C and R are changing. These changing values are called *transients*.

Charging a capacitor
Figure 7.108 shows a capacitor, initially having no charge on its plates, connected in series with resistor R across a d.c. supply. When the switch is closed:

(i) the initial current flowing, i, is given by $i = V/R$, and the capacitor acts as if it is a short-circuit when $v_C = 0$,
(ii) the current then begins to charge the capacitor so that v_C builds up rapidly across the plates,

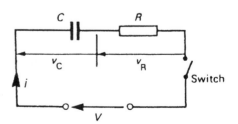

Figure 7.108

(iii) v_R falls to $V - v_C$ (since $V = v_C + v_R$ at all times) and the charging current i reduces to $(V - v_C)/R$,

(iv) eventually the capacitor is charged to the full supply voltage, V, current $i = 0$ and the capacitor acts as an open circuit. Curves of v_C and i against time are shown in Figure 7.109 and are natural or exponential curves of growth and decay.

(v) The *time constant* τ of the *CR* circuit shown in Figure 7.108 is defined as: the time taken for a transient to reach its final state if the initial rate of change is maintained. The time constant τ for any series-connected *C–R* circuit (as in Figure 7.108) is given by:

$$\text{time constant } \tau = CR \text{ seconds}$$

(vi) In the time $\tau = CR$ seconds, v_C rises to 63.2% of its final value V and, in practical situations, v_C rises to within 1% of its final value V in a time equal to 5τ seconds.

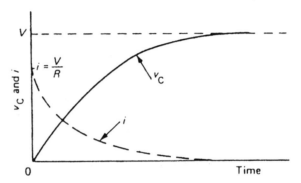

Figure 7.109

Example 7.108

A 20 μF capacitor is to be charged through a 100 kΩ resistor by a constant d.c. supply. Determine (a) the time constant for the circuit, and (b) the additional resistance required to increase the time constant to 5 s.

(a) Time constant, $\tau = CR = 20 \times 10^{-6} \times 100 \times 10^3 = \mathbf{2\,s}$

(b) When the time constant, $\tau = 5\,\text{s}$, then $5 = CR$, i.e. $5 = 20 \times 10^{-6} \times R$, from which, resistance,

$$R = \frac{5}{20 \times 10^{-6}} = \frac{5 \times 10^6}{20} = 250\,000\,\Omega \text{ or } 250\,\text{k}\Omega$$

Thus the additional resistance needed is $(250\,\text{k}\Omega - 100\,\text{k}\Omega) = \mathbf{150\,k\Omega}$

Discharging a capacitor

Figure 7.110 shows a capacitor C fully charged to voltage V, as described above, connected in series with a resistor R. When the

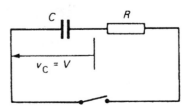

Figure 7.110

switch is closed the initial discharge current is given by $i = V/R$. As the capacitor loses its charge, v_C falls and hence i falls. The result is the natural decay curves shown in Figure 7.111. In the time $t = CR$ seconds, v_C falls to 36.8% of its initial voltage V and, in practical situations, v_C falls to less than 1% of its initial value in a time 5τ seconds.

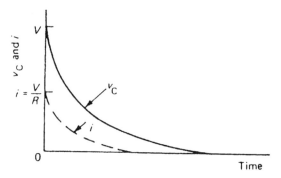

Figure 7.111

When a capacitor has been disconnected from the supply it may still be charged and it may retain this charge for some considerable time. Thus precautions must be taken to ensure that the capacitor is automatically discharged after the supply is switched off. This is done by connecting a high value resistor across the capacitor terminals.

Test your knowledge 7.58

1 A 15 μF capacitor is to be charged through a 300 kΩ resistor by a constant d.c. supply. Determine (a) the time constant of the circuit, and (b) the additional resistance needed to increase the time constant to 7.5 s.
2 A 6 nF capacitor is charged to 600 V before being connected across a 2 kΩ resistor. Determine (a) the initial discharge current, (b) the time constant of the circuit, and (c) the minimum probable time required for the voltage to fall to less than 1% of its initial value.

Example 7.109

A 0.1 μF capacitor is charged to 200 V before being connected across a 4 kΩ resistor. Determine (a) the initial discharge current, (b) the time constant of the circuit, and (c) the minimum time required to the voltage across the capacitor to fall to less than 2 V.

(a) Initial discharge current, $1 = \dfrac{V}{R} = \dfrac{200}{4 \times 10^3}$ = **0.05 A** or **50 mA**

(b) Time constant $\tau = CR = 0.1 \times 10^{-6} \times 4 \times 10^3$

$\qquad$ = **0.0004** or **0.4 ms**

(c) The minimum time for the capacitor voltage to fall to less than 2 V, i.e. less than 2/200 or 1% of the initial value is given by 5τ.

$\qquad 5\tau = 5 \times 0.4 = $ **2 ms**

In a *d.c. circuit*, a capacitor blocks the current except during the times there are changes in the supply voltage.

Effects of capacitance in a.c. circuits

In an a.c. circuit, a capacitor provides opposition to current flow which results in the voltage and current waveforms being 90° out of phase. This opposition is called *capacitive reactance* X_C and is given by:

$$X_C = \frac{1}{2\pi f C} \text{ ohms}$$

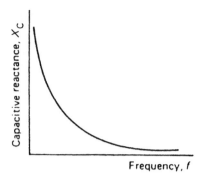

Figure 7.112

A typical graph showing the variation of capacitive reactance with frequency is shown in Figure 7.112. In a purely capacitive a.c. circuit current I is given by:

$$I = \frac{V}{X_C} \text{ amperes}$$

When a capacitor is connected to an a.c. supply its effects are present at all times since the voltage is continually changing. In a purely capacitive a.c. circuit the current waveform leads the voltage waveform by 90°.

Example 7.110

Determine the capacitive reactance of a capacitor of 10 μF when connected to a circuit of frequency (a) 50 Hz, (b) 20 kHz.

(a) Capacitive reactance $X_C = \dfrac{1}{2\pi fC} = \dfrac{1}{2\pi(50)(10 \times 10^{-6})}$

$$= \frac{10^6}{2\pi(50)(10)} = \mathbf{318.3\,\Omega}$$

(b) $X_C = \dfrac{1}{2\pi fC} = \dfrac{1}{2\pi(20 \times 10^3)(10 \times 10^{-6})}$

$$= \frac{10^6}{2\pi(20 \times 10^3)(10)} = \mathbf{0.796\,\Omega}$$

Hence as the frequency is increased from 50 Hz to 20 kHz, X_C decreases from 318.3 Ω to 0.796 Ω (see Figure 7.112).

Test your knowledge 7.59

1 Calculate the capacitive reactance of a 20 μF capacitor when connected to an a.c. circuit of frequency (a) 20 Hz, (b) 500 Hz, (c) 4 kHz.
2 A capacitor has a reactance of 40 Ω when operated on a 50 Hz supply. Determine the value of its capacitance.

Example 7.111

Calculate the current taken by a 23 μF capacitor when connected to a 240 V, 50 Hz supply.

$$\text{Current, } I = \frac{V}{X_C} = \frac{V}{\dfrac{1}{2\pi fC}} = 2\pi fCV$$

$$= 2\pi(50)(23 \times 20^{-6})(240) = \mathbf{1.73\,A}$$

Practical inductors

A component called an *inductor* is used when the property of inductance is required in a circuit. The basic form of an inductor is simply a coil of wire. Factors which affect the inductance of an inductor include:

(i) the number of turns of wire – the more turns the higher the inductance;

(ii) the cross-sectional area of the coil of wire – the greater the cross-sectional area the higher the inductance;

(iii) the presence of a magnetic core – when the coil is wound on an iron core the same current sets up a more concentrated magnetic field and the inductance is increased;

(iv) the way the turns are arranged – a short thick coil of wire has a higher inductance than a long thin one.

Two examples of practical inductors are shown in Figure 7.113, and the standard electrical circuit diagram symbols for air-cored and iron-cored inductors are shown in Figure 7.114.

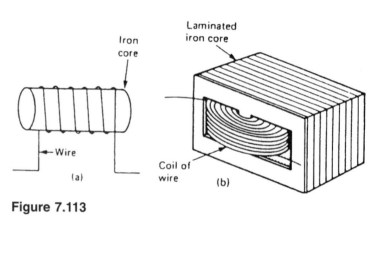

Figure 7.113

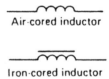

Figure 7.114

An iron-cored inductor is often called a *choke* since, when used in a.c. circuits, it has a choking effect, limiting the current flowing through it.

Inductance is often undesirable in a circuit. To reduce inductance to a minimum the wire may be bent back on itself, as shown in Figure 7.115, so that the magnetizing effect of one conductor is neutralized by that of the adjacent conductor. The wire may be coiled around an insulator, as shown, without increasing the inductance. Standard resistors may be non-inductively wound in this manner.

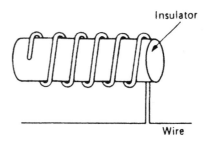

Insulator

Wire

Figure 7.115

Energy stored

An inductor posses an ability to store energy. The energy stored, W, in the magnetic field of an inductor is given by:

$$W = \frac{1}{2} LI^2 \text{ joules}$$

Example 7.112

An 8 H inductor has a current of 3 A flowing through it. How much energy is stored in the magnetic field of the inductor?

Energy stored, $W = \frac{1}{8} LI^2 = \frac{1}{2} (8)(3)^2 =$ **36 joules**

Test your knowledge 7.60

1 An inductor of 20 H has a current of 2.5 A flowing in it. Find the energy stored in the magnetic field of the inductor.
2 A flux of 30 mWb links with a 1200 turn coil when a current of 5 A is passing through the coil. Calculate (a) the inductance of the coil, (b) the energy stored in the magnetic field, and (c) the average e.m.f. induced if the current is reduced to zero in 0.20 seconds.

Example 7.113

A flux of 25 mWb links with a 1500 turn coil when a current of 3 A passes through the coil. Calculate (a) the inductance of the coil, (b) the energy stored in the magnetic field, and (c) the average e.m.f. induced if the current falls to zero in 150 ms.

(a) Inductance, $L = \dfrac{N\phi}{I} = \dfrac{(1500)(25 \times 10^{-3})}{3} =$ **12.5 H**

(b) Energy stored in field, $W = \dfrac{1}{2} LI^2 = \dfrac{1}{2} (12.5)(3)^2 =$ **56.25J**

(c) Induced e.m.f., $E = N\dfrac{\phi}{t} = (1500)\dfrac{25 \times 10^{-3}}{150 \times 10^{-3}} =$ **250 V**

Effects of inductance on a d.c. circuit

A coil of wire possesses both inductance and resistance, each turn of the coil contributing to both its self-inductance and its resistance. It is not possible to obtain pure inductance. An inductive circuit is usually represented as resistance and inductance connected in series.

When a d.c. voltage is connected to a circuit having inductance L and resistance R there is a short period of time immediately after the voltage is connected, during which the current flowing in the circuit and the voltages across L and R are changing. These changing values are called *transients*.

Current growth

(a) When the switch S shown in Figure 7.116 is closed then

$$V = v_L + v_R \qquad (7.20)$$

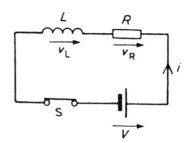

Figure 7.116

(b) The battery voltage V is constant,

$$v_L = L \times \frac{\text{change of current}}{\text{change of time}}$$

i.e. $v_L = L \left(\dfrac{\Delta I}{t} \right)$, and $v_R = iR$

Hence at all times

$$V = L \left(\frac{\Delta I}{t} \right) + iR \qquad (7.21)$$

(c) At the instant of closing the switch, the rate of change of current is such that it induces an e.m.f. in the inductance which is equal and opposite to V.

Hence $V = v_L + 0$, i.e. $v_L = V$.

From equation (7.20), $v_R = 0$ and $i = 0$.

(d) A short time later at time t_1 seconds after closing S, current i_1 is flowing, since there is a rate of change of current initially, resulting in a voltage drop of $i_1 R$ across the resistor. Since V, which is constant, is given by $V = v_L + v_R$, the induced e.m.f. v_L is reduced and equation (7.21) becomes

$$V = L \left(\frac{\Delta I_1}{t_1} \right) + i_1 R$$

(e) A short time later still, say at time t_2 seconds after closing the switch, the current flowing is i_2, and the voltage drop across the resistor increases to $i_2 R$. Since v_R increases, v_L decreases.

(f) Ultimately, some time after closing S, the current flow is entirely limited by R, the rate of change of current is zero and hence v_L is zero. Thus $V = iR$. Under these conditions, steady state current flows, usually signified by I. Thus $I = V/R$, $v_R = IR$ and $v_L = 0$ at steady state conditions.

(g) Curves showing the changes in v_L, v_R and i with time are shown in Figure 7.117 and show that v_L is a maximum value initially

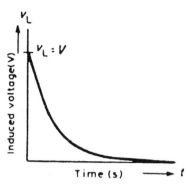

(a) Induced voltage transient

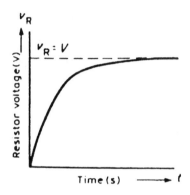

(b) Resistor voltage transient

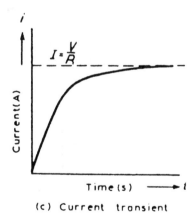

(c) Current transient

Figure 7.117

(i.e. equal to V), decaying exponentially to zero, whereas v_R and i grow from zero to their steady-state values of V and $I = (V/R)$, respectively.

The time taken for the current in an inductive circuit to reach its final value depends on the values of L and R. The ratio L/R is called the *time constant* τ of the circuit, i.e.

$$\tau = \frac{L}{R} \text{ seconds}$$

In the time τ seconds the current rises to 63.2% of its final value I and in practical situations the current rises to within 1% of its final value in a time equal to 5τ seconds.

Current decay

When a series $L - R$ circuit is connected to a d.c. supply, as shown in Figure 7.118, with S in position A, a current $I = V/R$ flows after a short time, creating a magnetic field ($\phi \propto I$) associated with the inductor. When S is moved to position B, the current decreases, causing a decrease in the strength of the magnetic field. Flux linkages occur generating a voltage v_L, equal to $L(\Delta I/t)$. By Lenz's law, this voltage keeps current i flowing in the circuit, its value being limited by R. Since $V = v_L + v_L$, $0 = v_L + v_R$ and $v_L = -v_R$, i.e. v_L and v_R are equal in magnitude but opposite in direction. The current decays exponentially to zero and since v_R is proportional to the current flowing, v_R decays exponentially to zero. Since $v_L = v_R$, v_L also decays exponentially to zero. The curves representing these transients are shown in Figure 7.119. Summarizing, in a d.c. circuit, inductance has no effect on the current except during the time when there are *changes* in the supply current (i.e. immediately following switching on or switching off).

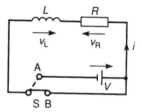

Figure 7.118

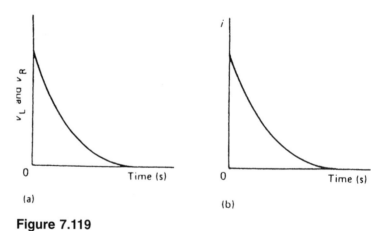

Figure 7.119

Energy stored in the magnetic field of an inductor exists because a current provides the magnetic field. When the d.c. supply is switched off the current falls rapidly, the magnetic field collapses causing a large induced e.m.f. which will either cause an arc across the switch contacts or will break down the insulation between adjacent turns of the coil. The high induced e.m.f. acts in a direction which tends to keep the current flowing, i.e. in the same direction as the applied voltage. The energy from the magnetic field will thus be aided by the supply voltage in maintaining an arc, which could cause severe damage to the switch. To reduce the induced e.m.f. when the

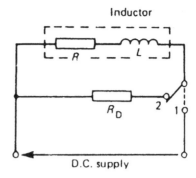

Inductor

Figure 7.120

1 A coil of resistance 20 Ω and inductance 500 mH is connected to a d.c. supply of 160 V. Determine (a) the final value of current, (b) the time constant, (c) the current after a time equal to the time constant from the instant the supply voltage is connected, and (d) the expected time for the current to rise to within 1% of its final value.

2 A coil of inductance 0.5 H and resistance 6 Ω is connected in parallel with a resistance of 15 Ω to a 120 V d.c. supply. Determine (a) the current in the 15 Ω resistance, (b) the steady-state current in the coil, and (c) the current in the 15 Ω resistance at the instant the supply is switched off.

supply switch is opened, a discharge resistor R_D is connected in parallel with the inductor as shown in Figure 7.120. The magnetic field energy is dissipated as heat in R_D and R and arcing at the switch contacts is avoided.

Example 7.114

A coil of inductance 0.04 H and resistance 10 Ω is connected to a 120 V d.c. supply. Determine (a) the final value of current, (b) the time constant of the circuit, (c) the value of current after a time equal to the time constant from the instant the supply voltage is connected, (d) the expected time for the current to rise to within 1% of its final value.

(a) Final steady current $I = \dfrac{V}{R} = \dfrac{120}{10} = \mathbf{12\,A}$

(b) Time constant of the circuit, $\tau = \dfrac{L}{R} = \dfrac{120}{10} = \mathbf{0.004\,s}$ or $\mathbf{4\,ms}$

(c) In the time τ s the current rises to 63.2% of its final value of 12 A, i.e. in 4 ms the current rises to $0.632 \times 12 = \mathbf{7.58\,A}$.

(d) The expected time for the current to rise to within 1% of its final value is given by 5τ, i.e. $5 \times 4 = \mathbf{20\,ms}$.

Effects of inductance in an a.c. circuit

In an a.c. circuit containing inductance, induced e.m.f. $e = L(\Delta I/t)$ is present at nearly all times. The higher the frequency the greater the induced e.m.f. The opposition offered by the induced e.m.f. to an applied voltage tends to limit the current in an a.c. circuit. This opposition is called *inductive reactance*, X_L, and is given by:

$X_L = 2\pi f L$ ohms

where f = frequency in hertz and L = inductance in henrys.

A graph of inductive reactance against frequency is shown in Figure 7.121 and shows that a linear relationship exists between X_L and f.

In a purely inductive a.c. circuit the current waveform lags the voltage waveform by 90°.

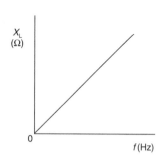

Figure 7.121

Example 7.115

(a) Calculate the reactance of a coil of inductance 0.32 H when it is connected to a 50 Hz supply. (b) A coil has a reactance of 124 Ω in a circuit with a supply of frequency 5 kHz. Determine the inductance of the coil.

(a) Inductive reactance $X_K = 2\pi fL = 2\pi(50)(0.32) = \mathbf{100.5\,\Omega}$

(b) Since $X_L = 2\pi fL$, inductance $L = \dfrac{X_L}{2\pi f} = \dfrac{124}{2\pi(5000)}$ H $= \mathbf{3.95\,mH}$

---

1 Calculate the inductive reactance of a coil of inductance 0.2 H when it is connected to (a) a 50 Hz, (b) a 600 Hz, and (c) a 4 kHz supply.

2 A coil of inductance 0.2 H has an inductive reactance of 754 Ω when connected to an a.c. supply. Calculate the frequency of the supply.

3 A coil of inductance 25 mH is connected to a 200 V, 100 Hz supply. Determine the current flowing.

Example 7.116

A coil has an inductance of 40 mH and negligible resistance. Calculate its inductive reactance and the resulting current if connected to (a) a 240 V, 50 Hz supply, and (b) a 100 V, 1 kHz supply.

(a) Inductive reactance, $X_L = 2\pi fL = 2\pi(50)(40 \times 10^{-3}) = \mathbf{12.57\,\Omega}$

$$\text{Current, } I = \frac{V}{X_L} = \frac{240}{12.57} = \mathbf{19.09\,A}$$

(b) Inductive reactance, $X_L = \pi(1000)(40 \times 10^{-3}) = \mathbf{251.3\,\Omega}$

$$\text{Current, } I = \frac{V}{X_L} = \frac{100}{251.3} = \mathbf{0.398\,A}$$

Introduction to electrical measuring instruments and measurements

Tests and measurements are important in designing, evaluating, maintaining and servicing electrical circuits and equipment. In order to detect electrical quantities such as current, voltage, resistance or power, it is necessary to transform an electrical quantity or condition into a visible indication. This is done with the aid of instruments (or meters) that indicate the magnitude of quantities either by the position of a pointer moving over a graduated scale (called an analogue instrument) or in the form of a decimal number (called a digital instrument).

Analogue instruments

All analogue electrical indicating instruments require three essential devices:

(a) *A deflecting or operating device*. A mechanical force is produced by the current or voltage which causes the pointer to deflect from its zero position.
(b) *A controlling device*. The controlling force acts in opposition to the deflecting force and ensures that the deflection shown on the meter is always the same for a given measured quantity. It also prevents the pointer always going to the maximum deflection. There are two main types of controlling device – spring control and gravity control.
(c) *A damping device*. The damping force ensures that the pointer comes to rest in its final position quickly and without undue oscillation. There are three main types of damping used – eddy-current damping, air-friction damping and fluid-friction damping.

There are basically two types of scale, linear and non-linear. A *linear scale* is shown in Figure 7.122(a), where the divisions or graduations are evenly spaced. The voltmeter shown has a range 0–100 V, i.e. a full-scale deflection (f.s.d.) of 100 V. A *non-linear scale* is shown in Figure 7.122(b). The scale is cramped at the beginning and the graduations are uneven throughout the range. The ammeter shown has a f.s.d. of 10 A.

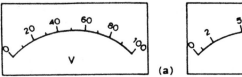

Figure 7.122

Shunts and multipliers

An *ammeter*, which measures current, has a low resistance (ideally zero) and must be connected in series with the circuit.

A *voltmeter*, which measures p.d., has a high resistance (ideally infinite) and must be connected in parallel with the part of the circuit whose p.d. is required.

There is no difference between the basic instrument used to measure current and voltage since both use a milliammeter as their basic part. This is a sensitive instrument which gives f.s.d. for currents of only a few milliamperes. When an ammeter is required to measure currents of larger magnitude, a proportion of the current is diverted through a low-value resistance connected in parallel with the meter. Such a diverting resistor is called a *shunt*.

From Figure 7.123(a), $V_{PQ} = V_{RS}$. Hence $I_a r_a = I_S R_S$. Thus the value of the shunt

$$R_S = \frac{I_a r_a}{I_s} \text{ ohms}$$

Table 7.3

	Moving-coil	*Moving-iron*	*Moving-coil rectifier*
Suitable for measuring	Direct current and voltages	Direct and alternating currents and voltages (reading in r.m.s. value)	Alternating current and voltage (reads average value but scale is adjusted to give r.m.s. value for sinusoidal waveforms)
Scale	Linear	Non-linear	Linear
Method of control	Hairsprings	Hairsprings	Hairsprings
Method of damping	Eddy current	Air	Eddy current
Frequency limits	–	20–200 Hz	20–100 kHz
Advantages	1 Linear scale 2 High sensitivity 3 Well shielded from stray magnetic fields 4 Lower power consumption	1 Robust construction 2 Relatively cheap 3 Measures d.c. and a.c. 4 In frequency range 20–100 Hz reads r.m.s. correctly regardless of supply waveform	1 Linear scale 2 High sensitivity 3 Well shielded from stray magnetic fields 4 Lower power consumption 5 Good frequency range
Disadvantages	1 Only suitable for d.c. 2 More expensive than moving-iron type 3 Easily damaged	1 Non-linear scale 2 Affected by stray magnetic fields 3 Hysteresis errors in d.c. circuits 4 Liable to temperature errors 5 Due to the inductance of the solenoid, readings can be affected by variation of frequency	1 More expensive than moving-iron type 2 Errors caused when supply is non-sinusoidal

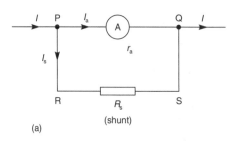

(a)

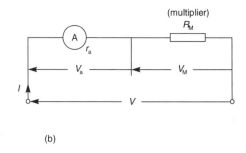

(b)

Figure 7.123

The milliammeter is converted into a voltmeter by connecting a high resistance (called a *multiplier*) in series with it as shown in Figure 7.123(b). From Figure 7.123(b), $V = V_a + V_M = Ir_a + IR_m$. Thus the value of the multiplier

$$R_M = \frac{V - Ir_a}{I} \text{ ohms}$$

Example 7.117

A moving-coil instrument gives a f.s.d. when the current is 40 mA and its resistance is 25 Ω. Calculate the value of the shunt to be connected in parallel with the meter to enable it to be used as an ammeter for measuring currents up to 50 A.

The circuit diagram is shown in Figure 7.124.

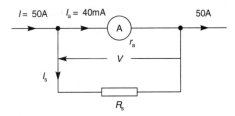

Figure 7.124

where r_a = resistance of instrument = 25 Ω
  r_s = resistance of shunt
  I_a = maximum permissible current flowing in instrument
    = 40 mA = 0.04 A
  I_s = current flowing in shunt
  I = total circuit current required to give f.s.d. = 50 A

Since $I = I_a + I_s$ then $I_s = I - I_a = 50 - 0.04 = 49.96$ A. $V = I_a r_a = I_s R_S$,

hence

$$R_S = \frac{I_a r_a}{I_s} = \frac{(0.04)(25)}{49.96} = 0.020\,02 \,\Omega = \mathbf{20.02\,m\Omega}$$

Thus for the moving-coil instrument to be used as an ammeter with a range 0–50 A, a resistance of value 20.02 mΩ needs to be connected in parallel with the instrument.

Example 7.118

A moving-coil instrument having a resistance of 10 Ω gives a f.s.d. when the current is 8 mA. Calculate the value of the multiplier to be connected in series with the instrument so that it can be used as a voltmeter for measuring p.d.s up to 100 V.

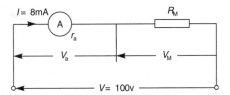

Figure 7.125

1 A moving-coil instrument gives f.s.d. for a current of 10 mA. Neglecting the resistance of the instrument, calculate the approximate value of series resistance needed to enable the instrument to measure up to (a) 20 V, (b) 100 V, (c) 250 V.

2 A meter of resistance 50 Ω has a f.s.d. of 4 mA. Determine the value of shunt resistance required in order that f.s.d. should be (a) 15 mA, (b) 20 A, (c) 100 A.

The circuit diagram is shown in Figure 7.125,

where r_a = resistance of instrument = 10 Ω
R_M = resistance of multiplier
I = total permissible instrument current = 8 mA = 0.008 A,
V = total p.d. required to give f.s.d. = 100 V

$$V = V_a + V_M = Ir_a + IR_m, \text{ i.e. } 100 = (0.008)(10) + (0.008)R_M$$

or $100 - 0.08 = 0.008\ R_M$, thus

$$R_M = \frac{99.92}{0.008} = 12\,490\ \Omega = \mathbf{12.49\,k\Omega}$$

Hence for the moving-coil instrument to be used as a voltmeter with a range 0–100 V, a resistance of value 12.49 kΩ needs to be connected in series with the instrument.

Electronic voltmeter

An *electronic voltmeter* can be used to measure with accuracy e.m.f. or p.d. from millivolts to kilovolts by incorporating in its design amplifiers and attenuators. The loading effect of an electronic voltmeter is minimal.

Digital voltmeter

A *digital voltmeter (DVM)* has, like the electronic voltmeter, a high input resistance. For power frequencies and d.c. measurements a DVM will normally be preferable to an analogue instrument.

The ohmmeter

An ohmmeter is an instrument for measuring electrical resistance. A simple ohmmeter circuit is shown in Figure 7.126(a). Unlike the ammeter or voltmeter, the ohmmeter circuit does not receive the energy necessary for its operation from the circuit under test. In the ohmmeter this energy is supplied by a self-contained source of

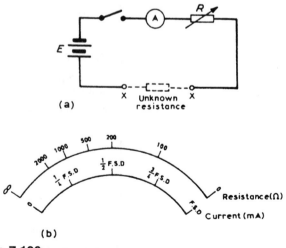

Figure 7.126

voltage, such as a battery. Initially, terminals XX are short-circuited and R adjusted to give f.s.d. on the milliammeter. If current I is at a maximum value and voltage E is constant, then resistance $R = E/I$ is at a minimum value. Thus f.s.d. on the milliammeter is made zero on the resistance scale. When terminals XX are open-circuited no current flows and R (= E/O) is infinity, ∞.

The milliammeter can thus be calibrated directly in ohms. A cramped (non-linear) scale results and is 'back to front', as shown in Figure 7.126(b). When calibrated, an unknown resistance is placed between terminals XX and its value determined from the position of the pointer on the scale. An ohmmeter designed for measuring low values of resistance is called a *continuity tester*. An ohmmeter designed for measuring high values of resistance (i.e. megohms) is called an *insulation resistance tester* (e.g., *megger*).

Multimeters

Instruments are manufactured that combine a moving-coil meter with a number of shunts and series multipliers, to provide a range of readings on a single scale graduated to read current and voltage. If a battery is incorporated then resistance can also be measured. Such instruments are called *multimeters* or *universal instruments* or *multirange instruments*. An 'Avometer' is a typical example. A particular range may be selected either by the use of separate terminals or by a selector switch. Only one measurement can be performed at one time. Often such instruments can be used in a.c. as well as d.c. circuits when a rectifier is incorporated in the instrument.

Wattmeters

A *wattmeter* is an instrument for measuring electrical power in a circuit. Figure 7.127 shows typical connections of a wattmeter used for measuring power supplied to a load. The instrument has two coils:

(i) a current coil, which is connected in series with the load, like an ammeter, and
(ii) a voltage coil, which is connected in parallel with the load, like a voltmeter.

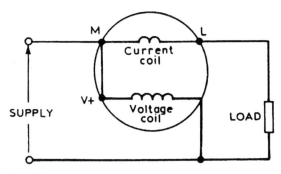

Figure 7.127

Cathode ray oscilloscope

The cathode ray oscilloscope (CRO) may be used in the observation of waveforms and for the measurement of voltage, current, frequency, phase and periodic time. For examining periodic waveforms the electron beam is deflected horizontally (i.e. in the X direction) by a sawtooth generator acting as a timebase. The signal to be examined is applied to the vertical deflection system (Y direction) usually after amplification.

Oscilloscopes normally have a transparent grid of 10 mm by 10 mm squares in front of the screen, called a graticule. Among the timebase controls is a 'variable' switch which gives the sweep speed as time per centimetre. This may be in s/cm, ms/cm or µs/cm, a large number of switch positions being available. Also on the front panel of a CRO is a Y amplifier switch marked in volts per centimetre, with a large number of available switch positions.

(i) With *direct voltage measurements*, only the Y amplifier 'volts/cm' switch on the CRO is used. With no voltage applied to the Y plates the position of the spot trace on the screen is noted. When a direct voltage is applied to the Y plates the new position of the spot trace is an indication of the magnitude of the voltage.

For example, in Figure 7.128(a), with no voltage applied to the Y plates, the spot trace is in the centre of the screen (initial position) and then the spot trace moves 2.5 cm to the final

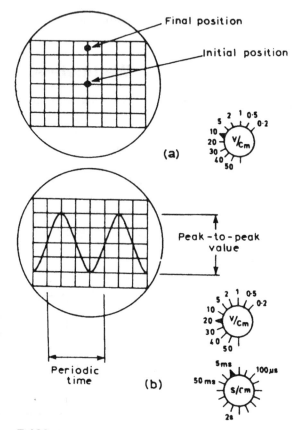

(a)

(b)

Final position

Initial position

Peak-to-peak value

Periodic time

Figure 7.128

position shown, on application of a d.c. voltage. With the 'volts/cm' switch on 10 volts/cm the magnitude of the direct voltage is 2.5 cm × 10 volts/cm, i.e. 25 volts.

(ii) With *alternating voltage measurement*, let a sinusoidal waveform be displayed on a c.r.o. screen as shown in Figure 7.128(b). If the s/cm switch is on, say, 5 ms/cm, then the *periodic time T* of the sinewave is 5 ms/cm × 4 cm, i.e. **20 ms** or **0.02 s.**

Since

$$\text{frequency } f = \frac{1}{T}, \text{ frequency} = \frac{1}{0.02} = \textbf{50 Hz}$$

If the 'volts/cm' switch is on, say, 20 volts/cm, then the *amplitude* or *peak value* of the sinewave shown is 20 volts/cm × 2 cm, i.e. 40 V.
  Since

$$\text{r.m.s. voltage} = \frac{\text{peak voltage}}{\sqrt{2}}$$

$$\text{r.m.s. voltage} = \frac{40}{\sqrt{2}} = \textbf{28.28 V}$$

Double beam oscilloscopes are useful whenever two signals are to be compared simultaneously. The c.r.o. demands reasonable skill in adjustment and use. However its greatest advantage is in observing the shape of a waveform – a feature not possessed by other measuring instruments.

Example 7.119

For the c.r.o. square voltage waveform shown in Figure 7.129 determine (a) the periodic time, (b) the frequency and (c) the peak-to-peak voltage. The 'time/cm' (or timebase control) switch is on 100 μs/cm and the 'volts/cm' (or signal amplitude control) switch is on 20 V/cm.

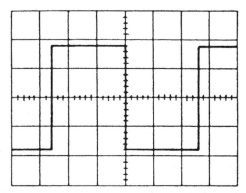

Figure 7.129

(a) The width of one complete cycle is 5.2 cm, hence the periodic time, $T = 5.2\,\text{cm} \times 100 \times 10^{-6}\,\text{s/cm} = \textbf{0.52 ms}$.

(b) Frequency, $f = \dfrac{1}{T} = \dfrac{1}{0.52 \times 10^{-3}} = \textbf{1.92 kHz}$

(c) The peak-to-peak height of the display is 3.6 cm, hence the peak-to-peak voltage = 3.6 cm × 20 V/cm = **72 V**.

Example 7.120

For the double-beam oscilloscope displays shown in Figure 7.130 determine (a) their frequency, (b) their r.m.s. values, (c) their phase difference. The 'time/cm' switch is on 100 μs/cm and the 'volts/cm' switch is on 2 V/cm.

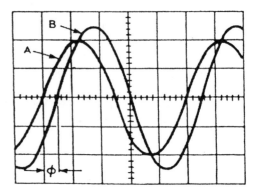

Figure 7.130

(a) The width of each complete cycle is 5 cm for both waveforms. Hence the periodic time, T, of each waveform is 5 cm × 100 μs/cm, i.e. 0.5 ms

Frequency of each waveform

$$f = \frac{1}{T} = \frac{1}{0.5 \times 10^{-3}} = \textbf{2 kHz}$$

(b) The peak value of waveform A is 2 cm × 2 V/cm = **4 V**.

Hence the r.m.s. value of waveform A $= \dfrac{4}{\sqrt{2}} =$ **2.83 V**.

The peak value of waveform B is 2.5 cm × 2 V/cm = **5 V**.

Hence the r.m.s. value of waveform B $= \dfrac{5}{\sqrt{2}} =$ **3.54 V**.

(c) Since 5 cm represents 1 cycle, then 5 cm represents 360°, i.e. 1 cm represents (360/5) = 72°.

The phase angle ϕ = 0.5 cm = 0.5 cm × 72°/cm = 36°.

Hence waveform A leads waveform B by **36°.**

Test your knowledge 7.64

A sinusoidal voltage trace displayed by a c.r.o. is shown in Figure 7.131. If the 'time/cm' switch is on 500 μs/cm and the 'volts/cm' switch is on 5 V/cm, find, for the waveform, (a) the frequency, (b) the peak-to-peak voltage, (c) the amplitude, (d) the r.m.s. value.

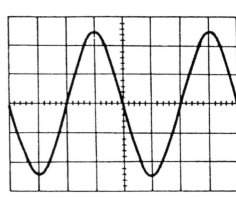

Figure 7.131

Activity 7.8

List, and briefly describe, the errors most likely to occur in measurements of electrical quantities.

Measurement of fluid flow

The measurement of fluid flow is of great importance in many industrial processes, some examples including air flow in the ventilating ducts of a coal mine, the flow rate of water in a condenser at a power station, the flow rate of liquids in chemical processes, the control and monitoring of the fuel, lubricating and cooling fluids of ships and aircraft engines, and so on. Fluid flow is one of the most difficult of industrial measurements to carry out, since flow behaviour depends on a great many variables concerning the physical properties of a fluid.

There are available a large number of fluid flow measuring instruments generally called *flowmeters*, which can measure the flow rate of liquids (in m^3/s) or the mass flow rate of gaseous fluids (in kg/s). The two main categories of flowmeters are differential pressure flowmeters and mechanical flowmeters.

Differential pressure flowmeters

When certain flowmeters are installed in pipelines they often cause an obstruction to the fluid flowing in the pipe by reducing the cross-sectional area of the pipeline. This causes a change in the velocity of the fluid, with a related change in pressure. Figure 7.132 shows a section through a pipeline into which a flowmeter has been inserted. The flow rate of the fluid may be determined from a measurement of the difference between the pressures on the walls of the pipe at specified distances upstream and downstream of the flowmeter. Such devices are known as *differential pressure flowmeters*. The pressure difference in Figure 7.132 is measured using a manometer connected to appropriate pressure tapping points. The pressure is seen to be greater upstream of the flowmeter than downstream, the pressure difference being shown as *h*.

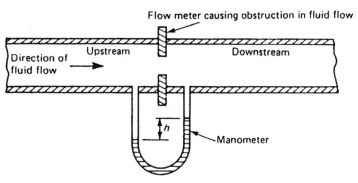

Figure 7.132

Calibration of the manometer depends on the shape of the obstruction, the positions of the pressure tapping points and the physical properties of the fluid.

In industrial applications, the pressure difference is detected by a differential pressure cell, the output from which is either an amplified pressure signal or an electric signal. Examples of differential pressure flowmeters commonly used include:

(a) Orifice plate
(b) Venturi tube
(c) Flow nozzles
(d) Pitot-static tube

British Standard reference BS 1042: Part 1: 1964 and Part 2A: 1973 'Methods for the measurement of fluid flow in pipes' gives specifications for measurement, manufacture, tolerances, accuracy, sizes, choice and so on, of differential flowmeters.

Mechanical flowmeters

With mechanical flowmeters a sensing element situated in a pipeline is displaced by the fluid flowing past it. Examples of mechanical flowmeters commonly used include:

1 Deflecting vane flowmeter
2 Turbine type meters
   (i)   Cup anemometer
   (ii) Rotary vane positive displacement meters
   (iii) Turbine flowmeter

Three further flowmeters are:

3 Float and tapered-tube meter
4 Electromagnetic flowmeter
5 Hot-wire anemometer.

Test your knowledge 7.65

Choose the most appropriate fluid flow measuring device for the following circumstances:
(a) The most accurate, permanent installation for measuring liquid flow rate.
(b) To determine the velocity of low-speed aircraft and ships.
(c) Accurate continuous volumetric measurement of crude petroleum products in a duct of 500 mm bore.
(d) To give a reasonable indication of the mean flow velocity, while maintaining a steady pressure difference on a hydraulic test rig.
(e) For an essentially constant flow rate with reasonable accuracy in a large pipe bore, with a cheap and simple installation.

Activity 7.9

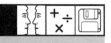

An engineering company, Whirlwind Wind Tunnels, manufactures a range of wind tunnels in which scale models of engineering structures can be tested. In its latest wind tunnel, the company needs to incorporate an accurate flowmeter and front panel display. The company has asked you to advise them on the selection of a suitable flowmeter and make recommendations about how this can be interfaced to a display. Which type would you recommend and why?

Prepare a briefing pack for the Board of Directors and include appropriate visual aids, charts, diagrams and handouts. Present your recommendations in the form of a verbal presentation lasting no more than 10 minutes.

Measurement of strain

An essential requirement of engineering design is the accurate determination of stresses and strains in components under working conditions. 'Strength of materials' is a subject relating to the physical nature of substances which are acted upon by external forces. No solid body is perfectly rigid, and when forces are applied to it changes in dimensions occur. Such changes are not always perceptible to the human eye since they are so small. For example, a spanner will bend slightly when tightening a nut, and the span of a bridge will sag under the weight of a car.

In designing a structure, such as an electricity transmission tower carrying overhead power lines or support pillars and spans of new designs of bridges, the engineer is greatly concerned about the mechanical properties of the materials he is going to use. Many laboratory tests have been designed to provide important information about materials. Such tests include tensile, compression, torsion, impact, creep and fatigue tests and each attempts to provide information about the behaviour of materials under working conditions.

The measurement of extension, and thus strain, is achieved in the laboratory with an instrument called an *extensometer*. Although some extensometers can be used in such practical situations as a crane under load, it is more usual to use in these situations an electrical device called a *strain gauge*.

A knowledge of stress and strain is the foundation of economy and safety in design.

Activity 7.10

Describe the principle of operation and construction of the following:

(a) Lindley extensometer
(b) Huggenburger extensometer
(c) Houndsfield extensometer

Present your findings in the form of a brief written report and include appropriate diagrams and sketches.

Multiple choice questions

1 Which of the following temperatures is absolute zero?

  A 0°C
  B −173°C
  C −273°C
  D −373°C.

2 The energy used by a 3 kW heater in 2 minutes is

  A 25 J
  B 360 J
  C 3000 J
  D 360 000 J

3 Which pair of the pairs of quantities listed below has two scalar quantities in it?

A energy and force
B mass and energy
C force and mass
D force and velocity.

4 The normal force between two surfaces is 40 N and the force required to maintain a constant speed of sliding is 20 N. The dynamic coefficient of friction is

A 20 N
B 2 N
C 60 N
D 0.5.

5 Which of the following is a unit of heat?

A joule
B newton
C kelvin
D watt.

6 Three 6 Ω resistors are connected together in various arrangements of series, parallel and series/parallel. Which of the following values **cannot** be obtained when all three resistors are being used?

A 2 Ω
B 9 Ω
C 12 Ω
D 18 Ω.

Questions 7 and 8 refer to the graph shown at Figure 7.133 which shows the velocity of a body during the first 30 s of its motion.

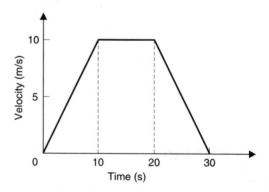

Figure 7.133

7 The total distance travelled in 30 s is

A 100 m
B 200 m
C 300 m
D 400 m.

8 The average velocity of the body during the first 30 seconds is

A 0 m/s

B 5 m/s

C $6\frac{2}{3}$ m/s

D 10 m/s.

9 A force of 10 N is applied at right angles to the handle of a spanner, 50 cm from the centre of the nut. The moment on the nut is

A 20 N/m

B 60 N cm

C 5 cm/N

D 5 Nm.

10 The largest number of 60 W bulbs which can be operated from a 240 V supply fitted with a 5 A fuse is

A 20

B 12

C 48

D 4.

11 5 kJ of work is done by a force in moving an object uniformly through 100 m in 2 minutes. The force applied is

A 50 N

B 20 N

C 500 N

D 2.4 N

12 When two wires of different metals are twisted together and heat applied to the junction, an e.m.f. is produced. This effect is used in a thermocouple to measure:

A expansion

B heat

C e.m.f.

D temperature.

13 Which of the following devices does not make use of the magnetic effect of an electric current?

A a transformer

B a filament lamp

C a m.c. ammeter

D a relay.

14 The magnitude of the resultant of the vectors shown in Figure 7.134 is

A 13 N

B 17 N

C 7 N

D 60 N

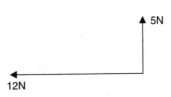

Figure 7.134

15 A point on a wheel has a constant angular velocity of 4 rad/s. The angle turned through in 1 minute is

A 30π rad
B 240 rad
C 15 rad
D 480π rad

16 The current I flowing in resistor R in the circuit shown at Figure 7.135 is

A $I_1 - I_2$
B $I_2 - I_1$
C I_2
D $I_1 + I_2$.

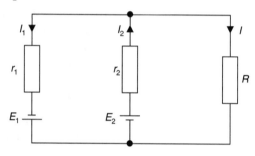

Figure 7.135

17 A circular rod of cross-sectional area 1 cm² has a tensile force of 100 kN applied to it. The stress in the rod is

A 1 MPa
B 100 kPa
C 1 GPa
D 10 MPa

18 The gauge pressure of a fluid in a pipe is 80 kPa and the atmospheric pressure is 100 kPa. The absolute pressure of the fluid in the pipe is

A 180 kPa
B 8 MPa
C 20 kPa
D 1.25 kPa

19 Which of the following statements is false?

A Boyle's law applies at constant temperature
B The pressure of a given mass of gas decreases as the volume is increased at constant temperature
C Isothermal changes are those which occur at constant pressure
D At constant pressure, Charles' law applies.

20 An alternating voltage of peak value 300 V is applied to a lamp. Which of the following direct voltages, if applied to the lamp, would cause the lamp to light with the same brilliance?

A 300 V
B 191.1 V
C 424.2 V
D 212.1 V

Answers to test your knowledge

7.1　1　(a)　$120\,\text{m}^2$　　　(b)　$1.2 \times 10^6\,\text{cm}^2$
　　　　(c)　$0.12 \times 10^9\,\text{mm}^2$
　　　2　(a)　$4000\,\text{cm}^3$　(b)　$0.004\,\text{m}^3$　(c)　$4 \times 10^6\,\text{mm}$

7.2　1　$7000\,\text{kg/m}^3$
　　　2　501
　　　3　$9000\,\text{kg/m}^3$

7.3　1　$4.3\,\text{kN}$ at $-25°$
　　　2　$26.7\,\text{N}$ at $-82°$

7.4　1　$2.56\,\text{N}$ at $-20.04°$
　　　2　$53.5\,\text{kN}$ at $37°$ to force 1 (i.e. $117°$ to the horizontal)

7.5　1　$474.6\,\text{N}$ at $-141°\,7'$
　　　2　$14.69\,\text{kN}$ at $-25°\,96'$

7.6　1　$10\,\text{min}\,40\,\text{s}$
　　　1　(a)　$72\,\text{km/h}$　　　(b)　$20\,\text{m/s}$

7.7　1　(a)　$46\,\text{min}\,36\,\text{s}$　　(b)　$42.86\,\text{km/h}$
　　　　(c)　$45\,\text{km}$　　　　　(d)　$53.4\,\text{km/h}$

7.8　1　$9.26 \times 10^{-4}\,\text{m/s}^2$
　　　2　$1.42\,\text{s}$
　　　3　$39.2\,\text{km/h}$

7.9　1　(a)　$\frac{5}{9}\,\text{m/s}^2$　　　(b)　$750\,\text{N}$
　　　2　$0.560\,\text{m/s}^2$

7.10　1　$12.5\,\text{kg}$

7.11　1　$200\,\text{mm}$
　　　2　$F_1 = 3.5\,\text{kN}$, $F_2 = 1.5\,\text{kN}$

7.12　1　$2.625\,\text{kN}$, $5.375\,\text{kN}$
　　　2　$36\,\text{kN}$

7.13　$= 90\,\text{rad/s}$, $v = 16.2\,\text{m/s}$

7.14　(a)　　$0.4\pi\,\text{rad/s}^2$ or $1.257\,\text{rad/s}^2$
　　　(b)　　$0.1\pi\,\text{m/s}^2$ or $0.314\,\text{m/s}^2$
　　　(c)　　187.5 revolutions

7.15　$800\,\text{N}$

7.16　1　$490\,\text{J}$
　　　2　(a)　$2.5\,\text{J}$　　(b)　$2.1\,\text{J}$
　　　3　$14.72\,\text{kJ}$

7.17　1　$420\,\text{J}$
　　　2　$4\,\text{m}$

7.18　1　(a)　$80\,\text{N}$　　(b)　$200\,\text{W}$
　　　2　(a)　$450\,\text{W}$　　(b)　$600\,\text{W}$
　　　3　(a)　$1500\,\text{W}$　(b)　$510\,\text{mm/s}$

7.19　1　$8.31\,\text{m}$
　　　2　$281.25\,\text{kJ}$
　　　3　$176.6\,\text{kJ}$, $176.6\,\text{kJ}$

7.20　1　$250\,\text{MPa}$
　　　2　$12.78\,\text{mm}$

7.21 1 0.3 mm
    2 (a) 127.3 MPa   (b) 0.001 25 or 0.125%
    3 (a) 157.1 kN   (b) 80.03 MPa

7.22 1 10 mm
    2 (a) 15.92 MPa   (b) 0.332 mm
    3 (a) 140 MPa   (b) 11.0 kN

7.23 1 2.4 kg m/s
    2 64 kg
    3 (a) 18 m/s in the direction in which the bodies are initially travelling
       (b) 6 m/s in the direction that the 30 g mass is initially travelling

7.24 1 70 Nm
    2 160 mm

7.25 1 343 kPa
    2 30 MN
    3 758 mm

7.26   (a) Bourdon gauge
       (b) MacLeod gauge
       (c) Mercury filled U-tube manometer
       (d) Inclined manometer
       (e) Fortin barometer

7.27 1 743 mm
    2 15.24 N

7.28 1 (a) 210 K   (b) −48°C
    2 130 J/(kg °C)
    3 220°C

7.29 1 18.08 MJ
    2 24.70 MJ

7.30 1 (a) 2 kΩ   (b) 10 kΩ   (c) 25 kΩ
    2 (a) 18.18 Ω (b) 10.0 mΩ (c) 2.0 mΩ

7.31 1 50.0928 m
    2 0.0425%
    3 (a) 4.1993 m (b) 4.2214 m

7.32 1 29.7 mm^3
    2 $\alpha = 9 \times 10^{-6}$ K^{-1}
      (a) 17.28 mm^2 (b) 162 mm^3

7.33 1 22.5 kN
    2 282 K or 9°C

7.34 1 141 kPa
    2 180 kPa

7.35 1 177°C
    2 2.75 kg
    3 256 J/(kg K)

7.36 1 16 A
    2 4 A

7.37 1 20 kΩ, 125 mA
    (a) 2400 Ω or 2.4 kΩ
    (b) 600 000 Ω or 600 kΩ or 0.6 MΩ

7.38 1 80 mW
   2 (a) 500 V   (b) 25 kW
   3 2 kW, 12 kWh, 84p
   4 £10.29

7.39   (a) 5 A   (b) 13 A

7.40 1 1.44 Ω
   2 0.017 μΩ m
   3 0.180 Ω

7.41 1 23.83 Ω
   2 69.28°C

7.42 1 (a) 2.17 V   (b) 1.6 V   (c) 0.7 V
   2 (a) 0.25 A   (b) 14.5 V

7.43   0.5 A, 4.5 V, 2.75 W
7.44   (a) 6 Ω   (b) 6 V
   3.6 kWh

7.45 1 (a) 2 Ω   (b) 4 A
   2 (a) all four in parallel
     (b) two in series, in parallel with another two in series
     (c) three in parallel in series with one
     (d) two in parallel, in series with two in series
   3 (a) 4 A   (b) 44 A

7.46   (a) 38 Ω   (b) $I_1 = 4$ A
   $I_2 = 6$ A, $I_3 = I_4 = 5$ A

7.47   (a) 50 V   (b) lamps A and B will not operate

7.48   0.5 A flowing into the positive terminal of 3 V source (i.e. charging),
    1 A flowing from the positive terminal of 5 V source (i.e. discharging),
    0.5 A flowing in 8 Ω resistor

7.49 1 1.5 T
   2 250 mm

7.50 1 21 N, 14.8 N
   2 (a) upwards
     (b) to the right
     (c) out of the paper
     (d) S on left, N on right

7.51 1 200 m/s
   2 (a) 3.75 mV (b) 3.25 mV (c) 1.875 mV

7.52 1 48 V
   2 3 H
   3 45 ms

7.53 1 3 H, 500 V
   2 (a) 120 V   (b) 24 mWb

7.54 1 (a) 0.4 s   (b) 10 ms   (c) 25 μs
     2 625 Hz

7.55 1 (i)   62.5 Hz   (ii) 10 A   (iii) 10 A
      (iv) 1   (v) 1
     2 235.5 V, 166.5 V

7.56 1 $E = 250$ kV/m
       (a) 2.213 μC/m^2 (b) 5.089 μC/m^2
     2 600 V
     3 2 s

7.57 1 (a) 0.02 μF   (b) 0.4 mJ
     2 (a) 240 V   (b) 41.67 μF

7.58 1 (a) 4.5 s   (b) 200 kΩ
     2 (a) 0.3 A   (b) 12 μs   (c) 60 μs

7.59 1 (a) 397.9 Ω   (b) 15.92 Ω   (c) 1.989 Ω
     2 79.58 μF

7.60 1 62.5 J
     2 (a) 7.2 H   (b) 90 J   (c) 180 V

7.61 1 (a) 8 A   (b) 25 ms   (c) 5.06 A   (d) 0.125 s
     2 (a) 8 A   (b) 20 A   (c) 20 A

7.62 1 (a) 62.83 Ω   (b) 754 Ω   (c) 5.027 kΩ
     2 600 Hz
     3 12.73 A

7.63 1 (a) 2 kΩ   (b) 10 kΩ   (c) 25 kΩ
     2 (a) 18.18 Ω   (b) 10.0 mΩ   (c) 2.0 mΩ

7.64   (a) 500 Hz   (b) 25 V   (c) 12.5 V   (d) 8.84 V

7.65   (a) Venturimeter
       (b) Pitot-static tube
       (c) Turbine flowmeter
       (d) Float and tapered-tube flowmeter
       (e) Orifice plate

Unit 8   Mathematics for engineering

Summary

This section aims to develop in the reader an understanding of the mathematical skills essential to engineering. The material is divided into five sections, each involving typical electrical, electronic and mechanical engineering problems.

Algebra

Indices

The lowest factors of 2000 are $2 \times 2 \times 2 \times 2 \times 5 \times 5 \times 5$. These factors are written as $2^4 \times 5^3$, where 2 and 5 are called *bases* and the numbers 4 and 3 are called *indices*.

When an index is an integer it is called a *power*. Thus, 2^4 is called 'two to the power of four', and has a base of 2 and an index of 4. Similarly, 5^3 is called 'five to the power of 3' and has a base of 5 and an index of 3.

Special names may be used when the indices are 2 and 3, these being called 'squared' and 'cubed', respectively. Thus 7^2 is called 'seven squared' and 9^3 is called 'nine cubed'. When no index is shown, the power is 1, i.e. 2^1 means 2.

Reciprocal

The *reciprocal* of a number is when the index is -1 and its value is given by 1 divided by the base. Thus the reciprocal of 2 is 2^{-1} and its value is $\frac{1}{2}$ or 0.5. Similarly, the reciprocal of 5 is 5^{-1} which means $\frac{1}{5}$ or 0.2

Square root

The *square root* of a number is when the index is $\frac{1}{2}$, and the square root of 2 is written as $2^{(1/2)}$ or $\sqrt{2}$. The value of a square root is the value of the base which when multiplied by itself gives the number. Since $3 \times 3 = 9$, then $\sqrt{9} = 3$. However, $(-3) \times (-3) = 9$, so $\sqrt{9} = -3$.

There are always two answers when finding the square root of a number and this is shown by putting both a + and a − sign in front of the answer to a square root problem. Thus $\sqrt{9} = \pm 3$ and $4^{(1/2)} = \sqrt{4} = \pm 2$, and so on.

Laws of indices

When simplifying calculations involving indices, certain basic rules or laws can be applied, called the *laws of indices*. These are given below:

(i) When multiplying two or more numbers having the same base, the indices are added. Thus $3^2 \times 3^4 = 3^{2+4} = 3^6$.

(ii) When a number is divided by a number having the same base, the indices are subtracted. Thus $3^5/3^2 = 3^{5-2} = 3^3$.

(iii) When a number which is raised to a power is raised to a further power, the indices are multiplied. Thus $(3^5)^2 = 3^{5 \times 2} = 3^{10}$.

(iv) When a number has an index of 0, its value is 1. Thus $3^0 = 1$.

(v) A number raised to a negative power is the reciprocal of that number raised to a positive power. Thus $3^{-4} = 1/3^4$. Similarly, $1/2^{-3} = 2^3$.

(vi) When a number is raised to a fractional power the denominator of the fraction is the root of the number and the numerator is the power. Thus

$$8^{(2/3)} = \sqrt[3]{8^2} = (2)^2 = 4$$

and

$$25^{(1/2)} = \sqrt{25^1} = \pm 5$$

Example 8.1

Evaluate: (a) $5^2 \times 5^3$, (b) $3^2 \times 3^4 \times 3$ and (c) $2 \times 2^2 \times 2^5$.

From law (i):

(a) $5^2 \times 5^3 = 5^{(2+3)} = 5^5 = 5 \times 5 \times 5 \times 5 \times 5 = \textbf{3125}$

(b) $3^2 \times 3^4 \times 3 = 3^{(2+4+1)} = 3^7 = 3 \times 3 \times \ldots$ to 7 terms $= \textbf{2187}$

(c) $2 \times 2^2 \times 2^5 = 2^{(1+2+5)} = 2^8 = \textbf{256}$

Example 8.2

Find the value of: (a) $7^5/7^3$ and (b) $5^7/5^4$.

From law (ii):

(a) $\dfrac{7^5}{7^3} = 7^{(5-3)} = 7^2 = \textbf{49}$

(b) $\dfrac{5^7}{5^4} = 5^{(7-4)} = 5^3 = \textbf{125}$

Example 8.3

Evaluate: (a) $5^2 \times 5^3 \div 5^4$ and (b) $(3 \times 3^5) \div (3^2 \times 3^3)$.

From laws (i) and (ii):

(a) $5^2 \times 5^3 \div 5^4$

$$= \frac{5^2 \times 5^3}{5^4} = \frac{5^{(2+3)}}{5^4}$$

$$= \frac{5^5}{5^4} = 5^{(5-4)}$$

$$= 5^1 = \mathbf{5}$$

(b) $(3 \times 3^5) \div (3^2 \times 3^3) = \frac{3 \times 3^5}{3^2 \times 3^3} = \frac{3^{(1+5)}}{3^{(2+3)}}$

$$= \frac{3^6}{3^5} = 3^{6-5}$$

$$= 3^1 = \mathbf{3}$$

Example 8.4

Simplify: (a) $(2^3)^4$ and (b) $(3^2)^5$, expressing the answers in index form.

From law (iii):

(a) $(2^3)^4 = 2^{3 \times 4} = \mathbf{2^{12}}$

(b) $(3^2)^5 = 3^{2 \times 5} = \mathbf{3^{10}}$

Example 8.5

Evaluate: $\dfrac{(10^2)^3}{10^4 \times 10^2}$.

From the laws of indices:

$$\frac{(10^2)^3}{10^4 \times 10^2} = \frac{10^{(2 \times 3)}}{10^{(4+2)}} = \frac{10^6}{10^6} = 10^{6-6} = 10^0 = \mathbf{1}$$

Example 8.6

Evaluate (a) $4^{1/2}$ (b) $16^{3/4}$ (c) $27^{2/3}$ (d) $9^{-1/2}$.

(a) $4^{1/2} = \sqrt{4} = \mathbf{\pm 2}$

(b) $16^{3/4} = \sqrt[4]{16^3} = (2)^3 = \mathbf{8}$

(Note that it does not matter whether the 4th root of 16 is found first or whether 16 cubed is found first – the same answer will result.)

(c) $27^{2/3} = \sqrt[3]{27^2} = (3)^2 = \mathbf{9}$

(d) $9^{-1/2} = \dfrac{1}{9^{1/2}} = \dfrac{1}{\sqrt{9}} = \dfrac{1}{\pm 3} = \mathbf{\pm \dfrac{1}{3}}$

In questions 1 to 3, simplify the expressions given, expressing the answers in index form.

1 (a) $3^3 \times 3^4$ (b) $4^2 \times 4^3 \times 4^4$

2 (a) $\dfrac{2^4}{2^3}$ (b) $\dfrac{3^7}{3^2}$

3 (a) $(7^2)^3$ (b) $(3^3)^2$

4 Evaluate

(a) $\dfrac{1^{-1}}{3^2}$ (b) $81^{0.25}$

(c) $16^{-1/4}$ (d) $\dfrac{4^{1/2}}{9}$

Standard form

A number written with one digit to the left of the decimal point and multiplied by 10 raised to some power is said to be written in *standard form*. Thus: 5837 is written as 5.837×10^3 in standard form, and 0.0415 is written as 4.15×10^{-2} in standard form.

When a number is written in standard form, the first factor is called the *mantissa* and the second factor is called the *exponent*. Thus the number 5.8×10^3 has a mantissa of 5.8 and an exponent of 10^3.

(i) Numbers having the same exponent can be added or subtracted in standard form by adding or subtracting the mantissae and keeping the exponent the same. Thus:

$$2.3 \times 10^4 + 3.7 \times 10^4 = (2.3 + 3.7) \times 10^4 = 6.0 \times 10^4,$$

and

$$5.9 \times 10^{-2} - 4.6 \times 10^{-2} = (5.9 - 4.6) \times 10^{-2}$$
$$= 1.3 \times 10^{-2}$$

When numbers have different exponents, one way of adding or subtracting the numbers is to express one of the numbers in non-standard form, so that both numbers have the same exponent. Thus:

$$2.3 \times 10^4 + 3.7 \times 10^3 = 2.3 \times 10^4 + 0.37 \times 10^4$$
$$= (2.3 + 0.37) \times 10^4$$
$$= 2.67 \times 10^4$$

Alternatively,

$$2.3 \times 10^4 + 3.7 \times 10^3 = 23\,000 + 3700$$
$$= 26\,700 = 2.67 \times 10^4$$

(ii) The laws of indices are used when multiplying or dividing numbers given in standard form. For example,

$$(22.5 \times 10^3) \times (5 \times 10^2) = (2.5 \times 5) \times (10^{3+2)}$$
$$= 12.5 \times 10^5 \text{ or } 1.25 \times 10^6$$

Similarly,

$$\frac{6 \times 10^6}{1.5 \times 10^2} = \frac{6}{1.5} \times (10^{4-2)} = 4 \times 10^2$$

Example 8.7

Express in standard form: (a) 38.71 (b) 3746 (c) 0.0124

For a number to be in standard form, it is expressed with only one digit to the left of the decimal point. Thus:

(a) 38.71 must be divided by 10 to achieve one digit to the left of the decimal point and it must also be multiplied by 10 to maintain the equality, i.e.

$$38.71 \times \frac{38.71}{10} \times 10 = \mathbf{3.871 \times 10} \text{ in standard form}$$

Test your knowledge 8.2

In questions 1 and 2, express in standard form

1 (a) 73.9   (b) 1128.4
  (c) 197.62

2 (a) 0.2401   (b) 0.0174
  (c) 0.00923

In questions 3 and 4, evaluate in standard form

3 (a) $4.831 \times 10^2 + 1.24 \times 10^3$
  (b) $3.24 \times 10^{-3} - 1.11 \times 10^{-4}$

4 (a) $\dfrac{6 \times 10^{-3}}{3 \times 10^{-5}}$

  (b) $\dfrac{(2.4 \times 10^3)(3 \times 10^{-2})}{(4.8 \times 10^4)}$

(b) $3746 = \dfrac{3746}{1000} \times 1000 = \mathbf{3.746 \times 10^3}$ in standard form

(c) $0.0124 = 0.0124 \times \dfrac{100}{100} = \dfrac{1.24}{100} = \mathbf{1.24 \times 10^{-2}}$ in standard form

Logarithms

With the use of calculators firmly established, logarithmic tables are now rarely used for calculations. However, the theory of logarithms is important, for there are several scientific and engineering laws that involve the rules of logarithms.

If a number y can be written in the form a^x, then the index x is called the 'logarithm of y to the base a'

i.e. if $y = a^x$ then $x = \log_a y$

Thus, since $1000 = 10^3$, then $3 = \log_{10} 1000$

Check this using the 'log' button on your calculator.

(a) Logarithms having a base of 10 are called *common logarithms* and $\log_{10}$ is usually abbreviated to lg.

The following values may be checked by using a calculator:

lg $17.9 = 1.2528\ldots$, lg $462.7 = 2.6652\ldots$ and

lg $0.0173 = -1.7619\ldots$

(b) Logarithms having a base of e (where 'e' is a mathematical constant approximately equal to 2.7183) are called *hyperbolic*, or *natural logarithms*, and $\log_e$ is usually abbreviated to ln. The following values may be checked by using a calculator:

ln $3.15 = 1.1474\ldots$, ln $362.7 = 5.8935\ldots$ and

ln $0.156 = -1.8578\ldots$

There are three rules of logarithms, which apply to any base:

(i) To multiply two numbers:

$\log (A \times B) = \log A + \log B$

The following may be checked by using a calculator:

lg $10 = 1$; also lg 5 + lg 2

$= 0.698\,97\ldots + 0.301\,029\ldots = 1$

Hence lg $(5 \times 2) = $ lg $10 = $ lg 5 + lg 2

(ii) To divide two numbers

$\log \dfrac{A}{B} = \log A - \log B$

The following may be checked using a calculator:

$\ln \dfrac{5}{2} = \ln 2.5 = 0.91629\ldots$

Also $\ln 5 - \ln 2 = 1.60943\ldots - 0.69314\ldots$

$$= 0.91629\ldots$$

Hence $\ln \dfrac{5}{2} = \ln 5 - \ln 2$

(iii) To raise a number to a power:

$$\log A^n = n \log A$$

The following may be checked using a calculator:

$$\lg 5^2 = \lg 25 = 1.39794\ldots$$

Also $2 \lg 5 = 2 \times 0.69897\ldots = 1.39794\ldots$

Hence $\lg 5^2 = 2 \lg 5$

Example 8.8

Evaluate (a) $\log_3 9$ (b) $\log_{10} 10$ (c) $\log_{16} 8$.

(a) Let $x = \log_3 9$ then $3^x = 9$ from the definition of a logarithm, i.e. $3^x = 3^2$, from which $x = 2$. Hence

$$\log_3 9 = 2$$

(b) Let $x = \log_{10} 10$ then $10^x = 10$ from the definition of a logarithm, i.e. $10^x = 10$, from which $x = 1$. Hence

$$\log_{10} 10 = 1 \text{ (which may be checked by a calculator)}$$

(c) Let $x = \log_{16} 8$ then $16^x = 8$, from the definition of a logarithm, i.e. $(2^4)^x = 2^3$, i.e. $2^{4x} = 2^3$ from the laws of indices, from which

$$4x = 3 \text{ and } x = \frac{3}{4}. \text{ Hence}$$

$$\log_{16} 8 = \frac{3}{4}$$

Example 8.9

Evaluate (a) $\lg 0.001$ (b) $\ln e$ (c) $\log_3 1/81$.

(a) Let $x = \lg 0.001 = \log_{10} 0.001$ then $10^x = 0.001$, i.e., $10^x = 10^{-3}$, from which $x = -3$. Hence

$\lg 0.001 = -3$ (which may be checked by a calculator).

(b) Let $x = \ln e = \log_e e$ then $e^x = e$, i.e., $e^x = e^1$ from which $x = 1$. Hence

$\ln e = 1$ (which may be checked by a calculator).

(c) Let $x = \log_3 \dfrac{1}{81}$ then $3^x = \dfrac{1}{81} = \dfrac{1}{3^4} = 3^{-4}$, from which $x = -4$. Hence

$$\log_3 \frac{1}{81} = -4$$

Example 8.10

Solve the following equations:

(a) lg x = 3   (b) $\log_2 x = 3$ (c) $\log_5 x = -2$.

(a) If lg x = 3 then $\log_{10} x = 3$ and $x = 10^3$, i.e. **x = 1000**

(b) If $\log_2 x = 3$ then **x = 2^3 = 8**

(c) If $\log_5 x = -2$ then **x = 5^{-2} = $\dfrac{1}{5^2}$ = $\dfrac{1}{25}$**

Example 8.11

Simplify log 64 − log 128 + log 32

$$64 = 2^6, 128 = 2^7 \text{ and } 32 = 2^5$$

Hence

log 64 − log 128 + log 32 = $\log 2^6 - \log 2^7 + \log 2^5$

= 6 log 2 − 7 log 2 + 5 log 2 by the third law of logarithms

= **4 log 2**

Test your knowledge 8.3

In questions 1 and 2, evaluate

1 (a) $\log_{10} 10000$ (b) $\log_8 2$

2 (a) $\log_5 125$ (b) lg 0.01

3 Solve the equation $\log_3 x = 2$

4 Simplify log 27 − log 9 + log 81.

Indicial equations

The laws of logarithms may be used to solve certain equations involving powers – called *indicial equations*. For example, to solve, say, $3^x = 27$, logarithms to a base of 10 are taken of both sides, i.e.

$$\log_{10} 3^x = \log_{10} 27$$

and

$$x \log_{10} 3 = \log_{10} 27 \text{ by the third law of logarithms.}$$

Rearranging gives $x = \dfrac{\log_{10} 27}{\text{Log}_{10} 3} = \dfrac{1.4314\ldots}{0.4771\ldots} = 3$

which may be readily checked

(Note, (log 8/log 2) is **not** equal to lg (8/2))

Example 8.12

Solve the equation $2_x = 3$, correct to 4 significant figures.

Taking logarithms to base 10 of both sides of $2^x = 3$ gives:

$$\log_{10} 2^x = \log_{10} 3$$
i.e. $x \log_{10} 2 = \log_{10} 3$

Rearranging gives:

$$x = \frac{\log_{10} 3}{\log_{10} 2} = \frac{0.47712125\ldots}{0.30102999\ldots} = \textbf{1.5850}$$

correct to 4 significant figures

Solve the following equations for x

1 $\log x^4 - \log x^3$
   $= \log 5x - \log 2x$

2 $3^x = 6.41$ (correct to 3 decimal places)

3 $x^{1.5} = 14.91$ (correct to 4 significant figures)

4 $0.027^x = 3.26$ (correct to 4 decimal places)

Example 8.13

Solve the equation $x^{3.2} = 41.15$, correct to 4 significant figures.

Taking logarithms to base 10 of both sides gives:

$$\log_{10} x^{3.2} = \log_{10} 41.15$$

$$3.2 \log_{10} x = \log_{10} 41.15$$

Hence $\log_{10} x = \dfrac{\log_{10} 41.15}{3.2} = 0.50449$

Thus $x = $ antilog $0.50449 = 10^{0.50449} = \mathbf{3.195}$ correct to 4 significant figures

---

Basic algebraic operations

Algebra is that part of mathematics in which the relations and properties of numbers are investigated by means of general symbols. For example, the area of a rectangle is found by multiplying the length by the breadth; this is expressed algebraically as $A = l \times b$, where A represents the area, l the length and b the breadth.

The basic laws introduced in arithmetic are generalized in algebra. Let a, b, c and d represent any four numbers. Then:

(i) $a + (b + c) = (a + b) + c$

(ii) $a(bc) = (ab)c$

(iii) $a + b = b + a$

(iv) $ab = ba$

(v) $a(b + c) = ab + ac$

(vi) $\dfrac{a + b}{c} = \dfrac{a}{c} + \dfrac{b}{c}$

(vii) $(a + b)(c + d) = ac + ad + bc + bd$

Example 8.14

Evaluate $3ab - 2bc + abc$ when $a = 1$, $b = 3$ and $c = 5$

Replacing a, b and c with their numerical values gives:

$$3ab - 2bc + abc = 3 \times 1 \times 3 - 2 \times 3 \times 5 + 1 \times 3 \times 5$$
$$= 9 - 30 + 15 = \mathbf{-6}$$

Example 8.15

Find the sum of $3x$, $2x$, $-x$ and $-7x$.

The sum of the positive terms is $3x + 2x = 5x$

The sum of the negative terms is $x + 7x = 8x$

Taking the sum of the negative terms from the sum of the positive terms gives:

$$5x - 8x = \mathbf{-3x}$$

Alternatively

$$3x + 3x + (-x) + (-7x) = 3x + 2x - x - 7x = \mathbf{-3x}$$

Example 8.16

Find the sum of $4a$, $3b$, c, $-2a$, $-5b$ and $6c$.

Each symbol must be dealt with individually.

for the 'a' terms: $+4a - 2a = 2a$

for the 'b' terms: $+3b - 5b = -2b$

for the 'c' terms: $+c + 6c = 7c$

Thus $4a + 3b + c + (-2a) + (-5b) + 6c = 4a + 3b + c -2a - 5b + 6c$

$$= \mathbf{2a - 2b + 7c}$$

Example 8.17

Find the sum of $5a - 2b$, $2a + c$, $4b - 5d$ and $b - a + 3d - 4c$.

The algebraic expressions may be tabulated as shown below, forming columns for the as, bs, cs and ds. Thus:

$$
\begin{array}{rrrrr}
+5a & - 2b & & & \\
+2a & + & & c & \\
& + 4b & & & - 5d \\
- a & + b & - 4c & + 3d &
\end{array}
$$

Adding gives: $\mathbf{6a + 3b - 3c - 2d}$

Example 8.18

Subtract $2x + 3y - 4z$ from $x - 2y + 5z$

$$
\begin{array}{rrr}
x & - 2y & + 5z \\
2x & + 3y & - 4z
\end{array}
$$

Subtracting gives: $\mathbf{-x - 5y + 9z}$

(Note that $+5z - -4z = +5z + 4z = 9z$)

An alternative method of subtracting algebraic expressions is to 'change the signs of the bottom line and add'. Hence:

$$
\begin{array}{rrr}
x & - 2y & + 5z \\
-2x & - 3y & + 4z
\end{array}
$$

Adding gives: $\mathbf{-x - 5y + 9z}$

Example 8.19

Multiply $2a + 3b$ by $a + b$

Each term in the first expression is multiplied by a, then each term in the first expression is multiplied by b, and the two results are added. The usual layout is shown below:

$$
\begin{array}{r}
2a + 3b \\
a + b \\
\hline
\end{array}
$$

Multiplying by $a \rightarrow$ $2a^2 + 3ab$

Multiplying by $b \rightarrow$ $+ 2ab + 3b^2$

Adding gives: $\mathbf{2a^2 + 5ab + 3b^2}$

Example 8.20

Divide $2x^2 + x - 3$ by $x - 1$.

$2x^2 + x - 3$ is called the *dividend* and $x - 1$ the *divisor*. The usual layout is shown below with the dividend and divisor both arranged in descending powers of the symbols.

$$
\begin{array}{r}
2x + 3 \\
\hline
x - 1 \overline{)\, 2x^2 + x - 3} \\
2x^2 - 2x \\
\hline
3x - 3 \\
3x - 3 \\
\hline
\bullet \quad \bullet
\end{array}
$$

Dividing the first term of the dividend by the first term of the divisor, i.e. $(2x^2/x)$ gives $2x$, which is put above the first term of the dividend as shown. The divisor is then multiplied by $2x$, i.e. $2x(x - 1) = 2x^2 - 2x$, which is placed under the dividend as shown. Subtracting gives $3x - 3$. The process is then repeated, i.e. the first term of the divisor is divided into $3x$, giving 3, which is placed under the $3x - 3$. The remainder, on subtraction, is zero, which completes the process.

Thus $(2x^2 + x - 3) \div (x - 1) = \mathbf{(2x + 3)}$

(A check can be made on this answer by multiplying $(2x + 3)$ by $(x - 1)$, which should equal $2x^2 + x - 3$)

Test your knowledge 8.5

1 Evaluate $3pq^2r^3$ when $p = 2/3$, $q = -2$ and $r = -1$

2 From $4x - 3y + 2z$ subtract $x + 2y - 3z$

3 Multiply $5x - 2y$ by $x + y$

4 Divide $3x^2 + xy - 2y^2$ by $x + y$

Laws of Indices

Expressed algebraically, the laws of indices are:

(i) $a^m \times a^n = a^{m \div n}$

(ii) $\dfrac{a^m}{a^n} = a^{m-n}$

(iii) $(a^m)^n = a^{mn}$

(iv) $a^{m/n} = \sqrt[n]{a^m}$

(v) $a^{-n} = \dfrac{1}{a^n}$

(vi) $a^0 = 1$

Example 8.21

Simplify $a^3b^2c \times ab^3c^5$

Grouping like terms gives: $a^3 \times a \times b^2 \times b^3 \times c \times c^5$

Using the first law of indices gives: $a^{3+1} \times b^{2+3} \times c^{1+5}$

i.e. $a^4 \times b^5 \times c^6$ i.e. $\boldsymbol{a^4b^5c^6}$

Example 8.22

Simplify $a^3b^2c^4/abc^{-2}$ and evaluate when $a = 3$, $b = 1/8$ and $c = 2$.

Using the second law of indices,

$$\frac{a^3}{a} = a^{3-1} = a^2, \frac{b^2}{b} = b^{2-1} = b$$

and

$$\frac{c^4}{c^{-2}} = c^{4-2} = c^6. \quad \text{Thus } \frac{a^3b^2c^4}{abc^{-2}} = \boldsymbol{a^2bc^6}$$

When $a = 3$, $b = 1/8$ and $c = 2$,

$$a^2bc^6 = (3)^2 \frac{1}{8}(2)^6 = (9)\frac{1}{8}(64) = \boldsymbol{72}$$

Example 8.23

Simplify $\dfrac{x^2y^3 + xy^2}{xy}$.

Algebraic expressions of the form $\dfrac{a + b}{c}$ can be split into $a/c + b/c$.

Thus

$$\frac{x^2y^3 + xy^2}{xy} = \frac{x^2y^3}{xy} + \frac{xy^2}{xy} = x^{2-1}y^{3-1} + x^{1-1}y^{2-1}$$

$$= \boldsymbol{xy^2 + y}$$

(since $x^0 = 1$, from the sixth law of indices).

Example 8.24

Simplify $(p^3)^{1/2}(q^2)^4$.

Using the third law of indices gives:

$$p^{3 \times (1/2)}q^{2 \times 4}$$

i.e.

$$\boldsymbol{p^{(3/2)}q^8}$$

1 Simplify $\dfrac{(x^2y^3z)\,(x^3y^4z^2)}{(xyz)}$

and evaluate when

$x = 2$, $y = -\dfrac{1}{2}$ and $x = 3$

2 Simplify $\dfrac{a^3b + a^2b^3}{a^2b^2}$

3 Simplify $\dfrac{(a^3\sqrt{b}\,c^{-2})(ab)^{-1/2}}{(\sqrt{a})(c^{-3})}$

Example 8.25

Simplify $(a^3b)(a^{-4}b^{-2})$, expressing the answer with positive indices only.

Using the first law of indices gives: $a^{3+\,-4}b^{1+\,-2} = \boldsymbol{a^{-1}b^{-1}}$

Using the fifth law of indices gives: $a^{-1}b^{-1} = \dfrac{1}{a^{+1}b^{+1}} = \dfrac{1}{\boldsymbol{ab}}$

Brackets and factorization

When two or more terms in an algebraic expression contain a common factor, then this factor can be shown outside of a bracket. For example

$$ab + ac = a(b + c)$$

which is simply the reverse of law (v) of indices, and

$$6px + 2py - 4pz = 2p(3x + y - 2z)$$

This process is called *factorization*.

Example 8.26

Remove the brackets and simplify the expression

$$(3a + b) + 2(b + c) - 4(c + d)$$

Both b and c in the second bracket have to be multiplied by 2, and c and d in the third bracket by -4 when the brackets are removed. Thus:

$$(3a + b) + 2(b + c) - 4(c + d) = 3a + b + 2b + 2c - 4c - 4d$$

Collecting similar terms together gives: $\boldsymbol{3a + 3b - 2c - 4d}$

Example 8.27

Simplify $a^2 - (2a - ab) - a(3b + a)$

When the brackets are removed, both $2a$ and $-ab$ in the first bracket must be multiplied by -1 and both $3b$ and a in the second bracket by $-a$. Thus

$$a^2 - (2a - ab) - a(3b + a) = a^2 - 2a + ab - 3ab - a^2$$

Collecting similar terms together gives: $-2a - 2ab$

Since $-2a$ is a common factor the answer can be expressed as $\boldsymbol{-2a(1 + b)}$

Example 8.28

Simplify $(a + b)(a - b)$

Each term in the second bracket has to be multiplied by each term in the first bracket. Thus:

$$(a + b)(a - b) = a(a - b) + b(a - b) = a^2 - ab + ab - b^2 = \boldsymbol{a^2 - b^2}$$

Alternatively

$$\begin{array}{r} a + b \\ a - b \\ \hline \end{array}$$

Multiplying by $a \rightarrow$ $a^2 + ab$

Multiplying by $-b \rightarrow$ $- ab - b^2$

Adding gives: $a^2 \qquad - b^2$

Example 8.29

Remove the brackets from the expession $2[p^2 - 3(q + r) + q^2]$.

In this example there are two brackets and the 'inner' one is removed first.

Hence $2[p^2 - 3(q + r) + q^2] = 2[p^2 - 3q - 3r + q^2]$

$$= \boldsymbol{2p^2 - 6q - 6r + 2q^2}$$

Example 8.30

Remove the brackets and simplify the expression

$$2a - [3\{2(4a - b) - 5(a + 2b)\} + 4a]$$

Removing the innermost brackets gives:

$$2a - [3\{8a - 2b - 5a - 10b\} + 4a]$$

Collecting together similar terms gives:

$$2a - 3[\{3a - 12b\} + 4a]$$

Removing the 'curly' brackets gives:

$$2a - [9a - 36b + 4a]$$

Collecting together similar terms gives:

$$2a - [13a - 36b]$$

Removing the outer brackets gives:

$$2a - 13a + 36b$$

i.e.

$$\boldsymbol{-11a + 36b \text{ or } 36b - 11a}$$

Example 8.31

Factorize (a) $xy - 3xz$, (b) $4a^2 + 16ab^3$, (c) $3a^2b - 6ab^2 + 15ab$

For each part of this problem, the HCF of the terms will become one of the factors. Thus:

(a) $xy - 3xz$ = $x(y - 3z)$

(b) $4a^2 + 16ab^3$ = $4a(a + 4b^3)$

(c) $3a^2b - 6ab^2 + 15ab = 3ab(a - 2b + 5)$

Fundamental laws and precedence

The *laws of precedence* which apply to arithmetic also apply to algebraic expressions. The order is Brackets, Of, Division, Multiplication, Addition and Subtraction (i.e. **BODMAS**).

Example 8.32

Simplify $2a + 5a \times 3a - a$

Multiplication is performed before addition and subtraction thus:

$$2a + 5a \times 3a - a = 2a + 15a^2 - a$$
$$= a + 15a^2 = a(1 + 15a)$$

Example 8.33

Simplify $(a + 5a) \times 2a - 3a$

The order of precedence is brackets, multiplication, then subtraction. Hence

$$(a + 5a) \times 2a - 3a = 6a \times 2a - 3a = 12a^2 - 3a$$
$$= 3a(4a - 1)$$

Example 8.34

Simplify $a \div 5a + 2a - 3a$

The order of precedence is division, then addition and subtraction. Hence

$$a \div 5a + 2a - 3a = \frac{a}{5a} + 2a - 3a = \frac{1}{5} + 2a - 3a$$
$$= \frac{1}{5} - a$$

Simplify the following:

1 $(3a - a) \div 2a - a$

2 $3b + 2 \div 3b + 2 \times 4 - 5b$

3 $2t^2 - (4st)(2t) \div 4s + st$

4 $\dfrac{1}{3}$ of $3p + 4p\,(3p - p)$

Example 8.35

Simplify $(3c + 2c)(4c + c) \div (5c - 8c)$

The order of precedence is brackets, division and multiplication. Hence:

$$(3c + 2c)(4c + c) \div (5c - 8c) = 5c \times 5c \div -3c$$

$$= 5c \times \frac{5c}{-3c}$$

$$= 5c \times \frac{5}{3} = -\frac{25}{3}c$$

Expressions, equations and identities

$(3x - 5)$ is an example of an *algebraic expression*, whereas $3x - 5 = 1$ is an example of an *equation* (i.e. it contains an 'equals' sign).

An equation is simply a statement that two quantities are equal. For example,

$$1\,\text{m} = 1000\,\text{mm} \quad \text{or} \quad y = mx + c.$$

An *identity* is a relationship which is true for all values of the unknown, whereas an equation is only true for particular values of the unknown. For example, $3x - 5 = 1$ is an equation, since it is only true when $x = 2$, whereas $3x \equiv 8x - 5x$ is an identity since it is true for all values of x. (Note '$\equiv$' means 'is identical to'.)

Simple linear equations (or equations of the first degree) are those in which an unknown quantity is raised only to the power 1.

To '*solve an equation*' means 'to find the value of the unknown'.

Any arithmetic operation may be applied to an equation *as long as the equality of the equation is maintained.*

Simple equations

Example 8.36

Solve the equation $4x = 20$.

Dividing each side of the equation by 4 gives: $\dfrac{4x}{4} = \dfrac{20}{4}$

(Note that the same operation has been applied to both the left-hand side (LHS) and the right-hand side (RHS) of the equation so the quality has been maintained.)

Cancelling gives **$x = 5$**, which is the solution to the equation. Solutions to simple equations should always be checked and this is accomplished by substituting the solution into the original equation. In this case,

$$\text{LHS} = 4(5) = 20 = \text{RHS}.$$

Example 8.37

Solve $\dfrac{2x}{5} = 6$.

The LHS is a fraction and this can be removed by multiplying both sides of the equation by 5. Hence

$$5\,\frac{2x}{5} = 5(6)$$

Cancelling gives: $2x = 30$

Dividing both sides of the equation by 2 gives: $\dfrac{2x}{2} = \dfrac{30}{2}$ i.e. **$x = 15$**

Example 8.38

Solve $6x + 1 = 2x + 9$

In such equations the terms containing x are grouped on one side of the equation and the remaining terms grouped on the other side of the equation. Changing from one side of an equation to the other must be accompanied by a change of sign.

Thus since $6x + 1 \;= 2x + 9$

then $\qquad 6x - 2x = \;\;9 - 1$

$$4x = \;\;8$$
$$\frac{4x}{4} \quad \frac{8}{4}$$

i.e. $\qquad\qquad$ **$x = 2$**

Check: LHS of original equation $= 6(2) + 1 = 13$
$\qquad\quad$ RHS of original equation $= 2(2) + 9 = 13$

Hence the solution $x = 2$ is correct.

Example 8.39

Solve $3(x - 2) = 9$.

Removing the bracket gives: $3x - 6 \;=\; 9$

Rearranging gives: $\qquad\qquad 3x = \;\;9 + 6$

$$3x = 15$$
$$\frac{3x}{3} \quad \frac{15}{3}$$

i.e. $\qquad\qquad$ **$x = 5$**

Check: LHS $= 3(5 - 2) = 3(3) = 9 = $ RHS

Hence the solution $x = 5$ is correct.

Example 8.40

Solve $\dfrac{3}{x} = \dfrac{4}{5}$.

The lowest common multiple (LCM) of the denominators, i.e. the lowest algebraic expression that both x and 5 will divide into, is $5x$. Multiplying both sides by $5x$ gives:

$$5x\,\frac{3}{x} = 5x\,\frac{4}{5}$$

Cancelling gives:

$$15 = 4x \tag{1}$$

$$\frac{15}{4} = \frac{4x}{4}$$

i.e.

$$x = \frac{15}{4} \text{ or } 3\frac{3}{4}$$

Check: LHS $= \dfrac{3}{3\frac{3}{4}} = \dfrac{3}{\frac{15}{4}} = 3\,\dfrac{4}{15} = \dfrac{12}{15} = \dfrac{4}{5} = $ RHS

(Note that when there is only one fraction on each side of an equation, 'cross-multiplication' can be applied. In this example, if

$$\frac{3}{x} = \frac{4}{5}$$

then $(3)(5) = 4x$, which is a quicker way of arriving at equation (1) above.)

Example 8.41

Solve $2\sqrt{d} = 8$

To avoid possible errors it is usually best to arrange the term containing the square root on its own. Thus

$$\frac{2\sqrt{d}}{2} = \frac{8}{2}$$

i.e.

$$\sqrt{d} = 4$$

Squaring both sides gives: $d = 16$, which may be checked in the original equation.

Example 8.42

Solve $x^2 = 25$.

This example involves a square term and thus is not a simple equation (it is, in fact, a quadratic equation). However, the solution of such an equation is often required and is therefore included for completeness.

Solve the following equations:

1 $x + 3 = 7$

2 $4 - 3p = 2p - 11$

3 $\dfrac{2y}{5} + \dfrac{3}{4} + 5 = \dfrac{1}{20} - \dfrac{3y}{2}$

4 $\dfrac{\sqrt{b} + 3}{\sqrt{b}} = 2$

5 $8 = \dfrac{y^2}{2}$

Whenever a square of the unknown is involved, the square root of both sides of the equation is taken. Hence

$$\sqrt{x^2} = \sqrt{25}$$

i.e.

$$x = 5$$

However, $x = -5$ is also a solution of the equation because $(-5) \times (-5) = +25$. Therefore, whenever the square root of a number is required there are always two answers, one positive, the other negative.

The solution of $x^2 = 25$ is thus written as **$x = \pm 5$**

Practical problems involving simple equations

Example 8.43

A copper wire has a length 1 of 1.5 km, a resistance R of $5\,\Omega$ and a resistivity of $17.2 \times 10^{-6}\,\Omega$ mm. Find the cross-sectional area, a, of the wire, given that $R = l/a$.

Since $R = l/a$ then

$$5\,\Omega = \frac{(1.72 \times 10^{-6}\,\Omega\ \text{mm})(1500 \times 10^3\,\text{mm})}{a}$$

From the units given, a is measured in mm². Thus

$$5a = 17.2 \times 10^{-6} \times 1500 \times 10^3$$

$$a = \frac{17.2 \times 10^{-6} \times 1500 \times 10^3}{5}$$

$$= \frac{17.2 \times 1500 \times 10^3}{10^6 \times 5} = \frac{17.2 \times 15^3}{10 \times 5} = 5.16$$

Hence the cross-sectional area of the wire is **5.16 mm²**.

Example 8.44

The temperature coefficient of resistance α may be calculated from the formula $R_t = R_0(1 + \alpha t)$. Find α given $R_t = 0.928$, $R_0 = 0.8$ and $t = 40$

Since $R_t = R_0(1 + \alpha t)$ then $0.928 = 0.8[1 + \alpha(40)]$

$$0.928 = 0.8 + (0.8)(\alpha)(40)$$

$$0.928 - 0.8 = 32\alpha$$

$$0.128 = 32\alpha$$

Hence

$$\alpha = \frac{0.128}{32} = \mathbf{0.004}$$

Example 8.45

The distance s metres travelled in time t seconds is given by the formula $s = ut + 1/2at^2$, where u is the initial velocity in m/s and a is the acceleration in m/s². Find the acceleration of the body if it travels 168 m in 6 s, with an initial velocity of 10 m/s

$$s = ut + \frac{1}{2} at^2, \text{ and } s = 168, u = 10 \text{ and } t = 6$$

Hence

$$168 = (10)(6) + \frac{1}{2} a(6)^2$$

$$168 = 60 + 18a$$

$$168 - 60 = 18a$$

$$108 = 18a$$

$$a = \frac{108}{18} = 6$$

Hence the acceleration of the body is **6 m/s²**

Test your knowledge 8.10

1 A rectangular box with square ends has its length 15 cm greater than its breadth and the total length of its edges is 2.04 m. Find the width of the box and its volume.

2 $v^2 = u^2 + 2as$ is an equation of linear motion. Find u, given $v = 30$, $a = -20$ and $s = 6.4$

3 A painter is paid £4.20 per hour for a basic 36 hour week, and overtime is paid at one and a third times this rate. Determine how many hours the painter has to work in a week to earn £212.80.

4 The stress f in a material of a thick cylinder can be obtained from

$$\frac{D}{d} = \sqrt{\frac{f + p}{f = p}}.$$

Calculate the stress given that $D = 21.5$, $d = 10.75$ and $p = 1800$.

Example 8.46

The extension x metres of an aluminium tie bar of length 1 metre and cross-sectional area A square metres when carrying a load of F newtons is given by the modulus of elasticity $E = Fl/Ax$. Find the extension of the tie bar (in mm) if $E = 70 \times 10^9$ N/m², $F = 20 \times 10^6$ N, $A = 0.1$ m² and $l = 1.4$ m

$$E = Fl/Ax. \quad \text{Hence } 70 \times 10^9 \frac{N}{m^2} = \frac{(20 \times 10^6 \text{ N})(1.4 \text{ m})}{(0.1 \text{ m}^2)(x)}$$

(the unit of x is thus metres).

$$70 \times 10^9 \times 0.1 \times x = 20 \times 10^6 \times 1.4$$

$$x = \frac{20 \times 10^6 \times 1.4}{70 \times 10^9 \times 0.1}$$

Cancelling gives: $x = \dfrac{2 \times 1.4}{6 \times 100} \text{ m} = \dfrac{2 \times 1.4}{7 \times 100} \times 1000 \text{ mm}$

Hence the extension of the tie bar, **$x = 4$ mm**

Introduction to simultaneous equations

Only one equation is necessary when finding the value of a *single unknown quantity* (as with simple equations). When an equation contains *two unknown quantities* it has an infinite number of solutions. When two equations are available connecting the same two unknown values then a unique solution is possible. Similarly, for three unknown quantities it is necessary to have three equations in order to solve for a particular value of each of the unknown quantities, and so on.

Equations which have to be solved together to find the unique values of the unknown quantities, which are true for each of the equations, are called *simultaneous equations*. There are two methods of solving simultaneous equations analytically:

(a) by *substitution*, and (b) by *elimination*.

Solving simultaneous equations

Example 8.47

Solve the following equations for x and y (a) by substitution, and (b) by elimination:

$$x + 2y = -1 \tag{1}$$

$$4x - 3y = 18 \tag{2}$$

(a) *By substitution*

From equation (1): $x = -1 - 2y$

Substituting this expression for x into equation (2) gives:

$$4(-1 - 2y) - 3y = 18$$

This is now a simple equation in y.

Removing the bracket gives:

$$-4 - 8y - 3y = 18$$

$$-11y = 18 + 4 = 22$$

$$y = \frac{22}{-11} = -2$$

Substituting $y = -2$ into equation (1) gives:

$$x + 2(-2) = -1$$

$$x - 4 = -1$$

$$x = -1 + 4 = 3$$

Thus **$x = 3$** and **$y = -2$** is the solution to the simultaneous equations

(Check: In equation (2), since $x = 3$ and $y = -2$,

$$\text{LHS} = 4(3) - 3(-2)$$

$$= 12 + 6 = 18 = \text{RHS})$$

(b) *By elimination*

$$x + 2y -1 \tag{1}$$

$$4x - 3y = 18 \tag{2}$$

If equation (1) is multiplied throughout by 4 the coefficient of x will be the same as in equation (2), giving:

$$4x + 8y = -4 \tag{3}$$

Subtracting equation (3) from equation (2) gives:

$$
\begin{array}{ll}
4x - \quad 3y = 18 & (2) \\
4x + \quad 8y = -4 & (3) \\
\hline
0 - 11y = 22 &
\end{array}
$$

Hence $y = \dfrac{22}{-11} = -2$

(Note, in the above subtraction, $18 - -4 = 18 + 4 = 22$.)

Substituting $y = -2$ into either equation (1) or equation (2) will give $x = 3$ as in method (a). The solution $x = 3$, $y = -2$ is the only pair of values that satisfies both of the original equations.

Example 8.48

Solve $7x - 2y = 26$ (1)

     $6x + 5y = 29$ (2)

When equation (1) is multiplied by 5 and equation (2) by 2 the coefficients of y in each equation are numerically the same, i.e. 10, but are of opposite sign.

   5 × equation (1) gives: $35x - 10y = 130$ (3)
   2 × equation (2) gives: $12x + 10y = 58$ (4)

   Adding equation (3) and (4) gives: $47x + 0 = 188$

Hence $x = \dfrac{188}{47} = 4$

(Note that when the signs of common coefficients are *different* the two equations are *added*, and when the signs of common coefficients are the *same* the two equations are *subtracted*.

Substituting $x = 4$ in equation (1) gives:

     $7(4) - 2y = 26$
       $28 - 2y = 26$
      $28 - 26 = 2y$
          $2 = 2y$
Hence $y = 1$

Checking, by substituting $x = 4$, $y = 1$ in equation (2), gives:

   LHS $= 6(4) + 5(1) = 24 + 5 = 29 = $ RHS

Thus the solution is $x = 4$, $y = 1$, since these values maintain the equality when substituted in both equations.

Example 8.49

Solve $\dfrac{2}{x} + \dfrac{3}{y} = 7$ (1)

    $\dfrac{1}{x} - \dfrac{4}{y} = -2$ (2)

In this type of equation a substitution can initially be made.

   Let $\dfrac{1}{x} = a$ and $\dfrac{1}{y} = b$

Thus equation (1) becomes: $\qquad 2a + 3b = 7 \qquad$ (3)

and equation (2) becomes: $\qquad a - 4b = -2 \qquad$ (4)

Multiplying equation (4) by 2 gives: $2a - 8b = -4 \qquad$ (5)

Subtracting equation (5) from equation (3) gives:

$$0 + 11b = 11$$

i.e. $\qquad b = 1$

Substituting $b = 1$ in equation (3) gives:

$$2a + 3 = 7$$
$$2a = 7 - 3 = 4$$

i.e. $\qquad a = 2$

Checking, substituting $a = 2$, $b = 1$ in equation (4) gives:

$$\text{LHS} = 2 - 4(1) = 2 - 4 = -2 = \text{RHS}$$

Hence $a = 2$, $b = 1$

However, since $\dfrac{1}{x} = a$ then $x = \dfrac{1}{a} = \dfrac{1}{2}$

and since $\qquad \dfrac{1}{y} = b$ then $y = \dfrac{1}{b} = \dfrac{1}{1} = 1$

Hence the solution is

$$x = \frac{1}{2}, \ y = 1,$$

which may be checked in the original equations.

Test your knowledge 8.11

Solve the following simultaneous equations

1. $2x + 5y = 7$
   $x + 3y = 4$

2. $3p = 2q$
   $4p + q + 11 = 0$

3. $2.5x + 0.75 - 3y = 0$
   $1.6x = 1.08 - 1.2y$

4. $\dfrac{x-1}{3} + \dfrac{y+2}{5} = \dfrac{2}{15}$

   $\dfrac{1-x}{6} + \dfrac{5+y}{2} = \dfrac{5}{6}$

Practical problems involving simultaneous equations

Example 8.50

The law connecting friction F and load L for an experiment is of the form $F = aL + b$, where a and b are constants. When $F = 5.6$, $L = 8.0$ and when $F = 4.4$, $L = 2.0$. Find the values of a and b and the value of F when $L = 6.5$.

Substituting $F = 5.6$, $L = 8.0$ into $F = aL + b$ gives:

$$5.6 = 8.0a + b \qquad (1)$$

Substituting $F = 4.4$, $L = 2.0$ into $F = aL + b$ gives:

$$4.4 = 2.0a + b \qquad (2)$$

Subtracting equation (2) from equation (1) gives:

$$1.2 = 6.0 a$$

$$a = \frac{1.2}{6.0} = \frac{1}{5}$$

Substituting $a = \dfrac{1}{5}$ into equation (1) gives:

$$5.6 = 8.0\,\dfrac{1}{5} + b$$

$$5.6 = 1.6 + b$$

$$5.6 - 1.6 = b$$

i.e. $\qquad b = 4$

Checking, substituting $a = \dfrac{1}{5}$, $b = 4$ in equation (2), gives:

$$RHS = 2.0\,\dfrac{1}{5} + 4 = 0.4 + 4 = 4.4 = LHS$$

Hence $\boldsymbol{a = \dfrac{1}{5}}$ and $\boldsymbol{b = 4}$

When $L = 6.5$, $F = aL + b = \dfrac{1}{5}(6.5) + 4 = 1.3 + 4$, i.e. $\boldsymbol{F = 5.30}$

Example 8.51

The distance s metres from a fixed point of a vehicle travelling in a straight line with constant acceleration, a metre/s^2, is given by

$$s = ut + \dfrac{1}{2}at^2$$

where u is the initial velocity in m/s and t the time in seconds. Determine the initial velocity and the acceleration given that $s = 42\,m$ when $t = 2\,s$ and $s = 144\,m$ when $t = 4\,s$. Find also the distance travelled after 3 s.

Substituting $s = 42$, $t = 2$ into $s = ut + \dfrac{1}{2}at^2$ gives:

$$42 = 2u + \dfrac{1}{2}a(2)^2$$

i.e. $42 = 2u + 2a$ \hfill (1)

Substituting $s = 144$, $t = 4$ into $s = ut + \dfrac{1}{2}at^2$ gives:

$$144 = 4u + \dfrac{1}{2}a(4)^2$$

i.e. $144 = 4u + 8a$ \hfill (2)

Multiplying equation (1) by 2 gives:

$84 = 4u + 4a$ \hfill (3)

Subtracting equation (3) from equation (2) gives:

$$60 = 0 + 4a$$

$$a = \dfrac{60}{4} = 15$$

Substituting $a = 15$ into equation (1) gives:

$$42 = 2u + 2(15)$$
$$42 - 30 = 2u$$
$$u = \frac{12}{2} = 6$$

Substituting $a = 15$, $u = 6$ in equation (2) gives:

$$RHS = 4(6) + 8(15) = 24 + 120 = 144 = LHS$$

Hence the initial velocity, $u = 6$ m/s and the acceleration, $a = 15$ m/s^2

Distance travelled after 3 s is given by $s = ut + \frac{1}{2}at^2$ where $t = 3$, $u = 6$ and $a = 15$

Hence $s = 6(3) + \frac{1}{2}(15)(3)^2$

$$= 18 + 67\frac{1}{2}$$

i.e. distance travelled after 3 s = **85.5 m**

Evaluation of formulae

The statement $v = u + at$ is said to be a *formula* for v in terms of v, a and t. v, u, a and t are called *symbols*. The single term on the left-hand side of the equation, v, is called the *subject of the formula*.

Provided values are given for all the symbols in a formula except one, the remaining symbol can be made the subject of the formula and may be evaluated by using a calculator.

Example 8.52

In an electrical circuit the voltage V is given by Ohm's law, i.e. $V = IR$. Find, correct to 4 significant figures, the voltage when $I = 5.36$ A and $R = 14.76$ Ω.

$$V = IR = (5.36)(14.76)$$

Hence voltage **V = 79.11 V**, correct to 4 significant figures.

Example 8.53

The surface area A of a hollow cone is given by $A = \pi rl$. Determine the surface area when $r = 3.0$ cm, $l = 8.5$ cm and $\pi = 3.14$.

$$A = \pi rl = (3.14)(3.0)(8.5) \text{ cm}^2$$

Hence surface area **A = 80.07 cm^2**

Example 8.54

Velocity v is given by $v = u + at$. If $u = 9.86$ m/s, $a = 4.25$ m/s^2 and $t = 6.84$ s, find v, correct to 3 significant figures.

$$v = u + at = 9.86 + (4.25)(6.84)$$

$$= 9.86 + 29.07 = 38.93$$

Hence velocity v = **38.9 m/s**, correct to 3 significant figures.

1 The area, A, of a circle is given by $A = \pi r^2$. Determine the area correct to 2 decimal places, given $\pi = 3.142$ and $r = 5.23$ m.
2 Force F newtons is given by the formula $F = (Gm_1m_2)/d^2$, where m_1 and m_2 are masses, d their distance apart and G is a constant. Find the value of the force given that $G = 6.67 \times 10^{-11}$, $m_1 = 7.36$, $m_2 = 15.5$ and $d = 22.6$. Express the answer in standard form, correct to 3 significant figures.
3 The volume V cm^3 of a right circular cone is given by

$$V = \frac{1}{3}\pi r^2 h.$$

Given that $r = 4.321$ cm, $h = 18.35$ cm and $\pi = 3.142$, find the volume correct to 4 significant figures.
4 The current I amperes in an a.c. circuit is given by

$$I = \frac{V}{\sqrt{(R^2 + X^2)}}.$$

Evaluate the current when $V = 250$, $R = 11.0$ and $X = 16.2$

Example 8.55

The power P watts dissipated in an electrical circuit may be expressed by the formula $P = V^2/R$. Evaluate the power, correct to 3 significant figures, given that $V = 17.48$ V and $R = 36.12$ Ω

$$P = \frac{V^2}{R} = \frac{(17.48)^2}{36.12} = \frac{305.6}{36.12}$$

Hence power, P = **8.46 W**, correct to 3 significant figures.

Example 8.56

The time of swing, t seconds, of a simple pendulum is given by $t = 2\pi\sqrt{(l/g)}$. Determine the time, correct to 3 decimal places, given that $\pi = 3.142$, $l = 12.0$ and $g = 9.81$.

$$t = 2\pi\sqrt{\frac{1}{g}} = (2)(3.142)\sqrt{\frac{12.0}{9.81}}$$

$$= (2)(3.142)\sqrt{(1.223)}$$

$$= (2)(3.142)(1.106)$$

Hence time t = **6.950 seconds**, correct to 3 decimal places.

Transposition of formulae

When the symbol other than the subject is required to be calculated it is usual to rearrange the formula to make a new subject. This rearranging process is called *transposing the formula* or *transposition*.

The rules used for transposition of formulae are the same as those used for the solution of simple equations – basically, *that the equality of an equation must be maintained.*

Example 8.57

Transpose $p = q + r + s$ to make r the subject.

The aim is to obtain r on its own on the left-hand side (LHS) of the equation. Changing the equation around so that r is on the LHS gives:

$$q + r + s = p \qquad (1)$$

Subtracting $(q + s)$ from both sides of the equation gives:

$$q + r + s - (q + s) = p - (q + s)$$

Thus

$$q + r + s - q - s = p - q - s$$

i.e. $\boldsymbol{r = p - q - s}$ $\qquad (2)$

It is shown with simple equations, that a quantity can be moved from one side of an equation to the other with an appropriate change of sign. Thus equation (2) follows immediately from equation (1) above.

Example 8.58

When a body falls freely through a height h, the velocity v is given by $v^2 = 2gh$. Express this formula with h as the subject.

Rearranging gives: $2gh = v^2$

Dividing both sides by 2g gives: $\dfrac{2gh}{2g} - \dfrac{v^2}{2g}$, i.e. $\boldsymbol{h = \dfrac{v^2}{2g}}$

Example 8.59

Transpose the formula $v = u + (ft)/m$, to make f the subject.

Rearranging gives: $u + \dfrac{ft}{m} = v$, and $\dfrac{ft}{m} = v - u$

Multiplying each side by m gives:

$$m\,\frac{ft}{m} = m(v - u), \text{ i.e. } ft = m(v - u)$$

Dividing both sides by t gives:

$$\frac{ft}{t} = \frac{m}{t}(v - u), \text{ i.e. } \boldsymbol{f = \frac{m}{t}(v - u)}$$

Example 8.60

A formula for the distance moved by a body is given by $s = \dfrac{1}{2}(v + u)t$.

Rearrange the formula to make u the subject.

Rearranging gives: $\dfrac{1}{2}(v + u)t = s$

Multiplying both sides by 2 gives: $(v + u)t = 2s$

Dividing both sides by t gives: $\dfrac{(v + u)t}{t} = \dfrac{2s}{t}$

i.e. $v + u = \dfrac{2s}{t}$

Hence $\boldsymbol{u = \dfrac{2s}{t} - v}$ or $\dfrac{2s - vt}{t}$

Make the symbol indicated in brackets the subject of each of the following formulae:

1 $a = \dfrac{F}{m}$ (m)

2 $l_2 = l_1 (1 + \alpha\theta)$ (α)

3 $t = 2\pi\sqrt{\dfrac{l}{g}}$ (g)

4 $I = \dfrac{E - e}{R + r}$ (R)

5 $p = \dfrac{a^2x + a^2y}{r}$ (a)

Example 8.61

The impedance of an a.c. circuit is given by $Z = \sqrt{(R^2 + X^2)}$. Make the reactance, X, the subject.

Rearranging gives: $\sqrt{(R^2 + X^2)} = Z$

Squaring both sides gives: $R^2 + X^2 = Z^2$

Rearranging gives: $X^2 = Z^2 - R^2$

Taking the square root of both sides gives: $\boldsymbol{X = \sqrt{(Z^2 - R^2)}}$

Introduction to quadratic equations

An *equation* is a statement that two quantities are equal. To '*solve an equation*' means 'to find the value of the unknown'. The value of the unknown is called the *root* of the equation.

A *quadratic equation* is one in which the highest power of the unknown quantity is 2. For example, $x^2 - 3x + 1 = 0$ is a quadratic equation.

There are four methods of *solving quadratic equations*. These are: (i) by factorization (where possible), (ii) by 'completing the square', (iii) by using the 'quadratic formula', or (iv) graphically (see the third section of this chapter).

Solution of quadratic equations by factorization

Multiplying out $(2x + 1)(x - 3)$ gives $2x^2 - 6x + x - 3$, i.e. $2x^2 - 5x - 3$. The reverse process of moving from $2x^2 - 5x - 3$ to $(2x + 1)(x - 3)$ is called *factorizing*.

If the quadratic expression can be factorized this provides the simplest method of solving a quadratic equation. For example, if $2x^2 - 5x - 3 = 0$, then, by factorizing:

$(2x + 1)(x - 3) = 0$

Hence either $(2x + 1) = 0$, i.e. $x = \dfrac{1}{2}$

or $(x - 3) = 0$, i.e. $x = 3$

The technique of factorizing is often one of 'trial and error'.

Example 8.62

Solve the equations (a) $x^2 + 2x - 8 = 0$ and (b) $3x^2 - 11x - 4 = 0$ by factorization.

(a) $x^2 + 2x - 8 = 0$. The factors of x^2 are x and x. These are placed in brackets thus: $(x\ )(x\ )$

The factors of -8 are $+8$ and -1, or -8 and $+1$, or $+4$ and -2, or -4 and $+2$.

The only combination to give a middle term of $+2x$ is $+4$ and -2, i.e.

$$x^2 + 2x - 8 = (x - 2)(x + 4)$$

(Note that the product of the two inner terms added to the product of the two outer terms must equal the middle term, $+2x$ in this case.) The quadratic equation $x2 + 2x - 8 = 0$ thus becomes $(x + 4)(x - 2) = 0$. Since the only way that this can be true is for either the first or the second, or both factors to be zero, then

either $(x + 4) = 0$ i.e. $x = -4$

or $(x - 2) = 0$ i.e. $x = 2$

Hence the roots of $x^2 + 2x - 8 = 0$ are $x = -4$ and 2.

(b) $3x^2 - 11x - 4 = 0$

The factors of $3x^2$ are $3x$ and x. These are placed in brackets thus:

$(x\ )(3x\ )$

The factors of -4 are -4 and $+1$, or $+4$ and -1, or -2 and 2.

Remembering that the product of the two inner terms added to the product of the two outer terms must equal $-11x$, the only combination to give this is -4 and $+1$, i.e.

$$3x^2 - 11x - 4 = (3x + 1)(x - 4)$$

The quadratic equation $3x^2 - 11x - 4 = 0$ thus becomes $(3x + 1)(x - 4) = 0$.

Hence,

either $(3x + 1) = 0$ i.e. $x = \dfrac{1}{3}$

or $(x - 4) = 0$ i.e. $x = 4$

and both solutions may be checked in the original equation.

Example 8.63

Determine the roots of (a) $x^2 - 6x + 9 = 0$, and (b) $4x^2 - 25 = 0$, by factorization.

(a) $x^2 - 6x + 9 = 0$. Hence $(x - 3)(x - 3) = 0$, i.e. $(x - 3)^2 = 0$ (the left-hand side is known as *a perfect square*). Hence $x = 3$ is the only root of the equation $x^2 - 6x + 9 = 0$.

(b) $4x^2 - 25 = 0$ (the left-hand side is *the difference of two squares*, $(2x)^2$ and $(5)^2$). Hence $(2x + 5)(2x - 5) = 0$

Hence either $(2x + 5) = 0$ i.e. $x = -\dfrac{5}{2}$

or $(2x - 5) = 0$ i.e. $x = \dfrac{5}{2}$

Example 8.64

The roots of a quadratic equation are $\dfrac{1}{3}$ and -2. Determine the equation.

If the roots of a quadratic equation are α and β then $(x - \alpha)$ $(x - \beta) = 0$.

Hence if $\alpha = \dfrac{1}{3}$ and $\beta = -2$, then

$$x - \frac{1}{2}(x - (-2)) = 0$$

$$x - \frac{1}{2}(x + 2) = 0$$

$$x^2 - \frac{1}{3}x + 2x - \frac{2}{3} = 0$$

$$x^2 + \frac{5}{3}x - \frac{2}{3} = 0$$

Hence $3x^2 + 5x - 2 = 0$

Test your knowledge 8.15

In questions 1 to 3 solve the equations by factorization:

1 $x^2 + x - 6 = 0$

2 $2x^2 - x - 6 = 0$

3 $15x^2 + 2x - 8 = 0$

4 Find the equation in x whose roots are (a) 5 and -5 (b) 1.2 and -0.4.

Solution of quadratic equations by 'completing the square'

An expression such as x^2 or $(x + 2)^2$ or $(x - 3)^2$ is called a perfect square.

> If $x^2 = 3$ then $x = \pm\sqrt{3}$
>
> If $(x + 2)^2 = 5$ then $x + 2 = \pm\sqrt{5}$ and $x = -2 \pm \sqrt{5}$
>
> If $(x - 3)^2 = 8$ then $x - 3 = \pm\sqrt{8}$ and $x = 3 \pm \sqrt{8}$

Hence if a quadratic equation can be rearranged so that one side of the equation is a perfect square and the other side of the equation is a number, then the solution of the equation is readily obtained by taking the square roots of each side as in the above equation. The process of rearranging one side of a quadratic equation into a perfect square before solving is called *'completing the square'*.

$$(x + a)^2 = x^2 + 2ax + a^2$$

Thus in order to make the quadratic expression $x^2 + 2ax$ into a perfect square it is necessary to add (half the coefficient of $x)^2$, i.e.

$$\frac{2a^2}{2} \text{ or } a^2$$

For example, $x^2 + 3x$ becomes a perfect square by adding $(3/2)^2$, i.e.

$$x^2 + 3x + \frac{3^2}{2} = x + \frac{3^2}{2}$$

The method is demonstrated in the following worked problems.

Example 8.65

Solve $2x^2 + 5x = 3$ by 'completing the square'.

The procedure is as follows:

1 Rearrange the equation so that all terms are on the same side of the equals sign (and the coefficient of the x^2 term is positive).

Hence $2x^2 + 5x - 3 = 0$.

2 Make the coefficient of the x^2 term unity. In this case this is achieved by dividing throughout by 2. Hence

$$\frac{2x^2}{2} + \frac{5x}{2} - \frac{3}{2} = 0$$

i.e. $x^2 + \frac{5}{2}x - \frac{3}{2} = 0$

3 Rearrange the equations so that the x^2 and x terms are on one side of the equals sign and the constant is on the other side. Hence

$$x^2 + \frac{5}{2}x = \frac{3}{2}$$

4 Add to both sides of the equation (half the coefficient of x)^2. In this case the coefficient of x is $\frac{5}{2}$. Half the coefficient squared is therefore $(5/4)^2$. Thus

$$x^2 + \frac{5}{2}x + \frac{5^2}{4} = \frac{3}{2} + \frac{5^2}{4}$$

The LHS is now a perfect square, i.e.

$$x + \frac{5^2}{4} = \frac{3}{2} + \frac{5^2}{4}$$

5 Evaluate the RHS. Thus

$$x + \frac{5^2}{4} = \frac{3}{2} + \frac{25}{16} = \frac{24 + 25}{16} = \frac{49}{16}$$

6 Taking the square root of both sides of the equation (remembering that the square root of a number gives a ± answer). Thus

$$\sqrt{x + \frac{5^2}{4}} = \sqrt{\frac{49}{16}}$$

i.e. $x + \frac{5}{4} = \pm\frac{7}{4}$

7 Solve the simple equation. Thus

$$x = -\frac{5}{4} \pm \frac{7}{4}$$

i.e. $x = -\frac{5}{4} + \frac{7}{4} = \frac{2}{4} = \frac{1}{2}$

and $x = -\frac{5}{4} - \frac{7}{4} = -\frac{12}{4} = -3$

Hence $x = \frac{1}{2}$ or -3 are the roots of the equation $2x^2 + 5x = 3$.

Solution of quadratic equations by formulae

Let the general form of a quadratic equation be given by:

$$ax^2 + bx + c = 0$$

where a, b and c are constants.

Dividing $ax^2 + bx + c = 0$ by a gives:

$$x^2 + \frac{b}{c}c + \frac{c}{a} = 0$$

Rearranging gives:

$$x^2 + \frac{b}{a}x = -\frac{c}{a}$$

Adding to each side of the equation the square of half the coefficient of the term in x to make the LHS a perfect square gives:

$$x^2 + \frac{b}{a}x + \frac{b^2}{2a} = \frac{b^2}{2a} - \frac{c}{a}$$

Rearranging gives:

$$x + \frac{b^2}{2a} = \frac{b^2}{4a^2} - \frac{c}{a} = \frac{b^2 - 4ac}{4a^2}$$

Taking the square root of both sides gives:

$$x + \frac{b}{2a} = \sqrt{\frac{b^2 - 4ac}{4a^2}} = \frac{\pm\sqrt{(b^2 - 4ac)}}{2a}$$

Hence $x = -\dfrac{b}{2a} \pm \dfrac{\sqrt{(b^2 - 4ac)}}{2a}$

i.e. the quadratic formula is $x = \dfrac{-b \pm \sqrt{(b^2 - 4ac)}}{2a}$

(This method of solution is 'completing the square' – as shown earlier.) Summarizing:

$$\text{if } ax^2 + bx + c = 0 \text{ then } x = \frac{-b \pm \sqrt{(b^2 - 4ac)}}{2a}$$

This is known as the *quadratic formula*.

Example 8.66

Solve (a) $x^2 + 2x - 8 = 0$ and (b) $3x^2 - 11x - 4 = 0$ by using the quadratic formula.

(a) Comparing $x^2 + 2x - 8 = 0$ with $ax^2 + bx + c = 0$ gives $a = 1$, $b = 2$ and $c = -8$

Substituting these values into the quadratic formula

$$x = \frac{-b \pm \sqrt{(b^2 - 4ac)}}{2a}$$

gives:

$$x = \frac{-2 \pm \sqrt{[(2)^2 - 4(1)(-8)]}}{2(1)}$$

$$= \frac{-2 \pm \sqrt{(4 + 32)}}{2} = \frac{-2 \pm \sqrt{36}}{2}$$

$$= \frac{-2 \pm 6}{2} = \frac{-2 + 6}{2} \text{ or } \frac{-2 - 6}{2}$$

Hence $x = \frac{4}{2} = 2$ or $\frac{-8}{2} = -4$

(b) Comparing $3x^2 - 11x - 4 = 0$ with $ax^2 + bx + c = 0$ gives $a = 3$, $b = -11$ and $c = -4$. Hence

$$x = \frac{-(-11) \pm \sqrt{[(-22)^2 - 4(3)(-4)]}}{2(3)}$$

$$= \frac{+11 \pm \sqrt{(121 + 48)}}{6} = \frac{11 \pm \sqrt{169}}{6}$$

$$= \frac{11 \pm 13}{6} = \frac{11 + 13}{6} \text{ or } \frac{11 - 13}{6}$$

Hence $x = \frac{24}{6} = 4$ or $\frac{-2}{6} = -\frac{1}{3}$

Test your knowledge 8.17

Solve the following equations by using the quadratic formula:

1 $2x^2 + 5x - 3 = 0$

2 $3x^2 - 11x - 4 = 0$

3 $x^2 - 27x + 38 = 0$
   (correct to 4 significant figures)

Practical problems involving quadratic equations

There are many *practical problems* where a quadratic equation has first to be obtained, from given information, before it is solved.

Example 8.67

Calculate the diameter of a solid cylinder which has a height of 82.0 cm and a total surface area of 2.0 m²

Total surface area of a cylinder = curved surface area + 2 circular ends

$$= 2\pi rh + 2\pi r^2 \text{ (where } r = \text{radius and } h = \text{height)}$$

Since the total surface area = 2.0 m² and the height h = 82 cm or 0.82 m, then

$$2.0 = 2\pi r(0.82) + 2\pi r^2$$

i.e. $2\pi r^2 + 2\pi r(0.82) - 2.0 = 0$

Dividing throughout by 2π gives:

$$r^2 + 0.82r - \frac{1}{\pi} = 0$$

Using the quadratic formula:

$$r = \frac{-0.82 \pm \sqrt{[(0.82)^2 - 4(1)(-\frac{1}{\pi})]}}{2(1)}$$

$$= \frac{-0.82 \pm \sqrt{1.9456}}{2} = \frac{-0.82 \pm 1.3948}{2}$$

$$= 0.2874 \text{ or } -1.1074$$

Thus the radius r of the cylinder is 0.2874 m (the negative solution being neglected).

Hence the diameter of the cylinder $= 2 \times 0.2874$

$$= \mathbf{0.5748\ m} \text{ or } \mathbf{57.5\ cm}$$
correct to 3 significant figures

Example 8.68

A shed is 4.0 m long and 2.0 m wide. A concrete path of constant width is laid all the way around the shed. If the area of the path is 9.50 m² calculate its width to the nearest centimetre.

Figure 8.1 shows a plan view of the shed with its surrounding path of width t metres.

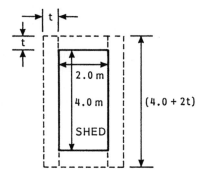

Figure 8.1

Area of path $= 2(2.0 \times t) + 2t(4.0 + 2t)$

i.e $9.50 = 4.0t + 8.0t + 4t^2$

or $4t^2 + 12.0t - 9.50 = 0$

Hence $t = \dfrac{-(12.0) \pm \sqrt{[(12.0)^2 - 4(4)(-9.50)]}}{2(4)}$

$$= \frac{-12.0 \pm \sqrt{296.0}}{8} = \frac{-12.0 \pm 17.20465}{8}$$

Hence $t = 0.6506$ m or -3.65058 m

(Neglecting the negative result which is meaningless, the width of the path, $t = \mathbf{0.651\ m}$ or $\mathbf{65\ cm}$, correct to the nearest centimetre.

Test your knowledge 8.18

1 The area of a rectangle is 23.6 cm² and its width is 3.10 cm shorter than its length. Determine the dimensions of the rectangle, correct to 3 significant figures.

2 The bending moment M of a beam at a point in a beam is given by

$$M = \frac{3x\,(20 - x)}{2}$$

where x metres is the distance from the point of support. Determine the values of x when the bending moment is 50 Nm.

3 If the total surface area of a solid cone is 486.2 cm² and its slant height is 15.3 cm, determine its base diameter.

The exponential function

An exponential function is one which contains e^x, e being a constant called the exponent and having an approximate value of 2.7183. The exponent arises from the natural laws of growth and decay and is used as a base for natural logarithms.

Evaluating exponential functions

The value of e^x may be determined by using:

(a) the power series for e^x, or
(b) a calculator, or
(c) tables of exponential functions.

The most common method of evaluating an exponential function is by using a scientific notation calculator, this now having replaced the use of tables. However, let us first look briefly at the power series for e^x.

The power series for e^x

The value of e^x can be calculated to any required degree of accuracy since it is defined in terms of the following *power series*:

$$e^x = 1 + x + \frac{x^2}{2!} + \frac{x^3}{3!} + \frac{x^4}{4!} + \ldots \tag{1}$$

(where $3! = 3 \times 2 \times 1$ and is called 'factorial 3').

The series is valid for all values of x.

The series is said to *converge*, i.e. if all the terms are added, an actual value for e^x (where x is a real number) is obtained. The more terms that are taken, the closer will be the value of e^x to its actual value. The value of the exponent e, correct to say 4 decimal places, may be determined by substituting $x = 1$ in the power series of equation (1). Thus

$$e^1 = 1 + 1 + \frac{(1)^2}{2!} + \frac{(1)^3}{3!} + \frac{(1)^4}{4!} + \frac{(1)^5}{5!} + \frac{(1)^6}{6!} + \frac{(1)^7}{7!} + \frac{(1)^8}{8!} + \ldots$$

$$= 1 + 1 + 0.5 + 0.16667 + 0.04167 + 0.00833 + 0.00139$$
$$+ 0.00020 + 0.00002 + \ldots$$

$$= 2.71828\ldots$$

i.e.

$$e = 2.7183 \text{ correct to 4 decimal places}$$

Use of a calculator

Most scientific notation calculators contain an 'e^x' function which enables all practical values of e^x and e^{-x} to be determined, correct to 8 or 9 significant figures. For example:

$$e^1 \quad = 2.7182818$$

$$e^{2.4} \quad = 11.023176$$

$$e^{-1.618} = 0.19829489$$

correct to 8 significant figures.

In practical situations the degree of accuracy given by a calculator is often far greater than is appropriate. The accepted convention is that the final result is stated to one significant figure greater than the least significant measured value. Use your calculator to check the following values:

$$e^{0.12} = 1.1275, \text{ correct to 5 significant figures}$$

$$e^{-1.47} = 0.22993, \text{ correct to 5 decimal places}$$

$$e^{-0.431} = 0.6499, \text{ correct to 4 decimal places}$$

$$e^{9.32} = 11159, \text{ correct to 5 significant figures}$$

$$e^{-2.785} = 0.0617291, \text{ correct to 7 decimal places}$$

Example 8.69

Using a calculator, evaluate, correct to 5 significant figures:

(a) $e^{2.731}$ (b) $e^{-3.162}$ (c) $\dfrac{5}{3} e^{5.253}$

(a) $e^{2.731} = 15.348227 \ldots = \mathbf{15.348}$, correct to 5 significant figures

(b) $e^{-3.162} = 0.04234097\ldots = \mathbf{0.042341}$, correct to 5 significant figures

(c) $\dfrac{5}{3} e^{5.253} = \dfrac{5}{3}(191.138825\ldots) = \mathbf{318.56}$, correct to 5 significant figures

---

Example 8.70

Use a calculator to determine the following, each correct to 4 significant figures:

(a) $3.72e^{0.18}$ (b) $53.2e^{-1.4}$ (c) $\dfrac{5}{122} e^{7}$

(a) $3.72e^{0.18} = (3.72)(1.197217\ldots) = \mathbf{4.454}$, correct to 4 significant figures

(b) $53.2e^{-1.4} = (53.2)(0.246596\ldots) = \mathbf{13.12}$, correct to 4 significant figures

(c) $\dfrac{5}{122} e^{7} = \dfrac{5}{122}(1096.6331\ldots) = \mathbf{44.94}$, correct to 4 significant figures

---

Test your knowledge 8.19

Use a calculator to evaluate the given functions correct to 4 significant figures.

1 (a) $e^{5.31}$ (b) $2e^{-1.76}$

2 (a) $5.3e^{1.83}$ (b) $\dfrac{e^{4.92}}{7.37}$

3 (a) $\dfrac{e^{1.5} - e^{-1.5}}{2}$ (b) $\dfrac{4e^{2.37}}{5e^{-1.62}}$

Natural logarithms

Logarithms having a base of e are called *hyperbolic* or *natural logarithms* and the natural logarithm of x is written as $\log_e x$, or more commonly $\ln x$.

Evaluating natural logarithms

The value of a natural logarithm may be determined by using:

(a) a calculator, or
(b) a relationship between common and natural logarithms, or
(c) natural logarithm tables.

The most common method of evaluating a natural logarithm is by a scientific notation calculator, this now having replaced the use of four-figure tables, and also the relationship between common and natural logarithms,

$$\log_e y = 2.3026 \log_{10} y$$

Most scientific notation calculators contain a 'ln x' function which displays the value of the natural logarithm of a number when the appropriate key is pressed.

Using a calculator,

$$\ln 4.692 = 1.5458589\ldots = 1.5459, \text{ correct to 4 decimal places}$$

and $\ln 35.78 = 3.57738907\ldots = 3.5774$, correct to 4 decimal places

Use your calculator to check the following values:

$\ln 1.732 = 0.54928$, correct to 5 significant figures

$\ln 1 = 0$

$\ln 0.52 = -0.6539$, correct to 4 decimal places

$\ln 593 = 6.3852$, correct to 5 significant figures

$\ln 1750 = 7.4674$, correct to 4 decimal places

$\ln 0.17 = -1.772$, correct to 4 significant figures

$\ln 0.00032 = -8.04719$, correct to 6 significant figures

$\ln e^3 = 3$

$\ln e^1 = 1$

From the last two examples we can conclude that

$$\log_e e^x = x$$

This is useful when solving equations involving exponential functions.

For example, to solve $e^{3x} = 8$, take natural logarithms of both sides, which gives $\ln e^{3x} = \ln 8$

i.e. $3x = \ln 8$

from which $x = \dfrac{1}{3} \ln 8 = \textbf{0.6931}$, correct to 4 decimal places.

Example 8.71

Using a calculator evaluate correct to 5 significant figures: (a) 47.291 (b) ln 0.06213 (c) 3.2 ln 762.923

(a) $\ln 47.291 = 3.8563200\ldots = \textbf{3.8563}$, correct to 5 significant figures

(b) $\ln 0.06213 = -2.7785263\ldots = \textbf{-2.7785}$, correct to 5 significant figures

(c) $3.2 \ln 762.923 = 3.2(6.6371571\ldots) = \textbf{21.239}$, correct to 5 significant figures

Test your knowledge 8.20

1 Plot a graph of $y = 2e^{0.3x}$ over a range of $x = -3$ to $x = 3$. Hence determine the value of y when $x = 2.2$ and the value of x when $y = 1.6$.

In questions 2 and 3, use a calculator to evaluate the given functions, correct to 4 significant figures.

2 (a) $\ln 4.621$ (b) $\ln 0.1624$

3 (a) $\dfrac{2 \ln 46.82}{7.68}$ (b) $\dfrac{3 \ln 5.62}{2 \lg 5.62}$

4 Solve $6 = 1.2e^{-2x}$, correct to 3 decimal places.

5 Given $20 = 60(1 - e^{t/2})$ determine the value of t, correct to 3 significant figures.

Test your knowledge 8.21

1 Two quantities x and y are related by the equation $y = ae^{-kx}$, where a and k are constants. (a) Determine the value of y when $a = 2.114$, $k = -3.20$ and $x = 1.429$. (b) Determine the value of x when $y = 115.4$, $a = 17.8$ and $k = 4.65$.

2 The pressure p pascals at height h metres above ground level is given by $p = p_0 e^{-h/c}$, where p_0 is the pressure at ground level and C is a constant. When p_0 is 1.012×10^5 Pa and the pressure at a height of 1420 m is 9.921×10^4 Pa, determine the value of C.

3 The temperature θ_2 of a winding which is being heated electrically at time t is given by: $\theta_2 = \theta_1(1 - e^{-t/\tau})$ where θ_1 is the temperature (in degrees Celsius) at time $t = 0$ and τ is a constant. Calculate
   (a) θ_1, correct to the nearest degree, when θ_2 is 50°C, t is 30 s and τ is 60 s.
   (b) the time t, correct to 1 decimal place, for θ_2 to be half the value of θ_1.

Example 8.72

Evaluate the following:

(a) $\dfrac{\ln e^{2.5}}{\lg 100.5}$

(b) $\dfrac{4e^{2.3} \lg 2.23}{\ln 2.23}$ (correct to 3 decimal places)

(a) $\dfrac{\ln e^{2.5}}{\lg 10^{0.5}} = \dfrac{2.5}{0.5} = \mathbf{5}$

(b) $\dfrac{4e^{2.23} \lg 2.23}{\ln 2.23} = \dfrac{4(9.29986607\ldots)(0.34830486\ldots)}{(0.80200158\ldots)}$

$= \mathbf{16.156}$, correct to 3 decimal places

Laws of growth and decay

The laws of exponential growth and decay are of the form $y = Ae^{kx}$ and $y = A(1 - e^{kx})$, where A and k are constants. The laws occur frequently in engineering and science and examples of quantities related by a natural law include:

(i)	Linear expansion	$l = l_0 e^{\alpha\theta}$
(ii)	Change in electrical resistance with temperature	$R_\theta = R_0 e^{\alpha\theta}$
(iii)	Tension in belts	$T_1 = T_0 e^{\mu\alpha}$
(iv)	Newton's law of cooling	$\theta = \theta_0 e^{-kt}$
(v)	Biological growth	$y = y_0 e^{kt}$
(vi)	Discharge of a capacitor	$q = Qe^{-t/CR}$
(viii)	Radioactive decay	$N = N_0 e^{-t}$
(ix)	Decay of current in an inductive circuit	$i = Ie^{-Rt/L}$
(x)	Growth of current in a capacitive circuit	$i = I(1 - e^{t/CR})$

Example 8.73

The resistance r of an electrical conductor at temperature θ°C is given by $R = R_0 e^{\alpha\theta}$, where α is a constant and $R_0 = 5 \times 10^3$ ohms. Determine the value of α when $R = 6 \times 10^3$ ohms and $\theta = 1500$°C. Also, find the temperature when the resistance R is 5.4×10^3 ohms.

Transposing $R = R_0 e^{\alpha\theta}$ gives $\dfrac{R}{R_0} = e^{\alpha\theta}$

Taking natural logarithms of both sides gives:

$$\ln \dfrac{R}{R_0} = \ln e^{\alpha\theta} = \alpha\theta$$

Hence:

$$\alpha = \dfrac{1}{\theta} \ln \dfrac{R}{R_0} = \dfrac{1}{1500} \ln \dfrac{6 \times 10^3}{5 \times 10^3}$$

$$= \dfrac{1}{1500}(0.1823)$$

Hence $\alpha = \mathbf{1.215 \times 10^{-4}}$

From above, $\ln \dfrac{R}{R_0} = \alpha\theta$ hence $\theta = \dfrac{1}{\alpha} \ln \dfrac{R}{R_0}$

When $R = 5.4 \times 10^3$, $\alpha = 1.215 \times 10^{-4}$ and $R_0 = 5 \times 10^3$

$$\theta = \frac{1}{1.215 \times 10^{-4}} \ln \frac{5.4 \times 10^3}{5 \times 10^3}$$

$$= \frac{10^4}{1.215} \,(7.696 \times 10^{-2}) = \textbf{633.4°C}$$

Example 8.74

In an experiment involving Newton's law of cooling, the temperature $\theta(°C)$ is given by $\theta = \theta_0 e^{-kt}$. Find the value of constant k when $\theta_0 = 56.6°C$, $\theta = 16.5°C$ and $t = 83.0$ seconds.

Transposing $\theta = \theta_0 e^{-kt}$ gives $\dfrac{\theta}{\theta_0} = e^{-kt}$ from which $\dfrac{\theta_0}{\theta} = \dfrac{1}{e^{-kt}} = e^{-kt}$

Taking natural logarithms of both sides gives: $\ln \dfrac{\theta_0}{\theta} = kt$

from which,

$$k = \frac{1}{t} \ln \frac{\theta_0}{\theta} = \frac{1}{83.0} \ln \frac{56.6}{16.5} = \frac{1}{83.0}(1.2326)$$

Hence $\textbf{\textit{k} = 1.485} \times \textbf{10}^{-2}$

Trigonometry

Trigonometry is the branch of mathematics which deals with the measurement of sides and angles of triangles, and their relationships with each other.

Trigonometric ratios of acute angles

(a) With reference to the right-angled triangle shown in Figure 8.2:

(i) sine $\theta = \dfrac{\text{opposite side}}{\text{hypotenuse}}$, i.e. $\sin \theta = \dfrac{b}{c}$

(ii) cosine $\theta = \dfrac{\text{adjacent side}}{\text{hypotenuse}}$, i.e. $\cos \theta = \dfrac{a}{c}$

(iii) tangent $\theta = \dfrac{\text{opposite side}}{\text{adjacent side}}$, i.e. $\tan \theta = \dfrac{b}{a}$

(iv) secant $\theta = \dfrac{\text{hypotenuse}}{\text{adjacent side}}$, i.e. $\sec \theta = \dfrac{c}{a}$

(v) cosecant $\theta = \dfrac{\text{hypotenuse}}{\text{opposite side}}$, i.e. $\operatorname{cosec} \theta = \dfrac{c}{b}$

(vi) cotangent $\theta = \dfrac{\text{adjacent side}}{\text{opposite side}}$, i.e. $\cot \theta = \dfrac{a}{b}$

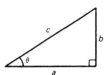

Figure 8.2

(b) From above,

(i) $\dfrac{\sin \theta}{\cos \theta} = \dfrac{\dfrac{b}{c}}{\dfrac{a}{c}} = \dfrac{b}{a} = \tan \theta$, i.e. $\tan \theta = \dfrac{\sin \theta}{\cos \theta}$

(ii) $\dfrac{\cos \theta}{\sin \theta} = \dfrac{\dfrac{a}{c}}{\dfrac{b}{c}} = \dfrac{a}{b} = \cot \theta$, i.e. $\cot \theta = \dfrac{\cos \theta}{\sin \theta}$

(iii) $\sec \theta = \dfrac{1}{\cos \theta}$

(iv) $\operatorname{cosec} \theta = \dfrac{1}{\sin \theta}$ (Note 's' and 'c' go together)

(v) $\cot \theta = \dfrac{1}{\tan \theta}$

Secants, cosecants and cotangents are called the *reciprocal ratios*.

Example 8.75

From Figure 8.3, find $\sin D$, $\cos D$ and $\tan F$.

Figure 8.3

By Pythagoras' theorem, $17^2 = 8^2 + EF^2$, from which, $EF = \sqrt{(17^2 - 8^2)} = 15$

$$\sin D = \frac{EF}{DF} = \frac{15}{17} \text{ or } \mathbf{0.8824}$$

$$\cos D = \frac{DE}{DF} = \frac{8}{17} \text{ or } \mathbf{0.4706}$$

$$\tan F = \frac{DE}{EF} = \frac{8}{15} \text{ or } \mathbf{0.5333}$$

Example 8.76

If $\cos X = \dfrac{9}{41}$ determine the value of the other five trigonometric ratios.

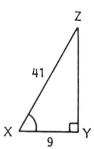

Figure 8.4

Figure 8.4 shows a right-angled triangle. Since $\cos X = \dfrac{9}{41}$, then XY = 9 units and XZ = 41 units.

Using Pythagoras' theorem: $41^2 = 9^2 + YZ^2$

from which $YZ = \sqrt{(41^2 - 9^2)} = 40$ units.

Thus

$$\sin X = \mathbf{\frac{40}{41}}, \tan X = \frac{40}{9} = \mathbf{4\,\frac{4}{9}}$$

$$\operatorname{cosec} X = \frac{41}{40} = \mathbf{1\,\frac{1}{40}}, \sec X = \frac{41}{9} = \mathbf{4\,\frac{5}{9}}$$

and $\cot X = \mathbf{\dfrac{9}{40}}$

---

1 If $\sin A = \dfrac{9}{41}$,

   find $\cos A$ and $\tan A$
2 Determine the values of the six trigonometric ratios for angle θ shown in the right-angled triangle ABC shown in Figure 8.5.

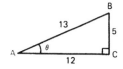

Figure 8.5

Example 8.77

If $\sin \theta = 0.625$ and $\cos \theta = 0.500$ determine, without using a calculator, the values of $\operatorname{cosec} \theta$, $\sec \theta$, $\tan \theta$ and $\cot \theta$.

$$\operatorname{cosec} \theta = \frac{1}{\sin \theta} = \frac{1}{0.625} = \mathbf{1.60}$$

$$\sec \theta = \frac{1}{\cos \theta} = \frac{1}{0.500} = \mathbf{2.00}$$

$$\tan \theta = \frac{\sin \theta}{\cos \theta} = \frac{0.625}{0.500} = \mathbf{1.25}$$

$$\cot \theta = \frac{\cos \theta}{\sin \theta} = \frac{0.500}{0.625} = \mathbf{0.80}$$

Evaluating trigonometric ratios

Four-figure tables are available which gives sines, cosines, tangents, secants, cosecants and cotangents for angles between 0° and 90°. However, the easiest method of evaluating trigonometric functions of any angle is by using a calculator.

The following values, correct to 4 decimal places, may be checked:

$$\sin 18° = 0.3090, \text{ cosine } 56° = 0.5592$$

$$\text{tangent } 29° = 0.5543, \text{ sine } 172° = 0.1392$$

$$\text{cosine } 115° = -0.4226, \text{ tangent } 178° = -0.0349$$

$$\text{sine } 241.63° = -0.8799, \text{ cosine } 331.78° = 0.8811$$

$$\text{tangent } 296.42° = -2.0127$$

Most calculators contain only sine, cosine and tangent functions. Thus to evaluate secants, cosecants and cotangents, reciprocals need to be used.

The following values, correct to 4 decimal places, may be checked:

$$\text{secant } 32° = \frac{1}{\text{cosine } 32°} = 1.1792$$

$$\text{secant } 215.12° = \frac{1}{\text{cosine } 215.12°} = -1.2226$$

$$\text{cosecant } 75° = \frac{1}{\text{sine } 75°} = 1.0353$$

$$\text{cosecant } 321.62° = \frac{1}{\text{sine } 321.62°} = -1.6106$$

$$\text{cotangent } 41° = \frac{1}{\text{tangent } 41°} = 1.1504$$

$$\text{cotangent } 263.59° = \frac{1}{\text{tangent } 263.59°} = 0.1123$$

To evaluate, say, sine 42° 23' using a calculator means finding

$$\text{sine } 42\frac{23°}{60} \text{ since there are 60 minutes in 1 degree.}$$

$$\frac{23}{60} = 0.3833, \text{ thus } 42°\,23' = 42.3833°$$

Thus sine 42° 23' = sine 42.3833 = 0.6741, correct to 4 decimal places. Similarly,

$$\text{cosine } 72°\,38' = \text{cosine } 72\frac{38°}{60}$$

$$= 0.2985, \text{ correct to 4 decimal places.}$$

Example 8.78

Evaluate, correct to 4 decimal places: (a) sine 11°, (b) sine 121.68°, (c) sine 259° 10'

(a) sine 11° = **0.1908**
(b) sine 121.68° = **0.8510**

(c) sine 259° 10' = sine 259 $\dfrac{10°}{60}$ = **−0.9822**

Example 8.79

Evaluate, correct to 4 decimal places: (a) cosine 23°, (b) cosine 159.32°, (c) cosine 321° 41'

(a) cosine 23° = **0.9205**
(b) cosine 159.32° = **−0.9356**

(c) cosine 321° 41' = cosine 321 $\dfrac{41°}{60}$ = **0.7846**

Example 8.80

Evaluate, correct to 4 significant figures: (a) tangent 276°, (b) tangent 131.29°, (c) tangent 76° 58'

(a) tan 276° = **−9.514**
(b) tan 131.29° = **−1.139**

(c) tan 76° 58' = tan 76 $\dfrac{58°}{60}$ = **4.320**

Example 8.81

Evaluate, correct to 4 significant figures: (a) sin 2.162, (b) cos $(3\pi/8)$, (c) tan 1.16.

(a) sin 2.162 means the sine of 2.162 radians. Hence a calculator needs to be on the radian function.

   Hence sin 2.162 = **0.8303**.

(b) cos $(3\pi/8)$ = cos 1.178097 . . . = **0.3827**.
(c) tan 1.16 = **2.296**.

Example 8.82

Evaluate, correct to 4 decimal places: (a) secant 5.37, (b) cosecant $\pi/4$, (c) cotangent $\pi/24$.

(a) Again, with no degrees sign, it is assumed that 5.37 means 5.37 radians.

   Hence sec 5.37 = $\dfrac{1}{\cos 5.37}$ = **1.0044**

(b) $\operatorname{cosec} (\pi/4) = \dfrac{1}{\sin (\pi/4)} = \dfrac{1}{\sin 0.785398 \ldots} = \mathbf{1.2732}$

(c) $\cot (5\pi/24) = \dfrac{1}{\tan (5\pi/24)} = \dfrac{1}{\tan 0.654498 \ldots} = \mathbf{1.5279}$

Example 8.83

Determine the acute angle: (a) arcsin 0.7321, (b) arccos 0.4174, (c) arctan 1.4695

(a) Note that 'arcsin θ' is an abbreviation for 'the angle whose sine is equal to θ'. 0.7321 is entered into a calculator and then the inverse sine (or $\sin^{-1}$) key is pressed. Hence arcsin 0.7321 = 47.06273. . .° Subtracting 47 leaves 0.06273. . .° Multiplying by 60 gives 4' to the nearest minute.

Hence arcsin 0.7321 = **47.06°** or **47° 4'**

Alternatively, in radians, arcsin 0.7321 = **0.821 radians**.

(b) arccos 0.4174 = **65.33°** or **65° 20'** or **1.140 radians**.

(c) arctan 1.4695 = **55.76°** or **55° 46'** or **0.973 radians**.

In questions 1 to 4, evaluate correct to 4 decimal places.
1 (a) sine 154.21°
   (b) cosine 211.46°
2 (a) tangent 76.47°
   (b) secant 302° 16'
3 (a) cosecant 83° 41'
   (b) cotangent (−52.16°)

4 (a) $\cos \dfrac{4\pi}{3}$

   (b) cosec 1.263
5 Determine the acute angle:
   (a) arcsin 0.6478
   (b) arccot 2.3416
6 Evaluate

$$\dfrac{4.2 \tan 49° 26' - 3.7 \sin 66° 1'}{7.1 \cos 29° 34'}$$

correct to 3 significant figures.

Example 8.84

Evaluate, correct to 4 decimal places: (a) sine (−112°), (b) tangent (−217.29°), (c) secant (−93° 16')

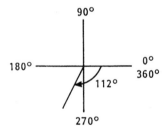

Figure 8.6

(a) Positive angles are shown anticlockwise and negative angles are shown clockwise. From Figure 8.6, −112° is actually the same as +248° (i.e. 360° − 112°).

Hence by calculator sine (−112°) = sine 248° = **−0.9272**

(b) tangent (−217.29°) = −0.7615 (which is the same as tan (360° − 217.29°), i.e. tan 142.71°)

(c) $\operatorname{secant} (-93° 16') = \dfrac{1}{\operatorname{cosine} \left(-93 \dfrac{16°}{60}\right)} = \mathbf{-17.5490}$

Graphs of trigonometric functions

By drawing up tables of values from 0° to 360°, graphs of $y = \sin A$, $y = \cos A$ and $y = \tan A$ may be plotted. Values obtained with a calculator (correct to 3 decimal places – which is more than sufficient for plotting graphs), using 30° intervals, are shown below, with the respective graphs shown in Figure 8.7.

(a) $y = \sin A$

A	0	30°	60°	90°	120°	150°	180°
$\sin A$	0	0.500	0.866	1.000	0.866	0.500	0

A	210°	240°	270°	300°	330°	360°
$\sin A$	−0.500	−0.866	−1.000	—0.866	−0.500	0

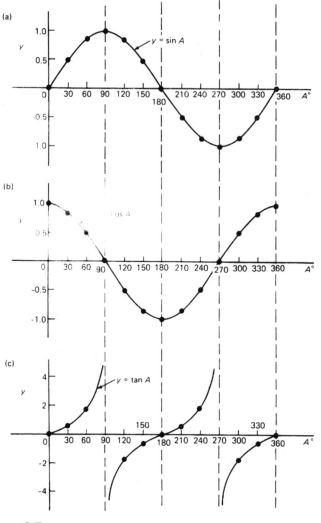

Figure 8.7

(b) $y = \cos A$

A	0	30°	60°	90°	120°	150°	180°
$\cos A$	1.000	0.866	0.500	0	−0.500	−0.866	−1.000

A		210°	240°	270°	300°	330°	360°
$\cos A$		−0.866	−0.500	0	0.500	0.866	1.000

(c) $y = \tan A$

A	0	30°	60°	90°	120°	150°	180°
$\tan A$	0	0.577	1.732	∞	−1.732	−0.577	0

A		210°	240°	270°	300°	330°	360°
$\tan A$		0.577	1.732	∞	−1.732	−0.577	0

From Figure 8.7 it is seen that:

(i)   Sine and cosine graphs oscillate between peak values of ±1.
(ii) The cosine curve is the same shape as the sine curve but displaced by 90°.
(iii) The sine and cosine curves are continuous and they repeat at intervals of 360°; the tangent curve appears to be discontinuous and repeats at intervals of 180°.

Angles of any magnitude

(i)   Figure 8.8 shows rectangular axes XX′ and YY′ intersecting at origin 0. As with graphical work, measurements made to the right and above 0 are positive while those to the left and downwards are negative. Let 0A be free to rotate about 0. By convention, when 0A moves anticlockwise angular measurement is considered positive, and vice versa.

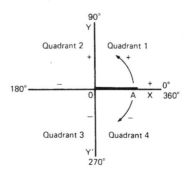

Figure 8.8

(ii) Let 0A be rotated anticlockwise so that θ1 is any angle in the first quadrant and let perpendicular AB be constructed to form the right-angled triangle 0AB (see Figure 8.9). Since all three sides of the triangle are positive, all six trigonometric ratios are positive in the first quadrant. (Note: 0A is always positive since it is the radius of a circle.)

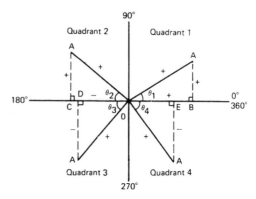

Figure 8.9

(iii) Let 0A be further rotated so that θ2 is any angle in the second quadrant and let AC be constructed to form the right-angled triangle 0AC. Then:

$$\sin\theta_2 = \frac{+}{+} = +, \cos\theta_2 = \frac{-}{+} = -, \tan\theta_2 = \frac{+}{-} = -$$

$$\operatorname{cosec}\theta_2 = \frac{+}{+} = +, \sec\theta_2 = \frac{+}{-} = -, \cot\theta_2 = \frac{-}{+} = -$$

(iv) Let 0A be further rotated so that θ_3 is any angle in the third quadrant and let AD be constructed to form the right-angled triangle 0AD. Then:

$$\sin\theta_3 = \frac{-}{+} = - \text{ (and hence cosec } \theta_3 \text{ is } -)$$

$$\cos\theta_3 = \frac{-}{+} = - \text{ (and hence sec } \theta_3 \text{ is } -)$$

$$\tan\theta_3 = \frac{-}{-} = + \text{ (and hence cot } \theta_3 \text{ is } +)$$

(v) Let 0A be further rotated so that θ_4 is any angle in the fourth quadrant and let AE be constructed to form the right-angled triangle 0AE. Then:

$$\sin\theta_4 = \frac{-}{+} = - \text{ (and hence cosec } \theta_4 \text{ is } -)$$

$$\cos\theta_4 = \frac{+}{+} = + \text{ (and hence sec } \theta_4 \text{ is } +)$$

$$\tan\theta_4 = \frac{-}{+} = - \text{ (and hence cot } \theta_4 \text{ is } -)$$

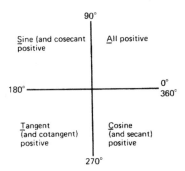

Figure 8.10

(vi) The results obtained in (ii) to (v) are summarized in Figure 8.10. The letters underlined spell the word CAST when starting in the fourth quadrant and moving in an anticlockwise direction.

(v) In the first quadrant of Figure 8.7 all the curves have positive values; in the second only sine is positive; in the third only tangent is positive; in the fourth only cosine is positive (exactly as summarized in Figure 8.10).

A knowledge of angles of any magnitude is needed when finding, for example, all the angles between $0°$ and $360°$ whose sine is, say, 0.3261. If 0.3261 is entered into a calculator and then the inverse sine key pressed (or $\sin^{-1}$ key) the answer $19.03°$ appears. However there is a second angle between $0°$ and $360°$ which the calculator does not give. Sine is also positive in the second quadrant (either from CAST or from Figure 8.7(a)). The other angle is shown in Figure 8.11 as angle θ where $\theta = 180° - 19.03° = 160.97°$. Thus $19.03°$ **and** $160.97°$ are the angles between $0°$ and $360°$ whose sine is 0.3261 (check that $\sin 160.97° = 0.3261$ on your calculator).

Be careful! Your calculator only gives you one of these answers. The second answer needs to be deduced from a knowledge of angles of any magnitude, as shown in the following problems.

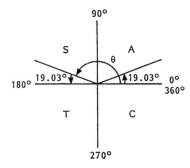

Figure 8.11

Example 8.85

Determine all the angles between $0°$ and $360°$ (a) whose sine is -0.4638 and (b) whose tangent is 1.7629.

(a) The angles whose sine is 0.4638 occurs in the third and fourth quadrants since sine is negative in these quadrants (see Figure 8.12(a)). From Figure 8.12(b), $\theta = \arcsin 0.4638 = 27°38'$.

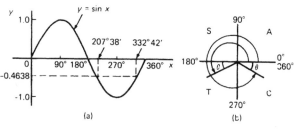

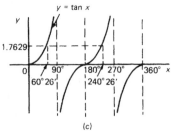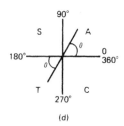

Figure 8.12

Measured from 0°, the two angles between 0° and 360° whose sine is −0.4638 are 180° + 27°38′, i.e. **207°38′** and 360° − 27°38′, i.e. **332°22′**. (Note that a calculator generally only gives one answer, i.e. −27.632588°.)

(b) A tangent is positive in the first and third quadrants (see Figure 8.12(c)). From Figure 8.12(d), θ = arctan 1.7629 = 60°26′. Measured from 0°, the two angles between 0° and 360° whose tangent is 1.7629 are **60°26′** and 180° + 60°26′, i.e. **240°26′**.

Example 8.86

Solve for angles of α between 0° and 360°:

(a) arcsec (−2.1499) = α   (b) arccot 1.3111 = α

(a) Secant is negative in the second and third quadrants (i.e. the same as for cosine). From Figure 8.13(a), θ = arcsec 2.1499 = 62°17′. Measured from 0°, the two angles between 0° and 360° whose secant is −2.1499 are

$$\alpha = 180° - 62°17' = \mathbf{117°43'}$$

and $\alpha = 180° + 62°17' = \mathbf{242°17'}$

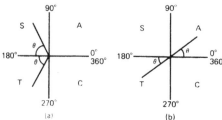

Figure 8.13

(b) Cotangent is positive in the first and third quadrants (i.e. same as for tangent). From Figure 8.13(b), θ = arccot 1.3111 = 37°20′. Hence

$$\alpha = \mathbf{37°20'} \text{ and } 180° + 37°20' = \mathbf{217°20'}$$

In questions 1 to 3, determine all the angles between 0° and 360°:

1 whose sine is −0.5438
2 whose cosine is 0.6841
3 whose secant is −1.7487.
4 Solve arctan 0.7613 = θ for values of θ between 0° and 360°.

Solution of right-angled triangles

To 'solve a right-angled triangle' means 'to find the unknown sides and angles'. This is achieved by using (i) the theorem of Pythagoras, and/or (ii) trigonometric ratios.

Example 8.87

Sketch a right-angled triangle ABC such that B = 90°, AB = 5 cm and BC = 12 cm. Determine the length of AC and hence evaluate sin c, cos c and tan c.

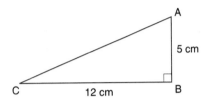

Figure 8.14

Triangle ABC is shown in Figure 8.14. By Pythagoras' theorem, AC = $\sqrt{(5^2 + 12^2)}$ = 13. By definition:

$$\sin C = \frac{\text{opposite side}}{\text{hypotenuse}} = \frac{5}{13} \text{ or } \mathbf{0.3846}$$

$$\cos C = \frac{\text{adjacent side}}{\text{hypotenuse}} = \frac{12}{13} \text{ or } \mathbf{0.9231}$$

$$\tan C = \frac{\text{opposite side}}{\text{adjacent side}} = \frac{5}{12} \text{ or } \mathbf{0.4167}$$

Example 8.88

In triangle PQR shown in Figure 8.15, find the lengths of PQ and PR.

Figure 8.15

$$\tan 38° = \frac{PQ}{PR} = \frac{PQ}{7.5}$$

Hence PQ = 7.5 tan 38° = 7.5(0.7813) = **5.860 cm**.

$$\cos 38° = \frac{QR}{PR} = \frac{7.5}{PR}$$

Hence PR = $\dfrac{7.5}{\cos 38°} = \dfrac{7.5}{0.7880}$ = **9.518 cm**.

(Check: Using Pythagoras' theorem $(7.5)^2 + (5.860)^2 = 90.59 = (9.518)^2$)

Angles of elevation and depression

(a) If, in Figure 8.16, BC represents horizontal ground and AB a vertical flagpole, then the *angle of elevation* of the top of the flagpole, A, from the point C is the angle that the imaginary straight line AC must be raised (or elevated) from the horizontal CB, i.e. angle θ.

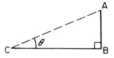

Figure 8.16

(b) If, in Figure 8.17, PQ represents a vertical cliff and R a ship at sea, then the *angle of depression* of the ship from point P is the angle through which the imaginary straight line PR must be lowered (or depressed) from the horizontal to the ship, i.e. angle θ.

(Note, PRQ is also θ – the alternate angles between parallel lines.)

Figure 8.17

Example 8.89

An electricity pylon stands on horizontal ground. At a point 80 m from the base of the pylon, the angle of elevation of the top of the pylon is 23°. Calculate the height of the pylon to the nearest metre.

Figure 8.18

Figure 8.18 shows the pylon AB and the angle of elevation of A from point C is 23°.

$$\tan 23° = \frac{AB}{BC} = \frac{AB}{80}$$

Hence height of pylon AB = 80 tan 23°

$$= 80(0.4245) = 33.96 \text{ m}$$

$$= \textbf{34 m} \text{ to the nearest metre}$$

Example 8.90

The angle of depression of a ship viewed at a particular instant from the top of a 75 m vertical cliff is 30°. Find the distance of the ship from the base of the cliff at this instant. The ship is sailing away from the cliff at constant speed and 1 minute later its angle of depression from the top of the cliff is 20°. Determine the speed of the ship in km/h.

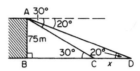

Figure 8.19

Figure 8.19 shows the cliff AB, the initial position of the ship at C and the final position at D. Since the angle of depression is initially 30° then

ACB = 30° (alternate angles between parallel lines).

$$\tan 30° = \frac{AB}{BC} = \frac{75}{BC}$$

Hence:

$$BC = \frac{75}{\tan 30°} = \frac{75}{0.5774}$$

$$= \mathbf{129.9\,m} = \text{initial position of ship}$$

In triangle ABD,

$$\tan 20° = \frac{AB}{BD} = \frac{75}{BC + CD} = \frac{75}{129.9 + x}$$

Hence:

$$129.9 + x = \frac{75}{\tan 20°} = \frac{75}{0.3640} = 206.0\,m$$

from which $x = 206.0 - 129.9 = 76.1\,m$

Thus the ship sails 76.1 m in 1 minute, i.e. 60 s, hence speed of ship

$$= \frac{\text{distance}}{\text{time}} = \frac{76.1}{60}\,m/s = \frac{76.1 \times 60 \times 60}{60 \times 1000}\,km/h = \mathbf{4.566\,km/h}$$

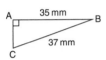
Sine and cosine rules

To '*solve a triangle*' means 'to find the values of unknown sides and angles'. If a triangle is *right angled*, trigonometric ratios and the theorem of Pythagoras may be used for its solution. However, for a *non-right-angled triangle*, trigonometric ratios and Pythagoras' theorem *cannot* be used. Instead, two rules, called the sinerule and the cosine rule, are used.

Sine rule

With reference to triangle ABC of Figure 8.21, the *sine rule* states:

$$\frac{a}{\sin A} = \frac{b}{\sin B} = \frac{c}{\sin C}$$

Figure 8.21

The rule may be used only when:

(i)   1 side and any 2 angles are initially given, or
(ii) 2 sides and an angle (not the included angle) are initially given

Cosine rule

With reference to triangle ABC of Figure 8.21, the *cosine rule* states:

$$a^2 = b^2 + c^2 - 2bc \cos A$$
$$\text{or } b^2 = a^2 + c^2 - 2ac \cos B$$
$$\text{or } c^2 = a^2 + b^2 - 2ab \cos C$$

The rule may be used only when:

(i)   2 sides and the included angle are initially given, or
(ii) 3 sides are initially given.

Area of any triangle

The *area of any triangle* such as ABC of Figure 8.21 is given by:

(i) $\frac{1}{2} \times$ base $\times$ perpendicular height, or

(ii) $\frac{1}{2} ab \sin C$, or $\frac{1}{2} ac \sin B$ or $\frac{1}{2} bc \sin A$, or

(iii) $\sqrt{[s(s-a)(s-b)(s-c)]}$, where $s = \dfrac{a+b+c}{2}$

Example 8.91

In the triangle XYZ, $X = 51°$, $Y = 67°$ and $YZ = 15.2$ cm. Solve the triangle and find its area.

The triangle XYZ is shown in Figure 8.22. Since the angles in a triangle add up to 180°, then $Z = 180° - 51° - 67° = 62°$.

Figure 8.22

Applying the sine rule:

$$\frac{15.2}{\sin 51°} = \frac{y}{\sin 67°} = \frac{z}{\sin 62°}$$

Using $\dfrac{15.2}{\sin 51°} = \dfrac{y}{\sin 67°}$ and transposing gives:

$$y = \frac{15.2 \sin 67°}{\sin 51°} = \mathbf{18.00\,cm} = \mathbf{XZ}$$

Using $\dfrac{15.2}{\sin 51°} = \dfrac{z}{\sin 62°}$ and transposing gives:

$$z = \frac{15.2 \sin 62°}{\sin 51°} = \mathbf{17.27\,cm} = \mathbf{XY}$$

Area of triangle XYZ $= \dfrac{1}{2} xy \sin Z$

$$= \frac{1}{2} (15.2)(18.00) \sin 62°$$

$$= \mathbf{120.8\,cm^2}$$

(or area $= \dfrac{1}{2} xz \sin Y = \dfrac{1}{2} (15.2)(17.27) \sin 67° = \mathbf{120.8\,cm^2}$)

It is always worth checking with triangle problems that the longest side is opposite the largest angle, and vice versa. In this problem, *Y* is the largest angle and thus XZ should be the longest of the three sides.

Example 8.92

Solve the triangle ABC given $B = 78°51'$, AC = 22.31 mm and AB = 17.92 mm. Find also its area.

Triangle ABC is shown in Figure 8.23.

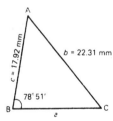

Figure 8.23

Applying the sine rule:

$$\frac{22.31}{\sin 78°51'} = \frac{17.92}{\sin C}$$

from which, $\sin C = \dfrac{17.92 \sin 78°51'}{22.31} = 0.7881$

Hence $C = \arcsin 0.7881 = 50°0'$ or $128°0'$. Since $B = 78°51'$, *C* cannot be $128°0'$, since $128°0' + 78°51'$ is greater than 180°. Thus only $C = 52°0'$ is valid. Angle $A = 180° - 78°51' - 52°0' = 49°9'$.

Applying the sine rule:

$$\frac{a}{\sin 49°9'} = \frac{22.31}{\sin 78°51'}$$

from which,

$$a = \frac{22.31 \sin 49°9'}{\sin 78°51'} = 17.20 \, \text{mm}$$

Hence $A = 49°9'$, $C = 52°0'$ and $BC = 17.20 \, \text{mm}$

Area of triangle ABC $= \dfrac{1}{2}\, ac \sin B = \dfrac{1}{2}\,(17.20)(17.92) \sin$

$78°51' = \mathbf{151.2 \, mm^2}$

Example 8.93

Solve the triangle PQR and find its area given that QR = 36.5 mm, PR = 29.6 mm and Q = 36°.

Triangle PQR is shown in Figure 8.24.

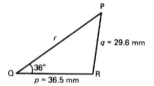

Figure 8.24

Applying the sine rule:

$$\frac{29.6}{\sin 36°} = \frac{36.5}{\sin P}$$

from which,

$$\sin P = \frac{36.5 \sin 36°}{29.6} = 0.7248$$

Hence P = arcsin 0.7248 = 46°27' or 133°33'

When P = 46°27' and Q = 36° then R = 180° − 46°27' − 36° = 97°33'

When P = 133°33' and Q = 36° then R = 180° − 133°33' − 36° = 10°27'

Thus, in this problem, there are *two* separate sets of results and both are feasible solutions. Such a situation is called the *ambiguous case*.

Case 1. P = 46°27', Q = 36°, R = 97°33', p = 36.5 mm and q = 29.6 mm.

From the sine rule:

$$\frac{r}{\sin 97°33'} = \frac{29.6}{\sin 36°}$$

from which,

$$r = \frac{29.6 \sin 97°33'}{\sin 36°} = \mathbf{49.92 \, mm}$$

Area $= \dfrac{1}{2}\, pq \sin R = \dfrac{1}{2}\,(36.5)(29.6) \sin 97°33' = \mathbf{535.5 \, mm^2}$

Case 2. P = 133°33', Q = 36°, R = 10°27', p = 36.5 mm and q = 29.6 mm.

From the sine rule:

$$\frac{r}{\sin 10°27'} = \frac{29.6}{\sin 36°}$$

from which,

$$r = \frac{29.6 \sin 10°27'}{\sin 36°} = \textbf{9.134 mm}$$

$$\text{Area} = \frac{1}{2} pq \sin R = \frac{1}{2}(36.5)(29.6) \sin 10°27' = \textbf{97.98 mm}^2$$

Triangle PQR for case 2 is shown in Figure 8.25.

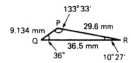

Figure 8.25

Example 8.94

A triangle ABC has sides a = 9.0 cm, b = 7.5 cm and c = 6.5 cm. Determine its three angles and its area.

Triangle ABC is shown in Figure 8.26. It is usual first to calculate the largest angle to determine whether the triangle is acute or obtuse. In this case the largest angle is A (i.e. opposite the longest side).

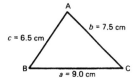

Figure 8.26

Applying the cosine rule:

$$a^2 = b^2 + c^2 - 2bc \cos A$$

from which,

$$2bc \cos A = b^2 + c^2 - a^2$$

and

$$\cos A = \frac{b^2 + c^2 - a^2}{2bc} = \frac{7.5^2 + 6.5^2 - 9.0^2}{2(7.5)(6.5)} = 0.1795$$

Hence A = arccos 0.1795 = **79°40'** (or 280°20'), which is obviously impossible). The triangle is thus acute angled since cos A is positive. (If cos A had been negative, angle A would be obtuse, i.e. lie between 90° and 180°)

Applying the sine rule:

$$\frac{9.0}{\sin 79°40'} = \frac{7.5}{\sin B}$$

from which,

$$\sin B = \frac{7.5 \sin 79°40'}{9.0} = 0.8198$$

Hence B = arcsin 0.8198 = **55°4'**

$$C = 180° - 79°40' - 55°4' = \mathbf{45°16'}$$

Area = $\sqrt{[s(s-a)(s-b)(s-c)]}$, where

$$s = \frac{a+b+c}{2} = \frac{9.0 + 7.5 + 6.5}{2} = 11.5 \text{ cm}$$

Hence area = $\sqrt{[11.5(11.5 - 9.0)(11.5 - 7.5)(11.5 - 6.5)]}$

$$= \sqrt{[11.5(2.5)(4.0)(5.0)]}$$

$$= \mathbf{23.98 \text{ cm}^2}$$

Alternatively, area = $\frac{1}{2} ab \sin C = \frac{1}{2}(9.0)(7.5) \sin 45°16' = \mathbf{23.98 \text{ cm}^2}$

Example 8.95

Solve triangle XYZ (Figure 8.27) and find its area given that $Y = 128°$, XY = 7.2 cm and YZ = 4.5 cm.

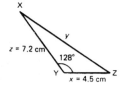

Figure 8.27

Applying the cosine rule:

$$y^2 = x^2 + z^2 - 2xz \cos Y$$

$$= (4.5)^2 + (7.2)^2 - \{2(4.5)(7.20) \cos 128°\}$$

$$= 20.25 + 51.84 - \{-39.89\}$$

$$= 20.25 + 51.84 + 39.89 = 112.0$$

$$y = \sqrt{(112.0)} = \mathbf{10.58 \text{ cm}}$$

Applying the cosine rule:

$$\frac{10.58}{\sin 128°} = \frac{7.2}{\sin Z}$$

from which,

$$\sin Z = \frac{7.2 \sin 128°}{10.58} = 0.5363$$

Hence Z = arcsin 0.5363 = **32°26'** (or 147°34' which, here, is impossible).

$$X = 180° - 128° - 32°26' = \mathbf{19°34'}$$

Area = $\frac{1}{2} xz \sin Y = \frac{1}{2}(4.5)(7.2) \sin 128° = \mathbf{12.77 \text{ cm}^2}$

Test your knowledge 8.26

1 Solve the triangle ABC and find its area given $A = 31°$, $C = 72°$ and $a = 9.6$ mm.
2 Solve triangle DEF and find its area given that EF = 35.0 mm, DE = 25.0 mm and $E = 64°$
3 Solve triangle XYZ and find its area given $x = 12.0$ cm, $y = 9.0$ cm and $z = 10.0$ cm.

Practical situations involving trigonometry

There are a number of *practical situations* where the use of trigonometry is needed to find unknown sides and angles of triangles. This is demonstrated in the problems that follow.

Example 8.96

Two voltage phasors are shown in Figure 8.28. If $V_1 = 40\,V$ and $V_2 = 100\,V$ determine the value of their resultant (i.e. length OA) and the angle the resultant makes with V_1.

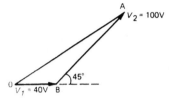

Figure 8.28

Angle OBA = $180° - 45° = 135°$. Applying the cosine rule:

$$OA^2 = V_1^2 + V_2^2 - 2V_1V_2 \cos OBA$$

$$= 40^2 + 100^2 - \{2(40)(100) \cos 135°\}$$

$$= 1600 + 10\,000 - \{-5657\}$$

$$= 1600 + 10\,000 + 5657 = 17\,257$$

The resultant OA = $\sqrt{(17\,257)} = 131.4\ V$

Applying the sine rule:

$$\frac{131.4}{\sin 135°} = \frac{100}{\sin AOB}$$

from which,

$$\sin AOB = \frac{100 \sin 135°}{131.4} = 0.5381$$

Hence angle AOB = arcsin $0.5381 = 32°33'$ (or $147°27'$ which is impossible in this case).

Hence the resultant voltage is **131.4 volts** at **32°33'** to **V_1**.

Example 8.97

In Figure 8.29, PR represents the inclined jib of a crane and is 10.0 m long. PQ is 4.0 m long. Determine the length of tie QR and the inclination of the jib to the vertical.

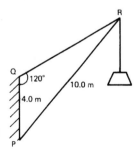

Figure 8.29

Applying the sine rule:

$$\frac{PR}{\sin 120°} = \frac{PQ}{\sin R}$$

from which,

$$\sin R = \frac{PQ \sin 120°}{PR} = \frac{(4.0) \sin 120°}{10.0} = 0.3464$$

Hence R = arcsin 0.3464 = 20°16' (or 159°44', which is impossible in this case).

P = 180° − 120° − 20°16' = **39°44'**, which is the inclination of the jib to the vertical.

Applying the sine rule:

$$\frac{10.0}{\sin 120°} = \frac{QR}{\sin 39°44'}$$

from which,

$$QR = \frac{10.0 \sin 39°44'}{\sin 120°} = \textbf{7.38 m} = \text{length of tie}$$

Test your knowledge 8.27

1 A room 8.0 m wide has a span roof which slopes at 33° on one side and 40° on the other. Find the length of the roof slopes, correct to the nearest centimetre.

2 PQ and QR are the phasors representing the alternating currents in two branches of a circuit. Phasor PQ is 20.0 A and is horizontal.
Phasor QR (which is joined to the end of PQ to form triangle PQR) is 14.0 A and is at an angle of 35° to the horizontal. Determine the resultant phasor PR and the angle it makes with phasor PQ.

3 A man leaves a point walking at 6.5 km/h in a direction E 20° N (i.e. a bearing of 70°). A cyclist leaves the same point at the same time in a direction E 40° S (i.e. a bearing of 130°) travelling at a constant speed. Find the average speed of the cyclist if the walker and cyclist are 80 km apart after 5 hours.

Example 8.98

The area of a field is in the form of a quadrilateral ABCD as shown in Figure 8.30. Determine its area.

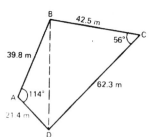

Figure 8.30

A diagonal drawn from B to D divides the quadrilateral into two triangles.

Area of quadrilateral ABCD

= area of triangle ABD + area of triangle BCD

$$= \frac{1}{2}(39.8)(21.4) \sin 114° + \frac{1}{2}(42.5)(62.3) \sin 56°$$

= 389.04 + 1097.5

= **1487 m²**

Trigonometric identities

A *trigonometric identity* is an expression that is true for all values of the unknown variable.

$$\tan \theta = \frac{\sin \theta}{\cos \theta}, \cot \theta = \frac{\cos \theta}{\sin \theta}, \sec \theta = \frac{1}{\cos \theta},$$

$$\operatorname{cosec} \theta = \frac{1}{\sin \theta} \text{ and } \cot \theta = \frac{1}{\tan \theta}$$

are examples of trigonometric identities.

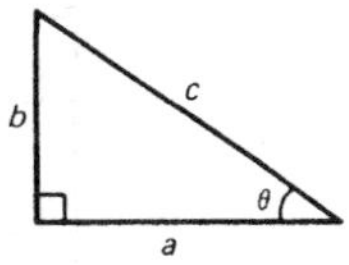

Figure 8.31

Applying Pythagoras' theorem to the right-angled triangle shown in Figure 8.31 gives:

$$a^2 + b^2 = c^2 \tag{1}$$

Dividing each term of equation (1) by c^2 gives:

$$\frac{a^2}{c^2} + \frac{b^2}{c^2} = \frac{c^2}{c^2}, \text{ i.e. } \frac{a^2}{c^2} + \frac{b^2}{c^2} = 1$$

$$(\cos \theta)^2 + (\sin \theta)^2 = 1$$

Hence $\cos^2 \theta + \sin^2 \theta = 1.$ $\tag{2}$

Dividing each term of equation (1) by a^2 gives:

$$\frac{a^2}{a^2} + \frac{b^2}{a^2} = \frac{c^2}{b^2}, \text{ i.e. } 1 + \frac{a^2}{b^2} = \frac{c^2}{a^2}$$

Hence $1 + \tan^2 \theta = \sec^2 \theta$ $\tag{3}$

Dividing each term of equation (1) by b^2 gives:

$$\frac{a^2}{b^2} + \frac{b^2}{b^2} = \frac{c^2}{b^2}, \text{ i.e. } \frac{a^2}{b^2} + 1 = \frac{c^2}{b^2}$$

Hence $\cot^2 \theta + 1 = \operatorname{cosec}^2 \theta$ $\tag{4}$

Equations (2), (3) and (4) are three further examples of trigonometric identities.

Example 8.99

Prove the identity $\sin^2 \theta \cot \theta \sec \theta = \sin \theta$

With trigonometric identities it is necessary to start with the left-hand side (LHS) and attempt to make it equal to the right-hand side (RHS) or vice versa. It is often useful to change all of the trigonometric ratios into sines and cosines where possible. Thus

$$\text{LHS} = \sin^2 \theta \cot \theta \sec \theta = \sin^2 \theta \, \frac{\cos \theta}{\sin \theta} \, \frac{1}{\cos \theta}$$

$$= \sin \theta \text{ (by cancelling)} = \text{RHS}$$

Example 8.100

Prove that $\dfrac{\tan x + \sec x}{\sin x\left(\dfrac{\tan x}{\sec x}\right)} = 1$

$$\text{LHS} = \frac{\tan x + \sec x}{\sec x\left(1 + \dfrac{\tan x}{\sec x}\right)} = \frac{\dfrac{\sin x}{\cos x} + \dfrac{1}{\cos x}}{\dfrac{1}{\cos x}\left(1 + \dfrac{(\sin x/\cos x)}{(1/\cos x)}\right)}$$

$$= \frac{\dfrac{\sin x + 1}{\cos x}}{\dfrac{1}{\cos x}\left(1 + \dfrac{\sin x}{\cos x}\right)\dfrac{\cos x}{1}}$$

$$= \frac{\dfrac{\sin x + 1}{\cos x}}{\dfrac{1}{\cos x}[1 + \sin x]} = \frac{\sin x + 1}{\cos x}\frac{\cos x}{1 + \sin x}$$

$$= 1 \text{ (by cancelling)} = \text{RHS}$$

Example 8.101

Prove that $\dfrac{1 + \cot\theta}{1 + \tan\theta} = \cot\theta$

$$\text{LHS} = \frac{1 + \cot\theta}{1 + \tan\theta} = \frac{\dfrac{1 + \cos\theta}{\sin\theta}}{1 + \dfrac{\sin\theta}{\cos\theta}} = \frac{\dfrac{\sin\theta + \cos\theta}{\sin\theta}}{\dfrac{\cos\theta + \sin\theta}{\cos\theta}}$$

$$= \frac{\sin\theta + \cos\theta}{\sin\theta}\frac{\cos\theta}{\cos\theta + \sin\theta} = \frac{\cos\theta}{\sin\theta}$$

$$= \cot\theta = \text{RHS}$$

1 Show that the trigonometric identities $\cos^2\theta + \sin^2\theta = 1$, $1 + \tan^2\theta = \sec^2\theta$ and $\cot^2\theta + 1 = \csc^2\theta$ are valid when θ is
(a) 124°,
(b) 231° and (c) 312°46′.

2 Prove that $\cos^2 A - \sin^2 A = 1 - 2\sin^2 A$.

3 Show that $\tan\theta\cos\theta = \sin\theta$.

Example 8.102

Show that $\cos^2\theta - \sin^2\theta = 1 - 2\sin^2\theta$.

From equation (2), $\cos^2\theta + \sin^2\theta = 1$, from which, $\cos^2\theta = 1 - \sin^2\theta$

Hence,

$$\text{LHS} = \cos^2\theta - \sin^2\theta = (1 - \sin^2\theta) - \sin^2\theta$$

$$= 1 - \sin^2\theta - \sin^2\theta = 1 - 2\sin^2\theta = \text{RHS}$$

Graphs

Introduction to graphs

A *graph* is a pictorial representation of information showing how one quantity varies with another related quantity. The most common method of showing a relationship between two sets of data is to use *Cartesian* or *rectangular axes* as shown in Figure 8.32.

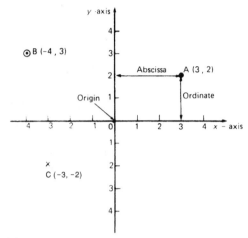

Figure 8.32

The points on a graph are called *coordinates*. Point A in Figure 8.32 has the coordinates (3,2), i.e. 3 units in the x direction and 2 units in the y direction. Similarly, point B has coordinates (−4,3) and C has coordinates (−3,−2). The origin has coordinates (0,0).

The straight line graph

Let a relationship between two variables x and y be $y = 3x + 2$

When $x = 0$, $y = 3(0) + 2 = 2$.

When $x = 1$, $y = 3(1) + 2 = 5$.

When $x = 2$, $y = 3(2) + 2 = 8$, and so on.

Thus coordinates (0,2), (1,5) and (2,8) have been produced from the equation by selecting arbitrary values of x, and are shown plotted in Figure 8.33. When the points are joined together a *straight-line graph* results.

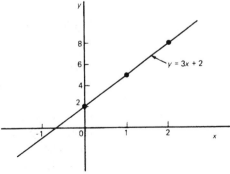

Figure 8.33

The *gradient* or *slope* of a straight line is the ratio of the change in the value of y to the change in the value of x between any two points on the line. If, as x increases, ($\rightarrow$), y also increases ($\uparrow$), then the gradient is positive.

In Figure 8.34(a) the gradient of

$$AC = \frac{\text{change in } y}{\text{change in } x} = \frac{CB}{BA} = \frac{7-3}{3-1} = \frac{4}{2} = 2.$$

If as x increases ($\rightarrow$), y decreases ($\downarrow$), then the gradient is negative.

In Figure 8.34(b), the gradient of

$$DF = \frac{\text{change in } y}{\text{change in } x} = \frac{FE}{ED} = \frac{11-2}{-3-0} = \frac{9}{3} = 3.$$

Figure 8.34(c) shows a straight line graph $y = 3$. Since the straight line is horizontal the gradient is zero.

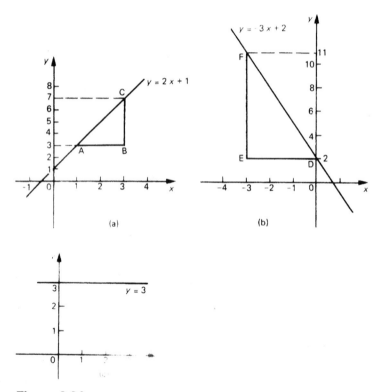

Figure 8.34

The value of y when $x = 0$ is called the *y-axis intercept*. In Figure 3.3(a) the y-axis intercept is 1 and in Figure 8.34(b) is 2.

If the equation of a graph is of the form $y = mx + c$, where m and c are constants, the graph will always be a straight line, m representing the gradient and c the y-axis intercept. Thus $y = 5x + 2$ represents a straight line of gradient 5 and y-axis intercept 2. Similarly, $y = -3x - 4$ represents a straight line of gradient -3 and y-axis intercept -4.

Summary of general rules to be applied when drawing graphs

(i)   Give the graph a title clearly explaining what is being illustrated.
(ii) Choose scales such that the graph occupies as much space as possible on the graph paper being used.
(iii) Choose scales so that interpolation is made as easy as possible. Usually scales such as 1 cm = 1 unit, or 1 cm = 2 units, or 1 cm = 10 units are used. Awkward scales such as 1 cm = 3 units or 1 cm = 7 units should not be used.
(iv) The scales need not start at zero, particularly when starting at zero produces an accumulation of points within a small area of the graph paper.
(v)   The coordinates, or points, should be clearly marked. This may be done either by a cross, or a dot and circle, or just by a dot (see Figure 8.32).
(vi) A statement should be made next to each axis explaining the numbers represented with their appropriate units.
(vii) Sufficient numbers should be written next to each axis without cramping.

Example 8.103

Plot the graph $y = 4x + 3$ in the range $x = -3$ to $x = +4$. From the graph, find (a) the value of y when $x = 2.2$, and (b) the value of x when $y = -3$.

Whenever an equation is given and a graph is required, a table giving corresponding values of the variable is necessary. The table is achieved as follows:

When $x = -3$, $y = 4x + 3 = 4(-3) + 3 = -12 + 3 = -9$

When $x = -2$, $y = 4(-2) + 3 = -8 + 3 = -5$, and so on.

Such a table is shown below:

x	-3	-2	-1	0	1	2	3	4
y	-9	-5	-1	3	7	11	15	19

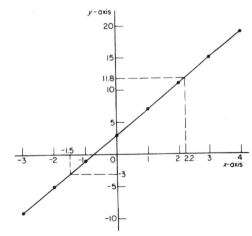

Figure 8.35

The coordinates (−3,−9), (−2,−5), (−1,−1), and so on, are plotted and joined together to produce the straight line shown in Figure 8.35. (Note that the scales used on the x and y axes do not have to be the same.) From the graph:

(a) when x = 2.2, **y = 11.8**, and

(b) when y = −3, **x = −1.5**

Activity 8.1

Plot the following graphs on the same axes between the range x = −4 to x = +4, and determine the gradients of each.

(a) $y = x$ (b) $y = x + 2$
(c) $y = x + 5$ (d) $y = x - 3$

Example 8.104

Plot the following graphs on the same axes between the values x = −3 to x = +3 and determine the gradient and y-axis intercept of each.

(a) $y = 3x$ (b) $y = 3x + 7$ (c) $y = -4x + 4$ (d) $y = -4x - 5$

A table of coordinates is drawn up for each equation.

(a) $y = 3x$

x	−3	−2	−1	0	1	2	3
y	−9	−6	−3	0	3	6	9

(b) $y = 3x + 7$

x	−3	−2	−1	0	1	2	3
y	−2	1	4	7	10	13	16

(c) $y = -4x + 4$

x	−3	−2	−1	0	1	2	3
y	16	12	8	4	0	−4	−8

(d) $y = -4x - 5$

x	−3	−2	−1	0	1	2	3
y	7	3	−1	−5	−9	−13	−17

Each of the graphs is plotted as shown in Figure 8.36, and each is a straight line, y = 3x and y = 3x + 7 are parallel to each other and thus have the same gradient. The gradient of AC is given by

$$AC = \frac{BC}{AC} = \frac{16 - 7}{3 - 0} = \frac{9}{3} = 3$$

Hence the gradient of both **y = 3x** and **y = 3x + 7 is 3**.

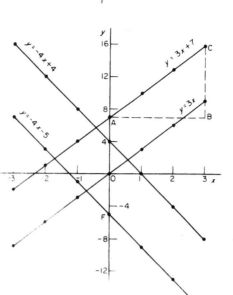

Figure 8.36

$y = -4x + 4$ and $y = -4x - 5$ are parallel to each other and thus have the same gradient. The gradient of DF is given by

$$DF = \frac{EF}{ED} = \frac{-5 - (-17)}{0 - 3} = \frac{12}{-3} = -4$$

Hence the gradient of both **$y = -4x + 4$** and **$y = -4x - 5$ is -4**

The y-axis intercept means the value of y where the straight line cuts the y-axis.

From Figure 8.36,

$y = 3x$ cuts the y-axis at $y = 0$

$y = 3x + 7$ cuts the y-axis at $y = +7$

$y = -4x + 4$ cuts the y-axis at $y = +4$

and $y = -4x - 5$ cuts the y-axis at $y = -5$

Some general conclusions can be drawn from the graphs shown in Figures 8.34 and 8.35.

When an equation is of the form $y = mx + c$, where m and c are constants, then

(i)   a graph of y against x produces a straight line,
(ii) m represents the slope or gradient of the line, and
(iii) c represents the y-axis intercept.

Thus, given an equation such as $y = 3x + 7$, it may be deduced 'on sight' that its gradient is $+3$ and its y-axis intercept is $+7$, as shown in Figure 8.36. Similarly, if $y = -4x - 5$, then the gradient is -4 and the y-axis intercept is -5, as shown in Figure 8.36.

When plotting a graph of the form $y = mx + c$, only two coordinates need be determined. When the coordinates are plotted a straight line is drawn between the two points. Normally, three coordinates are determined, the third one acting as a check.

Example 8.105

Determine the gradient of the straight line graph passing through the coordinates (−2,5) and (3,4)

A straight line graph passing through coordinates (x_1, y_1) and (x_2, y_2) has a gradient given by

$$m = \frac{y_2 - y_1}{x_2 - x_1} \text{ (see figure 8.37)}$$

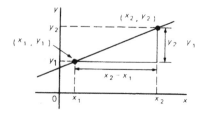

Figure 8.37

A straight line passes through (−2,5) and (3,4), hence

$$x_1 = -2, \ y_1 = 5, \ x_2 = 3$$

and $y_2 = 4$; hence gradient $m = \dfrac{y_2 - y_1}{x_2 - x_1} = \dfrac{4 - 5}{3 - (-2)} = -\dfrac{1}{5}$.

Activity 8.2

Plot the graph $3x + y + 1 = 0$ and $2y - 5 = x$ on the same axes and find their point of intersection.

Test your knowledge 8.29

1 The equation of a line is $4y = 2x + 5$. A table of corresponding values is produced and is shown below. Complete the table and plot a graph of y against x. Find the gradient of the graph.

x	−4	−3	−2	−1	0	1	2	3	4
y		−0.50			1.25				3.25

2 Without plotting graphs, determine the gradient and y-axis intercept values of the following equations:

(a) $y = 7x - 3$ (b) $3y = -6x + 2$ (c) $y - 2 = 4x + 9$ (d) $\dfrac{y}{3} = \dfrac{x}{3} - \dfrac{1}{5}$ (e) $2x + 9y + 1 = 0$

3 Determine the gradient of the straight line graph passing through the coordinates (−2,3) and (−1,3).

Practical problems involving straight line graphs

When a set of coordinate values are given or are obtained experimentally and it is believed that they follow a law of the form $y = mx + c$, then if a straight line can be drawn reasonably close to most of the coordinate values when plotted, this verifies that a law of the form $y = mx + c$ exists. From the graph, constants m (i.e. gradient) and c (i.e. y-axis intercept) can be determined. This technique is called *determination of law*.

Example 8.106

The temperature in degrees Celsius and the corresponding values in degrees Fahrenheit are shown in the table below. Construct rectangular axes, choose a suitable scale and plot a graph of degrees Celsius (on the horizontal axis) against degrees Fahrenheit (on the vertical scale).

°C	10	20	40	60	80	100
°F	50	68	104	140	176	212

From the graph find (a) the temperature in degrees Fahrenheit at 55°C, (b) the temperature in degrees Celsius at 167°F, (c) the Fahrenheit temperature at 0°C, and (d) the Celsius temperature at 230°F.

The coordinates (10,50), (20,68), (40,104), and so on are plotted as shown in Figure 8.38. When the coordinates are joined, a straight line is produced. Since a straight line results there is a linear relationship between degrees Celsius and degrees Fahrenheit.

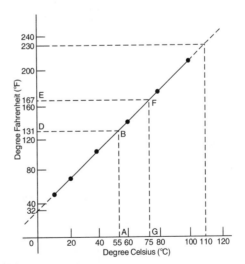

Figure 8.38

(a) To find the Fahrenheit temperature at 55°C a vertical line AB is constructed from the horizontal axis to meet the straight line at B. The point where the horizontal line BD meets the vertical axis indicates the equivalent Fahrenheit temperature.
Hence 55°C is equivalent to 131°F
This process of finding an equivalent value in between the given information in the above table is called *interpolation*.

(b) To find the Celsius temperature at 167°F, a horizontal line EF is constructed as shown in Figure 8.38. The point where the vertical line FG cuts the horizontal axis indicates the equivalent Celsius temperature.
Hence 167°F is equivalent to 75°C

(c) If the graph is assumed to be linear even outside of the given data, then the graph may be extended at both ends (shown by broken lines in Figure 8.38).
From figure 8.38, **0°C corresponds to 32°F**

(d) **230°F is seen to correspond to 110°C**.
The process of finding equivalent values outside of the given range is called *extrapolation*.

Example 8.107

In an experiment on Charles's law, the value of the volume of gas, V cubic metres, was measured for various temperatures $T°C$. Results are shown below.

V (m³)	25.0	25.8	26.6	27.4	28.2	29.0
$T°C$	60	65	70	75	80	85

Plot a graph of volume (vertical) against temperature (horizontal) and from it find (a) the temperature when the volume is 28.6 m³, and (b) the volume when the temperature is 67°C

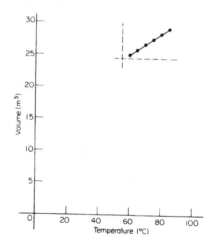

Figure 8.39

If a graph is plotted with both the scales starting at zero then the result is as shown in Figure 8.39. All of the points lie in the top right-hand corner of the graph, making interpolation difficult. A more accurate graph is obtained if the temperature axis starts at 55°C and the volume axis starts at 24.5 m³. The axes corresponding to these values is shown by the broken lines in Figure 8.39 and are called *false axes*, since the origin is not now at zero. A magnified version of this relevant part of the graph is shown in Figure 8.40. From the graph:

(a) when the volume is 28.6 m³, the equivalent temperature is **82.5°C**, and
(b) when the temperature is 67°C, the equivalent volume is **26.1 m³**.

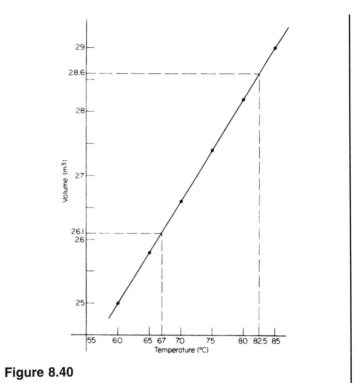

Figure 8.40

Example 8.108

Experimental tests to determine the breaking stress σ of rolled copper at various temperatures t gave the following results.

Stress σ N/cm^2	8.46	8.02	7.75	7.35	7.06	6.63
Temperature t °C	70	200	280	410	500	640

Show that the values obey the law $\sigma = AT + b$, where a and b are constants and determine approximate values for a and b. Use the law to determine the stress at 250°C and the temperature when the stress is 7.54 N/cm^2.

The coordinates (70,8.46), (200, 8.04), and so on, are plotted as shown in Figure 8.41. Since the graph is a straight line then the values obey the law $\sigma = at + b$, and the gradient of the straight line is

$$a = \frac{AB}{BC} = \frac{8.36 - 6.76}{100 - 600} = \frac{1.60}{-500} = \textbf{-0.0032}$$

Vertical axis intercept, **b = 8.68**.

Hence the law of the graph is $\sigma = \textbf{-0.0032}t + \textbf{8.68}$

When the temperature is 250°C, stress σ is given by

$$\sigma = -0.0032(250) + 8.68 = \textbf{7.88 N/cm}^2$$

Rearranging $\sigma = -0.0032t + 8.68$ gives

$$0.0032t = 8.68 - \sigma, \text{ i.e. } t = \frac{8.68 - \sigma}{0.0032}$$

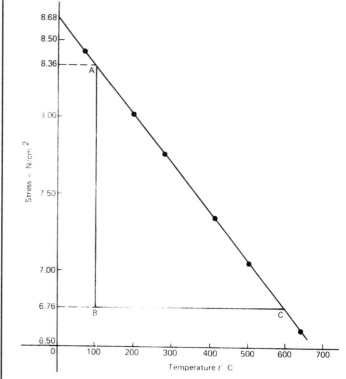

Figure 8.41

Hence when the stress $\sigma = 7.54$ N/cm², temperature

$$t = \frac{8.68 - 7.54}{0.0032} = \textbf{356.3°C}$$

---

1 The resistance R ohms of a copper winding is measured at various temperaturees t °C and the results are as follows:

R ohms	112	120	126	131	136
t °C	20	36	48	58	64

Plot a graph of R (vertically) against t (horizontally) and find from it (a) the temperature when the resistance is 122 Ω and (b) the resistance when the temperature is 52°C

2 In an experiment demonstrating Hooke's law, the strain in an aluminium wire was measured for various stresses. The results were:

Stress N/mm²	4.9	8.7	15.0	18.4	24.2	27.3
Strain	0.00007	0.00013	0.00021	0.00027	0.00034	0.00039

Plot a graph of stress (vertically) against strain (horizontally). Find:
(a) Young's modulus of Elasticity for aluminium, which is given by the gradient of the graph,
(b) the value of the strain at a stress of 20 N/mm², and
(c) the value of the stress when the strain is 0.00020.

Determination of law

Frequently, the relationship between two variables, say x and y, is not a linear one, i.e. when x is plotted against y a curve results. In such cases the non-linear equation may be modified to the linear form, $y = mx + c$, so that the constants, and thus the law relating the variables can be determined. This technique is called 'determination of law'.

Some examples of the reduction of equations to linear form include:

(i) $y = ax^2 + b$ compares with $Y = mX + c$, where $m = a$, $c = b$ and $X = x^2$. Hence y is plotted vertically against x^2 horizontally to produce a straight line graph of gradient 'a' and y-axis intercept 'b'

(ii) $y = \dfrac{a}{b} + b$

y is plotted vertically against $1/x$ horizontally to produce a straight line graph of gradient 'a' and y-axis intercept 'b'

(iii) $y = ax^2 + bx$

Dividing both sides by x gives $y/x = ax + b$
Comparing with $Y = mX + c$ shows that y/x is plotted vertically against x horizontally to produce a straight line graph of gradient 'a' and $y/$-*axis* intercept 'b'.

(iv) $y = ax^n$

Taking logarithms to a base of 10 of both sides gives:

$$\lg y = \lg(ax^n) = \lg a + \lg x^n$$

i.e. $\lg y = n \lg x + \lg a$

which compares with

$$Y = mX + c$$

and shows that $\lg y$ is plotted vertically against $\lg x$ horizontally to produce a straight line graph of gradient n and $\lg y$-axis intercept $\lg a$.

(v) $y = ab^x$

Taking logarithms to a base of 10 of both sides gives:

$$\lg y = \lg(ab^x)$$

i.e. $\lg y = \lg a + \lg b^x$

i.e. $\lg y = x \lg b + \lg a$

or $\lg y = (\lg b)x + \lg a$

which compares with

$$Y = mX + c$$

and shows that $\lg y$ is plotted vertically against x horizontally to produce a straight line graph of gradient $\lg b$ and $\lg y$-axis intercept $\lg a$.

(vi) $y = ae^{bx}$

Taking logarithms to a base of e of both sides gives:

$$\ln y = \ln (ae^{bx})$$

i.e. $\ln y = \ln a + \ln e^{bx}$

i.e. $\ln y = \ln a + bx \ln e$

i.e. $\ln y = bx + \ln a$

which compares with

$$Y = mX + c$$

and shows that $\ln y$ is plotted vertically against x horizontally to produce a straight line graph of gradient b and $\ln y$-axis intercept $\ln a$.

Example 8.109

Values of load L newtons and distance d metres obtained experimentally are shown in the following table.

Load, L (N)	32.3	29.6	27.0	23.2	18.3	12.8	10.0	6.4
distance, d (m)	0.75	0.37	0.24	0.17	0.12	0.09	0.08	0.07

Veriify that load and distance are related by a law of the form

$$L = \frac{a}{d} + b$$

and determine approximate values of a and b. Hence calculate the load when the distance is 0.20 m and the distance when the load is 20 N.

Comparing $L = \dfrac{a}{d} + b$ i.e. $L = a\dfrac{1}{d} + b$ with $Y = mX + c$ shows that L is to be plotted vertically against $1/d$ horizontally. Another table of values is drawn up as shown below.

L	32.3	29.6	27.0	23.2	18.3	12.8	10.0	6.4
d	0.75	0.37	0.24	0.17	0.12	0.09	0.08	0.07
$1/d$	1.33	2.70	4.17	5.88	8.33	11.1	1.25	14.3

A graph of L against $1/d$ is shown in Figure 8.42. A straight line can be drawn through the points, which verifies that load and distance are related by a law of the form

$$L = \frac{a}{d} + b.$$

Gradient of straight line, $a = \dfrac{AB}{BC} = \dfrac{31 - 11}{2 - 12} = \dfrac{20}{-10} = -2$

L-axis intercept, **b = 35**

Hence the law of the graph is $L = \dfrac{2}{d} + 35$

When the distance $d = 0.20$ m, load $L = \dfrac{-2}{0.20} + 35 = $ **25.0 N**

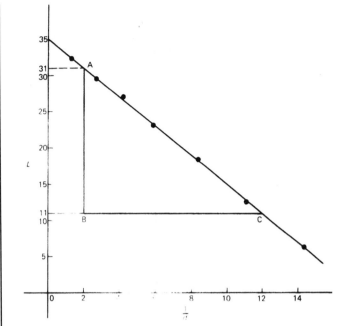

Figure 8.42

Rearranging $L = -\dfrac{2}{d} + 35$ gives

$\dfrac{2}{d} = 35 - L$ and $d = \dfrac{2}{35 - L}$

Hence when the load $L = 20$ N, distance $d = \dfrac{2}{35 - 20} = \dfrac{2}{15} = \textbf{0.133 m}$

Example 8.110

The current flowing in, and the power dissipated by, a resistor are measured experimentally for various values and the results are as shown below.

Current, I amperes	2.2	3.6	4.1	5.6	6.8
Power, P watts	116	311	403	753	1110

Show that the law relating current and power is of the form $P = RI^n$, where R and n are constants, and determine the law.

Taking logarithms to a base of 10 of both sides of $P = RI^n$ gives:

$\lg P = \lg(RI^n) = \lg R + \lg I^n = \lg R + n \lg I$

i.e. $\lg P = n \lg I + \lg R$, which is of the form $Y = mX + c$, showing that $\lg P$ is to be plotted vertically against $\lg I$ horizontally. A table of values for $\lg I$ and $\lg P$ is drawn up as shown below.

I	2.2	3.6	4.1	5.6	6.8
$\lg I$	0.342	0.556	0.613	0.748	0.833
P	116p	311	403	753	1110
$\lg P$	2.064	2.493	2.605	2.877	3.045

A graph of lg P against lg l is shown in Figure 8.43 and since a straight line results the law $P = Rl^n$ is verified.
  Gradient of straight line,

$$n = \frac{AB}{BC} = \frac{2.98 - 2.18}{0.8 - 0.4} = \frac{0.80}{0.4} = 2$$

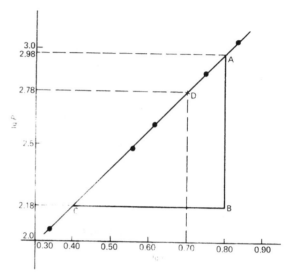

Figure 8.43

It is not possible to determine the vertical axis intercept on sight since the horizontal axis scale does not start at zero. Selecting any point from the graph, say point D, where lg $l = 0.70$ and lg $P = 2.78$, and substituting values into lg $P = n$ lg $l +$ lg R gives

$$2.78 = (2)(0.70) + \text{lg } R$$

from which   lg $R = 2.78 - 1.40 = 1.38$

Hence $R = $ angilog 1.38 $(= 10^{1.38}) = $ **24.0**

Hence the law of the graph is $P = 24.0\ l^2$

Activity 8.3

Experimental results of the safe load, L kilonewtons, applied to girders of varying spans, d metres, are shown below:

Span, d (m)	2.0	2.8	3.6	4.2	4.8
Load, L (kN)	475	339	264	226	198

It is believed that the relationship between load and span is $L = c/d$, where c is a constant. Determine (a) the value of constant c and (b) the safe load for a span of 3.0 m

Example 8.111

The current i (mA) flowing in a capacitor which is being discharged varies with time t (ms) as shown below.

i (mA)	203	61.14	22.49	6.13	2.49	0.615
t (ms)	100	160	210	275	320	390

Show that these results are related by a law of the form $i = Ie^{t/T}$, where I and T are constants. Determine the approximate values of I and T.

Taking natural logarithms of both sides if $i = Ie^{t/T}$ gives

$$\ln i = \ln(Ie^{t/T}) = \ln I + \ln e^{t/T} = \ln I + \frac{t}{T}\ln e$$

i.e. $\ln i = \ln I + \dfrac{t}{T}$ (since $\ln e = 1$)

or $\ln i = \dfrac{1}{T}t + \ln I$

which compares with $y = mx + c$, showing that $\ln i$ is plotted vertically against t horizontally. Another table of values is drawn up as shown below.

t	100	160	210	275	320	390
i	203	61.14	22.49	6.13	2.49	0.615
$\ln i$	5.31	4.11	3.11	1.81	0.91	−0.49

A graph of $\ln i$ against t is shown in Figure 8.44 and since a straight line results the law $i = Ie^{t/T}$ is verified.

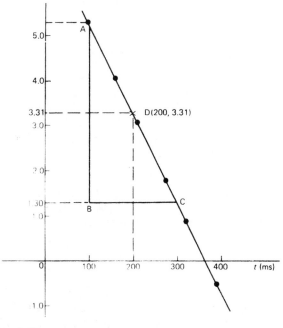

Figure 8.44

Gradient of straight line,

$$\frac{1}{T} = \frac{AB}{BC} = \frac{5.30 - 1.30}{100 - 300} = \frac{4.0}{-200} = -0.02$$

Hence $T = \dfrac{1}{-0.02} = \mathbf{-50}$

Selecting any point on the graph, say point D, where $t = 200$ and $\ln i = 3.31$, and substituting into

$$\ln i = \frac{1}{T} t + \ln I$$

gives

$$3.31 = -\frac{1}{50}(200) + \ln I$$

from which

$$\ln I = 3.31 + 4.0 = 7.31$$

and $I = $ antilog $7.31\ (= e^{7.31}) = 1495$ or $\mathbf{1500}$ correct to 3 significant figures.

Hence the law of the graph is $\boldsymbol{i = 1500e^{-t/50}}$.

Logarithmic scales

Graph paper is available where the scale markings along the horizontal and vertical axes are proportional to the logarithms of the numbers. Such graph paper is called *log–log graph paper*.

A *logarithmic scale* is shown in Figure 8.45 where the distance between, say 1 and 2, is proportional to lg 2 – lg 1, i.e. 0.3010 of the total distance from 1 to 10. Similarly, the distance between 7 and 8 is proportional to lg 8 – lg 7, i.e. 0.05799 of the total distance from

---

Test your knowledge 8.31

1 The head of pressure h and the flow velocity v are measured and are believed to be connected by the law $v = ah^b$, where a and b are constants. The results are as shown below.

h	10.6	13.4	17.2	24.6	29.3
v	9.77	11.00	12.44	14.88	16.24

Verify that the law is true and determine values of a and b.

2 The tension T in a belt passing round a pulley wheel and in contact with the pulley over an angle of θ radians is given by $T = T_0 e^{\mu\theta}$, where T_0 and μ are constants. Experimental results obtained are:

T newtons	47.9	52.8	60.3	70.1	80.9
θ radians	1.12	1.48	1.97	2.53	3.06

Determine approximate values of T_0 and μ. Hence find the tension when θ is 2.25 radians and the value of θ when the tension is 50.0 newtons.

Figure 8.45

1 to 10. Thus the distance between markings progressively decreases as the numbers increase from 1 to 10. With log–log graph paper the scale markings are from 1 to 9, and this pattern can be repeated several times. The number of times the pattern of markings is repeated on an axis signifies the number of *cycles*. When the vertical axis has, say, three sets of values from 1 to 9, then this log–log graph paper is called 'log 3 cycle $\times$ 2 cycle' (see Figure 8.46). Many different arrangements are available ranging from 'log 1 cycle x 1 cycle' through to 'log 5 cycle $\times$ 5 cycle'.

To depict a set of values, say, from 0.4 to 161, on an axis of log–log graph paper, 4 cycles are required, from 0.1 to 1, 1 to 10, 10 to 100 and 100 to 1000.

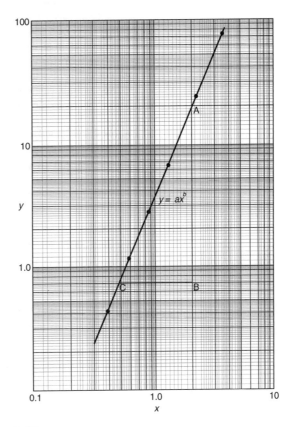

Figure 8.46

Graphs of the form $y = ax^n$

Taking logarithms to a base of 10 of both sides of $y = ax^n$ gives:

$$\lg y = \lg (ax^n) = \lg a + \lg x^n$$

i.e. $$\lg y = n \lg x + \lg a$$

which compares with $$Y = mX + c$$

Thus, by plotting lg y vertically against lg x horizontally, a straight line results, i.e. the equation $y = ax^n$ is reduced to linear form. With log–log graph paper available x and y may be plotted directly, without having first to determine their logarithms.

Example 8.112

Experimental values of two related quantities x and y are shown below:

x	0.41	0.63	0.92	1.36	2.17	3.95
y	0.45	1.21	2.89	7.10	20.79	82.46

The law relating x and y is believed to be $y = ax^b$, where a and b are constants. Verify that this law is true and determine the approximate values of a and b.

If $y = ax^b$ then lg $y = b$ lg $x +$ lg a, from above, which is of the form $Y = mX + c$, showing that to produce a straight line graph lg y is plotted vertically against lg x horizontally. x and y may be plotted directly on to log–log graph paper as shown in Figure 8.46. The values of y range from 0.45 to 82.46 and 3 cycles are needed (i.e. 0.1 to 1, 1 to 10 and 10 to 100). The values of x range from 0.41 to 3.95 and 2 cycles are needed (i.e. 0.1 to 1 and 1 to 10). Hence 'log 3 cycle $\times$ 2 cycle' is used as shown in Figure 8.46 where the axes are marked and the points plotted. Since the points lie on a straight line the law $y = ax^b$ is verified.

To evaluate constants a and b

Method 1. Any two points on the straight line, say points A and C, are selected, and AB and BC are measured (say in centimetres)

Then, gradient, $b = \dfrac{AB}{BC} = \dfrac{11.5 \text{ units}}{5 \text{ units}} = 2.3$

Since   lg $y = b$ lg $x +$ lg a, when $x = 1$, lg $x = 0$ and lg $y =$ lg a.

The straight line crosses the ordinate $x = 1.0$ at $y = 3.5$.

Hence lg $a =$ lg 3.5, i.e. **$a = 3.5$.**

Method 2. Any two points on the straight line, say points A and C, are selected. A has coordinates (2,17.25) and C has coordinates (0.5,0.7)

Since $y = ax^b$ then $17.25 = a(2)^b$ $\qquad\qquad\qquad$ (1)

and $\qquad\qquad\qquad\qquad 0.7 = a(0.5)^b$ $\qquad\qquad\qquad$ (2)

i.e. two simultaneous equations are produced and may be solved for a and b. Dividing equation (1) by equation (2) to eliminate a gives

$$\frac{17.25}{0.7} = \frac{(2)^b}{(0.5)^b} = \left(\frac{2}{0.5}\right)^b$$

i.e. $24.643 = (4)^b$

Taking logarithms of both sides gives lg $24.643 = b$ lg 4, i.e.

$$b = \frac{\text{lg } 24.643}{\text{lg } 4} = 2.3, \text{ correct to 2 significant figures}$$

Substituting $b = 2.3$ in equation (1) gives: $17.25 = a(2)^{2.3}$, i.e.

$$a \frac{17.25}{(2)^{2.3}} = \frac{17.25}{4.925} = 3.5, \text{ correct to 2 significant figures}$$

Hence the law of the graph is **$y = 3.5x^{2.3}$**

Example 8.113

The power dissipated by a resistor was measured for varying values of current flowing in the resistor and the results are as shown:

Current, I amperes	1.4	4.7	6.8	9.1	11.2	13.1
Power, P watts	49	552	1156	2070	3136	4290

Prove that the law relating current and power is of the form $P = RI^n$, where R and n are constants, and determine the law. Hence calculate the power when the current is 12 amperes and the current when the power is 1000 W.

Since $P = RI^n$ then $\lg P = n \lg I + \lg R$, which is of the form $Y = mX + c$, showing that to produce a straight line graph $\lg P$ is plotted vertically against $\lg I$ horizontally. Power values range from 49 to 4290, hence 3 cycles of log–log graph paper are needed (10 to 100, 100 to 1000 and 1000 to 10000). Current values range from 1.4 to 11.2, hence 2 cycles of log–log graph paper are needed (1 to 10 and 10 to 100).

Thus 'log 3 cycles × 2 cycles' is used as shown in Figure 8.47 (or, if not available, graph paper having a larger number of cycles per axis can be used). The coordinates are plotted and a straight line results which proves that the law relating current and power is of the form $P = RI^n$

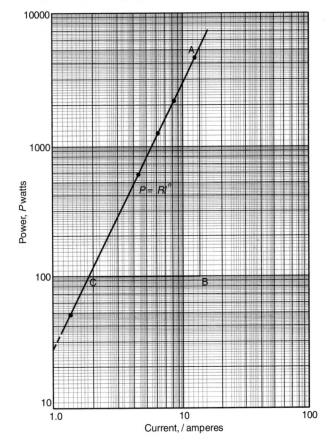

Figure 8.47

Gradient of straight line

$$n = \frac{AB}{BC} = \frac{14 \text{ units}}{7 \text{ units}} = 2$$

At point C, $I = 2$ and $P = 100$. Substituting these values into $P = RI^n$ gives:

$$100 = R(2)^2.$$

Hence $R = 100/(2)^2 = 25$ which may have been found from the intercept on the $I = 1.0$ axis in Figure 8.47.

Hence the law of the graph is **$P = 25I^2$**.

When current $I = 12$, power $P = 25(12)^2 = $ **3600 watts** (which may be read from the graph).

When power $P = 1000$, $1000 = 25I^2$

Hence $I^2 = \dfrac{1000}{25} = 40$

from which, $I = \sqrt{40} = $ **6.32 A**

Activity 8.4

The pressure p and volume v of a gas are believed to be related by a law of the form $p = cv^n$, where c and n are constants. Experimental values of p and corresponding values of v obtained in a laboratory are:

p pascals	2.28×10^5	8.04×10^5	2.03×10^6	5.05×10^6	1.82×10^7
v m³	3.2×10^{-2}	1.3×10^{-2}	6.7×10^{-3}	3.5×10^{-3}	1.4×10^{-3}

Verify that the law is true and determine approximate values of c and n

Graphs of the form $y = ae^{kx}$

Taking logarithms to a base of e of both sides of $y = ae^{kx}$ gives:

$$\ln y = \ln (ae^{kx}) = \ln a + \ln e^{kx} = \ln a + kx \ln e$$

i.e. $\ln y = kx + \ln a$ (since $\ln e = 1$)

which compares with $Y = mX + c$

Thus, by plotting $\ln y$ vertically against x horizontally, a straight line results, i.e. the equation $y = ae^{kx}$ is reduced to linear form. Since $\ln y = 2.3026 \lg y$, i.e. $\ln y = $ (a constant)($\lg y$), the same log–linear graph paper can be used for natural logarithms as for logarithms to a base of 10.

Example 8.114

The voltage, *v* volts, across an inductor is believed to be related to time, *t* (ms), by the law $v = Ve^{t/T}$, *where V and T are constants.* Experimental results obtained are:

v volts	883	347	90	55.5	18.6	5.2
t ms	10.4	21.6	37.8	43.6	56.7	72.0

Show that the law relating voltage and time is as stated and determine the approximate values of *V* and *T*. Find also the value of voltage after 25 ms and the time when the voltage is 30.0 V.

Since $v = Ve^{t/T}$ then $\ln v = \dfrac{1}{T} t + \ln V$

which is of the form $Y = mX + c$

Using 'log 3 cycle × linear' graph paper, the points are plotted as shown in Figure 8.48.

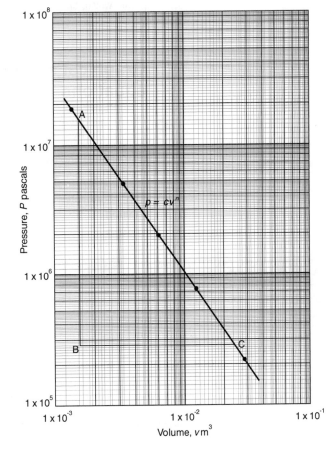

Figure 8.48

Since the points are joined by a straight line the law $v = Ve^{t/T}$ is verified.

Gradient of straight line,

$$\frac{1}{T} = \frac{AB}{BC} = \frac{\ln 100 - \ln 10}{36.5 - 64.2} = \frac{2.3026}{-27.7}$$

Hence $T = \dfrac{-27.7}{2.3026} = $ **−12.0**, correct to 3 significant figures.

Since the straight line does not cross the vertical axis at $t = 0$ in Figure 8.48, the value of V is determined by selecting any point, say A, having coordinates $(36.5, 100)$ and substituting these values into $v = Ve^{t/T}$. Thus

$$100 = Ve^{36.5/-12.0}$$

i.e. $\quad V = \dfrac{100}{e^{-36.5/12.0}} = $ **2090 volts**, correct to 3 significant figures

Hence the law of the graph is $v = 2090e^{-t/12.0}$

When time $t = 25$ ms, voltage $v = 2090e^{-25/12.0} = $ **260 V**

When the voltage is 30.0 volts, $30.0 = 2090e^{t/12.0}$, hence

$$e^{-t/12.0} = \frac{30.0}{2090} \text{ and } e^{t/12.0} = \frac{2090}{30.0} = 69.67$$

Taking natural logarithms gives: $\dfrac{t}{12.0} = \ln 69.67 = 4.2438$

from which, time $t = (12.0)(4.2438) = $ **50.9 ms**.

Graphical solution of simultaneous equations

Linear simultaneous equations in two unknowns may be solved graphically by:

(i) plotting the two straight lines on the same axes, and
(ii) noting their point of intersection.

The coordinates of the point of intersection give the required solution.

Test your knowledge 8.32

1 Quantities x and y are believed to be related by a law of the form $y = mn^x$. The values of x and corresponding values of y are:

x	0	0.5	1.0	1.5	2.0	2.5	3.0
y	1.0	3.2	10	31.6	100	316	1000

Verify the law and find the values of m and n.

2 At particular times, t minutes, measurements are made of the temperature, $\theta°C$, of a cooling liquid and the following results are obtained:

Temperature $\theta°C$	92.2	55.9	33.9	20.6	12.5
Time t minutes	10	20	30	40	50

Prove that the quantities follow a law of the form $\theta = \theta_0 e^{kt}$, where θ_0 and k are constants, and determine the approximate values of θ_0 and k.

Example 8.115

Solve graphically the simultaneous equations:

$$2x - y = 4$$
$$x + y = 5$$

Rearranging each equation into $y = mx + c$ form gives:

$$y = 2x - 4 \tag{1}$$
$$y = -x + 5 \tag{2}$$

Only three coordinates need be calculated for each graph since both are straight lines.

x	0	1	2
$y = 2x - 4$	-4	-2	0

x	0	1	2
$y = -x + 5$	5	4	3

Each of the graphs is plotted as shown in Figure 8.49. The point of intersection is at (3,2) and since this is the only point which lies simultaneously on both lines then **$x = 3$, $y = 2$** is the solution of the simultaneous equations.

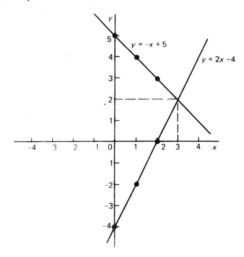

Figure 8.49

Activity 8.5

Solve graphically the equations:

$$1.20x + y = 1.80$$
$$x - 5.0y = 8.50$$

Graphical solutions of quadratic equations

A general *quadratic equation* is of the form $y = ax^2 + bx + c$, where a, b and c are constants and a is not equal to zero.

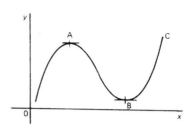

Figure 8.50

A graph of a quadratic equation always produces a shape called a *parabola*. The gradient of the curve between 0 and A and between B and C in Figure 8.50 is positive, while the gradient between A and B is negative. Points such as A and B are called *turning points*. At A the gradient is zero and, as *x* increases, the gradient of the curve changes from positive just before A to negative just after. Such a point is called a *maximum value*. At B the gradient is also zero, and, as *x* increases, the gradient of the curve changes from negative just before B to positive just after. Such a point is called a *minimum value*.

Quadratic graphs

(i) $y = ax^2$

Graphs of $y = x^2$, $y = 3x^2$ and $y = \dfrac{1}{2}x^2$

are shown in Figure 8.51.

All have minimum values at the origin (0,0).

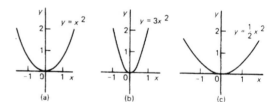

Figure 8.51

Graphs of $y = -x^2$, $y = -3x^2$ and $y = \dfrac{1}{2}x^2$

are shown in Figure 8.52.

All have maximum values at the origin (0,0).

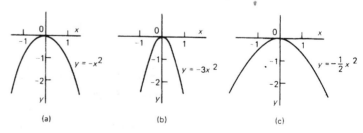

Figure 8.52

When $y = ax^2$,

    (a) curves are symmetrical about the y-axis,

    (b) the magnitude of 'a' affects the gradient of the curve

and (c) the sign of 'a' determines whether it has a maximum or minimum value.

(ii) $y = ax^2 + c$

Graphs of $y = x^2 + 3$, $y = x^2 - 2$, $y = -x^2 + 2$ and $y = -2x^2 - 1$ are shown in Figure 8.53.

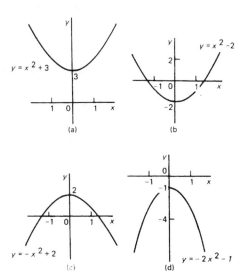

Figure 8.53

When $y = ax^2 + c$:

    (a) curves are symmetrical about the y-axis,

    (b) the magnitude of 'a' affects the gradient of the curve,

and (c) the constant 'c' is the y-axis intercept

(iii) $y = ax^2 + bx + c$

Whenever 'b' has a value other than zero the curve is displaced to the right or left of the y-axis. When b/a is positive, the curve is displaced $b/2a$ to the left of the y-axis, as shown in Figure 8.54(a). When b/a is negative the curve is displaced $b/2a$ to the right of the y-axis, as shown in Figure 8.54(b).

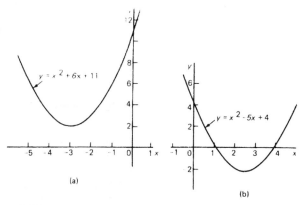

Figure 8.54

Quadratic equations of the form $ax^2 + bx + c = 0$ may be solved graphically by:

(i)   plotting the graph $y = ax^2 + bx + c$, and
(ii) noting the points of intersection on the x-axis (i.e. where $y = 0$).

The x values of the points of intersection give the required solutions since at these points both $y = 0$ and $ax^2 + bx + c = 0$. The number of solutions, or roots of a quadratic equation, depends on how many times the curve cuts the x-axis and there can be no real roots (as in Figure 8.54(a)) or one root (as in Figures 8.51 and 8.52) or two roots (as in Figure 8.54(b)).

Example 8.116

Solve the gradratic equation $4x^2 + 4x - 15 = 0$ graphically given that the solutions lie in the range $x = -3$ to $x = 2$. Determine also the coordinates and nature of the turning point of the curve.

Let $y = 4x^2 + 4x - 15$. A table of values is drawn up as shown below.

x									-3	-2	-1	0	1	2
$4x^2$									36	16	4	0	4	16
$4x$									-12	-8	-4	0	4	8
-15									-15	-15	-15	-15	-15	-15
$y = 4x^2 + 4x - 15$									9	-7	-15	-15	-7	9

A graph of $y = 4x^2 + 4x - 15$ is shown in Figure 8.55. The only points where $y = 4x^2 + 4x - 15$ and $y = 0$ are the points marked A and B. This occurs at **$x = 2.5$** and **$x = 1.5$** and these are the solutions of the quadratic equation $4x^2 + 4x - 15 = 0$. (By substituting $x = -2.5$ and $x = 1.5$ into the original equation the solutions may be checked.) The curve has a turning point at $(-0.5, -16)$ and the nature of the point is a *minimum*.

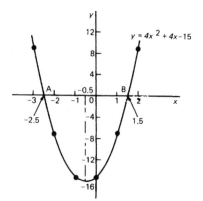

Figure 8.55

An alternative graphical method of solving $4x^2 + 4x - 15 = 0$ is to rearrange the equation as $4x^2 = -4x + 15$ and then plot two separate graphs – in this case $y = 4x^2$ and $y = -4x + 15$. Their points of intersection give the roots of equation $4x^2 = -4x + 15$, i.e. $4x^2 + 4x - 15 = 0$. This is shown in Figure 8.56, where the roots are $x = -2.5$ and $x = 1.5$ as before.

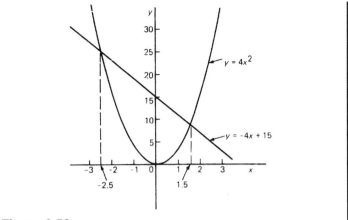

Figure 8.56

1 Sketch the following graphs and state the nature and coordinates of their turning points.

(a) $y = 4x^2$

(b) $y = 2x^2 - 1$

(c) $y = -x^2 + 3$

(d) $y = -\dfrac{1}{2}x^2 - 1$

2 Solve the quadratic equation $2x^2 + 7x + 6 = 0$ graphically, given that the solutions lie in the range $x = -2$ to $x = 3$. Determine also the nature and coordinates of its turning point.

Activity 8.6

Solve graphically the quadratic equation $-5x^2 + 9x + 7.2 = 0$ given that the solutions lie between $x = -1$ and $x = 3$. Determine also the coordinates of the turning point and state its nature.

Graphical solution of cubic equations

A *cubic equation* of the form $ax^3 + bx^2 + cx + d = 0$ may be solved graphically by: (i) plotting the graph $y = ax^3 + bx^2 + cx + d$, and (ii) noting the points of intersection on the x-axis (i.e. where $y = 0$). The x-values of the points of intersection give the required solution since at these points both $y = 0$ and $ax^3 + bx^2 + cx + d = 0$

The number of solutions, or roots of a cubic equation depends on how many times the curve cuts the x-axis and there can be one, two or three possible roots, as shown in Figure 8.57.

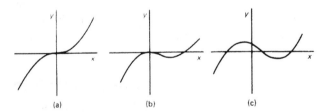

(a)   (b)   (c)

Figure 8.57

Example 8.117

Solve graphically the cubic equation $4x^3 - 8x^2 - 15x + 9 = 0$ given that the roots lie between $x = -2$ and $x = 3$. Determine also the coordinates of the turning points and distinguish between them.

Let $y = 4x^3 - 8x^2 - 15x + 9$. A table of values is drawn up as shown below.

x	−2	−1	0	1	2	3
$4x^3$	−32	−4	0	4	32	108
$-8x^2$	−32	−8	0	−8	−32	−72
$-15x$	30	15	0	−15	−30	−45
$+9$	9	9	9	9	9	9
y	−25	12	9	−10	−21	0

A graph of $y = 4x^3 - 8x^2 - 15x + 9$ is shown in Figure 8.58.

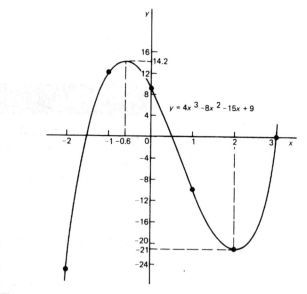

Figure 8.58

The graph crosses the x-axis (where $y = 0$) at

$$x = -1\frac{1}{2}, \; x = \frac{1}{2} \text{ and } x = 3,$$

and these are the solutions to the cubic equation $4x^3 - 8x^2 - 15x + 9 = 0$. The turning points occur at **(−0.6,14.2)**, which is a **maximum**, and **(2,−21)**, which is a **minimum**.

Introduction to Cartesian and polar coordinates

There are two ways in which the position of a point in a plane can be represented. These are:

(a) by *Cartesian coordinates*, i.e. (x,y); and
(b) by *polar coordinates*, i.e. (r,θ), where r is a 'radius' from a fixed point and θ is an angle from a fixed point.

From plotting graphs in previous sections, we are familiar with Cartesian coordinates. Polar coordinates provide us with another method of plotting points.

Changing from Cartesian into polar coordinates

In Figure 8.59, if lengths x and y are known, then the length of r can be obtained from Pythagoras' theorem since 0PQ is a right-angled triangle. Hence

$$r^2 = (x^2 + y^2)$$

from which

$$r = \sqrt{(x^2 + y^2)}$$

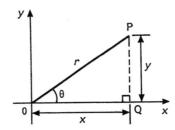

Figure 8.59

From trigonometric ratios,

$$\tan \theta = \frac{y}{x}$$

from which

$$\theta = \arctan y/x$$

$r = \sqrt{(x^2 + y^2)}$ and $\theta = \arctan (y/x)$ are the two formulae we need to change from Cartesian to polar coordinates. The angle θ, which may be expressed in degrees or radians, must *always* be measured from the positive x-axis, i.e. measured from the line 0Q in Figure 8.59. It is suggested that when changing from Cartesian to polar coordinates a diagram should always be sketched.

Example 8.118

Change the Cartesian coordinates (3,4) into polar coordinates. A diagram representing the point (3,4) is shown in Figure 8.60.

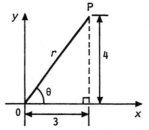

Figure 8.60

From Pythagoras' theorem, $r = \sqrt{(3^2 + 4^2)} = 5$ (note that −5 has no meaning in this context). By trigonometric ratios, $\theta = \arctan 4/3 = 53.13°$ or 0.927 rad (note that $53.13° = 53.13 \times (\pi/180)$ rad = 0.927 rad).

Hence (3,4) in Cartesian coordinates corresponds to (5,53.13°) or (5,0.927 rad) in polar coordinates.

Example 8.119

Express (−5,−12) in polar coordinates.

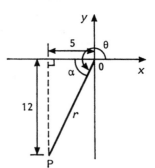

Figure 8.61

A sketch showing the position (−5,−12) is shown in Figure 8.61.

$$r = \sqrt{(5^2 + 12^2)} = 13$$

$$\alpha = \arctan \frac{12}{5} = 67.38° \text{ or } 1.176 \text{ rad}$$

Hence $\theta = 180° + 67.38° = 247.38°$

or $\theta = \pi + 1.176 = 4.318 \text{ rad}$

Thus (−5,−12) in Cartesian coordinates corresponds to **(13,247.38°)** or **(13,4.318 rad)** in polar coordinates.

Example 8.120

Express (2,−5) in polar coordinates.

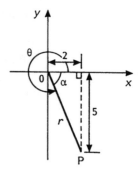

Figure 8.62

A sketch showing the position (2,−5) is shown in Figure 8.62.

$$r = \sqrt{(2^2 + 5^2)} = \sqrt{29} = 5.385 \text{ correct to 3 decimal places}$$

$$a = \arctan \frac{5}{2} = 68.20° \text{ or } 1.190 \text{ rad}$$

Hence $\theta = 360° − 68.20° = 291.80°$

or $\theta = 2\pi − 1.190 = 5.093 \text{ rad}$

Thus (2,−5) in Cartesian coordinates corresponds to **(5.385,291.80°)** or **(5.385,5.093 rad)** in polar coordinates.

Changing from polar into Cartesian coordinates

From the right-angled triangle 0PQ in Figure 8.63

$$\cos \theta = \frac{x}{r} \text{ and } \sin \theta = \frac{y}{r}, \text{ from trigonometric ratios}$$

Hence

$$x = r \cos \theta \text{ and } y = r \sin \theta$$

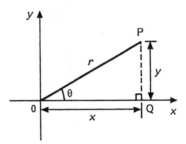

Figure 8.63

If lengths r and angle θ are known then $x = r \cos \theta$ and $y = r \sin \theta$ are the two formulae we need to change from polar to Cartesian coordinates.

Example 8.121

Express (6,137°) in Cartesian coordinates.

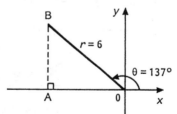

Figure 8.64

A sketch showing the position (6,137°) is shown in Figure 8.64.

$$x = r \cos \theta = 6 \cos 137° = -4.388$$

which corresponds to length 0A in Figure 8.66

$$y = r \sin \theta = 6 \sin 137° = 4.092$$

which corresponds to length AB in Figure 8.64.

Thus (6,137°) in polar coordinates corresponds to **(−4.388,4.092)** in Cartesian coordinates.

(Note that when changing from polar to Cartesian coordinates it is not quite so essential to draw a sketch. Use of $x = r \cos \theta$ and $y = r \sin \theta$ automatically produces the correct signs.)

Example 8.122

Express (4.5,5.16 rad) in Cartesian coordinates.

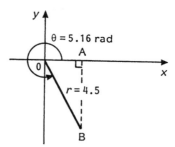

Figure 8.65

A sketch showing the position (4.5,5.16 rad) is shown in Figure 8.65.

$$x = r \cos \theta = 4.5 \cos 5.16 = 1.948$$

which corresponds to length OA in Figure 8.65.

$$y = r \sin \theta = 4.5 \sin 5.16 = -4.057$$

which corresponds to length AB in Figure 8.65.

Thus (1.948,−4.057) in Cartesian coordinates corresponds to **(4.5,5.16 rad)** in polar coordinates.

Test your knowledge 8.36

1 Change (4,32°) into Cartesian coordinates
2 Express (6.3,153°) in Cartesian coordinates
3 Change (2.5,4.5 rad) into Cartesian coordinates

Use of R → P and P → R functions on calculators

Another name for Cartesian coordinates is *rectangular* coordinates. Many scientific notation calculators possess R → P and P → R functions. The R is the first letter of the word rectangular and the P is the first letter of the word polar. Check the operation manual for your particular calculator to determine how to use these two functions. They make changing from Cartesian to polar coordinates, and vice versa, so much quicker and easier.

Sine and cosine curves

Graphs of sine and cosine waveforms

(i) A graph of $y = \sin A$ is shown by the broken line in Figure 8.66 and is obtained by drawing up a table of values. A similar table may be produced for $y = \sin 2A$.

$A°$	0	30	45	60	90	120	135	150	180
$2A$	0	60	90	120	180	240	270	300	360
$\sin 2A$	0	0.866	1.0	0.866	0	−0.866	−1.0	−0.866	0

$A°$	210	225	240	270	300	315	330	360
$2A$	420	450	480	540	600	630	660	720
$\sin 2A$	0.866	1.0	0.866	0	−0.866	−1.0	−0.866	0

A graph of $y = \sin 2A$ is shown in Figure 8.66

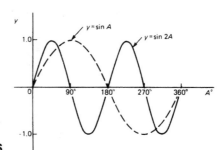

Figure 8.66

(ii) A graph of $y = \sin \dfrac{1}{2} A$

is shown in Figure 8.67 using the following table of values.

$A°$	0	30	60	90	120	150	180
$\dfrac{1}{2} A$	0	15	30	45	60	75	90
$\sin \dfrac{1}{2} A$	0	0.259	0.500	0.707	0.866	0.966	1.00

$A°$	210	240	270	300	330	360
$\dfrac{1}{2} A$	105	120	135	150	165	180
$\sin \dfrac{1}{2} A$	0.966	0.866	0.707	0.500	0.259	0

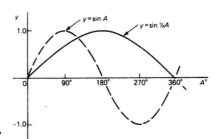

Figure 8.67

(iii) A graph of $y = \cos A$ is shown by the broken line in Figure 8.68 and is obtained by drawing up a table of values. A similar table may be produced for $y = \cos 2A$.

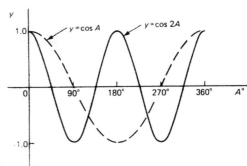

Figure 8.68

A°	0	30	45	60	90	120	135	150	180
2A	0	60	90	120	180	240	270	300	360
cos 2A	1.0	0.50	0	−0.50	−1.0	−0.50	0	0.50	1.0

A°	210	225	240	270	300	315	330	360
2A	420	450	480	540	600	630	660	720
cos 2A	0.50	0	-0.50	−1.0	−0.50	0	0.50	1.0

A graph of $y = \cos 2A$ is shown in Figure 8.68.

(iv) A graph of $y = \cos \dfrac{1}{2} A$

is shown in Figure 8.69 using the following table of values.

A°	0	30	60	90	120	150	180
$\dfrac{1}{2} A$	0	15	30	45	60	75	90
$\cos \dfrac{1}{2} A$	1.0	0.966	0.866	0.707	0.50	0.259	0

A°	210	240	270	300	330	360
$\dfrac{1}{2} A$	105	120	135	150	165	180
$\cos \dfrac{1}{2} A$	−0.259	−0.50	−0.707	−0.866	−0.966	−1.0

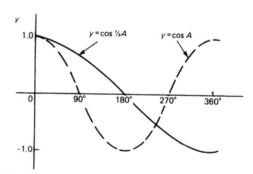

Figure 8.69

Periodic time and period

(i) Each of the graphs shown in Figures 8.66 to 8.69 will repeat themselves as angle A increases and are thus called *periodic functions*.

(ii) $y = \sin A$ and $y = \cos A$ repeat themselves every 360° (or 2π radians); thus 360° is called the *period* of these waveforms. $y = \sin 2A$ and $y = \cos 2A$ repeat themselves every 180° (or π radians); thus 180° is the period of these waveforms.

(iii) In general, if $y = \sin pA$ or $y = \cos pA$ (where p is a constant) then the period of the waveform is $360°/p$ (or $2\pi/p$ rad). Hence if $y = \sin 3A$ then the period is $360/3$, i.e. $120°$, and if $y = \cos 4A$ then the period is $360/4$, i.e. $90°$.

Amplitude

Amplitude is the name given to the maximum or peak value of a sine wave. Each of the graphs shown in Figures 8.66 to 8.69 has an amplitude of $+1$ (i.e. they oscillate between $+1$ and -1). However, if $y = 4 \sin A$, each of the values in the table is multiplied by 4 and the maximum value, and thus amplitude, is 4. Similarly, if $y = 5 \cos 2A$, the amplitude is 5 and the period is $360°/2$, i.e. $180°$.

Lagging and leading angles

(i) A sine or cosine curve may not always start at $0°$. To show this a periodic function is represented by $y = \sin(A \pm \alpha)$ or $y = \cos(A \pm \alpha)$ where α is a phase displacement compared with $y = \sin A$ or $y = \cos A$.

(ii) By drawing up a table of values, a graph of $y = \sin(A - 60°)$ may be plotted as shown in Figure 8.70. If $y = \sin A$ is assumed to start at $0°$ then $y = \sin(A - 60°)$ starts $60°$ later (i.e. has a zero value $60°$ later). Thus $y = \sin(A - 60°)$ is said to *lag* $y = \sin A$ by $60°$.

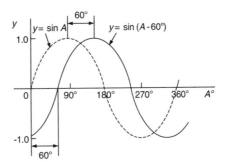

Figure 8.70

(iii) By drawing up a table of values, a graph of $y = \cos(A + 45°)$ may be plotted as shown in Figure 8.71. If $y = \cos A$ is assumed to start at $0°$ then $y = \cos(A + 45°)$ starts $45°$ earlier (i.e. has a zero value $45°$ earlier). Thus $y = \cos(A + 45°)$ is said to *lead* $y = \cos A$ by $45°$.

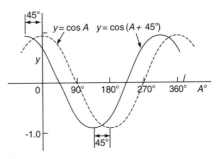

Figure 8.71

(iv) Generally, a graph of $y = \sin(A - \alpha)$ lags $y = \sin A$ by angle α, and a graph of $y = \sin(A + \alpha)$ leads $y = \sin A$ by angle α.

(v) A cosine curve is the same shape as a sine curve but starts 90° earlier, i.e. leads by 90°. Hence $\cos A = \sin(A + 90°)$.

Example 8.123

Sketch $y = \sin 3A$ between $A = 0°$ and $A = 360°$

Amplitude = 1; period = 360°/3 = 120°.

A sketch of $y = \sin 3A$ is shown in Figure 8.72

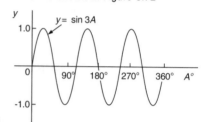

Figure 8.72

Example 8.124

Sketch $y = 3 \sin 2A$ from $A = 0$ to $A = 2\pi$ radians.

Amplitude = 3; period = $\dfrac{2\pi}{2} = \pi$ rads (or 180°).

A sketch of $y = 3 \sin 2A$ is shown in Figure 8.73.

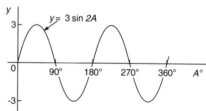

Figure 8.73

Test your knowledge 8.37

1 Sketch $y = 4 \cos 2x$ from $x = 0°$ to $x = 360°$

2 Sketch $y = 2 \sin \dfrac{3}{5} A$

over one cycle

3 Sketch $y = 7 \sin \left(2A - \dfrac{\pi}{3} \right)$

over one cycle

4 Sketch $y = 2 \cos \left(t - \dfrac{3\pi}{10} \right)$

over one cycle

Example 8.125

Sketch $y = 5 \sin(A + 30°)$ from $A = 0°$ to $A = 360°$

Amplitude = 5; period = 360°/1 = 360°

$5 \sin(A + 30°)$ leads $5 \sin A$ by 30° (i.e. starts 30° earlier).

A sketch of $y = 5 \sin(A + 30°)$ is shown in Figure 8.74.

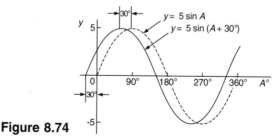

Figure 8.74

Graphs of exponential functions

Values of e^x and e^{-x}, obtained from a calculator, correct to 2 decimal places, over a range $x = -3$ to $x = 3$, are shown in the table below.

x	−3.0	−2.5	−2.0	−1.5	−1.0	−0.5	0
e^x	0.05	0.08	0.14	0.22	0.37	0.61	1.00
e^{-x}	20.09	12.18	7.39	4.48	2.72	1.65	1.00

x	0.5	1.0	1.5	2.0	2.5	3.0
e^x	1.65	2.72	4.48	7.39	12.18	20.09
e^{-x}	0.61	0.37	0.22	0.14	0.08	0.05

Figure 8.75 shows graphs of $y = e^x$ and $y = e^{-x}$

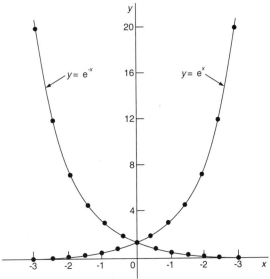

Figure 8.75

Activity 8.7

1 Plot a graph of $y = 3e^{0.2x}$ over the range $x = -3$ to $x = 3$. Hence determine the value of y when $x = 1.4$ and the value of x when $y = 4.5$.

2 Plot a graph of

$$y = \frac{1}{2} e^{-1.5x}$$

over a range $x = -1.5$ to $x = 1.5$ and hence determine the value of y when $x = -0.8$ and the value of x when $y = 3.5$.

3 Plot the decay curve $y = 4.13e^{-1.5x}$ and the growth curve $y = 2.4(1 - e^{-2x})$ on the same axes from $x = 0$ to $x = 1$, and determine their point of intersection.

Calculus

Introduction to calculus

Calculus is a branch of mathematics involving or leading to calculations dealing with continuously varying functions. Calculus is a subject which falls into two parts:

(i) *differential calculus* (or *differentiation*) and
(ii) *integral calculus* (or *integration*).

Differentiation is used in calculations involving velocity and acceleration, rates of change and maximum and minimum values of curves.

Integration is used to determine areas under curves, mean and r.m.s. values, volumes, centroids, second moments of area and in the solution of differential equations.

Functional notation

In an equation such as $y = 3x^2 + 2x - 5$, y is said to be a function of x and may be written as $y = f(x)$. An equation written in the form $f(x) = 3x^2 + 2x - 5$ is termed *functional notation*.

The value of $f(x)$ when $x = 0$ is denoted by $f(0)$, and the value of $f(x)$ when $x = 2$ is denoted by $f(2)$ and so on. Thus when $f(x) = 3x^2 + 2x - 5$, then

$$f(0) = 3(0)^2 + 2(0) - 5 = -5$$

and $f(2) = 3(2)^2 + 2(2) - 5 = 11$

and so on.

Example 8.126

If $f(x) = 4x^2 - 3x + 2$ find $f(0)$, $f(3)$, $f(-1)$ and $f(3) - f(-1)$.

$f(x) = 4x^2 - 3x + 2$

$f(0) = 4(0)^2 - 3(0) + 2 = \mathbf{2}$

$f(3) = 4(3)^2 - 3(3) + 2 = 36 - 9 + 2 = \mathbf{29}$

$f(-1) = 4(-1)^2 - 3(-1) + 2 = 4 + 3 + 2 = \mathbf{9}$

$f(3) - f(-1) = 29 - 9 = \mathbf{20}$

The gradient of a curve

(a) If a tangent is drawn at a point P on a curve, then the gradient of this tangent is said to be the *gradient of the curve* at P. In Figure 8.76, the gradient of the curve at P is equal to the gradient of the tangent PQ.

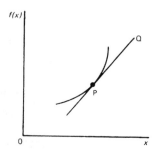

Figure 8.76

(b) For the curve shown in Figure 8.77, let the points A and B have coordinates (x_1, y_1) and (x_2, y_2), respectively. In functional notation, $y_1 = f(x_1)$ and $y_2 = f(x_2)$ as shown.

$$\text{The gradient of the chord AB} = \frac{BC}{AC} = \frac{BD - CD}{ED}$$

$$= \frac{f(x_2) - f(x_1)}{(x_2 - x_1)}$$

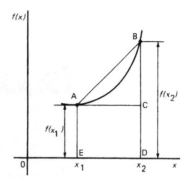

Figure 8.77

(c) For the curve $f(x) = x^2$ shown in Figure 8.78:

(i)   the gradient of chord AB $= \dfrac{f(3) - f(1)}{3 - 1} = \dfrac{9 - 1}{2} = 4$

(ii) the gradient of chord AC $= \dfrac{f(2) - f(1)}{2 - 1} = \dfrac{4 - 1}{1} = 3$

(iii) the gradient of chord AD $= \dfrac{f(1.5) - f(1)}{1.5 - 1}$

$$= \frac{2.25 - 1}{0.5} = 2.5$$

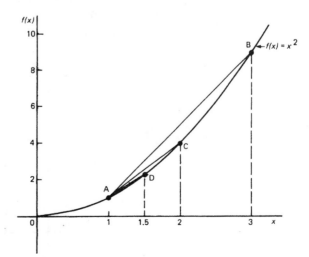

Figure 8.78

(iv) if E is the point on the curve $(1.1, f(1.1))$ then the gradient of

$$\text{chord AE} = \frac{f(1.1) - f(1)}{1.1 - 1} = \frac{1.21 - 1}{0.1} = 2.1$$

(v) if F is the point on the curve $(1.01, f(1.01))$ then the gradient

$$\text{of chord AF} = \frac{f(1.01) - f(1)}{1.01 - 1} = \frac{1.0201 - 1}{0.01} = 2.01$$

Thus as point B moves closer and closer to point A the gradient of the chord approaches nearer and nearer to the value 2. This is called the *limiting value* of the gradient of the chord AB and when B coincides with A the chord becomes the tangent to the curve.

Activity 8.8

Plot the curve $f(x) = 4x^2 - 1$ for values of x from $x = -1$ to $x = +4$. Label the coordinates $(3, f(3))$ and $(1, f(1))$ as J and K, respectively. Join points J and K to form the chord JK. Determine the gradient of chord JK. By moving J nearer and nearer to K determine the gradient of the tangent of the curve at K.

Differentiation from first principles

(i) In Figure 8.79, A and B are two points very close together on a curve, δx (delta x) and δy (delta y) representing small increments in the x and y directions, respectively.

Gradient of chord AB $= \delta y/\delta x$, however $\delta y = f(x + \delta x) - f(x)$

Hence $\dfrac{\delta y}{\delta x} = \dfrac{f(x + \delta x) - f(x)}{\delta x}$

As δx approaches zero, $\delta y/\delta x$ approaches a limiting value and the gradient of the chord approaches the gradient of the tangent at A.

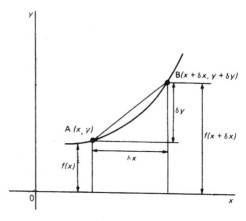

Figure 8.79

(ii) When determining the gradient of a tangent to a curve there are two notations used. The gradient of the curve at A in Figure 8.79 can either be written as

$$\underset{\delta x \to 0}{\text{limit}} \frac{\delta y}{\delta x} \quad \text{or} \quad \underset{\delta x \to 0}{\text{limit}} \frac{f(x + \delta x) - f(x)}{\delta x}$$

In *Leibniz notation*, $\dfrac{dy}{dx} = \underset{\delta x \to 0}{\text{limit}} \dfrac{\delta y}{\delta x}$

In *functional notation*, $f'(x) = \underset{\delta x \to 0}{\text{limit}} \dfrac{f(x + \delta x) - f(x)}{\delta x}$

(iii) dy/dx is the same as $f'(x)$ and is called the *differential coefficient* or the *derivative*. The process of finding the differential coefficient is called *differentiation*. Summarizing, the differential coefficient,

$$\frac{dy}{dx} = f'(x) = \underset{\delta x \to 0}{\text{limit}} \frac{\delta y}{\delta x} = \underset{\delta x \to 0}{\text{limit}} \frac{f(x + \delta x) - f(x)}{\delta x}$$

Example 8.127

Differentiate from first principle $f(x) = x^2$ and determine the value of the gradient of the curve at $x = 2$.

To 'differentiate from first principles' means 'to find $f'(x)$' by using the expression

$$f'(x) = \underset{\delta x \to 0}{\text{limit}} \frac{f(x + \delta x) - f(x)}{\delta x}$$

$f(x) = x^2$.

Substituting $(x + \delta x)$ for x gives $f(x + \delta x) = (x + \delta x)^2 = x^2 + 2x\delta x + \delta x^2$,

$$\text{hence } f'(x) = \underset{\delta x \to 0}{\text{limit}} \frac{(x^2 + 2x\delta x + \delta x^2) - (x^2)}{\delta x}$$

$$= \underset{\delta x \to 0}{\text{limit}} \frac{2x\delta x + \delta x^2}{\delta x} = \underset{\delta x \to 0}{\text{limit}} [2x + \delta x]$$

As $\delta x \to 0$, $[2x + \delta x] \to [2x + 0]$. Thus $f'(x) = 2x$, i.e. the differential coefficient of x^2 is $2x$. At $x = 2$, the gradient of the curve, $f'(x) = 2(2) = 4$.

Example 8.128

Find the differential coefficient of $y = 5x$.

By definition,

$$\frac{dy}{dy} = f'(x) = \underset{\delta x \to 0}{\text{limit}} \frac{f(x + \delta x) - f(x)}{\delta x}$$

The function being differentiated is $y = f(x) = 5x$. Substituting $(x + \delta x)$ for x gives $f(x + \delta x) = 5(x + \delta x) = 5x + 5\delta x$. Hence

$$\frac{dy}{dx} = f'(x) = \lim_{\delta x \to 0} \frac{(5x + 5\delta x) - (5x)}{dx}$$

$$= \lim_{\delta x \to 0} \frac{5\delta x}{\delta x} = \lim_{\delta x \to 0} \quad [5]$$

Since the term δx does not appear in [5] the limiting value as $\delta x \to 0$ of [5] is 5. Thus

$$\frac{dy}{dx} = 5,$$

i.e. the differential coefficient of $5x$ is 5. The equation $y = 5x$ represents a straight line of gradient 5. The 'differential coefficient' (i.e. dy/dx or $f'(x)$) means 'the gradient of the curve', and since the slope of the line $y = 5x$ is 5 this result can be obtained by inspection. Hence, in general, if $y = kx$ (where k is a constant), then the slope of the line is k and dy/dx or $f'(x) = k$.

Example 8.129

Find the derivative of $y = 8$.

$y = f(x) = 8$. Since there are no x-values in the original equation, substituting $(x + \delta x)$ for x still gives $f(x + \delta x) = 8$. Hence

$$\frac{dy}{dx} = f'(x) = \lim_{\delta x \to 0} \frac{f(x + \delta x) - f(x)}{\delta x}$$

$$= \lim_{\delta x \to 0} \frac{8 - 8}{\delta x} = 0$$

Thus, when $y = 8$, $\dfrac{dy}{dx} = 0$

The equation $y = 8$ represents a straight horizontal line and the gradient of a horizontal line is zero, hence the result could have been determined by inspection. 'Finding the derivative' means 'finding the gradient', hence, in general, for any horizontal line if $y = k$ (where k is a constant) then

$$\frac{dy}{dx} = 0.$$

Test your knowledge 8.39

1 Differentiate from first principles (a) $y = 4x^2$ (b) $y = 2x^3$
2 Find the differential coefficient of $y = 4x^2 + 5x - 3$ and determine the gradient of the curve at $x = -3$.

Differentiation of $y = ax^n$ by the general rule

From differentiation by first principles, a general rule for differentiating ax^n emerges, where a and n are any constants. This rule is:

$$\text{if } y = ax^n \text{ then } \frac{dy}{dx} = anx^{n-1}$$

or, if $f(x) = ax^n$ then $f'(x) = anx^{n-1}$

(Each of the results obtained in Examples 131 and 133 may be deduced by using this general rule.)

When differentiating, results can be expressed in a number of ways. For example:

(i) if $y = 3x^2$ then $\dfrac{dy}{dx} = 6x$,

(ii) if $f(x) = 3x^2$ then $f'(x) = 6x$,

(iii) the differential coefficient of $3x^2$ is $6x$,

(iv) the derivative of $3x^2$ is $6x$, and

(v) $\dfrac{d}{dx}(3x^2) = 6x$

Example 8.130

Using the general rule, differentiate the following with respect to x: (a) $y = 5x^7$, (b) $y = 3\sqrt{x}$, (c) $y = 4/x^2$.

(a) Comparing $y = 5x^7$ with $y = ax^n$ shows that $a = 5$ and $n = 7$. Using the general rule,

$$\frac{dy}{dx} = anx^{n-1} = (5)(7)x^{7-1} = \mathbf{35x^6}$$

(b) $y = 3\sqrt{x} = 3x^{1/2}$. Hence $a = 3$ and $n = \dfrac{1}{2}$

$$\frac{dy}{dx} = anx^{n-1} = (3)\left(\frac{1}{2}\right)x^{(1/2)-1} = \frac{3}{2}x^{-1/2} = \frac{3}{2x^{1/2}} = \frac{\mathbf{3}}{\mathbf{2\sqrt{x}}}$$

(c) $y = 4/x^2 = 4x^{-2}$. Hence $a = 4$ and $n = -2$

$$\frac{dy}{dx} = anx^{n-1} = (4)(-2)x^{-2-} = -8x^{-3} = -\frac{\mathbf{8}}{\mathbf{x^3}}$$

In questions 1 to 4, determine the differential coefficient with respect to the variable.

1 $y = 9x^3$

2 $y = \sqrt{x} - 5$

3 $y = \dfrac{1}{t^2} + 4$

4 $y = \dfrac{3}{\sqrt{x}} + \dfrac{1}{x} + 4$

5 Differentiate $y = 5x^2 - 2x + 3$ and find the gradient of the curve at $x = 1.5$.

Example 8.131

If $f(t) = 5t + \dfrac{1}{\sqrt{t^3}}$ find $f'(t)$.

$$f(t) = 5t + \frac{1}{\sqrt{t^3}} = 5t + \frac{1}{t^{3/2}} = 5t^1 + t^{-3/2}$$

Hence $f'(t) = (5)(1)t^{1-1} + \left(-\dfrac{3}{2}\right)t^{(-3/2)-1}$

$$= 5t^0 - \frac{3}{2}t^{-5/2}$$

i.e. $f'(t) = 5 - \dfrac{3}{2t^{5/2}} = 5 - \dfrac{3}{2\sqrt{t^5}}$

Differentiation of sin $a\theta$ and cos $a\theta$

Figure 8.82(a) shows a graph of $y = \sin\theta$. The gradient is continually changing as the curve moves from 0 to A to B to C to D. The gradient, given by $dy/d\theta$ may be plotted in a corresponding position below $y = \sin\theta$, as shown in Figure 8.80(b).

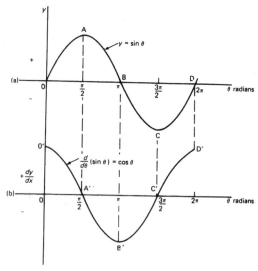

Figure 8.80

(i) At 0, the gradient is positive and is at its steepest. Hence 0' is a maximum positive value.

(ii) Between 0 and A the gradient is positive but is decreasing in value until at A the gradient is zero, shown as A'.

(iii) Between A and B the gradient is negative but is increasing in value until at B the gradient is at its steepest. Hence B' is a maximum negative value.

(iv) If the gradient of $y = \sin \theta$ is further investigated between B and C and C and D then the resulting graph of

$$\frac{dy}{d\theta}$$

is seen to be a cosine wave.

Hence the rate of change of $\sin \theta$ is $\cos \theta$, i.e.

$$\text{if } y = \sin \theta \text{ then } \frac{dy}{d\theta} = \cos \theta$$

It may also be shown that:

$$\text{if } y = \sin a\theta, \frac{dy}{d\theta} = a \cos a\theta \text{ (where } a \text{ is a constant)}$$

(v) If a similar exercise is followed for $y = \cos \theta$ then the graph of

$$\frac{dy}{d\theta}$$

is found to be a graph of $\sin \theta$, but displaced by π radians. It is, in fact, a graph of $-\sin \theta$. Thus

$$\text{if } y = \cos \theta, \frac{dy}{d\theta} = -\sin \theta$$

It may also be shown that

$$\text{if } y = \cos a\theta, \frac{dy}{d\theta} = -a \sin a\theta \text{ (where } a \text{ is a constant)}$$

1 Given $f(x) = 4 \sin 3x - 2 \cos 4x$ find $f'(x)$
2 An alternating current is given by $i = 8 \sin 50t$ amperes where t is the time in seconds. Find the rate of change of current when $t = 10$ ms

Example 8.132

Differentiate the following with respect to the variable: (a) $y = 2 \sin 5\theta$ (b) $f(t) = 3 \cos 2t$

(a) $y = 2 \sin 5\theta$

$$\frac{dy}{d\theta} = (2)(5) \cos 5\theta = \mathbf{10 \cos \theta}$$

(b) $f(t) = 3 \cos 2t$

$$f'(t)(3)(-2) \sin 2t = \mathbf{-6 \sin 2t}$$

Differentiation of e^{ax} and ln ax

If a graph of $y = e^x$ is plotted, and the gradient of the curve determined at intervals, and plotted in a corresponding position below $y = e^x$, it is found that the shape of the gradient curve is also e^x, i.e.

$$\text{if } y = e^x, \text{ then } \frac{dy}{dx} = e^x$$

It may also be shown that

$$\text{if } y = e^{ax}, \text{ then } \frac{dy}{dx} = ae^x$$

Therefore if $y = 2e^{6x}$, then

$$\frac{dy}{dx} = (2)(6e^{6x}) = 12e^{6x}$$

If a graph of $y = \ln x$ is plotted and the gradient of the curve determined at intervals, and plotted in a corresponding position below $y = \ln x$, it is found that the shape of the gradient curve produced is that of $1/x$, i.e.

$$\text{if } y = \ln x, \text{ then } \frac{dy}{dx} = \frac{1}{x}$$

It may also be shown that

$$\text{if } y = \ln ax, \text{ then } \frac{dy}{dx} = \frac{1}{x}$$

(Note that in the latter expression a does not appear in the $\dfrac{dy}{dx}$ term.)

Thus if $y = \ln 4x$, then $\dfrac{dy}{dx} = \dfrac{1}{x}$

Example 8.133

Differentiate the following with respect to the variable:

(a) $y = 3e^{2x}$ (b) $f(t) = \dfrac{4}{3e^{5t}}$

(a) If $y = 3e^{2x}$ then $\dfrac{dy}{dx} = (3)(2e^{3x}) = \mathbf{6e^{2x}}$

(b) If $f(t) = \dfrac{4}{3e^{5t}} = \dfrac{4}{3}e^{-5t}$, then

$$f'(t) = \frac{4}{3}(-5e^{-5t}) = \frac{-20}{3}e^{-5t} = \mathbf{\frac{-20}{3e^{5t}}}$$

Example 8.134

Differentiate $y = 5 \ln 3x$.

If $y = 5 \ln 3x$, $\dfrac{dy}{dx} = (5)\dfrac{1}{x} = \dfrac{5}{x}$

Summary of standard derivatives

The five differential coefficients used are summarized below.

y or $f(x)$	$\dfrac{dy}{dx}$ or $f'(x)$
ax^n	$an\,x^{n-1}$
$\sin ax$	$a \cos ax$
$\cos ax$	$-a \sin ax$
e^{ax}	ae^{ax}
$\ln ax$	$\dfrac{1}{x}$

Differentiate with respect to x:

1 $y = 4e^{2x} - \dfrac{3}{2e^{5x}} + 1$

2 $y = 5 \ln 2t + t - 1$

3 Differentiate $y = \dfrac{3}{x^3} + 3 \ln 4x$

$- 5 (\cos 2x + 2 \sin 3x) - \dfrac{1}{e^{2x}}$

Example 8.135

Find the gradient of the curve $y = 3x^2 - 7x + 2$ at the point $(1, -2)$.

If $y = 3x^2 - 7x + 2$, then gradient $= \dfrac{dy}{dx} = 6x - 7$

At the point $(1, -2)$, $x = 1$, hence **gradient** $= 6(1) - 7 = \mathbf{-1}$

Successive differentiation

When a function $y = f(x)$ is differentiated with respect to x the differential coefficient is written as dy/dx or $f'(x)$. If the expression is differentiated again, the second differential coefficient is obtained and is written as dy^2/dx^2 (pronounced dee two y by dee x squared) or $f''(x)$ (pronounced f double-dash x). By successive diffentiation further higher derivatives such as dy^3/dx^3 may be obtained.

Thus if $y = 5x^4$

$$\frac{dy}{dx} = 20x^3, \frac{d^2y}{dx^2} = 60x^2, \frac{d^3y}{dx^3} = 120x$$

$$\frac{d^4y}{dx^4} = 120 \text{ and } \frac{d^5y}{dx^5} = 0$$

Example 8.136

If $f(x) = 4x^5 - 2x^3 = x - 3$, find $f''(x)$

$f(x) = 4x^5 - 2x^3 + x - 3$

$f'(x) = 20x^4 - 6x^2 + 1$

$f''(x) = 80x^3 - 12x = 4x(20x^2 - 3)$

Example 8.137

Given $y = \dfrac{2}{3} x^3 - \dfrac{4}{x^2} + \dfrac{1}{2x} - \sqrt{x}$ determine $\dfrac{d^2y}{dx^2}$.

$$y = \frac{2}{3} x^3 - \frac{4}{x^4} + \frac{1}{2x} - \sqrt{x} = \frac{2}{3} x^3 - 4x^{-2} + \frac{1}{2} x^{-1} - x^{1/2}$$

$$\frac{dy}{dx} = \frac{2}{3} (3)x^2 - 4(-2)x^{-3} + \frac{1}{2} (-1)x^{-2} - \frac{1}{2} x^{-1/2}$$

i.e.

$$\frac{dy}{dx} = 2x^2 + 8x^{-3} - \frac{1}{2} x^{-2} - \frac{1}{2} x^{-1/2}$$

$$\frac{d^2y}{dx^2} = 4x - 24x^{-4} + x^{-3} + \frac{1}{4} x^{-3/2}$$

$$= 4x - \frac{24}{x^4} + \frac{1}{x^3} + \frac{1}{4\sqrt{x^3}}$$

---

1 If $y = 5x^4 - 2\sqrt{x} + \dfrac{1}{x}$

find $\dfrac{d^2y}{dx^2}$

2 Find the second differential of $2 \cos 3t + 4 \sin 2t - 3e^{2t} + 3 \ln 5t$.

Rates of change

(i) If a quantity y depends on and varies with a quantity x then the rate of change of y with respect to x is dy/dx. Thus, for example, the rate of change of pressure p with height h is dp/dh.

(ii) A rate of change with respect to time is usually just called 'the rate of change', the 'with respect to time' being assumed. Thus, for example, a rate of change of voltage, v is dv/dt and a rate of change of temperature θ is $d\theta/dt$, and so on.

Example 8.138

The length l metres of a certain metal rod at temperature $t°C$ is given by $l = 1 + 0.00003t + 0.0000003t^2$. Determine the rate of change of length, in mm/°C, when the temperature is (a) 100°C and (b) 250°C

The rate of change of length means dl/dt.

Since $l = 1 + 0.000003t + 0.0000003t^2$, then

$$\frac{dl}{dt} = 0.00003 + 0.0000006t$$

(a) When $y = 100°C$, $\dfrac{dl}{dt} = 0.00003 + (0.0000006)(100)$

$$= 0.00009 \text{ m/°C} = \mathbf{0.09\,mm/°C}$$

(b) When $t = 250°C$, $\dfrac{dl}{dt} = 0.00003 + (0.0000006)(250)$

$$= 0.00018 \text{ m/°C} = \mathbf{0.18\,mm/°C}$$

1 An alternating current, i amperes, is given by $i = 100 \sin 2\pi ft$, where f is the frequency in hertz and t the time in seconds. Determine the rate of change of current when $t = 12$ ms, given that $f = 50$ Hz.

2 The pressure p of the atmosphere at height h above ground level is given by $p = p_0 e^{-h/c}$, where p_0 is the pressure at ground level and c is a constant. Determine the rate of change of pressure with height when $p_0 = 10^5$ pascals and $c = 6 \times 10^4$ at 1500 m.

Example 8.139

Newton's law of cooling is given by $\theta = \theta_0 e^{-kt}$, where the excess of temperature at zero time is $\theta_0°C$ and at time t seconds is $\theta°C$. Determine the rate of change of temperature after 50 s, given that $\theta_0 = 15°C$ and $k = 0.02$

The rate of change of temperature is $d\theta/dt$. Since $\theta = \theta_0 e^{-kt}$ then

$$\frac{d\theta}{dt} = (\theta_0)(-k)e^{-kt} = -k\theta_0 e^{-kt}$$

Where $\theta_0 = 15$, $k = -0.02$ and $t = 50$, then

$$\frac{d\theta}{dt} = -(-0.02)(15)e^{-(-0.02)(50)}$$

$$= 0.3e^1 = \mathbf{0.815°C/s}$$

Maximum and minimum points

In Figure 8.81, the gradient (or rate of change) of the curve changes from positive between 0 and P to negative between P and Q and then positive again between Q and R. At point P the gradient is zero and, as x increases, the gradient of the curve changes from positive just before P to negative just after. Such a point is called a *maximum point* and

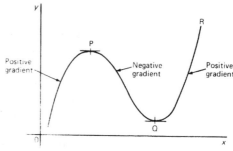

Figure 8.81

appears as the 'crest of a wave'. At point Q, the gradient is also zero and, as x increases, the gradient of the curve changes from negative just before Q to positive just after. Such a point is called a *minimum value*, and appears as the 'bottom of a valley'. Points such as P and Q are given the general name of *turning points*, or *stationary points*.

Procedure for finding and distinguishing between stationary points

(i)   Given $y = f(x)$, determine dy/dx (i.e. $f'(x)$).
(ii) Let $dy/dx = 0$ and solve for the values of x.
(iii) Substitute the values of x into the original equation, $y = f(x)$, to find the corresponding y-ordinate values. This establishes the coordinates of the stationary points.

To determine the nature of the stationary points:

Either

(iv) Determine the sign of the gradient of the curve just before and just after the stationary points. If the sign change for the gradient of the curve is:

   (a) *positive* to *negative* – the point is a *maximum* one;
   (b) *negative* to *positive* – the point is a *minimum* one.

or

(v) Find d^2y/dx^2 and substitute into it the values of x found in (ii). If the result is:

   (a) *positive* – the point is a *minimum* one;
   (b) *negative* – the point is a *maximum* one.

Consider the equation $y = x^2 - 2x + 3$. Gradient of the curve,

$$\frac{dy}{dx} = 2x - 2$$

At the turning point, the gradient is zero, hence $2x - 2 = 0$, from which $2x = 2$ and $x = 1$. When $x = 1$, $y = (1)^2 - 2(1) + 3 = 2$, hence at the coordinates $(1,2)$ a turning point occurs. To determine the nature of the turning point:

Method 1
Consider the gradient of the curve at a value of x just less than 1, say 0.9. At $x = 0.9$, gradient $= 2x - 2 = 2(0.9) - 2 = -0.2$.
   Now consider the gradient of the curve at a value of x just greater than 1, say 1.1
   At $x = 1.1$, gradient $= 2x - 2 = 2(1.1) - 2 = 0.2$.
   Hence the gradient has changed from negative just before the turning point at $x = 1$, to positive just after. This indicates a *minimum value*.

Method 2
If the gradient of the curve, $dy/dx = 2x - 2$, then $d^2y/dx^2 = 2$, which is positive, hence the turning point is a *minimum*.
   A graph of $y = x^2 - 2x + 3$ with the minimum point at $(1,2)$ is shown in Figure 8.82.

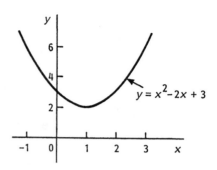

Figure 8.82

Example 8.140

Locate the turning point on the curve $y = 2x^2 - 4x$ and determine its nature by examining the sign of the gradient on either side.

Following the above procedure:

(i)   Since $y = 2x^2 - 4x$, $dy/dx = 4x - 4$
(ii) At a turning point, $dy/dx = 0$. Hence $4x - 4 = 0$ from which, $x = 1$
(iii) When $x = 1$, $y = 2(1)^2 - 4(1) = -2$

    Hence the **coordinates of the turning point are (1,–2)**

(iv) **If** x is slightly less than 1, say 0.9, then $dy/dx = 4(0.9) - 4 = -0.4$, i.e. negative. If x is slightly greater than 1, say 1.1, then $dy/dx = 4(1.1) - 4 = 0.4$, i.e. positive. Since the gradient of the curve is negative just before the turning point and positive just after **(1,–2) is a minimum point**.

Example 8.141

Find the maximum and minimum values of the curve $y = x^3 - 3x + 5$ by (a) examining the gradient on either side of the turning points, and (b) determining the sign of the second derivative.

Since $y = x^3 - 3x + 5$ then $dy/dx = 3x^2 - 3$
For a maximum or minimum value $dy/dx = 0$
Hence $3x^2 - 3 = 0$, from which, $3x^2 = 3$ and $x = \pm 1$
When $x = 1$, $y = (1)^3 - 3(1) + 5 = 3$
When $x = -1$, $y = (-1)^3 - 3(-1) + 5 = 7$
Hence $(1,3)$ and $(-1,7)$ are the coordinates of the turning points.

(a) Considering the point $(1,3)$:
    If x is slightly less than 1, say 0.9, then $dy/dx = 3(0.9)^2 - 3$, which is negative.
    If x is slightly more than 1, say 1.1, then $dy/dx = 3(1.1)^2 - 3$, which is positive.
    Since the gradient changes from negative to positive, **the point (1,3) is a minimum point**.

    Considering the point $(-1,7)$:
    If x is slightly less than −1, say −1.1, then $dy/dx = 3(-1.1)^2 - 3$, which is positive.
    If x is slightly more than −1, say −0.9, then $dy/dx = 3(-0.9)^2 - 3$, which is negative.
    Since the gradient changes from positive to negative, **the point (−1,7) is a maximum point**.

Test your knowledge 8.45

1 Find the turning points and distinguish between them for the curve

$$y = x^3 - 3x + 3$$

2 Locate the turning points on the following curves and determine whether they are maximum or minimum points:
(a) $y = 4\theta + e^{-\theta}$
(b) $y = 3(\ln \theta - \theta)$

(b) Since $dy/dx = 3x^2 - 3$, then $d^2y/dx^2 = 6x$

When $x = 1, \dfrac{dy^2}{dx^2}$ is positive, hence (1,3) is a **minimum value**

When $x = -1, \dfrac{dy^2}{dx^2}$ is negative, hence (−1,7) is a **maximum value**

Thus the **maximum value is 7** and the **minimum value is 3**

It can be seen that the second differential method of determining the nature of the turning points is, in this case, quicker than investigating the gradient.

Integration

The process of integration reverses the process of differentiation. In differentiation, if $f(x) = 2x^2$ then $f'(x) = 4x$. Thus the integral of $4x$ is $2x^2$, i.e. integration is the process of moving from $f'(x)$ to $f(x)$. By similar reasoning, the integral of $2t$ is t^2.

Integration is a process of summation or adding parts together and an elongated S, shown as $\int$, is used to replace the words 'the integral of'. Hence, from above, $\int 4x = 2x^2$ and $\int 2t$ is t^2.

In differentiation, the differential coefficient dy/dx indicates that a function of x *is being differentiated with respect to* x, the dx indicating that it is 'with respect to x'. In integration the variable of integration is shown by adding d (the variable) after the function to be integrated.

Thus $\int 4x \, dx$ means 'the integral of $4x$ with respect to x', and $\int 2t \, dt$ means 'the integral of $2t$ with respect to t'

As stated above, the differential coefficient of $2x^2$ is $4x$, hence $\int 4x \, dx = 2x^2$. However, the differential coefficient of $2x^2 + 7$ is also $4x$. Hence $\int 4x \, dx$ is also equal to $2x^2 + 7$. To allow for the possible presence of a constant, whenever the process of integration is performed, a constant 'c' is added to the result. Thus

$$\int 4x \, dx = 2x^2 + c \text{ and } \int 2t \, dt = t^2 + c$$

'c' is called the *arbitrary constant of integration*.

The general solution of $\int ax^n \, dx$

The general solution of integrals of the form $\int ax^n \, dx$, where a and n are constants and $n \neq -1$, is given by:

$$\int ax^n \, dx = \frac{ax^{n+1}}{n+1} + c$$

Using this rule gives:

$$\int 3x^4 \, dx = \frac{3x^{4+1}}{4+1} + c = \frac{3}{5} + c$$

and

$$\int \frac{4}{9} t^3 \, dr = \frac{4}{9} \frac{t^{3+1}}{3+1} + c = \frac{4}{9} \frac{t^4}{4} + c = \frac{1}{9} t^4 + c$$

Both of these results may be checked by differentiation.

Standard integrals

From earlier, $\dfrac{d}{dx}(\sin ax) = a\cos ax$.

Since integration is the reverse process of differentiation it follows that

$$\int a\cos ax\,dx = \sin ax + c$$

or $\quad \int \cos ax\,dx = \dfrac{1}{a}\sin ax + c$

By similar reasoning

$$\int \sin ax\,dx = \dfrac{1}{a}\cos ax + c$$

$$\int e^{ax}\,dx = \dfrac{1}{a}e^{ax} + c \text{ and } \int \dfrac{1}{x}\,dx = \ln x + c$$

Thus $\int ax^n\,dx = \dfrac{ax^{n+1}}{n+1} + c$ except when $n = -1$

When $n = -1$ then $\int x^{-1}\,dx = \int \dfrac{1}{x}\,dx = \ln x + c$

Summary of standard integrals

(i) $\quad \int ax^n\,dx = \dfrac{ax^{n+1}}{n+1} + 1c$ (except when $n = -1$)

(ii) $\quad \int \cos ax\,dx = \dfrac{1}{a}\sin ax + c$

(iii) $\quad \int \sin ax\,dx = -\dfrac{1}{a}\cos ax + c$

(iv) $\quad \int e^{ax}\,dx = \dfrac{1}{a}e^{ax} + c$

(v) $\quad \int \dfrac{1}{x}\,dx = \ln x + c$

Example 8.142

Determine (a) $\int 3x^2\,dx$ (b) $\int 2t^3\,dt$.

The general rule is $\int ax^n\,dx = \dfrac{ax^{n+1}}{n+1} + c$

(a) When $a = 3$ and $n = 2$ then

$$\int 3x^2\,dx = \dfrac{3x^{2+1}}{2+1} + c = \dfrac{3x^3}{3} + c = \boldsymbol{x^3 + c}$$

(b) When $a = 2$ and $n = 3$ then

$$\int 2t^3 \, dt = \frac{2t^{3+1}}{3+1} + c = \frac{2}{4} t^4 + c = \frac{1}{2} t^4 + c$$

Each of these results may be checked by differentiating them.

Example 8.143

Determine (a) $\int 8 \, dx$ (b) $\int \frac{2}{3} x \, dx$.

(a) $\int 8 \, dx$ is the same as $\int 8x^0 \, dx$, and, using the general rule when $a = 8$ and $n = 0$ gives

$$\int 8x^0 \, dx = \frac{8x^{0+1}}{0+1} + c = \mathbf{8x + c}$$

In general, if k is a constant then $k \, dx = kx + c$.

(b) When $a = \frac{2}{3}$ and $n = 1$ then

$$\int \frac{2}{3} x \, dx = \frac{2}{3} \frac{x^{1+1}}{(1+1)} + c = \frac{2}{3} \frac{x^2}{2} + c = \frac{1}{3} \mathbf{x^2 + c}$$

Example 8.144

Determine $\int \left(2 + \frac{5}{7} x - 6x^2 \right) dx$

$\int \left(2 + \frac{5}{7} x - 6x^2 \right) dx$ may be written as $\int 2 \, dx + \int \frac{5}{7} x \, dx - \int 6x^2 \, dx$,

i.e. each term is integrated separately. (This splitting up of terms only applies for addition and subtraction.)

Hence

$$\int \left(2 + \frac{5}{7} x - 6x^2 \right) dx$$

$$= \frac{2x^{0+1}}{0+1} + \frac{5}{7} \frac{x^{1+1}}{(1+1)} - \frac{6x^{2+1}}{(2+1)} + c$$

$$= 2x + \frac{5}{7} \frac{x^2}{2} - 6 \frac{x^3}{3} + c = \mathbf{2x + \frac{4}{14} x^2 - 2x^3 + c}$$

Note that when an integral contains more than one term there is no need to have an arbitrary constant for each; just a single constant at the end is sufficient.

Example 8.145

Determine (a) $\int \sqrt{x} \, dx$ (b) $\int \dfrac{3}{x^2} \, dx$.

When n is fractional or negative the general rule for integrals of the form $ax^n \, dx$ can still be applied.

(a) $\int \sqrt{x} \, dx = \int x^{1/2} \, dx$. Using the general rule, where $a = 1$ and $n = \dfrac{1}{2}$ gives:

$$\int x^{1/2} \, dx = \dfrac{(1)x^{(1/2)+1}}{\dfrac{1}{2}+1} + c = \dfrac{x^{3/2}}{\dfrac{3}{2}} + c$$

$$= \dfrac{2}{3} x^{3/2} + c = \dfrac{2}{3} \sqrt{x^3} + c$$

(b) $\int \dfrac{3}{x^2} \, dx = \int 3x^{-2} \, dx$

Using the general rule, where $a = 3$ and $n = -2$ gives:

$$\int 3x^{-2} \, dx = \dfrac{3x^{-2+1}}{-2+1} + c = \dfrac{3x^{-1}}{-1} + c$$

$$= -3x^{-1} + c = -\dfrac{3}{x} + c$$

Example 8.146

Determine (a) $\int 5 \cos 3x \, dx$ (b) $\int \dfrac{5}{e^{2x}} \, dx$

(a) $\int 5 \cos 3x \, dx = 5 \int \cos 3x \, dx$

$$= (5)\dfrac{1}{3} \sin 3x + c$$

$$= \dfrac{5}{3} \sin 3x + c$$

(b) $\int \dfrac{6}{e^{2x}} = \int 6e^{-2x} \, dx = 6 \int e^{-2x} \, dx$

$$= (6)\dfrac{1}{-2} e^{-2x} + c$$

$$= -3e^{-2x} + c \text{ or } \dfrac{-3}{e^{2x}} + c$$

Determine the following integrals:

1 $\int (5x^2 + 2x - 1) \, dx$

2 $\int \left(\dfrac{3}{x} - \dfrac{1}{x^2} + \dfrac{1}{2} \right) dx$

3 $\int (5 \sin 2x - 4 \cos 3x) \, dx$

4 $\int \left(3e^{4t} - \dfrac{2}{e^{3t}} \right) dt$

Limits and definite integrals

Integrals containing an arbitrary constant c in their results are called *indefinite integrals* since their precise value cannot be determined without further information.

Definite integrals are those in which limits are applied.

If an expression is written as $[x]_b^a$, is called the upper limit and a the lower limit. The operation of applying the limits is defined as $[x]_b^a = (b) - (a)$ The increase in the value of the integral x^2 as x increases from 1 to 3 is written as

$$\int_1^3 x^2 \, dx$$

Applying the limits gives:

$$\int_1^3 x^2 \, dx = \left[\frac{x^3}{3} + c \right]_1^3$$

$$= \left\{ \frac{(3)^3}{3} + c \right\} - \left\{ \frac{(1)^3}{3} + c \right\}$$

$$= (9 + c) - \left(\frac{1}{3} + c \right) = 8 \frac{2}{3}$$

Note that the 'c' term always cancels out when limits are applied and it need not be shown with definite integrals.

Example 8.147

Evaluate

(a) $\int_1^2 4x \, dx$ (b) $\int_{-2}^3 (5 - x^2) \, dx$

(a) $\displaystyle \int_1^2 4x \, dx = \left[\frac{4x^2}{2} \right]_1^2 = [2x^2]_1^2 = \{2(2)^2\} - \{2(1)^2\}$

$$= 8 - 2 = \mathbf{6}$$

(b) $\displaystyle \int_{-2}^3 (5 - x^2) dx = \left[5x - \frac{x^3}{3} \right]_{-2}^3 = \left\{ 5(3) - \frac{(3)^3}{3} \right\} - \left\{ 5(-2) - \frac{(-2)^3}{3} \right\}$

$$= \{15 - 9\} - \left\{ -10 - \frac{-8}{3} \right\} = 6 + 10 - \frac{8}{3}$$

$$= 13 \frac{1}{3}$$

Example 8.148

Evaluate:

(a) $\int_0^{\pi/3} 2 \sin 3x \, dx$

(b) $\int_1^2 \cos 2x \, dx$ (correct to 4 significant figures)

(a) $\displaystyle\int_0^{\pi/3} 2\sin 3x\,dx = \left[\frac{-2}{3}\cos 3x\right]_0^{\pi/3} = \frac{-2}{3}[\cos 3x]_0^{\pi/3}$

$\qquad\qquad = \frac{-2}{3}\left[\cos 3\frac{\pi}{3} - \cos 0\right]$

$\qquad\qquad = \frac{-2}{3}[\cos \pi - \cos 0]$

$\qquad\qquad = \frac{-2}{3}[-1 - 1]$ (note $\cos \pi$ means the cosine of π radians)

$\qquad\qquad = \frac{-2}{3}(-2) = \frac{4}{3}$ or $1\frac{1}{3}$

(b) $\displaystyle\int_1^2 \cos 2x\,dx = \left[\frac{1}{2}\sin 2x\right]_1^2 = \frac{1}{2}[\sin 2x]_1^2$

$\qquad\qquad = \frac{1}{2}[\sin 4 - \sin 2]$

(where $\sin 4$ means the sine of 4 radians)

$\qquad\qquad = \frac{1}{2}[(-0.75680\ldots) - (0.909297\ldots)]$

$\qquad\qquad = -0.8330$, correct to 4 significant figures

Test your knowledge 8.47

Evaluate the following definite integrals, where necessary correct to 4 significant figures:

1 (a) $\displaystyle\int_1^3 5x^2\,dx$

   (b) $\displaystyle\int_{-1}^2 (4 - x^2)\,dx$

2 $\displaystyle\int_0^2 x(3 + 2x)\,dx$

3 (a) $\displaystyle\int_0^{\pi/6} 4\sin 2x\,dx$

   (b) $\displaystyle\int_0^1 3\cos 4x\,dx$

4 $\displaystyle\int_1^2 \left(3e^{2x} - \frac{4}{x}\right)dx$

Areas under and between curves using integration

The area shown shaded in Figure 8.83 may be determined precisely by using integration.

$$\int_a^b y\,dx = \int_a^b f(x)\,dx$$

There are several instances in engineering and science where the area beneath a curve needs to be accurately determined. For example, the area between limits of: velocity/time graph gives distance travelled; force/distance graph gives work done; voltage/current graph gives power, and so on.

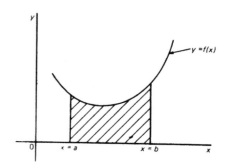

Figure 8.83

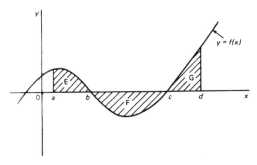

Figure 8.84

Should a curve drop below the *x*-axis, then $y \; (= f(x))$ becomes negative and $f(x)\,\mathrm{d}x$ is negative. When determining such areas by integration, a negative sign is placed before the integral. For the curve shown in Figure 8.84, the total shaded area is given by (area E + area F + area G).

By integration,

$$\text{total shaded area} = \int_a^b f(x)\,\mathrm{d}x - \int_b^c f(x)\,\mathrm{d}x + \int_c^d f(x)\,\mathrm{d}x$$

(Note that this is *not* the same as $\int_a^d f(x)\,\mathrm{d}x$)

It is usually necessary to sketch a curve in order to check whether it crosses the *x*-axis.

Example 8.149

Determine the area enclosed by $y = 2x + 3$, the *x*-axis and ordinates $x = 0$ and $x = 3$.

$y = 2x + 3$ is a straight line graph as shown in Figure 8.85, where the area enclosed by $y = 2x + 3$, the *x*-axis and ordinates $x = 0$ and $x = 3$ is shown shaded.

By integration

$$\text{shaded area} = \int_0^3 y\,\mathrm{d}x = \int_0^3 (2x + 3)\,\mathrm{d}x$$

$$= \left[\frac{2x^2}{2} + 3x \right]_0^3 = (9 + 9) - (0 + 0) = \textbf{18 square units}$$

This answer may be checked since the shaded area is a trapezium.

$$\text{Area of trapezium} = \frac{1}{2} \text{ (sum of parallel sides)(perpendicular distance between 2 parallel sides)}$$

$$= \frac{1}{2}(3 + 9)(3) = \textbf{18 square units}$$

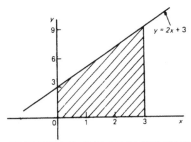

Figure 8.85

1 Determine the area enclosed by the curve $y = 3x^2 + 6$, the x-axis and ordinates $x = 1$ and $x = 4$.

2 A gas expands according to the law pV = constant. When the volume is $2\,m^3$ the pressure is $250\,kPa$. Find the work done as the gas expands from $1\,m^3$ to a volume of $4\,m^3$, given that work done

$$= \int_{V_1}^{V_2} p\,dv.$$

3 Sketch the curve $y = x^3 - 2x^2 - 3x$ between $x = -2$ and $x = 4$. Find the area enclosed by the curve and the x-axis.

Example 8.150

Determine the area enclosed by the curve $y = \cos\theta$, the ordinates $\theta = 0$ and $\theta = \pi/2$ and the θ-axis.

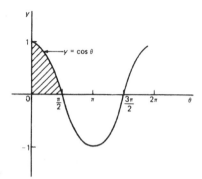

Figure 8.86

The graph of $y = \cos\theta$ is shown in Figure 8.86 and the required area is shown shaded.

$$\text{shaded area} = \int_0^{\pi/2} \cos\theta\,d\theta = [\sin\theta]_0^{\pi/2}$$

$$= \sin\frac{\pi}{2} - \sin 0 = \textbf{1 square unit}$$

Vectors and phasors

Introduction

Some physical quantities are entirely defined by a numerical value and are called *scalar quantities* or *scalars*. Examples of scalars include time, mass, temperature, energy and volume. Other physical quantities are defined by both a numerical value and a direction in space and these are called *vector quantities* or *vectors*. Examples of vectors include force, velocity, moment and displacement.

Vector addition

A vector may be represented by a straight line, the length of line being directly proportional to the magnitude of the quantity and the direction of the line being in the same direction as the line of action of the quantity. An arrow is used to denote the sense of the vector, that is, for a horizontal vector, say, whether it acts from left to right or vice versa. The arrow is positioned at the end of the vector and this position is called the 'nose' of the vector. Figure 8.87 shows a velocity of $20\,m/s$ at an angle of $45°$ to the horizontal and may be depicted by **oa** = $20\,m/s$ at $45°$ to the horizontal.

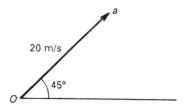

Figure 8.87

To distinguish between vector and scalar quantities, various ways are used, and the one adopted in this text is to denote vector quantities in bold print.

Thus, **oa** represents a vector quantity, but oa is the magnitude of the vector **oa**. Also, positive angles are measured in an anticlockwise direction from a horizontal, right facing line and negative angles in a clockwise direction from this line. Thus 90° is a line vertically upwards and −90° is a line vertically downwards. The resultant of adding two vectors together, say V_1 at an angle θ_1 and V_2 at angle $(-\theta_2)$, as shown in Figure 8.88 can be obtained by drawing **oa** to represent V_1 and then drawing **ar** to represent V_2. The resultant of $V_1 + V_2$ is given by **or**. This is shown in Figure 8.88(b), the vector equation being **oa + ar = or**. This is called the '*nose-to-tail*' *method* of vector addition.

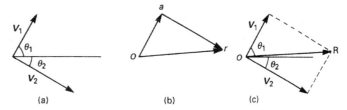

Figure 8.88

Alternatively, by drawing lines parallel to V_1 and V_2 from the noses of V_2 and V_1, respectively, and letting the point of intersection of these parallel lines be R, gives **OR** as the magnitude and direction of the resultant of adding V_1 and V_2, as shown in Figure 8.88(c). This is called the '*parallelogram*' *method* of vector addition.

Example 8.151

A force of 4 N is inclined at an angle of 45° to a second force of 7 N, both forces acting at a point. Find the magnitude of the resultant of these two forces and the direction of the resultant with respect to the 7 N force by both the 'triangle' and the 'parallelogram' methods.

The forces are shown in Figure 8.89(a). Although the 7 N force is shown as a horizontal line, it could have been drawn in any direction. Using the

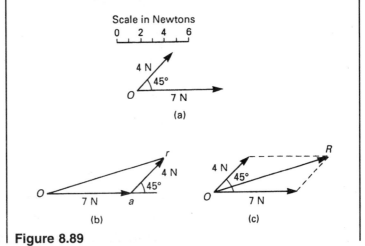

Figure 8.89

'nose-to-tail' method, a line 7 units long is drawn horizontally to give vector **oa** in Figure 8.89(b). To the nose of this vector **ar** is drawn 4 units long at an angle of 45° to **oa**. The resultant of vector addition is **or** and by measurement is 10.2 units long and at an angle of 16° to the 7 N force.

Figure 8.89(c) uses the 'parallelogram' method in which lines are drawn parallel to the 7 N and 4 N forces from the noses of the 4 N and 7 N forces, respectively. These intersect at R. Vector *OR* gives the magnitude and direction of the resultant of vector addition and as obtained by the 'nose-to-tail' method is 10.2 units long at an angle of 16° to the 7 N force. Thus by both methods, the resultant of vector addition is a **force of 10.2 N at an angle of 16° to the 7 N force**.

Example 8.152

Use a graphical method to determine the magnitude and direction of the resultant of the three velocities shown in Figure 8.90.

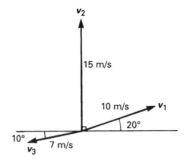

Figure 8.90

Often it is easier to use the 'nose-to-tail' method when more than two vectors are being added. The order in which the vectors are added is immaterial. In this case the order taken is v_1, then v_2, then v_3 but just the same result would have been obtained if the order had been, say, v_1, v_3 and finally v_2. v_1 is drawn 10 units long at an angle of 20° to the horizontal, shown by **oa** in Figure 8.91. v_2 is added to v_1 by drawing a line 15 units long vertically upwards from a, shown as **ab**. Finally, v_3 is added to $v_1 + v_2$ by drawing a line 7 units long at an angle at 190° from b, shown as **br**. The resultant of vector addition is **or** and by measurement is 17.5 units long at an angle of 82° to the horizontal. Thus

$$v_1 + v_2 + v_3 = \textbf{17.5 m/s at 82° to the horizontal}.$$

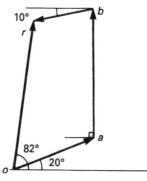

Figure 8.91

Resolution of vectors

A vector can be resolved into two component parts such that the vector addition of the component parts is equal to the original vector. The two components usually taken are a horizontal component and a vertical component. For the vector shown as **F** in Figure 8.92, the horizontal component is $F \cos \theta$ and the vertical component is $F \sin \theta$.

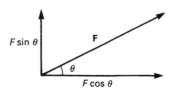

Figure 8.92

For the vectors $\mathbf{F}_1$ and $\mathbf{F}_2$ shown in Figure 8.93, the horizontal component of vector addition is

$$H = F_1 \cos \theta_1 + F_2 \cos \theta_2$$

and the vertical component of vector addition is

$$V = F_1 \sin \theta_1 + F_2 \sin \theta_2$$

Having obtained H and V, the magnitude of the resultant vector **R** is given by $\sqrt{(H^2 + V^2)}$ and its angle to the horizontal is given by arctan (V/H).

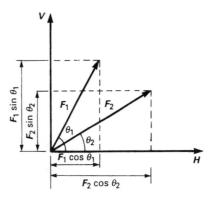

Figure 8.93

Example 8.153

Resolve the acceleration vector of $17\,\text{m/s}^2$ at an angle of 120° to the horizontal into a horizontal and a vertical component.

For a vector **A** at angle θ to the horizontal, the horizontal component is given by $A \cos \theta$ and the vertical component by $A \sin \theta$. Any convention of signs may be adopted, in this case horizontally from left to right is taken as positive and vertically upwards is taken as positive.

Horizontal component $H = 17 \cos 120° = \mathbf{-8.5\,m/s^2}$, acting from left to right

Vertical component $V = 17 \sin 120° = \textbf{14.72 m/s}^2$, acting vertically upwards

These component vectors are shown in Figure 8.94.

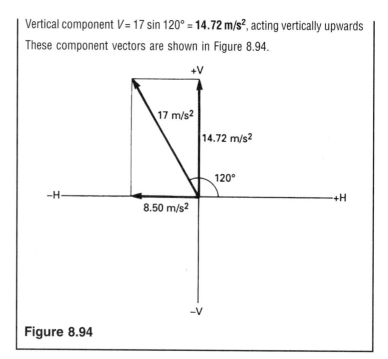

Figure 8.94

Vector subtraction

In Figure 8.95, a force vector **F** is represented by **oa**. The vector (**−oa**) can be obtained by drawing a vector from o in the opposite sense to **oa** but having the same magnitude, shown as *ob* in Figure 8.95, i.e. **ob** = (**−oa**).

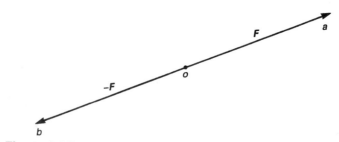

Figure 8.95

For two vectors acting at a point, as shown in Figure 8.96(a), the resultant of vector addition is **os** = **oa** + **ob**. Figure 8.96(b) shows vectors **ob** + (**−oa**), that is, **ob** − **oa** and the vector equation is **ob** − **oa** = **od**. Comparing **od** in Figure 8.96(b) with the broken line ab in Figure 8.96(a) shows that the second diagonal of the 'parallelogram' method of vector addition gives the magnitude and direction of vector subtraction of **oa** from **ob**.

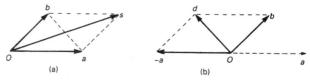

Figure 8.96

Example 8.154

Acceleration of a_1 = 1.5 m/s^2 at 90° and a_2 = 2.6 m/s^2 at 145° act at a point. Find $a_1 + a_2$ and $a_1 - a_2$ by (i) drawing a scale vector diagram and (ii) by calculation.

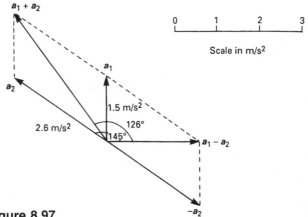

Figure 8.97

(i) The scale vector diagram is shown in Figure 8.97. By measurement,

$$a_1 + a_2 = \textbf{3.7 m/s}^2 \textbf{ at } \textbf{126°}$$

$$a_1 - a_2 = \textbf{2.1 m/s}^2 \textbf{ at } \textbf{0°}$$

(ii) Resolving horizontally and vertically gives:

Horizontal component of $a_1 + a_2$

$$\textbf{H} = 0 + 2.6 \cos 145° = -2.13$$

Vertical component of $a_1 + a_2$

$$\textbf{V} = 1.5 + 2.6 \sin 145° = 2.99$$

Magnitude of $a_1 + a_2 = \sqrt{(-2.13^2 + 2.99^2)} = 3.67$ m/s^2

Direction of $a_1 + a_2 = \arctan \dfrac{2.99}{-2.13}$

and must lie in the second quadrant since H is negative and V is positive

Arctan (2.99/−2.13) = −54.5°, and for this to be in the second quadrant, the true angle is 180° displaced, i.e. 180° − 54.5° or 125.5°. Thus

$$a_1 + a_2 = \textbf{3.67 m/s}^2 \textbf{ at } \textbf{125.5°}$$

Horizontal component of $a_1 - a_2$, that is $a_1 + (-a_2)$

$$= 0 + 2.6 \cos (145° - 180°)$$

$$= 2.6 \cos (-35°) = 2.13$$

Vertical component of $a_1 - a_2$, that is $a_1 + (-a_2)$

$$= 1.5 + 2.6 \sin (-35°) = 0$$

Magnitude of $a_1 - a_2 = \sqrt{(2.13^2 + 0_2)} = 2.13$ m/s^2

Direction of $a_1 - a_2 = \arctan \dfrac{0}{2.13} = 0°$

Thus $a_1 - a_2 = \textbf{2.13 m/s}^2 \textbf{ at } \textbf{0°}$

Activity 8.9

Calculate the resultant of (i) $\mathbf{v}_1 - \mathbf{v}_2 + \mathbf{v}_3$ and (ii) $\mathbf{v}_1 - \mathbf{v}_2 - \mathbf{v}_3$ when $\mathbf{v}_1 = 22$ units at 140°, $\mathbf{v}_2 = 40$ units at 190° and $\mathbf{v}_3 = 15$ units at 290°.

Sinusoidal form $A \sin(\omega t \pm \alpha)$

In Figure 8.98, let 0R represent a vector that is free to rotate anticlockwise about 0 at a velocity of ω rad/s. A rotating vector is called a *phasor*. After a time t seconds 0R will have turned through an angle ωt radians (shown as angle T0R in Figure 8.98). If ST is constructed perpendicular to 0R, then $\sin \omega t = \text{ST/0T}$, i.e. ST = 0T $\sin \omega t$.

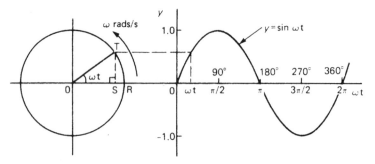

Figure 8.98

If all such vertical components are projected on to a graph of y against ωt, a sine wave results of amplitude 0R.

If phasor 0R makes one revolution (i.e. 2π radians) in T seconds, then the angular velocity, $\omega = 2\pi/T$ rad/s, from which, $T = 2\pi/\omega$ seconds.

T is known as the periodic time.

The number of complete cycles occurring per second is called the *frequency, f*

$$\text{Frequency} = \frac{\text{number of cycles}}{\text{second}}$$

$$= \frac{1}{T} = \frac{\omega}{2\pi} \text{ Hz, i.e. } f = \frac{\omega}{2\pi} \text{ Hz}$$

Hence angular velocity, $\omega = 2\pi f$ rad/s

Given a general sinusoidal periodic function $y = A \sin(\omega t \pm \alpha)$, then A = amplitude, ω = angular velocity, $2\pi/\omega$ = periodic time, T, $\omega/2\pi$ = frequency, f, and α = angle of lead or lag (compared with $y = A \sin \omega t$).

Test your knowledge 8.51

1 An alternting voltage is given by: $v = 200 \sin (400\pi t + 0.374)$ volts. Determine the amplitude, periodic time, frequency and phase angle (in degrees and minutes)

2 An alternating current is given by: $i = 15 \sin (100\pi t - 0.37)$ amperes. Find (a) the periodic time, (b) the frequency ,(c) the value of current when $t = 0$, (d) the value of the current when $t = 10$ ms, and (e) the time when the current is first a maximum.

Example 8.155

An alternating current is given by $i = 30 \sin (100\pi t + 0.27)$ amperes. Find the amplitude, periodic time, frequency and phase angle (in degrees and minutes).

$i = 30 \sin (100\pi t + 0.27)$ A

Amplitude = **30 A**

Angular velocity = 100π. Hence periodic time,

$$T = \frac{2\pi}{\omega} = \frac{2\pi}{100\pi} = \frac{1}{50} = \textbf{0.02 s or 20 ms}$$

Frequency, $f = \dfrac{1}{T} = \dfrac{1}{0.02} = \textbf{50 Hz}$

Phase angle, $\alpha = 0.27$ rad $= 0.27 \times \dfrac{180°}{\pi}$

$= \textbf{15° 28' leading } i = \textbf{30 sin (100}\pi\textbf{\textit{t}})$

Combination of two periodic functions of the same frequency

There are a number of instances in engineering and science where waveforms combine and where it is required to determine the single phasor (called the resultant) which could replace two or more separate phasors. Uses are found in electrical alternating current theory, in mechanical vibrations, in the addition of forces and with sound waves. There are several methods of determining the resultant and two such methods are shown below.

(i) Plotting the period functions graphically

This may be achieved by sketching the separate functions on the same axes and then adding (or subtracting) ordinates at regular intervals. (Alternatively, a table of values may be drawn up before plotting the resultant waveforms.)

Example 8.156

Plot the graph of $y_1 = 3 \sin A$ from $A = 0°$ to $A = 360°$. On the same axes plot $y_2 = 2 \cos A$. By adding ordinates plot $y_R = 3 \sin A + 2 \cos A$ and obtain a sinusodial expression for this resultant waveform.

$y_1 = 3 \sin A$ and $y_2 = 2 \cos A$ are shown plotted in Figure 8.99. Ordinates may be added at, say, 15° intervals. For example,

at   0°, $y_1 + y_2 = 0 + 2 = 2$

at   15°, $y_1 + y_2 = 0.78 + 1.93 = 2.71$

at 120°, $y_1 + y_2 = 2.60 + -1 = 1.6$

at 210°, $y_1 + y_2 = -1.50 - 1.73 = -3.23$, and so on

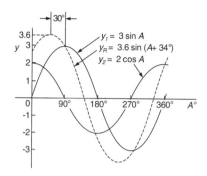

Figure 8.99

The resultant waveform, shown by the broken line, has the same period, i.e. 360°, and thus the same frequency as the single phasors. The maximum value, or amplitude, of the resultant is 3.6. The resultant waveform leads $y_1 = 3 \sin A$ by 34° or 0.593 rad. The sinusoidal expression for the resultant waveform is:

$$y_R = 3.6 \sin (A + 34°) \text{ or } y_R = 3.6 \sin (A + 0.593)$$

Activity 8.10

Plot the graphs of $y_1 = 4 \sin \omega t$ and $y_2 = 3 \sin (\omega t - \pi/3)$ on the same axis, over one cycle. By adding ordinates at intervals plot $y_R = y_1 + y_2$ and obtain a sinusoidal expression for the resultant waveform.

(ii) Resolution of phasors by drawing or calculation

The resultant of two periodic functions may be found from their relative positions when the time is zero. For example, if $y_1 = 4 \sin \omega t$ and $y_2 = 3 \sin (\omega t - \pi/3)$ then each may be represented as phasors as shown in Figure 8.100, y_1 being 4 units long and drawn horizontally and y_2 being 3 units long, lagging y_1 by $\pi/3$ radians or 60°. To determine the resultant of $y_1 + y_2$, y_1 is drawn horizontally as shown in Figure 8.101 and y_2 is joined to the end of y_1 at 60° to the horizontal. The resultant is given by y_R. This is the same as the diagonal of a parallelogram which is shown completed in Figure 8.102.

Figure 8.100

Figure 8.101

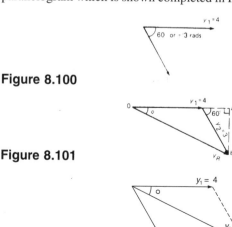

Figure 8.102

Resultant y_R, in Figures 8.101 and 8.102, is determined either by:

(a) scaled drawing and measurement, or
(b) by use of the cosine rule (and then sine rule to calculate angle ϕ), or
(c) by determining horizontal and vertical components of lengths oa and ab in Figure 8.101, and then using Pythagoras' theorem to calculate ob.

In this case by calculation, $y_R = 6.083$ and angle $\phi = 25.28°$ or 0.441 rad.

Thus the resultant may be expressed in sinusoidal form as $y_R = 6.083 \sin(\omega t - 0.441)$. If the resultant phasor, $y_R = y_1 - y_2$ is required, then y_2 is still 3 units long but is drawn in the opposite direction, as shown in Figure 8.103, and y_R is determined by measurement or calculation.

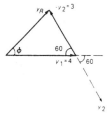

Figure 8.103

Example 8.157

Given $y_1 = 2 \sin t$ and $y_2 = 3 \sin(t + \pi/4)$, obtain an expression of the resultant $\mathbf{y_R} = \mathbf{y_1} + \mathbf{y_2}$, (a) by drawing and (b) by calculation.

(a) When time $t = 0$ the position of phasors y_1 and y_2 are as shown in Figure 8.104(a). To obtain the resultant, y_1 is drawn horizontally, 2 units long, y_2 is drawn 3 units long at an angle of $\pi/4$ rads or 45° and joined to the end of y_1 as shown in Figure 8.104(b). y_R is measured as 4.6 units long and angle ϕ is measured as 27° or 0.47 rad. Alternatively, y_R is the diagonal of the parallelogram formed as shown in Figure 8.104(c).

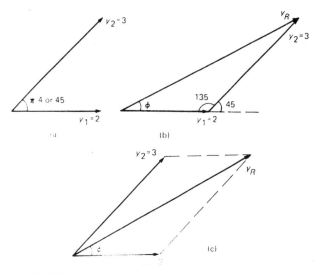

Figure 8.104

Hence, by drawing, $y_R = 4.6 \sin(\omega t + 0.47)$

(b) From Figure 8.104(b), and using the cosine rule:

$$y_R^2 = 2^2 + 3^2 - [2(2)(3) \cos 135°]$$

$$= 4 + 9 - [-8.485] = 21.49$$

Hence $y_R = \sqrt{(21.49)} = 4.64$

Using the sine rule:

$$\frac{3}{\sin \phi} = \frac{4.64}{\sin 135°}, \text{ from which } \sin \phi = \frac{3 \sin 135°}{4.64} = 0.4572$$

Hence $\phi = \arcsin 0.4572 = 27° 12'$ or 0.475 rad

By calculation, $\mathbf{y_R = 4.64 \sin(\omega t + 0.475)}$

Example 8.158

Two alternating voltages are given by $v_1 = 15 \sin \omega t$ volts and $v_2 = 25 \sin(\omega t - \pi/6)$ volts. Determine a sinusoidal expression for the resultant $v_R = v_1 + v_2$ by finding horizontal and vertical components.

The relative positions of v_1 and v_2 at time $t = 0$ are shown in Figure 8.105(a) and the phasor diagram is shown in Figure 8.105(b).

The horizontal component of $v_1 = oa + ab$

$$= 15 + 25 \cos 30°$$

$$= 36.65 \text{ V}$$

The vertical component of $v_R = bc$

$$= 25 \sin 30°$$

$$= 12.5 \text{ V}$$

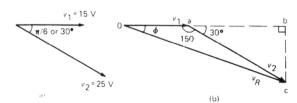

Figure 8.105

Hence

$$v_R \,(= oc) = \sqrt{[(36.65)^2 + (12.50)^2]} \text{ by Pythagoras' theorem}$$

$$= 38.72 \text{ volts}$$

$$\tan \phi = \frac{bc}{oc} = \frac{12.50}{36.65} = 0.3411$$

from which, $\phi = \arctan 0.3411 = 18° 50'$ or 0.329 radians.

Hence

$$\mathbf{v_R = v_1 + v_2 = 38.72 \sin(\omega t - 0.329) \, V}$$

Express each of the following in the form $A \sin(\omega t \pm \alpha)$, either by drawing or by calculation.

1 $7.2 \sin \omega t + 3.5 \sin\left(\omega t - \dfrac{\pi}{4}\right)$

2 $20 \sin \omega t + 13 \sin\left(\omega t + \dfrac{\pi}{6}\right)$

3 $6.4 \sin \omega t - 4.5 \sin\left(\omega t + \dfrac{\pi}{3}\right)$

Multiple choice questions

1    $\text{Volume} = \dfrac{\text{mass}}{\text{density}}$.

The density (in kg/m^3) when the mass is 2.532 kg and the volume is 162 cm^3 is

A   0.01563 kg/m^3
B   410.2 kg/m^3
C   15 630 kg/m^3
D   64.0 kg/m^3

2   The total resistance R_T of a parallel network is given by

$$\frac{1}{R_T} = \frac{1}{R_1} + \frac{1}{R_2} + \frac{1}{R_3}$$

When $R_T = 1.20\ \Omega$, $R_1 = 2.42\ \Omega$ and $R_3 = 6.84\ \Omega$, R_2 is given by

A   3.65 Ω
B   0.72 Ω
C   0.27 Ω
D   3.22 Ω

3   The time of swing, t seconds, of a simple pendulum is given by

$$t = 2\pi \sqrt{\left(\frac{l}{g}\right)}.$$

Given $l = 12.0$ and $g = 10.0$, the value of t, correct to 3 decimal places, is

A   6.883 s
B   9.048 s
C   5.736 s
D   6.882 s

4   In a system of pulleys the effort P required to raise a load W is given by $P = aW + b$, where a and b are constants.

If $W = 40$ when $P = 12$ and $W = 90$ when $P = 22$, the values of a and b are

A $a = 5, b = \dfrac{1}{4}$

B $a = 1, b = -28$

C $a = \dfrac{1}{3}, b = -8$

D $a = \dfrac{1}{5}, b = 4$

5   The length l metres of a certain metal rod at temperature $t\,°C$ is given by $l = 1 + 4 \times 10^{-5}t + 4 \times 10^{-7}t^2$.

The rate of change of length, in mm/°C, when the temperature is 400°C, is

A 3.6×10^{-4}
B   1.000 36
C   0.36
D 3.2×10^{-4}

6   A pylon stands on horizontal ground. At a point 80 m from the base of the pylon, the angle of elevation of the top of the pylon is 18°.

The height of the pylon is

A   76.1 m
B   24.7 m
C   246.2 m
D   26.0 m

7   A part of a graph of resistance R against voltage V for a filament lamp is shown in Figure 8.106. The relationship relating R and V is

A $R = 0.8\ V + 60$
B $R = 1.2\ V + 20$
C $R = 1.2\ V$
D $R = 0.8\ V + 15$

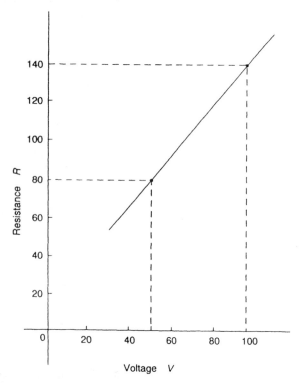

Figure 8.106

8 Forces of 12 N and 25 N act at a point and are inclined at 90° to each other. The resultant force and its direction relative to the 25 N force is

A 37 N at 90°
B 27.73 N at 64.36°
C 13 N at 90°
D 27.73 N at 25.64°

9 The equation of a curve is $y = 2x^3 - 6x + 1$. The minimum value of the curve is

A −6
B 1
C 5
D −3

10 The area enclosed by the curve $y = 3 \cos 2\theta$, the ordinates $\theta = 0$ and

$$\theta = \frac{\pi}{4}$$

and the θ axis is

A −3
B 1.5
C 6
D 3

Answers to test your knowledge

Algebra

8.1 1 (a) 3^7 (b) 4^9
     2 (a) 2   (b) 3^5
     3 (a) 7^6 (b) 3^6

     4 (a) 9   (b) ±3   (c) $\frac{1}{2}$ (d) $\pm\frac{2}{3}$

8.2 1 (a) 7.39×10 (b) 1.1284×10^3
       (c) 1.9762×10^2
     2 (a) 2.401×10^{-1} (b) 1.74×10^{-2}
       (c) 9.23×10^{-3}
     3 (a) 1.7231×10^3 (b) 3.129×10^{-3}
     4 (a) 2×10^2 (b) 1.5×10^{-3}

8.3 1 (a) 4   (b) $\frac{1}{3}$

     2 (a) 3   (b) −2
     3 9
     4 5 log 3

8.4 1 $1\frac{1}{2}$

     2 1.691
     3 6.058
     4 −0.3272

8.5 1 −8
2 $3x − 5y + 5z$
3 $5x^2 + 3xy − 2y^2$
4 $3x − 2y^2$

8.6 1 $2\dfrac{1}{4}$

2 $\dfrac{a + b^2}{b}$

3 $a^2 c$

8.7 1 $5x − 7y$
2 $2a^2 + ab − b^2$
3 $3 + 4y^2$
4 (a) $7ab(2b − 5)$ (b) $(x − y)(a + b)$

8.8 1 $1 − a$

2 $\dfrac{2}{3b} − 2b + 8$ or $2\left(\dfrac{1}{3b} − b + a\right)$

3 St
4 $p + 8p^2$ or $p(1 + 8p)$

8.9 1 4
2 3
3 −3
4 9
5 ±4

8.10 1 12 cm, 3888 cm^3
2 34
3 47 h
4 3000

8.11 1 $x = 1, y = 1$
2 $p = −2, q = −3$
3 $x = 0.3, y = 0.4$
4 $x = 2, y = −3$

8.12 1 5, −7
2 $a = 12, b = 0.4$
3 £185, £138

8.13 1 85.94 m^2
2 $1.49 × 10^{−11}$ N
3 358.8 cm^3
4 12.77 A

8.14 1 $m = \dfrac{F}{a}$

2 $\alpha = \dfrac{l_2 − l_1}{l_1 \theta}$

3 $g = \dfrac{4\pi^2 l}{t^2}$

$$4 \quad R = \frac{E - e - Ir}{I}$$

$$5 \quad a = \sqrt{\left(\frac{rp}{x + y}\right)}$$

8.15 1 2, −3

2 $2, -\dfrac{3}{2}$

3 $-\dfrac{4}{5}, \dfrac{2}{3}$

4 (a) $x^2 - 25 = 0$ (b) $x^2 - 0.8x - 0.48 = 0$

8.16 1 −0.438, −4.562

2 0.344, −1.105

8.17 1 $\dfrac{1}{2}, -3$

2 $-\dfrac{1}{3}, 4$

3 25.51, 1.490

8.18 1 6.61 cm by 3.55 cm

2 1.835 m or 18.165 m

3 13.82 cm

8.19 1 (a) 202.4   (b) 0.3441

2 (a) 33.04   (b) 18.59

3 (a) 2.129   (b) 43.24

8.20 1 $y = 3.87, x = -0.74$

2 (a) 1.531   (b) −1.818

3 (a) 1.002   (b) 3.454

4 −0.805

5 0.881

8.21 1 (a) 204.7   (b) −0.4020

2 71500

3 (a) 127°C   (b) 41.6 s

Trigonometry

8.22 1 $\cos A = \dfrac{40}{41}, \tan A = \dfrac{9}{40}$

2 $\sin \theta = 0.3846, \csc \theta = 2.6000$
$\cos \theta = 0.9231, \sec \theta = 1.0833$
$\tan \theta = 0.4167, \cot \theta = 2.4000$

8.23 1 (a) 0.4351   (b) −0.8530

2 (a) 4.1557   (b) 1.8731

3 (a) 1.0061   (b) −0.7768

4 (a) −0.5000   (b) 1.0493

5 (a) 40.38° or 40° 23' or 0.705 rad
(b) 23.13° or 23° 8' or 0.404 rad

6 0.247

8.24 1 212° 57' and 327° 3'
     2 46° 50' and 313° 10'
     3 124° 53' and 235° 7'
     4 37° 17' and 217° 17'

8.25 1 $C = 71° 4'$, $B = 18° 56'$, AC = 12.0 mm
     2 $Z = 66° 43'$, XZ = 7.906 mm, XY = 18.37 mm
     3 48 m
     4 60.85 m

8.26 1 $B = 77°$, $b = 18.16$ mm, $c = 17.73$ mm, area = 82.90 mm^2
     2 $e = 32.91$ mm, $F = 43° 4'$, $D = 72° 56'$, area = 393.2 mm^2
     3 $X = 78° 8'$, $Y = 47° 13'$, $Z = 56° 38'$, area = 44.04 cm^2

8.27 1 4.56 m, 5.38 m
     2 32.48 A, 14° 19'
     3 18.23 km/h

8.28 1 Proof
     2 Proof
     3 Proof

Graphs

8.29 1 Gradient $= \dfrac{1}{2}$

     2 (a) 7, −3   (b) $-2, \dfrac{2}{3}$ (c) 4, 11   (d) $\dfrac{3}{2}, \dfrac{-3}{4}$

     (e) $-\dfrac{2}{9}, -\dfrac{1}{9}$

     3 6

8.30 1 (a) 40°C   (b) 128 Ω
     2 (a) 70×10^9 N/mm^2 (b) 0.000285
     (c) 14 N/mm^2

8.31 1 $a = 3.0$, $b = 0.5$
     2 $T_0 = 35.4$ N, $\mu = 0.27$, 65.0 N, 1.28 rad

8.32 1 $m = 1$, $n = 10$
     2 $\theta_0 = 152$, $k = -0.05$

8.33 1 (a) MINIMUM (0,0)   (b) MINIMUM (0,−1)
     (c) MAXIMUM (0,3)   (d) MAXIMUM (0,−1)

     2 $x = -1\dfrac{1}{2}$ and 2

     MINIMUM $\left(-1\dfrac{3}{4}, -\dfrac{1}{8}\right)$

8.34 1 $x = -0.5$ and 2
     2 $x = -2$, 1 and 3
     MINIMUM (2.12, 4.10)
     MAXIMUM (−0.79, 8.21)

8.35 1 (5, 143.13°) or (5, 2.498 rad)
2 (5.39, 201.80°) or (5.39, 3.52 rad)

8.36 1 (3.39, 2.12)
2 (−5.61, 1 2.86)
3 (−0.53, −2.44)

8.37 1 Amplitude = 4; period = 360°/2 = 180°.
A sketch of $y = 4 \cos 2x$ is shown in Figure 8.107.

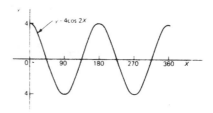

Figure 8.107

2 Amplitude = 2, period = $\dfrac{360°}{\dfrac{3}{5}} = \dfrac{360° \times 5}{3} = 600°$

A sketch of $y = 2 \sin \dfrac{3}{5} A$ is shown in Figure 8.108.

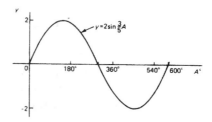

Figure 8.108

3 Amplitude = 7, period = $2\pi/2 = \pi$ radians.
In general, $y = \sin (pt - \alpha)$ lags $y = \sin pt$ by α/p, hence 7 sin
$(2A - \pi/3)$ lags 7 sin $2A$ by $\pi/(3/2)$, i.e. $\pi/6$ rad or 30°.
A sketch of $y = 7 \sin (2A - \pi/3)$ is shown in Figure 8.109.

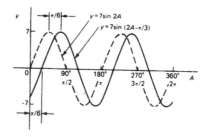

Figure 8.109

4 Amplitude = 2; period = $2\pi/\omega$.
2 cos ($\omega t - 3\pi/10$) lags 2 cos ωt by $3\pi/10$ radians.
A sketch of $y = 2\cos(\omega t - 3\pi/10)$ is shown in Figure 8.110.

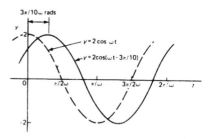

Figure 8.110

Calculus

8.38 1 –3, 4, 0, 21
      2 (i) –15   (ii) $41 + 31a + 5a^2$
         (iii) $31a + 5a^2$ (iv) $31 + 5a$

8.39 1 (a) $8x$ (b) $6x^2$
      2 $8x + 15$, –19

8.40 1 $27x^2$

      2 $\dfrac{1}{2\sqrt{x}}$

      3 $-\dfrac{2}{t^3}$

      4 $-\dfrac{3}{2\sqrt{x^3}} - \dfrac{1}{x^2}$

      5 $10x - 2$, 13

8.41 1 $12\cos 3x + 8\sin 4x$
      2 351 A/s

8.42 1 $8e^{2x} + \dfrac{15}{2e^{5x}}$

      2 $\dfrac{5}{t} + 1$

      3 $\dfrac{-9}{x^4} + \dfrac{3}{x} + 10(\sin 2x - 3\cos 3x) + \dfrac{1}{e^{2x}}$

8.43 1 $60x^2 + \dfrac{1}{2\sqrt{x^3}} + \dfrac{2}{x^3}$

      2 $-18\cos 3t - 16\sin 2t - 12e^{2t} - \dfrac{3}{t^2}$

8.44 1 −25420 A/s
    2 −1.63 Pa/m

8.45 1 max (−1, 5), min (1, 1)
    2 (a) (−1.3863, −1.5452) min   (b) (1, −3) max

8.46 1 $\dfrac{5x^3}{3} + x^2 - x + c$

    2 $3 \ln x + \dfrac{1}{x} + \dfrac{1}{2} x + c$

    3 $-\dfrac{5}{2} \cos 2x - \dfrac{4}{3} \sin 3x + c$

    4 $\dfrac{3}{4} e^{4t} + \dfrac{2}{3e^{3t}} + c$

8.47 1 (a) $43\dfrac{1}{3}$ (b) 9

    2 $11\dfrac{1}{3}$

    3 (a) 1   (b) −0.5676
    4 68.04

8.48 1 81 square units
    2 693.1 kJ

    3 $24\dfrac{1}{3}$ square units

Phasors and vectors

8.49 1 10.23 N at 16.05° to the 7 N vector
    2 17.39 m/s at 81.72° to the horizontal

8.50 1 7.27 m/s at 90.8°
    2 83.5 km/h at 71.6° to the vertical

8.51 1 200 V, 5 ms, 200 Hz, 21.43° leading
    2 (a) 20 ms
       (b) 50 Hz
       (c) −5.42 A
       (d) 5.42 A
       (e) 6.18 ms

8.52 1 9.99 sin ($\omega t - 0.25$)
    2 31.93 sin ($\omega t + 0.21$)
    3 5.69 sin ($\omega t - 0.75$)

Index